Physical Methods
in Chemical Analysis

VOLUME I, SECOND REVISED EDITION

Physical Methods in Chemical Analysis

Edited by

WALTER G. BERL

Applied Physics Laboratory
Johns Hopkins University
Silver Spring, Maryland

VOLUME I, SECOND REVISED EDITION

ACADEMIC PRESS • NEW YORK AND LONDON • 1960

Contributors to Volume I, Second Revised Edition

W. C. Bigelow, *Department of Chemical and Metallurgical Engineering, University of Michigan, Ann Arbor, Michigan*

Wallace R. Brode, *National Bureau of Standards, Washington, D.C.*

Chester J. Calbick, *Bell Telephone Laboratories, Murray Hill, New Jersey*

George L. Clark, *Department of Chemistry, University of Illinois, Urbana, Illinois*

Mary E. Corning, *National Bureau of Standards, Washington, D.C.*

William L. Davidson, *Food Machinery and Chemical Corporation, Princeton, New Jersey*

Robert D. Heidenreich, *Bell Telephone Laboratories, Murray Hill, New Jersey*

James H. Hibben, *United States Tariff Commission, Washington, D.C.* (Died June 15, 1959)

John A. Howsmon, *American Viscose Corporation, Marcus Hook, Pennsylvania*

Harald H. Nielsen, *Department of Physics, The Ohio State University, Columbus, Ohio*

Robert A. Oetjen, *Department of Astronomy, The Ohio State University, Columbus, Ohio*

Charles F. Robinson, *Research Division, Consolidated Electrodynamic Corporation, Pasadena, California*

J. Sherman, *Philadelphia Naval Shipyard, Philadelphia, Pennsylvania*

John K. Taylor, *National Bureau of Standards, Washington, D.C.*

Leroy W. Tilton, *National Bureau of Standards, Washington, D.C.*

Norman M. Walter, *American Viscose Corporation, Marcus Hook, Pennsylvania*

Preface

What are the functions of the chemical analyst? Are they not to provide and apply the tools and techniques with which the individual components of unknown chemical aggregates can be identified qualitatively and quantitatively? The entire science of chemistry, be it structural organic chemistry, reaction kinetics, or the biochemistry of living cells, rests squarely on this ability to disentangle the numerous strands of a complex system and to isolate those parts that are of significance to the problem under investigation. And the analyst is charged with the task of providing the means and methods which permit this identification quickly and accurately in more and more complex situations.

In the past quarter of a century a change, or rather a widening of horizons, has taken place in the domain of chemical analysis. The change has been gradual at first but is proceeding at a vastly accelerated pace at the present time. The nineteenth century saw an unparalleled flowering of what are now the "classical" methods of chemical analysis, namely the development of gravimetric and volumetric methods. The objective in these methods is to operate on an unknown sample in such a way that a chemical reaction takes place, specific to the components that are to be determined. One would weigh precipitates and residues, measure evolved or consumed gases, titrate acid-base and oxidation-reduction systems. The main problem was to discover type-specific reactions that lent themselves to the making of quantitative deductions and to refine and simplify the measuring techniques. Marvels of ingenuity, reliability, and accuracy resulted. In all cases, however, it was necessary to change the substrate permanently. This fact alone was a weakness needing remedy. But what was the analyst to do when confronted by complex hydrocarbon or amino acid mixtures where the mere qualitative separation represented an almost impossible task? And how could he solve with his classical tools the subtler questions of alloy and polymer structure, problems dealing with arrangement and design rather than the purely quantitative determination of elemental composition. Nevertheless, these are problems assigned to the analyst for solution. The answer is, of course, that the analytical chemist has added to his tools a new series of methods and devices, often developed for quite other purposes— namely, the instruments and techniques that determine the physical constants of chemical substances. A fertile field was uncovered with

vii

which to supplement the classical techniques. For in the sensitive and inventive hands of the analyst this supplementing of type-specific chemical reactions with the measurement of type-specific physical constants opens a wider field of usefulness than had been provided heretofore. Frequently, speed, accuracy, and specificity have been greatly enhanced. And of equal significance are the discoveries and utilization of powerful and improved methods of separation, indispensable in the investigation of complex systems where even the most refined of available methods are inadequate to distinguish and measure with sufficient precision.

In the following two volumes our aim has been to describe those physical methods that have either proved themselves of considerable value in quantitative analytical work or are destined to play an important role in the future. The reader will find a discussion of the various "Unit Operations," the techniques and instruments that can be used by the analyst in the identification, both qualitative and quantitative, of atomic, molecular, and ionic species, crystal phases and arrangements, surface structures and area, etc. Enough experimental and theoretical data have been assembled to minimize the need of consulting more specialized texts or the original literature, in the sense of enabling the reader to become familiar with the underlying principles of the methods and to analyze the applicability of the techniques to his specific problems.

The subject matter, wherever possible, is arranged in the following manner:

1) Survey and development of the theoretical base on which the "Unit Operation" rests, together with the derivation of the formulae and working equations necessary in the interpretation of the experimental results.

2) Discussion and description of the methods, types of apparatus, and equipment, general test procedures, preparation and selection of samples, evaluation of experimental data, and reference to alternate procedures.

3) Discussion of the various broad fields of application and prominent examples where the techniques have been successfully applied. Estimation of limitations, experimental error, and inherent accuracy. Probable future extensions and applications in other fields.

4) Literature references to specialized texts and to the journals where important segments of the experimental methods or applications are discussed.

In a field as extensive and as rapidly expanding as this one the practicing analyst is obliged to maintain close scrutiny over the current literature. He must, however, be sufficiently grounded in the basic principles of the various physical methods in order to carry out his tasks in the most intelligent, efficient, and scientific manner. It is hoped that the contributions to these volumes will aid him in this understanding.

The subject matter has been divided in such a way that all methods dealing with the interaction of radiation with matter (in addition to mass spectrometry) appear together in Volume I. Electrical, magnetic, and miscellaneous techniques and the methods of separation will appear in Volume II.

Preface to the Second Edition

Rapid advances are the rule in the field of analytical instrumentation where developments in physical measurements are quickly adapted to the specific needs of the analyst. Basically new techniques are constantly added to the "classical" physical measurements. The aim of the series of volumes on "Physical Methods in Chemical Analysis" is to present and discuss these techniques and their applications as soon as they have reached a stage of usefulness to the analyst.

Coincident with the development of new methods there are, of course, many important advances and refinements in areas already discussed in the earlier volumes. To present these advances in their proper perspective a second edition of Volumes I and II has become necessary. While the techniques under discussion are the same as in the first edition, the material has been rewritten, revised, and brought up to date.

The reviews present both the theoretical foundations and the analytical applications of a number of physical measurements in sufficient detail so that the principle of the method and the usefulness of the technique for solving a particular problem can be assessed readily.

It is a pleasure to thank the authors who have again given so generously of their time. It is with much regret that the untimely death of Dr. James H. Hibben must be recorded. The publishers have been helpful in every respect.

WALTER G. BERL

January, 1960

Contents

Absorption Phenomena of X-rays and γ-Rays
George L. Clark

X-Ray Diffraction Methods as Applied to Powders and Metals
William L. Davidson

X-Ray Diffraction as Applied to Fibers
JOHN A. HOWSMON AND NORMAN M. WALTER

Spectrophotometry and Absorptimetry
WALLACE R. BRODE AND MARY E. CORNING

Emission Spectrography
J. SHERMAN

Infrared Spectroscopy
HARALD H. NIELSEN AND ROBERT A. OETJEN

Raman Spectra
JAMES H. HIBBEN

Refractive Index Measurement
LEROY W. TILTON AND JOHN K. TAYLOR

Mass Spectrometry
CHARLES F. ROBINSON

Electron Microscopy
ROBERT D. HEIDENREICH AND CHESTER J. CALBRICK

Electron Diffraction
W. C. BIGELOW

Absorption Phenomena of X-Rays and γ-Rays

George L. Clark

Department of Chemistry, University of Illinois, Urbana, Illinois

1. Introduction

Today, more than sixty years after his momentous discovery of x-rays, it is easy to forget that Wilhelm Conrad Röntgen made the first observations on penetration and absorption of these rays and immediately instituted the first practical applications, which today are so well established in medical diagnosis, industrial radiography, microradiography, photometric analysis, gauging, absorption spectroscopy, photochemical reactions, biological effects, and medical therapy. For all but the last three, direct observation of differential absorption is involved; for the last three it is clear that absorption of rays must precede chemical and biological changes. Röntgen and his contemporaries had only the measurements of absorption for evaluation of quality (or wavelength distribution) until the discovery in 1912 of diffraction by crystals. With this discovery absorption phenomena as such were eclipsed, and in part nearly forgotten, and "shadowgraphs" of bones and tissues were taken more or less for granted. Within the past few years, with the advent of such useful instruments as r-meters, phosphors, electron multiplier tubes, and Geiger, proportional, and scintillation counters, there

1

has been a reawakening to the practical usefulness in many directions of observing absorption of x- and γ-ray beams in all types of materials. The ease and speed with which measurements can be made, in comparison with other techniques, has brought to the fore the analytical possibilities of absorptiometry or absorption photometry in academic and industrial laboratories. New automatic apparatus is on the market, and many new applications are being found (16, 45, 47). It is the purpose of this chapter to illustrate some of these applications of Röntgen's first experimental observations.

2. The Laws of Absorption

The absorption of x- and γ-rays follows the exponential equation

$$I_x = I_0 e^{-\mu x} \tag{1}$$

$$I_0/I_x = \exp(\mu x); \log I_0/I_x = \mu x \tag{2}$$

where I_x is the intensity of radiation of initial intensity I_0 after passage through x centimeters of homogeneous matter, e is the natural base of logarithms, and μ is the linear absorption coefficient. If the beam of radiation has a cross section of 1 cm.², then μ represents the fraction of energy absorbed per cubic centimeter of the absorber traversed. Because of a more frequent interest in absorption per gram instead of per cubic centimeter, a more useful form of eq. (1) is

$$I_x/I_0 = \exp[(-\mu/\rho) \cdot \rho x] \tag{3}$$

where ρ is the density of the absorbing layer, and μ/ρ is the mass absorption coefficient, which is a simple function of atomic number and is independent of physical state and temperature. The value of μ/ρ for a chemical compound is an additive function of the mass absorption coefficients of the constituent elements. Thus, in an example cited by Sproull (56), x-rays passing from the ceiling to the floor of a room containing hydrogen and oxygen may be 90% absorbed through the total height of gas, and on the floor there is 10% of the initial intensity. A spark is passed so as to cause combination to steam, without any change in absorption. When the steam is condensed to water, x-rays reaching the floor through the water or ice will also have 10% of initial intensity. For a given element μ/ρ increases with an increase in wavelength of the radiation absorbed, discontinuities appearing at the characteristic K, L, M, N, etc., absorption wavelengths. The μ/ρ values for many of the most important elements over a range of wavelengths are tabulated in the familiar handbooks of chemistry and physics.

The mechanism of the absorption process is shown by the fact that

$$\mu/\rho = \gamma/\rho + \sigma/\rho \tag{4}$$

where γ/ρ is the true or fluorescent mass coefficient, and σ/ρ is the coefficient due to scattering; μ/ρ is also a function of atomic number and of wavelength as shown by the equation

$$\mu/\rho = (CZ^4\lambda^3)N/A \tag{5}$$

where C is a constant over a range between characteristic absorption edges, Z is the atomic number, λ the wavelength, N Avogadro's number, and A the atomic weight.

The laws of absorption apply to single wavelengths (or monochromatic beams) even though x-ray tubes generate a whole spectrum of rays. Each such polychromatic beam, however, has an "effective" wavelength—that is, the wavelength of a monochromatic beam absorbed to the same extent. X-ray absorptiometry is classified into two techniques, depending on whether monochromatic or polychromatic beams are used.

3. Thickness Gauging

The exponential law indicates that absorption of a given x-ray beam of given intensity must vary with x, the thickness of the homogeneous material. This suggests the simplest application of an absorption technique, namely the evaluation of gauge and its constancy. Many materials occur in such shapes that micrometer thickness measurements are difficult or impossible. With an x- or γ-ray beam such determinations can be made without in any way touching the sample. It is necessary only to measure the diminution in initial intensity, I_0, in passage through a layer. This may be done with a fluoroscopic screen or a photographic film, although only roughly, since under the best conditions a difference in thickness of about 2% is required for visual differentiation of the blackening of the photographic emulsion. Still better is an ionization chamber or r-meter or Geiger counter, which can be made extremely sensitive so that a difference of the order of 0.1% is detectable. The logical practical equipment is a combination of phosphor and an electron multiplier photoelectric tube first used for intensity measurement in 1942 by Morgan (51), for preliminary chemical analysis by Liebhafsky and Winslow (48) in 1945, and for rapid examination of fuses by Smith (55) in 1945. Operations with amplifiers and automatic continuous operation have followed.

During the war it became necessary to roll thin metal sheets of constant gauge, free from defects, for various types of precision equipment. At a constant voltage and current, x-rays could be passed through the sheet traveling at 800 feet per minute on the rolling mill. The unabsorbed radiation passes into an electron multiplier tube, the current in which is amplified to be read on an ammeter or otherwise arranged to signal when there is variation in gauge of the sheet. Variations in primary x-ray intensity are compensated by a null method, since a beam from the opposite side of the target passes through a stationary sample of standard required gauge and then into another multiplier tube and the circuit linked with that registering absorption in the moving sheet. Deviations from balance activate a servomechanism which automatically readjusts the mill rolls more or less tightly (14). This technique of gauging is now established practice for a wide variety of rolled metal sheets. Continuous testing of deviations from concentricity of wire cores in insulation of high-tension cables is now established practice.

4. Thin Coating Measurement

A very important measurement frequently required is that of the thickness of electroplated layers and coatings of all kinds. The methods depending on capacitative or magnetic properties or optical observations of reflectivity are often inadequate and difficult. Evaluation by x-ray absorption measurements has been found highly satisfactory in rapidity and simplicity. Several alternative techniques have been devised.

In the most sensitive and widely used technique developed by Friedman and Birks (29) for measuring the thickness of single- or multiple-electroplated metal films, evaporated electrode coatings on piezoelectric crystals, and thin pigment layers in the range from 10^{-5} to 10^{-2} cm., the x-ray source and detector are both situated on the same side of the coating. The x-rays pass through the coating and are reflected from the crystalline substrate at the proper Bragg angle from one of the principal sets of planes back to the detector, their intensity being reduced by absorption due to the double transmission through the coating (Fig. 1). The commercially available focusing Geiger counter powder diffractometers are used directly for this purpose. If t is the coating thickness, θ is the angle of incidence of the x-ray beam on crystal planes hkl in the substrate, and μ is the linear absorption coefficient $(\mu/\rho)\rho$, the ratio of the diffracted intensity from the coated specimen, I_t, to the intensity from the uncoated base material is

$$I_t/I_0 = \exp\left[-2\mu(t/\sin\theta)\right] \tag{6}$$

Another important technique for measuring coating thickness depends on excitation by primary x-rays of the characteristic fluorescent radiation of the substrate and measurement of the attenuation in intensity in passing through the overlying coating. This method is satisfactory for determining the thickness over a range of 1 to 20 μ of zinc on iron and steel with primary copper radiation. The substrate metal must have a lower atomic number than that of the coating in order to avoid interference from characteristic rays from the coating. It has been successfully used by Beeghly (6) on tinplate; by Pellissier and Wicker (53) in the United States Steel Company laboratories; and by Zemany and Liebhafsky (65) in the General Electric Company laboratories on attenuation by iron foil of characteristic lines from silver or zirconium substrates. Other methods which have had limited application are: (1)

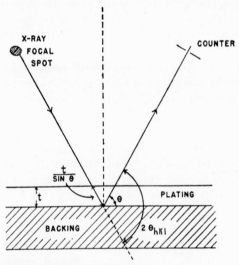

Fig. 1. Reflection of x-rays at diffraction angle θ from backing. Path length in plating is $2t/\sin \theta$.

measurements of intensity ratios of two diffraction lines of the substrate with the x-ray primary beam perpendicular to the specimen, the values being dependent on preferred orientation and strain in the specimen; (2) measurement of intensity ratios by Gray (32) and by Eisenstein (22) of pairs of diffraction interferences from substrate and coating (a routine method for layers of SrO on BaO oxide cathodes), also subject to error from textural variations; (3) measurement of the absorption factor of the beam from an irradiated sample in aluminum foil, by which Gerold (31) determined the thickness of a very thin chromium layer on brass with an intermediate nickel electrodeposited layer; (4) the method of Koh and Caugherty (39) for estimating the thickness of very thin coatings from the intensity of a characteristic line of the coating itself.

5. Porosity and Density Determinations

X-ray gauge methods are particularly useful on compressible materials such as leather, cellophane, cloth textiles, rubber blankets, plastic
films, and paper. It follows that porosity, as well as gauge, can be accurately determined, for x-rays measure only the true thickness of solid
matter through which they pass without reference to free spaces and
pores, whereas only the apparent thickness is measurable by mechanical
means such as micrometers. The porosity of the negative metallic lead
plates in storage batteries as a function of temperature of formation and
charging down to very low temperatures is an important factor, the
capacity of the plates being determined by the penetration of sulfuric
acid into the interior of the active mass. No possible mechanical measurement of the spongy mass could be made; but absorption of x-rays
through sections of the plate of the same area and same mass of active
material give the variations in thickness and porosity, the latter decreasing nonlinearly with temperature and also with capacity of the plate.

A highly quantitative measurement of porosity of rubber-composi-
tion storage battery separators has been made by Clark and Liu (18).
This property is critical, since sulfuric acid must diffuse through these
separators which must insulate adjacent negative and positive plates
from each other and prevent formation of lead trees. The average value
(55% porosity) compares closely with the value derived from laborious
pycnometric measurements, which cannot provide for closed pores unless
the sample is powdered.

X-ray absorption has also been used in petroleum geology exploration
to determine the porosity of sandstones, the oil saturation of drilling
cores (10) and related problems. Grohse (33) has found absorptiometry
with polychromatic beams to be a unique method for studying the
"fluidization" of a finely divided solid by a gas, as in beds of silicon
fluidized by air. Bed density profiles which reveal the character and
effectiveness of fluidization can be readily determined without disturbing
the bed with internal probes. Detonation waves (38), boundary layers
(61), and density in supersonic flow, well suited for nozzle calibration (63), are other applications of x-ray absorption.

6. Chemical Analysis from Absorptiometry

It is at once apparent that rapid chemical analysis can be made
to depend on differences in absorption of x-rays, for the concentration of
one chemical element in the presence of others determines the difference

in absorption between a sample and a reference. In 1929 Aborn and Brown (1) used x-ray apparatus with an ionization chamber to analyze gasoline for lead tetraethyl content, utilizing the large difference in mass absorption coefficients of carbon and hydrogen in gasoline and the lead. It was possible to achieve an accuracy of 1 part in 14,000.

In 1946 Sullivan and Friedman (57) successfully utilized a Geiger counter for x-ray absorption measurements for this same analysis of lead tetraethyl in gasoline. As shown in eq. (5), the mass absorption coefficient increases as the cube of the wavelength. In a single-component system it is logical to employ the longest wavelength transmitted by the sample, thus obtaining a maximum change in intensity for a given change in sample thickness. Leaded gasoline is a two-component system, however, in which the μ/ρ values change at different rates as the wavelength is varied. Hence an optimum wavelength generated at 17 kv. is used with an absorption cell length of 15 to 25 cm. A counter tube filled with krypton is designed such that 80% of the x-ray beam so generated is absorbed; or 80 out of 100 quanta entering the counter produce counts. At comparable sensitivity of the photomultiplier tube, the counter registered over 1000 counts per second. Standard deviation was 0.05 ml. of lead tetraethyl per gallon of gasoline, or 1%. Similarly a precision of 1% was obtained with samples containing a maximum of 0.46 ml./gal., corresponding to the detection of 0.005 ml. of lead tetraethyl per gallon or 0.0002% lead. The analysis can be made in one-tenth the time of any far less satisfactory chemical method.

In spite of the success of this analysis and the suggestion of many others applied to mixtures of gases, liquids, and solids, no suitable equipment was placed on the market until late in 1946. The General Electric x-ray photometer is now in routine and research use for a wide variety of analytical problems (54).

The general arrangement is illustrated in Fig. 2. A tungsten target x-ray tube with beryllium window is operated at 15 to 45 kv. and 1 to 20 ma. with an enclosed power unit. Above the x-ray unit is a synchronous motor-driven chopper which alternately interrupts one-half of the x-ray beam after the other. A variable-thickness aluminum attenuator is placed above the chopper in one beam. Duplicate sample tubes are placed in the two beams above the attenuator. Sample cells up to 25 inches long can be accommodated; those for liquids and gases are arranged for continuous flow of the sample. Both halves of the beam fall on a common fluorescent screen protected from visible light by a thin metallic filter. An electron multiplier phototube with associated power supply and amplifier determines when the beams are of equal intensity.

In operation a reference sample is placed in the cell above the attenuator, and the unknown in the other sample tube. The attenuator is adjusted until the balance indicator shows that the two beams are of equal intensity; this position indicates a certain thickness of aluminum, which is equal in absorption to the difference between the reference sample and the unknown. Prior calibration enables an immediate deter-

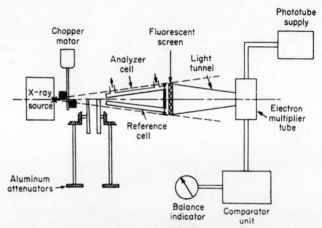

FIG. 2. X-ray photometer.

mination in terms of the amount of impurity or solute in the unknown. The instrument may operate automatically to indicate or record this result directly. The exploratory work leading to the development of this successful commercial equipment was done by Liebhafsky and associates (46, 64) for solids, liquids, and gases under simplest conditions. The relation between x-ray absorption and two masses (m_1 and m_2) of sample is

$$\log (I_1/I_2) = \log (i_1/i_2) = k(m_2 - m_1) \tag{7}$$

where I_1 and I_2 are intensities of x-ray beams transmitted, i_1 and i_2 are corresponding average output currents (from the phototube), and k is a proportionality factor. With a monochromatic beam

$$\log I_0/I = \log i_0/i = km \tag{8}$$

where I_0 and i_0 refer to the empty cell. With the commonly used polychromatic beam from a tungsten target tube, k varies inversely with m. It is defined by

$$\mu/\rho = 2.303ak \tag{9}$$

where a is the cross-sectional area of a cell containing m grams of sample; as already indicated, μ/ρ varies with λ^3, and the value of $\lambda_{\text{effective}}$ changes by absorption of the longer wavelengths. For quantitative analysis the effective wavelength must be determined for various thicknesses in order to determine μ/ρ in turn.

The analysis of gases is particularly interesting and significant. The equation is

$$2.303 \log i_0/i = \bar{} \mu_m \rho l \tag{10}$$

where μ_m is the mass absorption coefficient, ρ is the gas density, and l is the cell length in centimeters. Long wavelengths make possible a ratio of 6000 to 1 between outputs for hydrogen and chlorine.

The following examples of actual analyses for which the absorption photometer is employed are typical of an almost endless list of possibilities.

1. Characterization of plastics (for use in cell windows, all lying between beryllium and aluminum) (46).

2. Sulfur content of crude and refined oil. A quantitative study leading to routine commercial analyses is that of Levine and Okamoto (44). The equation is

$$\ln (I_{\mathrm{CHS}}/I_{\mathrm{CH}}) = (\mu'_{\mathrm{S}} - \mu'_{\mathrm{CH}}) \rho_{\mathrm{CHS}} X F_{\mathrm{S}}$$

where I is the intensity of the x-ray beam after passing through the S-containing petroleum hydrocarbon (CHS) and a pure hydrocarbon (CH, represented by calibrated polystyrene rods), μ' is the mass absorption coefficient (for S and CH), ρ_{CHS} is the petroleum density, X is the length of the absorber, and F_{S} is the mass fraction of S in the C—H base (to be determined). Accuracy of analysis is $\pm0.02\%$ S; one operator can analyze thirty samples per day much faster and more economically than by chemical means and with comparable accuracy, together with nondestruction of samples.

A number of other absorption measurements of sulfur have been reported (21, 37, 52). Of particular interest is the K-capture determination of sulfur in hydrocarbons by the absorption of rays from iron-55. In this isotope (half-life 2.94 years), one of the two S-electrons in the K-shell is captured by the nucleus, thereby transmuting the atom into the next lower atom in the periodic table, in this case manganese-55. In the process of filling the K-vacancy, the $K\alpha$- and $K\beta$-rays with a weighted wavelength of 2.07 A. are generated. Sulfur in the range 0.05 to 2.7% is easily and quickly determined by this essentially monochromatic absorptiometry and is in routine use in the Socony-Vacuum laboratories.

Other analyses may be made similarly with this isotope or Ni^{59}, Rh^{102}, or Cd^{109} which are engaged in K-capture. Hughes and Wilczewski (35) have compared speed, accuracy, and cost for sulfur determinations as shown in the tabulation.

Method	Speed				Relative cost	
	Elapsed time (hr.)	Operator time (min.)	Samples per day	Accuracy (S%)	Equip-ment	Operator time
Bomb sulfur	24	36	13	0.03–0.14	5	7.2
Lamp sulfur	3	29	16	0.03	1	5.8
X-ray absorption	0.12	7	48	0.09	20	1.4
K-capture	0.08	5	60	0.05	6	1.0

3. Quantitative "titration" of sulfhydryl (HS) groups. This extremely important analysis is carried out by assessing the amount of silver which can react with HS groups in proteins (28).

4. Tetraethyllead content of gasoline. Since the appearance of the photometer, other critical investigations have been made of the x-ray absorption method of analysis for tetraethyllead and reported in a symposium devoted entirely to the subject. Calingaert et al. (13) improved accuracy by reducing primary-voltage fluctuation on the x-ray tube to ±0.10 and further reduced sensitivity of the measurements of such fluctuations by a factor of 10 by introducing a polystyrene block in the reference beam. These authors found the method sensitive to 0.01 ml. of tetraethyl per gallon and the precision ±0.01 ml. for known gasoline-base stocks. The varying percentage of sulfur in gasoline was the chief obstacle to more accurate determination. Hughes and Hochgesang (34) found further advantage in using monochromatic radiation (preferably thorium lines near a lead absorption discontinuity, but for practical routine purpose the molybdenum K_a-doublet). The tetraethyllead fluid actually added to automotive gasoline consists of 61.48% $PbEt_4$, 17.86% $C_2H_2Br_2$, 18.81% $C_2H_2Cl_2$, 1.7% kerosene, and 0.124% dye, corresponding to 4.8% H, 26.7% C, 13.8% Cl, 15.4% Br, and 39.4% Pb; aviation mixture differs only in having 35.68% ethylene dibromide and no dichloride. A straight-line working curve derived from the usual mass absorption equation with Mo K_a-radiation is obtained by plotting log (P/P_0) or log (t/t_0) against $\rho(0.587 + 9.31f_S) + 0.0478C_T$, where P is the radiant power of the x-ray beam of initial power, P_0, after passing through the sample in an 8-ml. absorption cell (4⅛ inches long), t and t_0 are the corresponding times for a fixed Geiger count of 10,000, ρ is the density, f_S is the weight fraction of sulfur, and C_T is the concentration of tetraethyllead in milliliters per gallon. When the sulfur content is known, an exact correction is made; otherwise an average value accepted by the American Society for Testing Materials (ASTM) of 0.064% gives a satisfactory result.

It is interesting to compare accepted methods of tetraethyllead analysis. The saving in personnel time of the x-ray over the chemical method pays the equipment cost every 6 months, or in comparison with polarographic analysis every 8 months. Another x-ray method of analysis, by utilization of the intensity of the characteristic fluorescence spectrum for determination of lead and bromine, has been widely adopted. A Geiger count of only 1 minute at the peak of the L_a-line of lead gave a probable error of ±0.06 ml./gal. of gasoline, and for the Br K_a-line of ±0.16 ml./gal. Chlorine, sulfur, and other elements have negligible effect. Thus, accuracy and speed are comparable with those of the x-ray absorption technique.

5. Control of constancy of metal composition of metallo-organic compounds (60).

6. Additives in heavy-duty lubricating oils (60).

7. Ash content and quality of coal.

8. Heavy-metal content of glass.

9. Chlorine or fluorine content of polymers and plastics. Here values of μ/ρ are H = 0.435 (independent of wavelength), C = 0.567, Cl = 12.0, etc.

10. Bromine content in gaseous brominated derivatives.

11. Determination of formula of organic compounds (C, H, O). Typical results are as shown in the tabulation.

Compound	μ/ρ (measured)	μ/ρ (calculated)	Formula (experimental)	Formula (true)
Methyl alcohol	0.869	0.867	$CH_3O_{1.01}H$	CH_3OH
Acetone	0.734	0.728	$(CH_3)_2CO_{1.06}$	$(CH_3)_2CO$
Sucrose (solution)	0.869	0.884	$C_{12}H_{22}O_{10.8}$	$C_{12}H_{22}O_{11}$

At the Armour Research Foundation an excellent method has been devised for determining the per cent composition of compounds composed of light elements (4), involving determination of absorption by the unknown of monochromatic x-rays, excited by fluorescence, at several different wavelengths, and the subsequent solution of a series of simultaneous linear equations. For a compound composed solely of carbon, hydrogen, and oxygen, for example, the beam attenuation is

$$\frac{I}{I_0} = \exp\left[-\left(\frac{\mu_H}{\rho_H}\rho_H + \frac{\mu_C}{\rho_C}\rho_C + \frac{\mu_O}{\rho_O}\rho_O \right) X \right] \qquad (11)$$

where μ/ρ's are the mass absorption coefficients, ρ's are the element densities, and X is the sample thickness. At three different wavelengths the absorption coefficients for the three elements vary independently with wavelength. These equations for the three wavelengths are independent and can be solved for ρ_H, ρ_O, and ρ_C as unknowns if μ's are known and $\ln I_1/I_0$, $\ln I_2/I_0$, and $\ln I_3/I_0$ are experimentally determined. The characteristic radiations of Se, Rb, and Zr were used in the analysis of solution of ethanol and water with excellent agreement in percentage compositions with the theoretical values.

12. Concentration of fillers and impregnants in wood, paper, cloth, rubber, carbon, etc. Titus (58) gives in comprehensive detail the quantitative analyses by absorptiometry with polychromatic beams of treated carbon brushes used in aircraft, this being the point-by-point exploration method for many materials. The treatment consists usually in impregnating the brush stock with a solution of a salt ($PbCl_2$, $CdCl_2$, BaF_2, $BaBr_2$) to an extent that will leave the desired amount in the brush on water removal. The purpose of the treatment is to reduce or eliminate excessive wear of brushes in motors and generators operating at high altitudes.

13. Mineral content and efficiency of softening of water.

14. Soil composition (qualitatively on account of complexity).

15. Adsorbed contents of charcoals and silica gels.

16. Concentration of reagent solutions containing metallic ions. The latest example is the determination of uranium in solution (5), a matter of the greatest importance in contemporary atomic energy research. In the absence of contaminating elements the precision is ± 0.05 g./l. between limits of 0.1 to 10 g./l. The presence of Na^+, NH_4^+, F^-, and other light ions has no effect, but heavier ions require separations. These solutions may also be analyzed as in the case of tetraethyllead by fluorescence spectrum analysis, which has the advantage of no interference by contaminating elements. In various Atomic Energy Commission reports by M. C. Lambert *et al.*, absorptiometry has been applied to aqueous solutions of thirty-five compounds and ions of twenty-five elements widely distributed in the periodic table. These extensive and precise absorbance data greatly facilitate absorptiometry with polychromatic beams.

17. Alloy analysis, especially when one alloying element is appreciably heavier than the base metal. For such an alloy, with a high atomic number element H and a low atomic element L, with weights respectively m_H and m_L g. cm.$^{-2}$, and mass absorption coefficients μ_H/ρ_H and μ_L/ρ_L, the extinction or attenuation ($\log_e$ transmission), E, of a monochromatic beam is

$$E = \frac{\mu_H}{\rho_H} \cdot m_H + \frac{\mu_L}{\rho_L} \cdot m_L \tag{12}$$

The influence of m_H is compared with the extinction from a standard made from H:

$$E_{standard} = \frac{\mu_H}{\rho_H} \cdot m_{standard} \tag{13}$$

and a blank made from L:

$$E_{blank} = \frac{\mu_L}{\rho_L} \cdot m_{blank} \tag{14}$$

Thus the simple relation

$$m_H = \frac{(E - E_{blank}) \, m_{standard}}{E_{standard}} \tag{15}$$

permits calculation of the amount of the heavy element (27).

7. Analysis by Characteristic Absorption Spectrometry

Just as emission and absorption spectroscopic analyses in the optical ranges of the electromagnetic spectrum are such important instrumental techniques, so may characteristic x-ray emission lines and absorption edges be utilized by the chemist. It has long been known that each chemical element has one characteristic K absorption wavelength, three L, five M, seven N, etc., the relationship to atomic number being governed by Moseley's law. Thus, when an absorbing screen is placed in the path of an x-ray beam, and the transmitted beam is analyzed with the crystal spectrometer, sharp discontinuities or edges in the continuous spectrum may be found corresponding to the characteristic absorption wavelengths in the various series for each element present, these being independent of physical state or chemical combination. Not a great deal of use has been made of this particular technique over the years, probably because the emission spectra are somewhat more sensitive. The height of this edge or discontinuity is a quantitative measure of the amount of element in the unknown. This is governed by the equation

$$\frac{I_2}{I_1} = e^{-cp} \tag{16}$$

where I_2 is the intensity of the radiation leaving the absorption screen on the short-wavelength side of the discontinuity, I_1 is the intensity of the long-wave side, c is the coefficient which must be experimentally determined, and p is the amount of element present. In Table I are probably the best data available for values of c and m, the weight in milligrams per square centimeter for the production of an absorption edge with a 5% intensity difference in the two sides.

The method has been used successfully for analysis of barium in

TABLE I

Atomic number	Element	c, K edge	c, L edge	m, K edge	m, L edge
42	Mo	69		0.7	
47	Ag	45		1.1	
50	Sn	34		1.5	
51	Sb	31		1.6	
56	Ba	24		2.1	
58	Ce	22.5		2.2	
74	W	8		6.0	
82	Pb	5.7		16.0	
90	Th		50		1.0
92	U		45		1.1

glass, antimony, barium, and lanthanum, bismuth in alloys, and many others (16). It has not been successful for elements below the atomic number of molybdenum. With the advent of Geiger spectrometers, however, and new x-ray tubes delivering extremely intense beams up to 5,500,000 r./min., many of the former difficulties are eliminated. It is easily possible to make analyses for elements as low in atomic number as potassium with present equipment, and to magnesium or below with special provisions parallel with the progress in emission spectrometry.

8. Histochemical Analysis

Absorption spectroscopic analysis has been perfected to the stage of a histochemical procedure, permitting the chemical elementary analysis of single mammalian cells. Absorption of monochromatic x-radiation is measured by ionization chambers or Geiger counters, or photographically followed by microphotometry, for a series of wavelengths (isolated from primary or secondary fluorescent characteristic rays) lying on each side of a long-wave absorption edge of the sought-for element (23-25). Thus it is possible to determine phosphorus and calcium in a 10-μ-thick microtome section of a bony tissue within an area of 10×10 μ, and nitrogen and oxygen within an area of 50 to 100 μ^2 of a section 2 μ thick. The actual weights are of the order of 10^{-9} to 10^{-12} g. Since such small localized areas may be examined, the analysis may be directly correlated with the cytological picture. For these analyses the formula is

$$X = \frac{\ln (i_2/I_2) \cdot (\lambda_1/\lambda_2)^p - \ln (i_1/I_1)}{(\mu_1/\rho) - (\mu_2/\rho)(\lambda_1/\lambda_2)^p} \tag{17}$$

where X is the amount of the sought-for element in grams; the index 1 indicates the short-wave and 2 the long-wave side of the absorption edge for the element; I is the intensity of incident rays and i the intensity of transmitted rays; μ_1/ρ and μ_2/ρ are the mass absorption coefficients for the element sought at wavelengths λ_1 and λ_2; and the exponent p may be found in tables (19). If λ_1 lies very near λ_2, this reduces to

$$X = \frac{E_1 - E_2}{(\mu_1/\rho) - (\mu_2/\rho)} \cdot Y = \frac{E_1 - E_2}{k} \cdot Y \qquad (18)$$

where $E_1 = -\ln i_1/I$, $E_2 = -\ln i_2/I$, and $Y =$ area of analyzed surface. In the experiments for the determination of calcium (absorption edge 3.1 A.), the monochromatic beams had to be taken from a polychromatic beam of 7 kv.; for phosphorus (absorption edge 5.8 A.), the L_{α_1} line of niobium and the L_{β_1} line of zirconium; for nitrogen, the K-absorption edge of 31.1 A. requiring high vacuum.

Similarly, dry weights of cytological structures are determined with a filtered polychromatic beam of 1.5-kv. peak, or 8.3-A. minimum wavelength (26). The analysis is done by a comparative method with a carefully prepared step gauge of nitrocellulose foils as standard, approximately the composition and absorbing power of proteins. Since the images representing differential absorption are photographically registered, enlarged, and photometered, this is actually a quantitative application of microradiography. The total dry weight of individual ascites tumor cells, with a volume less than 4×10^{-9} cc., is found to be $3.95 \pm 0.20 \times 10^{-10}$ g., agreeing with results of microchemical analyses of samples of many cells (49). Mucus- and enzyme-secreting cells have a greater mass (0.1×10^{-12} g./μ^3) than acid-secreting cells (50). Extending these techniques, Brattgard and Hydén (11) obtained results on the mass, lipids (by chloroform extraction), pentose nucleoproteins (after digestion by crystalline ribonuclease), and residual cell proteins for various nerve cells—Deiters' cells and spinal ganglion and Purkinje cells, all of which are distinctly different in composition. This contribution by microradiography to medical chemistry opens the way for many others.

9. γ-Ray Absorptiometry

Since γ-rays are formed in nuclear processes which generally involve high energies, the wavelengths are shorter than those of x-rays generated by conventional means, and the mass absorption coefficients are appreciably smaller than those encountered ordinarily in x-ray absorptiometry. Of course x-rays generated by resonance transformers, Van de Graaff electrostatic generators, and betatrons with energies of 1 Mev. or above overlap the γ-ray range, or even extend beyond it at ⅓ to 1 Bev. Coefficients for γ-rays vary much less from element to element in comparison with x-rays at 0.1 Mev. (100 kv.) or less, so that the latter have the advantage in absorptiometric analyses. Actually the absorption characteristics of γ-rays (or x-rays in the same energy range) are very complex, as illustrated in Fig. 3, because of entrance of the process of pair

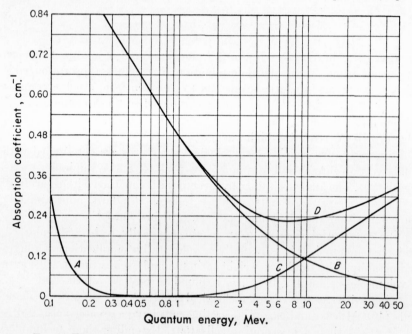

FIG. 3. Energy dependence of absorption coefficient for x-rays in iron. *A*, photoelectric effect; *B*, Compton effect; *C*, pair production; *D*, total absorption coefficient. From G. D. Adams, *Ind. Radiography* **4**, 3, 23 (1946).

production. The net result is that the values of μ/ρ, instead of linearly decreasing with increase in radiation energy, level off to a nearly constant value, depending on the absorbing material, which means that absolute sensitivity is obtained—that is, thick and thin sections are penetrated nearly alike, and radiographs are correctly exposed without screening thin sections to prevent overexposure. Thus absorption of γ-rays has its chief usefulness in thickness gauging and in radiography. The general process of γ-ray absorption is given by Bethe and Ashkin (9). Extensive data on γ-ray absorption coefficients are available because of the vitally important shielding problems in an atomic age. A large number of papers indicate rapid progress in nondestructive testing such as thickness gauging and radiography best done by isotopes cobalt-60, tantalum-182, cesium-137, iridium-192, and thulium-170. Especially valuable are papers by Aebersold (2), Brewer (12), Garrett *et al.* (30), Johnston *et al.* (36), and Untermyer (60). Berman and Harris (7) attained a precision of 0.01% in thickness measurements with cobalt-60. Leboeuf *et al.* (41) made a notable comparison of x-ray and γ-ray absorptiometry (including a mixture of americium and plutonium as source). The advantages of the latter are: extreme stability of source intensity; decreased instrument complexity and compact size; more nearly monoenergetic source; much wider range of photon energies—20 to 2000 kev.; lower cost. The chief disadvantage is low intensity, so that up to 50 kev. x-ray absorptiometry prevails. Bernhard and Chasek (8) applied γ-ray absorptiometry successfully to the measurement of soil density, as an indication of great present and future potentialities.

10. Combined Absorption-Diffraction Technique for Quantitative Analysis

In 1948 Alexander and Klug (3) devised a method for quantitative analysis of mixtures from powder diffraction patterns without the use of internal standards. The method was further developed and simplified in the Canadian Occupational Health Laboratory by Leroux *et al.* (43). The general theoretical equation is

$$X_1 = \left[\frac{I_1}{(I_1)_0} \right] \left(\frac{\mu_s{}^*}{\mu_1{}^*} \right) \tag{19}$$

where X_1 is the weight fraction of component 1; I_1 is the integrated intensity diffracted by a sample with mass absorption coefficient $\mu_s{}^*$ (or μ_s/ρ_s); and $(I_1)_0$ is the integrated intensity diffracted by a sample with mass absorption coefficient $\mu_1{}^*$ comprised solely of component 1. This equation holds for a monochromatic x-ray beam, but for a polychromatic beam the correct experimental expression for X requires a correction in the form of an exponent of 0.652 for the ratios, as the result of a critical study by Lennox (42). This technique was originally developed for analysis of industrial dusts for quartz, responsible for silicosis, but it is also standard procedure for routine analyses in such industries as ceramics, refractories, paint, and cement.

11. Radiography and Fluoroscopy

It is scarcely necessary to indicate that medical diagnostic radiography and industrial radiography, the best known and most widely practiced application of both x- and γ-rays, are direct consequences of differential absorption of rays by matter of varying homogeneity, thickness, and density. The shadow graphs are observed either on the fluoroscopic screen or the photographic film. So many excellent treatises are available that a review here of techniques and results is unnecessary. Here the progress in equipment is spectacular, as may be judged from the following list:

1. X-ray tubes only 7 or 8 feet long to operate at 1 and 2 million volts.

2. Resonance transformers with Freon gas insulation so efficient that with the tubes at the core the entire equipment may be included in mobile units; greatly improved and compact Van de Graaff electrostatic generators for operation at 2,000,000 volts.

3. The betatron or electron accelerator, developed by Kerst at the University of Illinois, in which the accelerating "donut" is also the x-ray tube producing beams up to 350,000,000 volts, far transcending the penetrating power of minimum wavelengths of γ-rays; a successful Allis-Chalmers 20,000,000-volt unit scarcely larger than an office desk, for radiography of sections up to 12 inches or more; automatic and multiple radiography both with these supervoltage units and with γ-rays from radioactive sources for thirty-six or more specimens tested at one time by arrangement on a circle around the source. In such a case supervoltage x-rays have largely replaced γ-radiography in industry because of the several hundredfold reduction in exposure time.

4. The Westinghouse surge generator, making possible radiographic exposures in a millionth of a second, for instantaneous photographs of moving objects such as bullets and artillery shells. The contribution to the science of ballistics in the past war is incalculable.

5. Monochromatic radiography. The limitations in resolving power, or in the radiographic detection of extraordinarily fine detail, with an x-ray beam of many wavelengths is apparent. This has suggested a re-examination of the possibilities of monochromatic rays (isolated by a crystal or less perfectly by appropriate filters) as applied to other industrial problems and to medical diagnosis. Many examples have been cited elsewhere (15).

6. Industrial fluoroscopy. Although this application so far is secondary to medical diagnosis, it is growing rapidly, since electronic intensification of images has greatly increased safety for the operators against over-exposure—a prohibitive factor in earlier attempts to use the fluoroscope for rapid, continuous inspection of products ranging from ball bearings and contact points, to grain for insect infestation, citrus fruit, and packaged fruits and meats. By electronic devices the images

formed by weak beams of x-rays are intensified on screens far removed from radiation exposure; such devices now permit automatic control of filling of ammunition shells, beverage bottles, and cans. Processes of mixing, diffusion, precipitation, and other reactions in chemical industries within opaque materials and vessels may be continuously observed and controlled. The viscosity of tooth pastes and similar products is measured by fluoroscopic observation of the rate of fall of metal balls. Long hoped for, industrial fluoroscopy is an accomplished fact and is growing rapidly as the result of meeting a challenge to a successful instrumentation.

12. Microradiography and X-Ray Microscopy

The use of monochromatic rays becomes more necessary, the smaller the specimen. Without ordinary lenses for magnification of x-rays, one must resort to photographic enlargement up to 300 or 400 diameters of radiographic images on very fine-grained photographic emulsion such as the Lippmann. This is the basis of microradiography, which complements ordinary photomicrography but is the representation of structure of a specimen in three dimensions rather than merely of a polished surface. Over many years attempts were made to perfect a microradiography with a polychromatic beam generated at very low voltages such as 4000 to 5000 volts. A new compact unit for contact microradiography operating at 1 to 5 kv. is produced by Philips especially for biological specimens and for microanalysis, as discussed in Section 8. For these long waves there is a favorable difference in absorption coefficients for various elements in thin specimens; but here again the polychromatic beam and the lack of penetration even through air presents difficulties. In 1939 the writer (17) advocated the use of monochromatic beams from easily available x-ray diffraction tubes operated at 30,000 volts or more. The result has been a successful development of a useful science. Here the idea of selecting the proper wavelength for maximum differentiation of constituents arose.

In Fig. 4 the values of $\mu_2 - \mu_1$, the difference of two linear absorption coefficients for constituents of an iron-copper binary alloy as a function of wavelength, are plotted as ordinate against wavelength. It is clear that there is a peak representing the largest possible difference in absorbing power; consequently the proper monochromatic wavelength corresponds to this peak to enable maximum delineation of phases in the enlarged photograph. By this method some of the most important alloys utilized in war materials, even five- and six-component systems, have been successfully analyzed in terms of phase structures, microdefects and porosity, and strain. An example for a lead-antimony alloy is illustrated in Fig. 5. For very small biological specimens, tissues, impregnated wood, and other organic materials microradiography has been a logical and useful extension of more usual macro or 1:1 radiography. Thus a new branch of histology depends on the absorption of x-rays in various areas

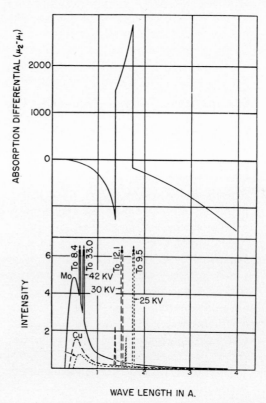

FIG. 4. Chart for absorption differential $\mu_2 - \mu_1$ for binary iron-copper alloy (above) and corresponding position of K_α-rays for molybdenum, copper, and cobalt (below), showing logical selection of copper radiation for maximum $\mu_2 - \mu_1$ differential.

of a section only a few thousandths of an inch thick. These sections also may be preferentially "stained," not with the dyes of microscopy, but with varying absorbents for x-rays.

Some tissues are particularly well adapted for microradiography. The follicles of the thyroid gland contain iodine and thus are opaque to x-rays; when the follicles are treated by acid, sodium nitrite, and chloroform to remove iodine, they become transparent. Epidermis shows absorbing layers, the basal layer that supplies nutrition to upper ones, and the outer densely packed keratinized layer. Sulfur is responsible for some opacity of intermediate layers; the cells show protoplasm fairly opaque, lighter nuclei, and very dark nucleoli. The variation in opacity of cells has a further bearing on radiosensitivity, since the greater the absorption, the greater is the amount of energy liberated by roentgen rays. It is generally true that the most sensitive cells are the most absorbent.

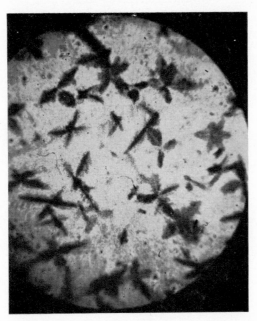

Fɪɢ. 5. Typical microradiograph of alloy of lead and antimony; lead-rich phase, light; antimony-rich phase, dark wınglike crystals. (100×)

Cancer tissue gives excellent microradiographic detail, such as keratosic and parakeratosic globes or rose-shaped cell nests in epidermal cancer.

Another microradiographic technique, developed by Trillat (59), makes use of the photoelectrons liberated by primary roentgen rays. Hard roentgen rays generated at 180 kv. pass through the Lippmann photographic film, which is insensitive, and then impinge upon a specimen closely pressed against the film. The liberated photoelectrons from the surface interact with the photographic emulsion and so produce a characteristic image, which may be enlarged. The specimen may be a photographic negative that may be reproduced exactly. Under these conditions the primary and the secondary fluorescent roentgen rays have negligible effects in comparison with the photoelectrons. In addition to this reflection technique, a transmission modification consists in the use of a thin lead foil as a generator of photoelectrons. The hard roentgen rays first pass through this foil, which is in contact with the specimen and this in turn with the film. Photoelectrons from the foil pass through the specimen and register the radiographic image on the film, which may be micro-

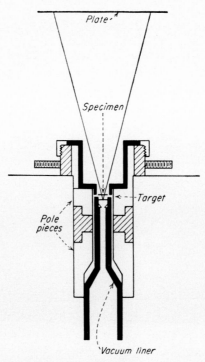

FIG. 6. Diagram of Cosslett-Nixon shadow microscope; objective lens, target specimen, plate portion.

radiographed with 4000-volt roentgen rays and give equally good differentiation with 180,000-volt rays that liberate the easily absorbed electrons.

It was inevitable that attempts should be made in microradiography and historadiography to avoid the limitations imposed in enlargements of contact images of graininess of photographic emulsions. The solution of this problem has taken two courses, with very successful results. (a) *Grainless medium.* From among various x-ray-sensitive substances which show no structure even in electron microscope ranges of enlargement, Ladd, *et al.* (40) found that faces of ammonium dichromate crystals and some polymers such as polyvinyl films were most useful. In both cases the solubility of the medium changes in proportion to the amount of exposure to the x-ray beam, with the result that the microradiographic image can be etched into a relief by suitable solvents. Anhydrous alcohols are used for developing the image on the dichromate crystals, and a 30% solution of acetone in water develops the image on the plastic sheets, in which crosslinking between polymer molecules has resulted from absorption. A cast, thin enough to permit the passage of an electron beam, is then made of the relief surface with silicon monoxide, carbon, or other materials generally used for making replicas for electron microscopy. This replica is shadow-cast with metal vapors directed at an angle to the surface and then examined in the electron microscope up to 200,000 diameters magnification. (b) *X-ray microscopy.* In ordinary microradiography sharp images can be gained only by intimate contact between specimen and film because the x-ray beam has a finite size. It follows that, if the x-rays were generated from a point source, it should be possible to place the photographic film at various distances from the specimen and thus obtain sharp-edged images inherently enlarged from the divergent beam through the specimen. Such a procedure, originally developed by Cosslett and Nixon (20), is now an accomplished fact, and the General Electric x-ray shadow microscope is a commercially produced instrument. Electrons from a filament are collimated into an extremely fine beam (Fig. 6) by means of magnetic lenses such as make electron microscopy possible. This beam impinges upon a thin piece of tungsten foil in the envelope of this special tube, and generates an x-ray beam from this point focal spot. After transmission through the thin specimen the enlarged image is directly registered on photographic films at distances up to several feet. The success of this microscope, especially with freeze-dried biological specimens of all types, alloys, clays and minerals, fabrics, and other materials, is quite remarkable.

References

1. Aborn, R. H., and Brown, R. H., *Ind. Eng. Chem. Anal. Ed.* **1**, 26 (1929).
2. Aebersold, P. C., *J. Soc. Non-Destructive Testing* **12**, No. 3, 19 (1954).
3. Alexander, L., and Klug, H. P., *Anal. Chem.* **20**, 886 (1948).
4. Armour Research Foundation, Final Report, Air Force Project A-070 (1957).
5. Bartlett, T. W., *Anal. Chem.* **23**, 705 (1951).
6. Beeghly, H. F., *J. Electrochem. Soc.* **97**, 152 (1950).
7. Berman, A. I., and Harris, J. N., *Rev. Sci. Instr.* **25**, 21 (1954).
8. Bernhard, R. K., and Chasek, M., *J. Soc. Non-Destructive Testing* **11**, No. 8, 17 (1953).
9. Bethe, H. A., and Ashkin, J., in "Experimental Nuclear Physics" (E. Segrè, ed.), Vol. 1, p. 304. 1953.

10. Boyer, R. L., Morgan, F., and Muskat, M., *Petrol. Technol.* **10**, No. 1, Tech. Publ. 2124, 19 pp. (1947).
11. Brattgard, S. O., and Hydén, H., *Acta Radiol, Suppl.* **94**, 48 pp. (1952); **39**, 494 (1953).
12. Brewer, D. E., *Iron Age* **172**, No. 27, 80 (1953).
13. Calingaert, G., Lamb, F. W., Miller, H. L., and Noakes, G. L., *Anal. Chem.* **22**, 1238 (1950).
14. Clapp, C. W., and Pohl, R. V., *Elec. Eng.* **67**, 441 (1948).
15. Clark, G. L., *Radiology* **49**, 483 (1947).
16. Clark, G. L., "Applied X-Rays," 4th ed., p. 961. McGraw-Hill, New York, 1955.
17. Clark, G. L., "Applied X-Rays," 4th ed., p. 238. McGraw-Hill, New York, 1955.
18. Clark, G. L., and Liu, C. H., *Anal. Chem.* **29**, in press.
19. Compton, A. H., and Allison, S. K., "X-Rays in Theory and Experiment," 2nd ed., p. 533. Van Nostrand, New York, 1940.
20. Cosslett, V. E., and Nixon, W. C., *Proc. Roy Soc.* **B140**, 442 (1952).
21. Cranston, R. W., Matthews, F. W. H., and Evans, N. (Sunbury Method), *J. Inst. Petrol.* **40**, 55 (1954).
22. Eisenstein, A., *J. Appl. Phys.* **17**, 874 (1946).
23. Engström, A., *Acta Radiol. Suppl.* **63**, 106 (1946).
24. Engström, A., *Biochim. et Biophys. Acta* **1**, 428 (1947).
25. Engström, A., *Rev. Sci. Inst.* **18**, 681 (1947).
26. Engström, A., and Carlström, D., *Svensk Kem. Tidskr.* **67**, 107 (1955).
27. Engström, and Parrish, W., *Svensk Kem. Tidskr.* **68**, 445 (1956).
28. Engström, A., and Wegsted, L., *Acta Chem. Scand.* **3**, 1442 (1949).
29. Friedman, H., and Birks, L. S., *Rev. Sci. Instr.* **17**, 99 (1946).
30. Garrett, C., Morrison, A., and Rice, G., *Am. Soc. Testing Materials, Spec. Tech. Pub.* **145**, 9 (1953).
31. Gerold, V., *Z. angew. Physik* **4**, 247 (1952).
32. Gray, R. R., *Phys. Rev.* **69**, 49 (1946).
33. Grohse, E. W., *A.I.Ch.E. Journal* **1**, 358 (1955).
34. Hughes, H. K., and Hochgesang, F. P., *Anal. Chem.* **22**, 1248 (1950).
35. Hughes, H. K., and Wilczewski, J. W., *Anal. Chem.* **26**, 1889 (1954).
36. Johnston, J. E., Faires, R. A., and Mille H. R. J., *Proc. 2nd Radioisotope Conf., Oxford, 1954.*
37. Kehl, W. L., and Hart, J. C., *Proc. Am. Petrol. Inst.* **Sect. III, 28**, 9 (1948).
38. Kistiakowsky, G. B., *J. Chem. Phys.* **19**, 1611 (1951).
39. Koh, P. K., and Caugherty, B. J., *J. Appl. Phys.* **23**, 427 (1952).
40. Ladd, W. A., Hess, W. M., and Ladd, W. M., *Science* **123**, 370 (1956).
41. Leboeuf, M. B., Miller, D. G., and Connally, R. E., *Nucleonics* **12**, No. 8, 18 (1954).
42. Lennox, D. H., *Anal. Chem.* **29**, 766 (1957).
43. Leroux, J., Lennox, D. H., and Kay, K., *Anal. Chem.* **25**, 740 (1953).
44. Levine, S. W., and Okamoto, A. H., *Anal. Chem.* **23**, 699 (1951).
45. Liebhafsky, H. A., *Anal. Chem.* **21**, 17 (1949); **22**, 15 (1950); **23**, 14 (1951).
46. Liebhafsky, H. A., Smith, J. A., Tanis, H. E., and Winslow, E. H., *Anal. Chem.* **19**, 861 (1947).
47. Liebhafsky, H. A., and Winslow, E. H., *Anal. Chem.* **28**, 583 (1956).
48. Liebhafsky, H. A., and Winslow, E. H., *Gen. Elec. Rev.* **48**, 36 (1945).
49. Lindstrom, B., *Acta Radiol. Suppl.* **125** (1955).
50. Lindstrom, B., and Moberger, G., *Expl. Cell Research* **9**, 68 (1955).

51. Morgan, R. H., *Am. J. Roentgenol. Radium Therapy* **48**, 88 (1942).
52. Mottlau, A. Y., and Driesens, C. E., Jr., *Anal. Chem.* **24**, 1852 (1952).
53. Pellissier, G. E., and Wicker, E. W., *Elec. Mfg.* **49**, 124 (1952).
54. Rich, T. A., and Michel, P. C., *Gen. Elec. Rev.* **50**, 45 (1947).
55. Smith, H. M., *Gen. Elec. Rev.* **48**, No. 3, 13 (1945).
56. Sproull, W. T., "X-Ray in Practice," p. 72. McGraw-Hill, New York, 1946.
57. Sullivan, M. V., and Friedman, H., *Ind. Eng. Chem. Anal. Ed.* **18**, 304 (1946).
58. Titus, A. C., *Power App. and Systems* **No. 14**, 1160 (October, 1954).
59. Trillat, J. J., *J. Appl. Phys.* **19**, 844 (1948).
60. Untermyer, S., *Nucleonics* **12**, No. 5, 35 (1954).
61. Vollmar, R. C., Petterson, E. E., and Petruzzelli, P. A., *Anal. Chem.* **21**, 1491 (1949).
62. Weltmann, R. N., and Kuhns, P. W., *Natl. Advisory Comm. Aeronaut. Tech. Note* **No. 3098** (1954).
63. Winkler, Eva M., *J. Appl. Phys.* **22**, 201 (1951).
64. Winslow, E. H., Smith, H. M., Tanis, H. E., and Liebhafsky, H. A., *Anal. Chem.* **19**, 866 (1947).
65. Zemany, P. D., and Liebhafsky, H. A., *J. Electrochem. Soc.* **103**, 157 (1956).

X-Ray Diffraction Methods as Applied to Powders and Metals

WILLIAM L. DAVIDSON

Food Machinery and Chemical Corporation, Princeton, New Jersey

1. Introduction

1.1 ADVANTAGES OF POWDER METHOD

In spite of the fact that it does not usually enable one to determine crystal structures completely, the powder method of x-ray analysis has several distinct advantages.

1. Most crystalline materials occur in nature as agglomerates. This means that such samples are already in suitable form for study by the powder method.

2. Many technological processes deal with material in a finely divided state or composites of small crystallites. The powder method enables us to study specimens in their normal state, avoiding perturbations which might otherwise arise from sample preparation.

3. All the information can be recorded at one time on a single film, permitting rapid analysis.

4. As little as 1 mg. of material is sufficient for study by the powder method.

5. The technique involved in securing powder patterns is extremely simple. A novice can take excellent diffraction patterns after receiving a few hours of instruction.

6. The interpretation of powder patterns is in the main simple and straightforward. A cursory knowledge of crystallography ordinarily will enable one to carry out valuable studies with this tool.

For these reasons it is probably safe to say that more diffraction patterns are currently taken via the powder method than by all other methods combined.

1.2. PRODUCTION OF X-RAYS

X-rays are electromagnetic waves, similar in character to light but of much shorter wavelength. They are generated when high-velocity electrons impinge on a target. The target is usually a metal surface, molyb-

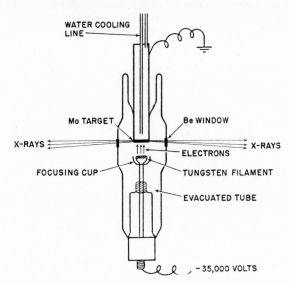

FIG. 1. Molybdenum x-ray tube of type used in diffraction work. Electrons from heated tungsten filament bombard a molybdenum target and generate x-rays. The latter emerge through low-absorption beryllium windows. Tubes with target of copper, iron, cobalt, nickel, tungsten, and chromium are also available.

denum and copper being the most popular target materials for producing the x-rays used in diffraction studies. Figure 1 illustrates the conventional means by which x-rays are generated.

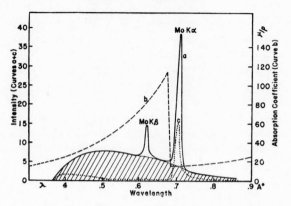

FIG. 2. Curve (a) plots the x-ray intensity from the tube of Fig. 1 as a function of wavelength. Curve (b) shows how the mass absorption coefficient of zirconium varies with wavelength. Curve (c) illustrates the filtering effect of 0.008 cm. of zirconium on the radiation. The Mo K_β and white radiation are substantially removed from the beam, whereas almost half of the Mo K_α intensity remains. This provides a beam sufficiently monochromatic for most powder work.

If one were to examine the x-rays coming from the target of Fig. 1, he would discover that the intensity varied with wavelength as shown in Fig. 2, curve (a).

1.3. TYPES OF X-RADIATION

Two kinds of x-radiation are distinguished, depending on the mechanism of production. The shaded region under curve (a) comprises the *white* or *general radiation*. This radiation results from interaction of the electrons with target nuclei. It is present irrespective of applied voltage or target material, although the shape of the curve changes as either of these quantities is varied. In fact there is always a sharp cutoff at the wavelength λ_{min} given by the following expression:

$$\lambda_{min} = \frac{12,450}{V_0} \tag{1}$$

where V_0 is the potential difference across the tube (volts); λ will be in units of 10^{-8} cm. or angstroms (A.).

If the voltage is increased beyond a certain critical value, sharp radiation peaks begin to appear, superposed on the white spectrum. These peaks constitute the *characteristic x-rays*, since they depend on the target element. From the Bohr picture of an atom, the critical voltage may be defined as that which gives a bombarding electron sufficient energy to eject one of the shell electrons from a target atom. When this happens an electron from one of the outer shells immediately negotiates a jump, replacing the dislodged electron. During the transition a quantum of characteristic x-radiation is emitted. If an electron is removed from the K-shell and the "jumping" electron comes from the L-shell, the radiation is termed K_a; if the jumping electron arises from the M-shell, K_β, etc.

There are two L-electrons in slightly different energy states which may interact with the K-shell. Consequently, the K_a-radiation is really a close doublet, K_{a_1} and K_{a_2}. The wavelength difference is so small that the two are not usually resolved on powder photographs. For calculations the wavelength is assumed to be the mean of K_{a_1} and K_{a_2}. Table I

TABLE I

Properties of Radiation Most Used in Diffraction Work

| Target | Minimum excitation potential (volts) | Characteristic wavelengths[a] | | | | Filter to remove K_β | Approx. filter thickness (in.) |
| | | kX | | A. | | | |
		K_{a_1}	K_{a_2}	K_{a_1}	K_{a_2}		
Mo	20,000	0.7078	0.7121	0.7093	0.7135	Zr	0.003
Cu	8,900	1.5374	1.5412	1.5405	1.5443	Ni	0.0008
Ni	8,300	1.6545	1.6584	1.6578	1.6618	Co	0.0008
Co	7,700	1.7853	1.7892	1.7889	1.7928	Fe	0.0006
Fe	7,100	1.9321	1.9360	1.9360	1.9399	Mn	0.0005
Cr	6,000	2.2850	2.2889	2.2896	2.2935	V	0.0005

[a] The wavelengths recorded in columns 3 and 4 were evaluated on the assumption that the spacing of the cleavage planes in calcite was 3.02945 A. More recent determinations indicate that this spacing is more nearly equal to 3.03560 A. This means that the wavelengths are too low by about 0.2%, and this is also true for all interplanar spacings obtained with these wavelengths. In the past, careful workers have negotiated this difficulty by expressing wavelengths and d values, not in angstrom units but in kX units, where a kX is defined as 1/2.8140 of the spacing of planes parallel to the unit cell faces (100) in NaCl. (The old measurements for this spacing gave a figure 2.814 A.) It has been agreed internationally that all kX values may be converted to angstroms through multiplication by the factor 1.00202 (104). Characteristic wavelengths have been listed both in kX and angstrom units. Wherever feasible throughout this chapter, spacings and wavelengths will be reported in true angstrom units. It should be confessed that distinguishing between these two units is mainly a matter of principle here, since most powder diffraction measurements include a probable error far greater than 0.2%.

records the K_a wavelengths and other pertinent data for the target elements most used in diffraction work.

Now, as the voltage is increased above the critical value V_0, the characteristic x-ray intensity increases about as $(V - V_0)^{1.7}$. Thus, although $V_0 = 20,000$ volts for Mo K, one normally uses considerably higher voltages in order to increase the x-ray output. For powder diffraction work a monochromatic beam of x-rays is needed. The usual way of achieving this is to introduce a selective filter into the x-ray beam where it emerges from the tube. This is illustrated later in Fig. 15.

1.4. ABSORPTION OF X-RAYS

When x-rays traverse matter, the beam intensity is reduced, partly by scattering and partly by a transformation of x-ray energy into that of moving electrons. The fraction of original beam (I/I_0) penetrating any thickness x of material is given by the well-known expression

$$\frac{I}{I_0} = e^{-\mu x} = e^{-(\mu/\rho)\rho x} \tag{2}$$

where μ is the linear absorption coefficient, and ρ is the density of the absorber; μ/ρ, the mass absorption coefficient, is often preferred, since it is independent of the state of the material.* Curve (b) in Fig. 2 shows how μ/ρ for Zr varies with the x-ray wavelength. The important feature of this plot is the sharp break at 0.688 A. This is known as the K absorption edge for Zr. X-rays with a wavelength shorter than this limit have energy $[E_{\text{x-ray}} \alpha(1/\lambda)]$ sufficient to knock electrons out of the Zr K-shell. In this way the initial beam is effectively attenuated, since the resulting Zr K x-rays are sent out in all directions. Owing to the phenomenon of resonance, the chance of ejecting a K-electron decreases slowly as the x-ray energy increases beyond the threshold value. On the other hand, an x-ray quantum with $\lambda > 0.688$ A. is unable to remove Zr K-electrons, and the absorption for such quanta assumes a very low value. Since the Zr K absorption edge falls between $\lambda_{\text{Mo } K_\alpha}$ and $\lambda_{\text{Mo } K_\beta}$, it is clear that a thin Zr foil will pass a high percentage of Mo K_α-radiation while absorbing most of the Mo K_β and general radiation. Curve (c) in Fig. 2 depicts the radiation of curve (a) after passing through a 0.008-cm. Zr foil. The Mo K_β-line is scarcely visible, but the Mo K_α-line retains almost half its original intensity. For most powder work this beam is sufficiently monochromatic.

If an ionization chamber or Geiger-Müller counter is to record the diffracted beam, a Ross filter may be used to advantage. This is in reality two filters, usually mounted so that one or the other may be readily positioned well in front of the ionization chamber or counter window. For Mo

---

* Values of μ/ρ for specified wavelengths are listed for many elements in the "Handbook of Chemistry and Physics," Chemical Rubber Publishing Company, Cleveland, Ohio. The Handbook also contains a wealth of crystallographic data for many compounds.

radiation one of the filters is Zr, the other Sr. The K absorption edge for Sr is 0.771 A. The thickness of the filters is adjusted so that above 0.771 A. and below 0.688 A. both absorb nearly equal fractions of the radiation. Between these two limits, however, the Sr filter is a heavy absorber, whereas the Zr absorbs very little. Therefore, the difference in readings obtained with one and then the other filter in place is due almost entirely to x-rays in this special wavelength region. This effectively eliminates counter background, secondary, and incoherently scattered radiation. For special applications requiring purely monochromatic radiation one must resort to reflection from a crystal.

2. X-Ray Diffraction

2.1. Need for X-Ray Diffraction Method

The instrument for extending normal vision is the optical microscope. The resolution of this instrument can be pushed to about 1000 A. Beyond this point the electron microscope takes over and extends the resolution limit some 25 A. But a single atom is barely 1 A. in diameter, so even the electron microscope is limited to a study of atomic aggregates. Clearly some other technique is indicated if we are to ascertain the exact location of the individual atoms which constitute matter. Although we never really see the atoms in our sample, through the interaction of x-rays with these atoms we can locate the positions of the latter quite accurately. We must thank two fortunate circumstances for the great success that has been achieved in revealing the structure of substances with x-rays.

1. *X-ray wavelengths are roughly of the same magnitude as the separation of atoms in matter.* This is a necessary condition for the diffraction phenomenon.

2. *Most solids are constructed from some elementary spatial unit duplicated over and over at regular intervals.* This is equivalent to saying that most solids are crystalline. A diffracted ray represents the integrated effect of many scattering centers, and hence a reasonable perfection in structure is required.

These two facts were realized by many people prior to 1912. In that year, however, the German scientist von Laue, by merging these two ideas, suggested that x-rays should be diffracted by crystalline materials. The phenomenon was verified a year later (63), and so a powerful new aid to scientific progress was born. Von Laue's mathematical interpretation of x-ray diffraction by using a three-dimensional array of scattering points was so involved that its full significance was not appreciated at once. It remained for the Braggs in England to show that equivalent results could be obtained by assuming that x-rays are *reflected* by sets of parallel planes in the crystal. The planes are always chosen so that they contain a heavy population of atom centers.

2.2. The Bragg Equation

Consider a two-dimensional array of atom centers as depicted in Fig. 3 with X-radiation incident at angle θ to the plane PP' and all points on

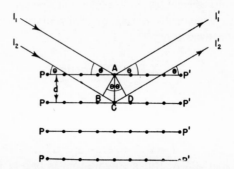

Fig. 3. The "reflection" of x-rays by parallel planes of scattering centers. When electromagnetic radiation traverses an atomic array, each electron present becomes a source of secondary radiation. The result may be pictured as a "reflection" of the x-rays by the atomic planes. Unlike an ordinary mirror, these planes reflect rays only for particular angles of incidence.

the wave front AB in phase. On the Bragg picture I_1 and I_2 will be reflected as shown. In order that points A and D be in phase after reflection, it is evident that $BC + CD$ must equal some multiple of the x-ray wavelength; i.e., $BC + CD = n\lambda$. Now AB and AD are perpendicular to I_2C and CI_2', respectively; and AC is perpendicular to PP'. Therefore $\angle BAC = \angle CAD = \theta$; thus $BC = CD = d \sin \theta$. Hence, the condition for constructive reflection is

$$n\lambda = 2d \sin \theta \tag{3}$$

This is the famed Bragg equation and is the fundamental relation underlying all x-ray diffraction measurements. It is important to remember that only for an angle of incidence such that $\sin \theta = n\lambda/2d$ will x-rays be reflected. At all other angles destructive interference will occur. Also, since $\sin \theta \leq 1$, it is clear that $n\lambda$ can never be greater than $2d$. For example, if we are dealing with atomic planes spaced 1 A. apart ($d = 1$ A.), no reflection of higher order than the second ($n = 2$) can be obtained with Mo K_a-radiation.

In using eq. (3) to calculate interplanar spacings one usually knows n and λ and has only to measure θ. In powder work the diffracted rays normally are allowed to fall on a photographic plate. From the resulting pattern and camera geometry θ can be readily determined for every reflection.

3. Elements of Crystal Structure

It would be quite erroneous to think that our knowledge of crystal structure dates only from the discovery of x-ray diffraction. Crystallographers had made remarkable strides in this direction long before the discovery of x-rays, even though their observations were limited to the external, optical, and cleavage features of crystals. X-rays in essence

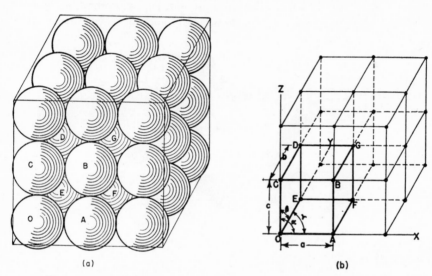

(a)   (b)

FIG. 4. (a) A small section of a hypothetical crystal of like atoms, magnified about one hundred million times. The sketch is purely for illustrative purposes; no *element* actually crystallizes in this fashion, although it could be thought of as representing the structure of KCl, since K⁺ and Cl⁻ have the same scattering power for x-rays. (b) A plot showing the location of the centers for the atoms in (a). These points (ignore the connecting lines) comprise the space-lattice for the crystal. The parallelepiped set off by heavy lines constitutes the unit cell.

permitted one to look inside the crystal and thus provided a potent tool for studying ultimate structures. Before x-rays can be used for this purpose, some knowledge of crystallography is necessary. To attain this end, several basic concepts must be mastered. These include the following: (1) Space-lattice. (2) Unit cell. (3) Crystal systems. (4) Elements of symmetry. (5) Point groups. (6) Space groups. (7) Miller indices. In

the following discussion we propose to consider these concepts in the
order listed.

3.1. SPACE-LATTICE

Were we able to see the ultimate structure of a simple crystal composed of like atoms, a small fragment might appear somewhat as pictured
in Fig. 4a. If we should now plot the position in space of each atom
center, a series of points would be obtained as shown in Fig. 4b. This
array of points constitutes the *space-lattice* for our crystal. A space-
lattice is defined as a series of points, formed by the intersection of three
sets of parallel planes, which locates equivalent positions in the crystal.
When more than one kind of atom is present, e.g., sodium chloride, each
type would possess its own space-lattice. Sometimes even for crystals

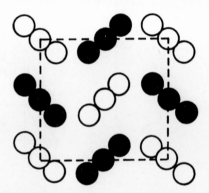

FIG. 5. Projection of a unit cell for crystalline benzene. The plane of all
benzene molecules is perpendicular to the plane of the paper, so only three
carbons are visible. For simplicity the hydrogen atoms are not shown. The
shaded molecules are displaced into the paper one half the length of a unit
cell. Note that a whole benzene molecule surrounds each lattice point.

containing but one atom type certain of the atoms fit one lattice whereas
others require a different one. In either event the combination of separate
lattices will then determine the symmetry properties of the crystal.
There are many ways in which planes may be erected to form our particular lattice, but the simplest is as shown in Fig. 4b, i.e., planes parallel
to *OCDE*, *OABC*, and *OAFE*. In the case we are considering, each lattice
point corresponds to an atom center. This is not essential. Sometimes we
find many atoms grouped around a lattice point. This can be seen in Fig.
5, which depicts a projection of the unit cell for crystalline benzene. The
only requirement is that each point represents an equivalent position in
the crystal.

3.2. UNIT CELL

The volume bounded by the labeled points in Fig. 4b is known as the *unit cell*, since it represents the smallest "brick" which, by repetition of itself in all directions, will build the crystal.

3.3. CRYSTAL SYSTEMS

It is clear that the lattice pictured can be referred to lines OX, OY, and OZ. These are termed the *crystallographic axes*. The system to which a crystal belongs is determined by the angles, α, β, and γ, formed by these axes and the relative lengths of the *primitive translations a, b,* and *c*. It has been found that all crystals can be fitted to one of just seven systems of coordinates. These represent the seven major divisions into which crystals are classified. Table II records these systems and the

TABLE II

Crystal Systems

System	Axes	Angles
1. Triclinic	$a \neq b \neq c$	$\alpha \neq \beta \neq \gamma \neq 90°$
2. Monoclinic	$a \neq b \neq c$	$\alpha = \gamma = 90°; \beta \neq 90°$
3. Orthorhombic	$a \neq b \neq c$	$\alpha = \beta = \gamma = 90°$
4. Tetragonal	$a = b \neq c$	$\alpha = \beta = \gamma = 90°$
5. Hexagonal	$a = b \neq c$	$\alpha = \beta = 90°; \gamma = 120°$
6. Rhombohedral	$a = b = c$	$\alpha = \beta = \gamma \neq 90°$
7. Cubic	$a = b = c$	$\alpha = \beta = \gamma = 90°$

properties of each. Some writers recognize only six systems, since by a transformation of axes rhombohedral crystals can be referred to hexagonal coordinates.

It is seen that the crystal considered above belongs to the cubic system, since $\alpha = \beta = \gamma = 90°$ and $a = b = c$. The arrangement of points which represents our crystal is termed a *simple* cubic lattice to distinguish it from two other possible space-lattices having cubic symmetry. All three of the cubic space-lattices are depicted in Fig. 6. In addition to the simple cubic arrangement the body-centered and face-centered lattices exist, so called because of additional lattice points appearing at the cube center and each face center, respectively. Note that, although the simple cubic cell contains eight lattice points, each must be shared equally with seven other cells meeting at the point. Thus the simple cube possesses but one complete point per unit cell. Similarly we notice that the body-centered cubic cell has two points (the body-centered point is not shared), whereas the face-centered cube has four points per unit cell (each of the six face-centered points is shared equally with one other

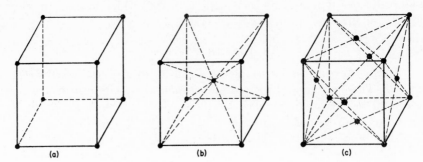

FIG. 6. A unit cell for each of the three cubic space-lattices: (a) simple cubic; (b) body-centered cubic (b.c.c.); (c) face-centered cubic (f.c.c.).

cell). This feature will prove important later for checking unit cell determinations. All told, fourteen space-lattices are geometrically possible. Each can be referred to one of the seven coordinate systems.

3.4. CRYSTAL SYMMETRY

The symmetry of any object is an expression of the fact that the object has identical properties in different directions. For example, the checkered diagram in Fig. 7 resumes its initial appearance after a rotation around O of 90°, 180°, 270°, or 360°. In crystal terminology O would

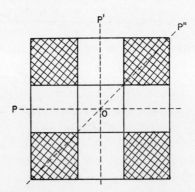

FIG. 7. A diagram to illustrate the concept of symmetry.

be called an axis of symmetry. When we consider figures in space, there are three types of symmetry operation which may be performed to bring equivalent points into coincidence. These are termed symmetry elements and include:

1. Axes of symmetry. Points in crystals may have two-, three-, four-, or sixfold axes. This implies rotation of 180°, 120°, 90°, or 60° to bring equivalent points into coincidence. As previously noted, our two-dimensional diagram, Fig. 7, has a fourfold axis through O.

2. Plane of symmetry. Here points on one side of the plane are mirror images of points on the other side. P,P' and P'' represent planes of symmetry for the checkered figure.

3. Center of symmetry. For this to hold true every point in the crystal must be matched by a corresponding point such that the line joining the two is bisected by the center of symmetry; O is such a center for Fig. 7.

3.5. POINT GROUPS

These operations can be used to describe the symmetry properties of crystals. Imagine a perfect cube. It has the following symmetry elements (these can be demonstrated quite readily by reference to an actual cube): (1) Three fourfold axes. (2) Four threefold axes. (3) Six twofold axes. (4) Three reflection planes (perpendicular to the fourfold axes). (5) Six reflection planes (perpendicular to the twofold axes). (6) Center of symmetry.

These elements collectively are termed the *point group* for a cube. It will also be found that each of the cubic lattices in Fig. 6 possesses this high symmetry. It is not essential, however, that *every* cubic crystal have *all* these symmetry elements. This fact can be ascertained by analogy, from consideration of the two-dimensional plots in Fig. 8. Here we are in

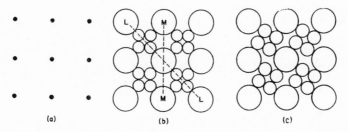

FIG. 8. Both (b) and (c) belong to the square lattice of (a). The planes of symmetry LL and MM in (b) are absent in (c), however. From W. H. Bragg and W. L. Bragg. "The Crystalline State," p. 74. Bell, London, 1934.

effect viewing the projection on a plane of a simple cubic lattice (29.8a) having atom clusters grouped around the lattice points. Figure 8b has all the symmetry properties associated with a square. This would correspond to the perfect cube in three dimensions. Figure 8c lacks several of the symmetry elements found in Fig. 8b (the planes of symmetry have disappeared). Yet this crystal has identical properties along X and Y and can be referred to a square lattice just as well as the grouping in Fig. 8b. If a crystal has the full symmetry of the system to which it belongs, it is called *holohedral;* if it possesses fewer symmetry elements, *hemihedral.*

All seven crystal systems have been analyzed with regard to the possible symmetry elements they can accommodate. Such an analysis leads to a total of thirty-two different point groups, and every known crystal can be assigned to one of these thirty-two *crystal classes,* as they are called. These are divided among the crystal systems so that each system has at least the following symmetry elements or their equivalent. (The number of classes associated with each system is also included.)

System	Minimum symmetry	No. of classes
Triclinic	None	2
Monoclinic	A twofold rotation axis	3
Orthorhombic	Two reflection planes perpendicular to each other	3
Tetragonal	A fourfold rotation axis	7
Rhombohedral	A threefold rotation axis	5
Hexagonal	A sixfold rotation axis	7
Cubic	Four threefold rotation axes (along the cube diagonal)	5

Crystallographers are able to make class assignments through studies on face angles and certain physical properties of the crystals. It must be emphasized that the point group assignment is basically a macroclassification. The ideas of space-lattices and atoms as ultimate units do not enter here, even though we have used them to illustrate the consequences of symmetry operations. Real progress in deducing ultimate crystal structure was delayed until it was realized that *atomic arrangement* is the *sine qua non* of a crystal, its outward appearance being an unimportant consequence of this. And it is a fact that the atomic arrangement bears little relation to the symmetry. Crystals closely related in their atomic groupings and bonding may differ widely in symmetry. As an example of this, it is found that benzene crystallizes in the orthorhombic system whereas hexamethylbenzene fits the triclinic system of much lower symmetry. It is by contributing information on the true arrangement of atoms in matter that x-rays have proved invaluable.

3.6. SPACE GROUPS

By its very nature the point group idea has a limited utility. By definition all the symmetry elements of each point group are associated with a central point, and translation is impossible. In order to describe the true atomic structural relationships in crystals a further concept is necessary. It remained for Federov, Schoenflies, and Barlow, working independently (circa 1890), to supply the missing link. Their contribution, incorporating the theory of *space groups,* combined the thirty-two classes of symmetry around a point with translation in three directions to other equivalent points. This successfully merged the point group and space-lattice. In so doing, new symmetry operations occur. These are the *screw axis* and the *glide plane.* The former rotates a structure $360°/n$ and at the same time translates it parallel to the axis. This operation, repeated n times, is equivalent to a translation of the space-lattice. The glide plane operation entails a reflection across the plane plus a translation parallel to the plane. These new operations are possible because each point of the structural unit need never return to its original position (as is required of a point group) but only to a similar position in another cell of the space-lattice. The space group may be defined as a set of self-consistent symmetry operations extending in space and associated with a space-lattice. Any symmetry operation or lattice translation brings all the remaining symmetry operations into self-coincidence. In all, 230 different space groups exist. Several notation schemes have been proposed to identify the various space groups. These may be found in any standard work on crystallography (30).

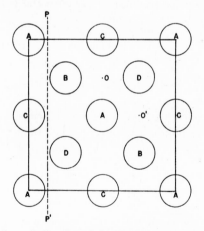

Fig. 9. Projection of the diamond unit cell to illustrate the function of screw axes O (clockwise), O' (counter-clockwise), and glide plane PP'.

Since the translations associated with a screw axis are of atomic dimensions, it is a fact that the finished crystal appearance does not distinguish between a mere rotation axis and a screw axis. The same situation obtains for a glide plane versus a straight reflection. To illustrate the importance of this, let us focus our attention on a diamond crystal. It shows externally the highest cubic symmetry. Therefore, one might naively demand a unit cell showing such symmetry. The actual situation is quite different, however. Looking down on a unit cell (Fig. 9), we see that the A carbon atoms occupy the top (and bottom) layers, B atoms comprise the second level, C atoms the middle layer, etc. Obviously this structure has no fourfold rotation axis, but O and O′ represent fourfold screw axes, clockwise and counterclockwise, respectively. These turn A into B, B into C, C into D, in a spiral manner. Likewise, there is no reflection plane parallel to a cube face, but PP′ is a glide plane. A reflection across PP′ together with motion downward a quarter cell length, parallel to PP′ and at 45° to the cell edge, makes A coincident with B, B with C, C with D, etc. Therefore, it is only by means of the space group concept combined with information obtained from x-ray diffraction that the basic structures of diamond and hundreds of other crystals, organic and inorganic, have been elucidated.

An ultimate structure determination normally requires data secured from single crystals by optical, goniometric, and x-ray diffraction methods. Since we are confining ourselves substantially to the powder method of analysis, the possibility of finding a complete structure will not usually arise. Even so, we shall see that powder patterns can provide us with a wealth of information having unique value to the fields of chemical and metallurgical analysis.

3.7. MILLER INDICES

Consider the unit cell for a face-centered lattice depicted in Fig. 10. In addition to the faces there are numerous other planes (e.g., ABYX, CDEF, XYZ) which may be passed through this cell, cutting lattice points. When extended through neighboring cells, each plane will cut corresponding lattice points. In addition, each plane will have associated with it a family of equally spaced parallel planes. It should be re-emphasized that the points contained in these planes are not the atoms themselves but represent equivalent points around which atoms are grouped. Nevertheless, we can assume that these planes will reflect x-rays, since the atomic arrangement around each point is symmetrical. For this reason it is important that we possess a notation that will allow us to index these planes in a logical manner. The scheme actually employed involves the use of so-called *Miller indices*. The planes are designated by the reciprocals of the fractional intercepts on the axes XYZ of the unit cell. For example, CDEF cuts X at ½a and is parallel to Y and Z. Hence the intercepts are ½, ∞, ∞, and the reciprocals 200. Thus we identify CDEF as a two-zero-zero (200) plane, the figures being enclosed by parentheses. Similarly *ABYX* is seen to be a (110) plane, and *XYZ* a (111) plane. It is evident that the cell faces have indices (100), (010), and (001). The general expression is written (*hkl*), *h* being the reciprocal of the fractional intercept on the *X*-axis, *k* and *l* being similar quantities for the *Y*- and *Z*-axes. If any of the reciprocals should be fractional, (*hkl*) is taken as the smallest set of integers which leaves the relative values unchanged. For example, if the reciprocals are ⅔, ⅓,½, the plane is written (983). If the intercepts of a plane on the axes are negative, then the indices of that plane are negative. Convention requires that the minus sign be placed above the number. For example, a plane striking the axes at $-\frac{1}{3}a$, $\frac{1}{2}b$, $1c$, would be written ($\bar{3}21$).

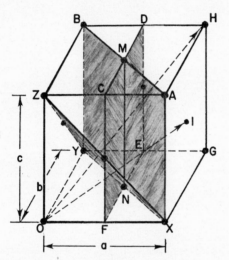

FIG. 10. Plot of unit cell for a face-centered structure to provide an understanding of nomenclature for planes and directions within a crystal.

If a particular line has components on the *XYZ* axes of *ua, vb, wc,* respectively, its *direction* is written [*uvw*], consistent with the requirement that *u, v, w* has minimum integral values. For example, in Fig. 10, *OI* has components $1a$, $\frac{1}{2}b$, $\frac{1}{2}c$. Hence direction *OI* is [1, ½, ½] or more properly [211]. Similarly *OH* = [111], *HO* = [$\overline{111}$]. In the cubic system a direction is always normal to the set of planes having identical indices; e.g., [111] is normal to (111), etc. Certain sets of crystal planes will intersect along a line or parallel lines. This line is termed a *zone axis* (such as *MN* of Fig. 10), and all planes which pass through this or parallel lines constitute a *zone*. Like a crystal direction, the zone axis is designated by indices in square brackets. *MN* (and parallel lines such as *OZ, BY, DE,* etc.) form the [001] zone axis, and planes *ABYX,*

CDEF, *AZOX*, *AHGX*, etc., all are a part of the [001] zone. The essential distinction between a direction and a zone axis is that the former passes through the origin, whereas the latter may not.

Special mention should be made regarding the notation for planes in the hexagonal system. By definition this system has two axes, X and Y, at an angle of 120°, with a third axis perpendicular to the plane of the first two. To take full advantage of the symmetry inherent in the hexagonal system, a fourth axis, W, is often added. W lies in the XY plane and makes an angle of 120° to both X and Y. The (hkl) indices for a

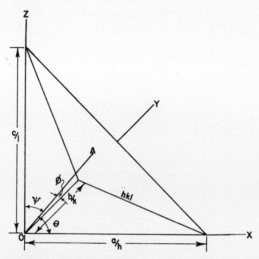

Fig. 11. OA represents the interplanar spacing d for the set (hkl). θ, ϕ, and ψ are the angles OA makes with X, Y, and Z, respectively. If the axes are mutually perpendicular, d can be readily evaluated in terms of a, b, c, h, k, l.

plane are now replaced by $(hkil)$, called Miller-Bravais indices; i refers to the intercept on W and is always equal to $-(h + k)$. To illustrate this point, the conventional (010) plane becomes (01$\bar{1}$0) in the new notation. Since i never enters into the calculation of interplanar spacings, it is often replaced by a dot; i.e., (01$\bar{1}$0) becomes (01·0).

4. Formulas for Interplanar Spacings

The spacing between adjacent planes of a set having indices (hkl) is usually written d_{hkl}. It is this d that occurs in the Bragg equation $n\lambda = 2d \sin \theta$. A certain simplification results if one includes n in the d. In this way every diffraction line can be thought of as a first-order reflection.

For instance, one would interpret a second-order reflection from the (111) set of planes as a first-order 222 reflection. Note that no parentheses surround the 222. This enables true planes to be distinguished from reflections. Obviously the above point of view requires that $d_{222} = \frac{1}{2}d_{111}$.

Now d_{hkl} is a function of the unit cell parameters a, b, c, α, β, γ. Let us derive an expression for d, limiting ourselves to the case where $\alpha = \beta = \gamma = 90°$. This expression will be adequate for the cubic, tetragonal, and orthorhombic systems.

In Fig. 11 we choose a plane (hkl) such that the neighboring plane of this set cuts the origin. Then OA, a normal to the plane represents the interplanar spacing d_{hkl}. It can be seen that

$$d_{hkl} = \frac{a}{h}\cos\theta = \frac{b}{k}\cos\phi = \frac{c}{l}\cos\psi \tag{4}$$

Now if $\cos\theta$, $\cos\phi$, and $\cos\psi$ are the direction cosines of the plane normal referred to the coordinate axes, it is true that

$$\cos^2\theta + \cos^2\phi + \cos^2\psi = 1 \tag{5}$$

Squaring the expressions in eq. (4) and putting them in eq. (5) gives

$$d^2\left(\frac{h^2}{a^2} + \frac{k^2}{b^2} + \frac{l^2}{c^2}\right) = 1 \tag{6}$$

or

$$d = \frac{1}{\sqrt{\dfrac{h^2}{a^2} + \dfrac{k^2}{b^2} + \dfrac{l^2}{c^2}}} \tag{7}$$

for the cubic system $a = b = c$, and eq. (7) reduces to

$$d = \frac{a}{\sqrt{h^2 + k^2 + l^2}} \tag{8}$$

In tetragonal crystals $a = b$, and we find

$$d = \frac{a}{\sqrt{h^2 + k^2 + \dfrac{l^2 a^2}{c^2}}} \tag{9}$$

The expression for d in the hexagonal system is

$$d = \frac{a}{\sqrt{\dfrac{4}{3}(h^2 + hk + k^2) + \dfrac{l^2 a^2}{c^2}}} \tag{10}$$

In the other crystal systems the equations for d are much more involved. It is fortunate that most solids crystallize in systems possessing high symmetry, for these are the ones most amenable to study by the powder method.

5. X-Ray Diffraction Technique

5.1. Major Methods and Equipment

X-ray diffraction apparatus for powder work can be classified in two major categories, depending on the method employed to register the diffraction pattern. If photographic film serves as the detecting medium, the recording unit is termed a diffraction camera and one is said to be utilizing the camera technique. On the other hand, if a radiation detector such as a Geiger counter fixed to a goniometer is used to detect the diffracted rays, the apparatus is termed a diffractometer. Each of these procedures boasts certain advantages and at the same time some disadvantages. The photographic procedure has a marked edge in terms of simplicity, and minimum sample requirements. By the same token an x-ray diffraction unit plus associated cameras will cost only one-third to one-half that of a recording x-ray diffractometer. The photographic film can record the complete diffraction pattern from a specimen, whereas the standard diffractometer provides only a one-dimensional scan. Consequently, errors caused by preferred orientation or coarse grain size are more liable to occur in diffractometer work, and very weak lines may be missed completely. On the other hand, for many applications the diffractometer possesses the great advantage of rendering results much more rapidly than is possible when one must load, expose, unload, develop, fix, dry, and measure film. Furthermore, the diffractometer can measure line intensities with greater precision than the film method, and the information is conveniently displayed on a strip chart. In addition, the diffractometer can be readily modified to function as an x-ray spectrometer, providing qualitative and quantitative information on elements present in a specimen by measurement of the fluorescent radiations excited. Thus, the choice between these two approaches will depend in large measure on financial considerations and the type of problems to be studied. Happily, only minor modifications are necessary to permit use of the same basic x-ray generation equipment with either film or goniometer attachments. It is the author's feeling that, in the interest of economy, simplicity, and versatility, a laboratory contemplating an investment in x-ray diffraction apparatus should first concentrate on photographic techniques. Later, the required diffractometer auxiliaries can be acquired as specific needs arise which justify the additional expenditure.

Today's commercial x-ray diffraction apparatus is quite compact, the basic unit being about the size of a console television set. It is completely self-contained, ray-proof, and requires but two external connections, one to a 110- or 220-volt a.c. source, the other to a water line for cooling purposes. All parts operating at high voltage are safely confined within the metal cabinet. Access doors are equipped with interlocking switches, making the apparatus quite safe. The American Crystallographic Association has compiled a detailed listing (August 15, 1956) of products and suppliers for x-ray diffraction studies.* Diffraction equipment supplied by any reputable manufacturer can be depended on for satisfactory service. Each make has a few special refinements, so it becomes a matter of individual preference as to which apparatus is chosen, much like the selection of an automobile. It is possible to have a hybrid arrangement wherein a powder camera, a back-reflection camera, a Weissenberg single-crystal camera, and a Geiger counter goniometer can be operated simultaneously from radiation supplied by a single four-window x-ray tube.

5.2. X-RAY GENERATION

The generation of x-rays for diffraction work is a step common to both the photographic and diffractometer techniques. The high-voltage supply is a transformer having an output peak voltage around 60,000. The primary is usually fed through an autotransformer, permitting a wide choice of voltage. The transformer voltage may be applied to the tube in numerous ways. The four most common are depicted in Fig. 12. With arrangement (a) or (b) one pulse of x-rays is produced per a.c. cycle. Methods (c) and (d) require additional rectifier tubes but yield two x-ray pulses per cycle. This effectively doubles the x-ray output compared to schemes (a) and (b) or alternately provides the same output with reduced filament emission in the x-ray tube. Under the latter condition tube life will be greatly increased.

With photographic recording, fluctuations in the voltage and current supplied to the x-ray tube are not serious, since any change in the x-ray beam affects all lines in the pattern equally. Fluctuating x-ray output is much more critical in a diffractometer, however, since the lines are scanned sequentially in time. Diffractometer manufacturers have solved this difficulty in one of two ways. The direct approach involves the addition of voltage and current stabilizer circuits, which holds the x-ray output constant to $\pm0.1\%$ for long periods of time irrespective of line fluctuations. The other solution involves the addition of a second radiation detector which continually intercepts a portion of the main beam or diffraction line from a thin foil in the main beam and thus serves as a moni-

---

* Persons interested in obtaining this listing are invited to write Dr. T. C. Furnas, Jr., 55 Johnson St., Brooklyn, New York.

tor. As an added feature, the electrical output from monitor and detector may be fed to a ratio recorder so that the chart record is a true picture of the intensity distribution in the diffraction pattern. Obviously, either of these solutions requires considerable additional circuitry.

In commercial installations, the x-ray target (anode) is grounded while the filament floats at the requisite negative potential. This enables one to carry cooling water to the target support with no insulation wor-

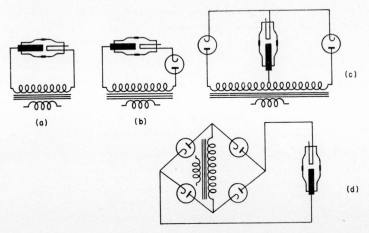

FIG. 12. Common rectification schemes used in diffraction apparatus. (a) Self-rectification. (b) Half-wave rectification employing one rectifier tube. (c) Full-wave rectification using two tubes. (d) Full-wave bridge rectifier. For the same output voltage the transformer used in (c) must produce twice as much voltage across the terminals as that given by (a), (b), or (d).

ries. Cooling is essential, since of the 600 watts in the electron stream only 1 to 2% appears as x-ray power, the remainder being dissipated as heat.

5.3. X-Ray Tube

Although for reasons of economy and versatility many European workers favor a demountable x-ray tube, i.e., one in which the filament and target may be readily replaced, the difficulties associated with securing and maintaining the requisite high vacuum have caused most workers in the United States to adopt sealed-off tubes. Such tubes are available commercially with any of the following targets: molybdenum, nickel, tungsten, copper, cobalt, iron, and chromium, and on special request even other elements. With reasonable care a tube will have an operating life ranging between 3000 and 10,000 hours. The tube consists of a highly evacuated glass envelope containing a spiral tungsten filament as an electron source, such as is pictured in Fig. 1. The electrons are focused to a sharp line on the target roughly 1 mm. by 12 mm. Special windows with low x-ray absorption (Lindemann glass 0.010 inch thick, beryllium metal 0.020 inch thick, or mica 0.005 inch thick) are built into the envelope to permit emergence of the beam.

Two windows "see" the electron target area end-on, so that it appears as a spot. When viewed at an angle of 6° below the horizontal, the target spot is foreshortened into an area of about 1 mm.². This gives effectively a strong point source of x-rays. For special microbeam diffraction applications tubes are available where the electron line focus on the target has a width of less than 0.1 mm.

For cameras employing circular pinhole geometry, a strong point source of x-rays is preferable. For slit-system collimation, setups which see the target line broadside are satisfactory and even preferable. Soller slits (see Fig. 19) may be added to a system employing an extended line source to retain high resolution and excellent line shape in the diffraction pattern.

Copper K_a-radiation is much used in diffraction studies, since its longer wavelength spreads the diffraction patterns over a wider angular interval than does Mo K_a, for example. This means that, with the same camera diameter, Cu radiation will permit greater precision in measurements of d values. Of course, this can be offset by utilizing a larger camera for work with a Mo target tube but at the cost of much longer exposures. Owing to its high thermal conductivity, a Cu target tube can be operated safely at a higher power loading than those with most other metals.

Another factor to be considered in the choice of radiation for diffraction studies is the possibility of exciting fluorescent radiation in the specimen. K-radiation from element A is capable of exciting the K-radiation in element B, provided B has an atomic number two or more units lower than A. (L-radiation may also be produced, but this is not usually troublesome.) This fluorescent radiation results in a general background on the film and may completely blot out the diffraction pattern when B is three or four atomic numbers below A. A specimen containing iron exhibits this phenomenon when examined with Cu K_a-radiation. Consequently, one who plans to concentrate on the study of ferrous materials would certainly select a tube with target other than Cu. Of course, the ideal is to own several different x-ray tubes, but this is not always economically possible. It so happens that the region of the periodic table immediately below Mo contains few elements of great technical importance. On this basis, a Mo target tube is often chosen to supplement the preferred Cu tube. For the study of organic compounds where long spacings are the rule, Cr radiation is gaining in favor.

It should be obvious that long-wavelength radiation is mandatory if back-reflection experiments are contemplated. In this region $2\theta \approx 180°$, $\theta \approx 90°$, and $\sin \theta \approx 1$. Therefore, the Bragg equation becomes approximately $\lambda \approx 2d$. This means that one should select a wavelength slightly less than twice the value of a fairly strong specimen reflection. Table III

TABLE III

Radiations Applicable to Specimens for Back-Reflection Experiments

Sample	Reflection	Relative intensity	2d (A.)	Suitable characteristic radiation	Mean λ of K_α-doublet (A.)
Fe	211	0.38	2.33	Cr K_α	2.29
	310	0.08	1.81	Co K_α	1.79
	222	0.03	1.65	Cu K_α	1.54
	321	0.10	1.53	Zn K_α	1.44
Cu	222	0.09	2.09	Fe K_α	1.93
	400	0.03	1.81	Co K_α	
Al	400	0.02	2.02	Fe K_α	
	420	0.04	1.81	Co K_α	
Mg	12.3	0.03	1.80	Co K_α	

records radiations suitable for a number of materials often studied by the back-reflection technique.

5.4. Protective and Safety Devices

Mention has been made of the interlocking switches which prevent access to energized high-voltage points. In addition there are numerous devices whose function is to protect the equipment in the event of overload, water failure, etc. Although not involved directly in the production of x-rays, these accessories are invaluable in protecting the unit against damage.

5.5. Standard X-Ray Cameras

Many types of camera have been used in the study of crystals by x-ray diffraction methods. Here we shall consider only those cameras which can be used with powder specimens.

A powder contains myriads of small crystallites oriented in every conceivable direction. When a beam of x-rays traverses such a sample, some crystallites can always be found which fulfill the Bragg condition for every possible interplanar spacing. The diffracted rays for one particular set of planes will be directed along the surface of a cone having its apex at the specimen and altitude along the incident beam direction. In general there will be many such cones of diffracted rays emanating from the sample, as pictured in Fig. 13. Four schemes are used to record these rays, each having its special field of utilization. They are illustrated in Figs. 14, 15, 16, and 17.

The conventional "powder camera," the type used for a majority of powder samples, since it records all the diffraction lines, is pictured in Fig. 14. Here a strip of film (35 mm. wide) is curved to form a cylinder with the specimen placed in the center and the whole enclosed in a light-tight container. With some powder cameras the film must be covered with black paper or aluminum foil. This proves a disadvantage only for soft

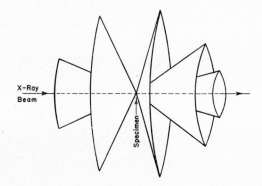

Fig. 13. The diffracted rays from a powder specimen form a series of concentric cones having a common apex at the sample position.

radiations such as those from iron and chromium. An important feature of any camera involves the manner in which the beam is conducted to and away from the specimen under study. Long paths in air are to be avoided, since air scattering will produce an unwanted background on the film. The sketch accompanying Fig. 14 depicts one scheme that has been used to minimize air scattering. Also apparent in this sketch is the *guarded* slit or pinhole, a feature common to all final collimating apertures. This arrangement allows for the trapping of rays which might be diffracted by material forming the edge of the defining aperture. The camera diameter is often chosen to be (1) 57.3 mm. or (2) 114.6 mm. (sometimes a bit larger to allow for film shrinkage). This choice means that (1) 1 mm. or (2) 2 mm. measured between corresponding lines represents $1°$ in 2θ. The camera of smaller diameter requires a shorter exposure time, but spacings are more accurately determined with the larger.

The pattern reproduced in Fig. 14 illustrates the Straumanis (95) method of loading film in a powder camera. Following this technique, one punches two holes in the film a distance apart equal to one-half the camera circumference and places the film so that the free ends meet roughly half-way between entrance and exit portals. In this way one is certain of recording the complete pattern; there are no missing regions near $\theta = 0$ or $\theta = 90°$. In addition, a doubled back-reflection record is available for accurate measurements. An added advantage ac-

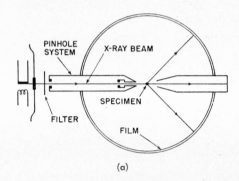

(a)

FIG. 14. (a) Schematic diagram showing essential features of powder camera. The exit tube is shown here extending almost to the specimen. This reduces air scattering.

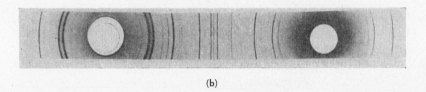

(b)

(b) Typical film obtained from cylindrical camera. Holes are cut in the film to permit entry and exit of x-ray beam. The Straumanis method of film placement was utilized here. See text. Courtesy of Picker X-Ray Corporation.

crues from the fact that lines around the exit and entrance ports center about points differing by exactly half the camera circumference. This enables one to deduce the effective camera diameter and correct for possible film shrinkage.

Figure 15 shows a flat cassette Laue-type camera. The specimen is mounted in front of the second pinhole, and the diffraction pattern is recorded on a flat film. The black disk directly in the x-ray path is a small blob of lead which intercepts the beam and prevents film halation during extended exposure. This camera is particularly suited to samples showing preferred orientation and also to those having large interplanar spacings.

The layout pictured in Fig. 16 is termed a back-reflection camera, since the recorded rays make an angle greater than 90° with the incident beam direction. This technique is ideal for large, thick samples. Pro-

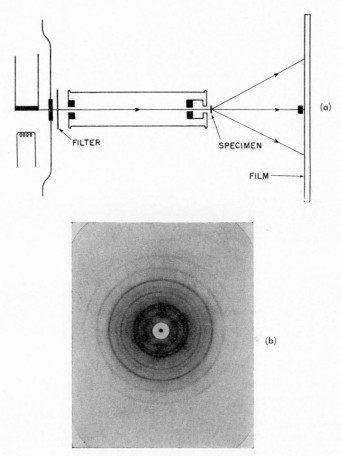

Fig. 15. (a) Schematic diagram of Laue camera arrangement. (b) Typical pattern obtained with this arrangement. This camera is especially suitable for samples showing preferred orientation or having large interplanar spacings. Courtesy of Picker X-Ray Corporation.

vision is made for rotating both sample and film to ensure smooth lines. The outstanding advantage of the back reflection camera is its extreme sensitivity to small lattice changes. This can be seen as follows:

The Bragg equation states

$$n\lambda = 2d_{hkl}\sin\theta \qquad (11)$$

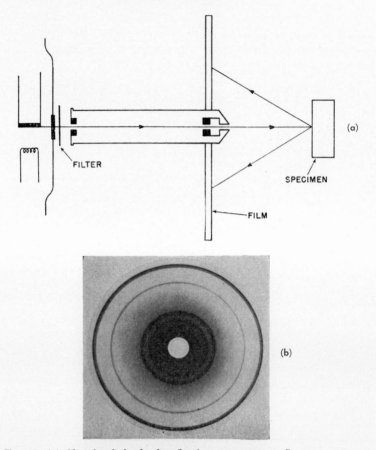

FIG. 16. (a) Sketch of the back-reflection arrangement. In some cameras of this type the collimating pinhole nearest the specimen may be moved independently, parallel to the beam direction. This adjustment makes it possible to satisfy the focusing conditions of Fig. 17 for any desired reflection, thus permitting very sharp rings. (b) Typical pattern taken with a back-reflection camera. Courtesy of Picker X-Ray Corporation.

To ascertain how θ varies with d_{hkl}, we differentiate eq. (11), obtaining

$$0 = 2d(d_{hkl}) \sin \theta + 2d_{hkl} \cos \theta \, d\theta \tag{12}$$

which can be written

$$\frac{d\theta}{d(d_{hkl})} = -\frac{\tan \theta}{d_{hkl}} \tag{13}$$

For values of θ near $90°$ (the back-reflection film covers this region, since $2\theta = 180°$), $\tan \theta$ has a very large value. This means that a small change Δd_{hkl} will cause a large θ change in this region.

For this reason lattice parameters can be evaluated with high accuracy from back-reflection patterns, and the method is much used in this connection.

5.6. Miscellaneous Cameras

Figure 17 illustrates the principle of the Seemann-Bohlin focusing camera which can be used for rapid recording of patterns. Here one bathes a large area of sample with x-rays and depends on a geometric principle to achieve sharp lines. If the slit (A), specimen (B), and film (C) lie on the circumference of a circle, all rays diffracted by the same family of planes in the specimen will be brought to a focus at the same point on the film. To see that this is so, let the rays shown repre-

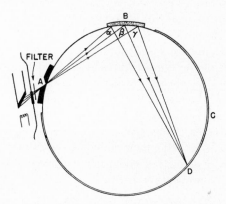

Fig. 17. Sketch to illustrate the focusing principle involved in focusing type of camera.

sent reflections from a common set of planes. Then $\alpha = \beta = \gamma$, since all are supplements of the same scattering angle, 2θ. But on any circle *equal angles inscribe equal arcs.* Since all three angles have point A in common, they must meet the circle at another common point such as D. The same argument holds for any other family of planes. Hilger and Watts Ltd. offer a miniature Seemann-Bohlin camera recommended for use with their microfocus (0.04-mm.) x-ray unit. Exposure times can be as little as 3 minutes with this combination.

Often one wishes to study the diffraction patterns from samples available only in micrograms or from selected small areas of larger samples. Here, microcameras are mandatory, employing collimated beams down to a few microns in diameter. Specimen-film distances are reduced correspondingly (to a few millimeters) so that exposure times are not prohibitive. Fankuchen and Mark (37), Chesley (22), Fried and Davidson (40), and Cahn (20), among others, have applied the microbeam technique to a variety of interesting problems. The microcamera designed by Chesley is available commercially from the North American Philips Company.

Special techniques are also necessary when diffraction patterns are desired from specimens maintained at very high or very low temperatures. A difficulty encountered in working at high temperatures is the necessity for keeping the photographic film sufficiently cool that deterioration of the emulsion does not occur. At low temperature the prevention of frost formation on the specimen mount or camera windows is sometimes a vexing problem. A powder camera designed for temperatures as high as 600°C. has been described by Buerger *et al.*, (19) and is available commercially from Otto von der Hyde, Box 1168, Maynard, Massachusetts. Unicam Instruments Ltd. (United States sales representative: Jarrell-Ash Co., 26 Farwell St., Newtonville 60, Massachusetts) offers a 1000°C. camera and an even more elegant high-temperature camera which can be operated on temperatures up to 1400°C. Hume-Rothery and Strawbridge (52) describe a powder camera attachment suitable for diffraction studies down to −110°C. The cooling medium is dry cold air obtained by boiling liquid air in a Dewar flask by means of an immersed electric heater. The cold air is circulated serially through a sequence of concentric cellophane chimneys surrounding the specimen. The air passes over a heating coil prior to passage through the outermost channel, thus preventing frosting.

5.7. Sample Preparation

In preparing a powder specimen the material should be ground in an agate mortar until it will pass through a 325-mesh screen. If the specimen is metallic, fine filings will suffice. There is always danger of lattice distortion here, so light pressure should be used in the filing operation. Of course the back-reflection method may be applied to the undisturbed bulk metal.

There are several ways of fabricating powder into a finished specimen. For a Laue camera it may simply be pressed between metal blocks to form a thin cake which is placed in front of the second pinhole. If the powder cake is too fragile, a small amount of amorphous binder (starch, gum tragacanth) can be added.

For the cylindrical camera the powder may be introduced into a thin-walled glass or cellophane capillary (about 0.4-mm. i.d.), the tube serving as a sample holder. If long-wavelength ($\lambda > 1$ A.) radiation is used, a paste of the powder and collodion can be pressed into a specimen tube and then partially extruded by means of a small wire ramrod.

The tube supports the specimen, and the bare section is irradiated. This avoids absorption of x-rays in the walls of a tube. If the material is in block or sheet form it can be mounted in the powder camera so that an edge intercepts the beam. Scattering will then result from a thin wedge-shaped section. This camera also has means for rotating the sample during exposure to smooth out spotty diffraction lines. Sometimes, however, it proves advantageous not to rotate the sample, inasmuch as variation in texture of the lines may assist in separating those due to different phases present in the sample. Various aids such as centering screws and fluorescent windows in the exit portal are usually incorporated for accurately centering the sample in the camera.

It will be noted that schemes shown in Fig. 14 and Fig. 15 are in a large measure transmission methods. Therefore, in the preparation of samples care must be exercised that the absorption be not too great. It is easy to show that for maximum diffracted intensity (forward direction) the optimum sample thickness is $1/\mu$, where μ is the linear absorption coefficient of the sample. This thickness would reduce the incident beam intensity to e^{-1} or about 37% of its original value. One can always dilute a highly absorbing sample with an amorphous material like flour in order to approach the above condition, using but a single capillary tube size.

5.8. EXPOSURE TIME AND FILM PROCESSING

The time required to secure a satisfactory pattern depends on many factors but in general will run from 30 minutes to 3 hours. The focusing camera is considerably faster (10 minutes perhaps); the back-reflection camera may require times running to 10 hours or more, since rays are diffracted at large angles with lower intensity. The commercial x-ray units are equipped with an automatic clock which shuts off the apparatus after a predetermined time. Once the exposure is complete, the film is removed from the camera and developed. X-ray film is orthochromatic, so the processing can be carried out under a ruby lamp. Special x-ray developers are available commercially. The usual time in developer is 4 minutes at 68°F. A 10- to 15-minute fix is suggested (twice the time to clear), followed by a wash of 30 minutes to 1 hour. The film is then allowed to dry and is at last ready for study.

5.9. MEASUREMENT OF PATTERN

Various comparators and viewing screens are marketed that permit accurate measurements on the diameters of the diffraction lines. The writer has found that a ground-glass viewing screen, together with a pair of sharp pointed dividers and a calibrated metal scale, provides satis-

WILLIAM L. DAVIDSON

Charts for Computation of d-Values in X-Ray Diffraction Chemical Analysis

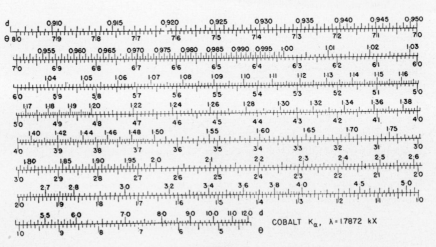

Fig. 18 (a)

Charts for Computation of *d*-Values in X-Ray Diffraction Chemical Analysis

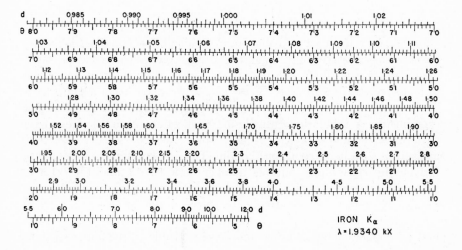

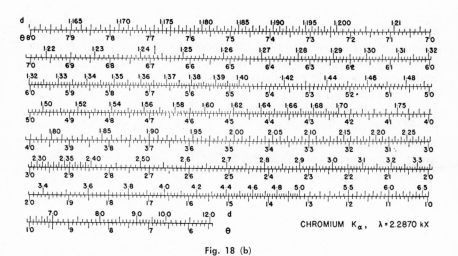

Fig. 18 (b)

FIG. 18. Charts that enable one to solve graphically the Bragg equation for interplanar spacings *d*. They were prepared by O. E. Brown and cover the five radiations most used in x-ray diffraction work (18).

factory equipment for measuring routine patterns. The dividers are set on corresponding lines of the film and then transferred to the scale for reading. The line diameter plus a knowledge of the camera geometry gives θ. As stated earlier, a camera diameter of 57.3 mm. or 114.6 mm. allows θ to be deduced without detailed calculation. Sin θ is then combined with the wavelength, λ, in the Bragg equation to yield an interplanar spacing, d. Figure 18 presents a series of charts which enables θ to be converted to d directly. These charts are taken from a publication by Brown (18) and cover the five wavelengths most used in diffraction experiments. A tabulation is made of the d values from all lines of the pattern. A relative intensity value is also assigned to each line, commensurate with its strength on the film. This is usually done semiquantitatively by selecting a suitable number between 0.1 and 1.0, 0.1 corresponding to a very weak line and 1.0 to the strongest. The reader may wonder why one does not attempt to place relative intensities on a firm quantitative footing by photometering the film. The answer is that the best microphotometer will miss lines easily visible to the naked eye and thus cannot provide a complete story.

5.10. Errors and Their Elimination

The following major factors serve to limit the accuracy attainable in deducing interplanar spacings from powder patterns. (1) Inadequate knowledge of specimen-film distance. (2) Shrinkage of film during processing. (3) Absorption of x-rays in sample. (4) Eccentricity of specimen and respect to axis in cylindrical cameras.

These first two factors can be corrected for quite simply. This entails two knife edges built into the camera so that they form sharp limits to the exposed film. The camera is calibrated by securing a pattern from a standard material. This pattern allows one to deduce the effective Bragg angle, θs, for a hypothetical diffraction line occurring at these limits. With other patterns from this camera the Bragg angle θ for any diffraction line is given by

$$\frac{\theta}{\theta s} = \frac{D}{Ds} \tag{14}$$

where D is the distance on the film from one arc of the line to its mate, and Ds is the distance between the knife-edge shadows.

When it is necessary to know lattice parameters with high accuracy all four factors should be taken into account. This can be accomplished in the following manner: a small amount of standard material such as sodium chloride or quartz is mixed with the unknown sample, and a pattern is recorded from the mixture. The well-known diffraction angles from the standard substance are plotted against measurements on the corresponding lines to give a calibration curve. The curve is then used to find accurate values of θ for lines due to the unknown. This procedure is more tedious than the first method but is considerably more accurate. The current procedure is used in conjunction with a back-reflection camera when the ultimate in accuracy is required. Such a combination will give d values that are reproducible to ± 0.0001 A. For some types of powder work it may not prove feasible to incorporate a standard material with the experimental specimen. In this event the sample tube can be divided into two compartments, the unknown occupying one section, and the standard in the other. Collimating slits serve to define the beam here, replacing the usual pinholes. A septum can be installed in the camera if desired to prevent superposition of the spectra. The two spectra will then appear side by side on the same film. The flat back-reflection camera contains a metal sector disk which exposes only a portion of the film at a time. This likewise permits side-by-side comparison spectra on the same film.

5.11. DIFFRACTOMETERS AND THEIR OPERATION

The detector unit of a diffractometer includes some type of radiation-sensing element which in turn is mounted on a single-circle goniometer. The detector can be an ionization chamber, Geiger counter, proportional counter, of fluorescent crystal-photomultiplier combination termed a scintillation counter. Although each of the devices possesses certain desirable attributes, the Geiger counter is most widely used in diffractometer work, since it is reliable, cheap, and requires only modest accessory equipment.

The pulses from the detector are amplified, shaped, equalized, and finally fed to a recorder. The latter can be a mechanical register or current-indicating device (counting rate meter). With the former, the pulses are first sent through an electronic scaling-down circuit because of the relatively slow response capability of the register. The rate meter is usually supplemented by a potentiometer-type pen recorder to permit making a permanent trace of the pattern.

5.12. DIFFRACTOMETER GEOMETRY

A modification of the Seemann-Bohlin (see Fig. 17) focusing arrangement known as Bragg-Brentano parafocusing is used almost universally in present-day diffractometers to maximize the diffracted radiation reaching the detector. For the same reason the line focus of the

x-ray tube itself occupies position A rather than the slit pictured. For
convenience and ease of preparation, the specimen surface is flat rather
than curved and thus does not completely coincide with the focusing
circle. To compensate for this, and to maintain a constant sample-
detector distance, the detector pivots about the specimen as center. The
sample mount is geared to the detector drive in such a way that it rotates
at half the angular velocity of the detector. Thus, the specimen surface
is always tangent to the focusing circle, and the normal to this point of
tangency bisects the angle between incident and diffracted radiation.

The use of an extended line source of x-rays causes further defocusing problems to arise from third-dimensional crossfire. At some expense
in intensity, however, this condition can be alleviated by the introduction
of Soller slits in the incident and diffracted beam paths, effectively
eliminating the divergent rays. Figure 19 is a schematic diagram showing

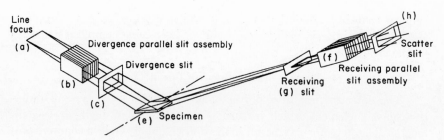

FIG. 19. Schematic diagram depicting x-ray optical arrangement. Courtesy
of North American Philips Co.

the x-ray optical arrangement of the sample-goniometer-detector combination employed in the Norelco diffractometer. With the setup shown the
detector can cover a range of 2θ from $0°$ to $160°$. Vertical spread is
limited by the divergence, receiving, and scatter slits. The first of these
determines the area of sample bathed by radiation. The receiving and
scatter slits define the diffracted beam reaching the Geiger tube. A series
of interchangeable slits is provided so that the most desirable compromise
between resolution and intensity can be achieved, depending on the particular demands. As mentioned above, the stacked Soller slits limit the
horizontal beam divergence and permit high resolution and excellent
line shape from an extended source of x-rays. Figure 20 records a diffraction pattern of quartz taken with the Norelco diffractometer, employing filtered Cu K_a-radiation. The high resolution present is pointed up
by the distinct α_1, α_2-doublet for all lines at $2\theta > 35°$ (the best powder
cameras do not resolve α_1, α_2-doublets until $2\theta \approx 90°$) and separation of
the five lines in a $1°$ interval around $68°$.

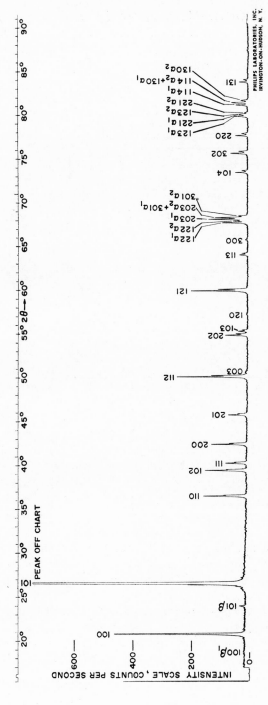

FIG. 20. Portion of a strip chart showing the diffraction pattern obtained from a quartz specimen over the range 2θ from $17°$ to $90°$ with the arrangement shown in Fig. 19. The x-ray source was Cu K_α with a 0.0006-inch Ni filter; effective angular aperture $1°$; scanning rate $\frac{1}{4}°$ (2θ) per minute; and time constant of the detector circuit 4 seconds.

5.13. GEIGER-MÜLLER TUBE DETECTOR

An ideal detector for diffracted x-rays should fulfill the following requirements:

1. A large proportion of the quanta incident on the detector should be registered.

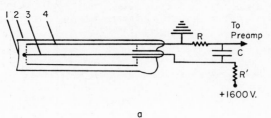

a

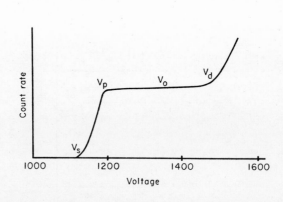

b

FIG. 21. (a) Geiger-Müller end window counter suitable for x-ray diffraction work. (1) mica window, (2) glass envelope, (3) central wire, and (4) metal cylinder. (b) Typical response curve for a GM counter as a function of voltage in the presence of a constant radiation source. The operating point, V_o, is chosen to be near the center of the plateau in order to minimize the effect of voltage fluctuations.

2. In order to minimize total equipment requirements the effect produced by a single quantum should be large.

3. The detector and associated apparatus should exhibit stable behavior over long periods of time.

4. The response of the detector to stimuli other than the desired x-rays should be small.

5. The system should show linear response to a wide range of intensities.

The Geiger counter scores high on all counts save the last, and even here suitable corrections can be made. Therefore, as mentioned earlier, it has found wide application as the prime detector in diffractometers. A typical Geiger tube suitable for x-ray work is depicted in Fig. 21a. Its essentials include a sealed glass envelope containing a central wire surrounded by a coaxial metal cylinder. External connections are as shown. A thin mica end window permits high x-ray transmission. The tube is filled to approximately atmospheric pressure with a special gas mixture. For soft x-radiation such as Cu, Ni, and Cr, argon is an excellent filling gas, a 10-cm. path of argon at atmospheric pressure absorbing more than 85% of these radiations. Of equal importance, argon is transparent to short-wavelength radiation. Thus, an argon-filled tube will effectively discriminate between the desired characteristic rays and unwanted white radiation, yielding a low background. When short-wavelength radiation such as Mo K_a is employed, the filling gas should be krypton for high counting efficiency. To make the tube self-quenching a small amount of halogen or organic vapor is added. The reader is referred to refs. 61, 65, 72, and 82 for an explanation of the phenomena underlying the functioning of a Geiger counter. Here, suffice it to say that, when a counter is exposed to a constant source of radiation and the voltage on the wire gradually increased, the counter response will be as shown in Fig. 21b. No counts occur until a threshold voltage, V_s, is reached. Between V_s and V_p the counting rate increases rapidly and the pulse amplitude is proportional to the energy of the incident quanta. This is the so-called proportional counter region. Between V_p and V_d there is little change in counting rate, and the pulse height is constant irrespective of the triggering radiation. Beyond V_d the counter enters a region of instability with a tendency toward incipient discharge whether or not a radiation source is present.

The interval V_p to V_d is called the counter plateau, and one normally sets the counter voltage, V_0, near the center of this region, since a fairly large change in counter voltage here will have but a slight effect on the counting rate. Stabilized high-voltage power supplies are commercially available wherein the voltage output is maintained constant to $\pm 0.1\%$ for extended periods. This is more than adequate for the precision required in most diffractometer studies.

The halogen added to the filling gas serves to quench the counter discharge by absorbing secondary photons. Thus, a few halogen molecules are destroyed each time the counter fires, and consequently the counter has a finite useful life. Most self-quenching counters have a life of 10^8 to 10^9 counts.

5.14. CORRECTION FOR NONLINEAR COUNTER RESPONSE

It was noted earlier that a Geiger counter does not show linear response over a wide range of x-ray intensities. This follows because there is a time interval after one pulse during which the voltage on the counter wire is below normal. The counter will be insensitive to an event occurring while the voltage is below a threshold value. For self-quenching counters this "dead time" is around 10^{-4} second. Inasmuch as the resolving time of the associated amplifying and scaling circuits is less than this by an order of magnitude, the counter itself is the controlling factor. The resolving time of the Geiger tube can be taken as representative of that for the entire counting system. A counter with a 10^{-4} second dead time will start missing an important number of events when the counting rate exceeds 100 per second. The observed counting rate, N, can be corrected to the true rate, N_0, by the following formula:

$$N_0 = \frac{N}{1 - NK\tau} \tag{15}$$

where τ is the resolving time for the Geiger tube, and K is a factor which recognizes that x-rays are not generated uniformly in time by a tube energized by a nonfiltered high-voltage supply but are produced in bunches. Arndt (3) finds K to be 3.2 for x-ray tubes employing half-wave or self-rectification and half this value (1.6) in the event of full-wave rectification. Methods for the determination of counter resolving time are beyond the scope of this review but can be found in the literature (9, 80, 86).

The above formula should not be applied when the counting correction exceeds 25%. For such cases a multifoil calibration technique (2) is recommended. Better still, to do appreciable work at high counting rates one should consider use of a beaded-wire Geiger tube or other device such as a proportional or scintillation counter boasting much shorter resolving times.

5.15. COUNTING STATISTICS

One might presume that after exercising adequate care in sample preparation, making certain of a highly stabilized x-ray source and counting system, and knowing the needed corrections for nonlinear counter response, the experimenter could feel completely confident of the data produced by his diffractometer. Unfortunately this is not quite true. X-ray quanta generation, like radioactive decay, is a random process both as to time and direction of emission. Thus, two measurements of the same x-ray beam over equal time intervals will not in general yield the same total count, owing to statistical fluctuations. Interestingly, photographically recorded diffraction patterns are not bothered by statistical considerations, since some 10^5 to 10^6 quanta must impinge on 1 mm.^{2} of film to produce reasonable blackening. For such large totals the statistical variations are negligible. It has already been noted, however, that speed is one of the prime advantages offered by the diffractometer. Consequently, to retain this advantage one cannot afford the luxury of counting longer than necessary to assure the desired precision and reproducibility. In what follows we shall consider how many counts must be accumulated to reduce the probable error from statistical fluctuations to a predetermined level. It should be appreciated that instrumental and sampling errors are not included in this determination.

If the true average number of counts resulting from a large number of experiments over equal time intervals in N_0, the spread of values from individual experiments is approximated by Gaussian distribution of mean value N_0 and standard deviation $\sigma = \sqrt{N_0} \approx \sqrt{N}$, where N is any individual determination. The probable deviation, i.e., the deviation in counts from N_0 which will encompass half the individual determinations, is given by $0.674\sigma \approx 0.674\sqrt{N}$. The probable error in per cent is thus

$$\text{P.E.}(\%) = \frac{0.674\sqrt{N}}{N}(100) = \frac{67.4}{\sqrt{N}} \tag{16}$$

From eq. (16) one can readily deduce the number of counts necessary to attain any desired degree of statistical accuracy. For example, 45, 4543, and 454,376 events must be counted to give a probable error of 10%, 1%, and 0.1%, respectively.

Inherent in the preceding is the tacit assumption that no background is present. Obviously, this is never true. If the gross count from a diffraction line is N, and the background count in the same general angular region is N_b, the net count due to the line is obviously $N - N_b$. The probable deviation here, however, is $0.674\sqrt{\sqrt{N}^2 + \sqrt{N_b}^2}$ and the percentage probable error is

$$\pm \frac{67.4\sqrt{N + N_b}}{N - N_b} \tag{17}$$

It follows that with $N = 500$ and no background ($N_b = 0$) the probable error would be $\pm 3\%$. With $N = 600$ and $N_b = 100$, however, the probable error is $\pm 3.5\%$, and if $N = 1000$ and $N_b = 500$ the probable error rises to $\pm 5.2\%$. Figure 22 plots the gross count, N, necessary to achieve a given probable error for a series of ratios of peak intensity to background (R). If the peak intensity is greater than ten times background, the curve for $R = \infty$ can be used without serious error.

5.16. OTHER FACTORS AFFECTING DIFFRACTOMETER MEASUREMENTS

It was previously noted that the slit geometry affects the resolution and intensities recorded by a diffractometer. In order to reproduce the profile of a diffraction line accurately, the counter entrance slit should be as narrow as possible. Furthermore, when the continuous traverse technique is employed, the time constant (RC) of the rate meter and the rate of scan have a decided influence on the recorded line shapes and

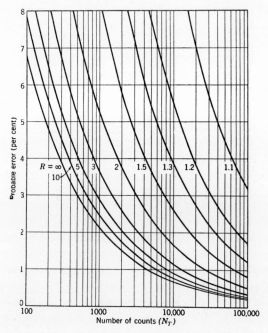

FIG. 22. Family of curves showing number of events N_T (diffracted intensity plus background) which must be counted to realize a given percentage probable error (ordinate) as a function of the ratio R (total counting rate/background counting rate). Courtesy of Klug and Alexander (60).

peak heights. Fortunately, the total area under a line and the line breadth at half peak intensity are not overly sensitive to variations in these instrumental parameters. Therefore, for most qualitative work comparison of total areas rather than peak heights is to be preferred. When the ultimate in accuracy is desired, one should dispense with continuous scanning and follow a point-by-point counting technique. If one wishes to determine each point with equal probable error the "fixed count" procedure is followed; i.e., at each goniometer position the time interval to yield a given total count is measured. Cooke-Yarborough (28) has suggested a modification of the fixed count method which involves the addition of periodic pulses at a constant low rate to the normal input. This reduces the counting time at the low intensity points, albeit at some sacrifice in probable error. Its adaptability to automatic operation is one of its outstanding virtues, however. A somewhat less precise procedure is the "fixed time" method wherein each point is counted for a given time. Clearly, in this instance, the probable error for the low-count regions will be greater than at the peaks. Counting rate computer attachments which will perform the preceding regimes automatically are commercially available. The reader is referred to an excellent paper by Parrish (77) which considers in detail the measurement of x-ray intensities with the diffractometer.

6. Chemical Analysis by X-Ray Diffraction

6.1. THE HANAWALT METHOD (47)

One of the most noteworthy successes of the powder method has been in the field of chemical analysis. The method has much to recommend it. In addition to its speed, economy, and simplicity, it possesses certain unique features.

1. The substances present reveal their true state of chemical combination. This advantage cannot be overemphasized. For example, cupric oxide gives a pattern distinctly different from that of cuprous oxide. In fact, a polymorphic material shows a unique pattern for each of its different forms. Figure 23 plots the patterns obtained from cupric oxide, cuprous oxide, and two forms of titanium dioxide.

2. The process almost classifies as a "micro" technique. One milligram or less of sample is usually adequate for an analysis.

3. Unknowns can often be studied *in situ*. For example, thin corrosion deposits on metallic surfaces can be examined with ease.

4. The analysis is nondestructive.

5. The record is permanent and can be filed for future study.

6. X-ray analysis does not require or produce any appreciable change in constitution of the sample. In other words, there need be no temperature changes, added reagents, etc. On the contrary, physical environment, including temperature, humidity, surrounding atmosphere, etc. can be adjusted freely to predetermined values.

In practice the identification of materials via their x-ray diffraction patterns is made feasible through the availability of the so-called Hanawalt card index file.

This was the major source of information for the original card file of the American Society for Testing Material (ASTM), which was first issued in 1941, covering some 1600 compounds. To this a supplementary set was added in 1947. This index has now been completely revised and issued in a new and more convenient format, under the auspices of ASTM, the American Crystallographic Association, the (British) Institute of Physics, and the National Association of Corrosion Engineers. Seven sections are available, and an additional section is normally issued annually. The various sections can be purchased separately and can be obtained as plain cards, Keysort cards, or IBM cards.*

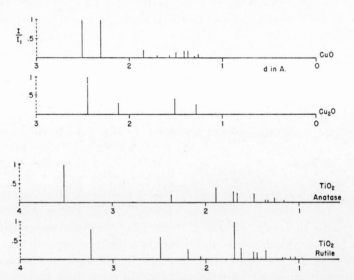

Fig. 23. Graphical plot of the powder patterns due to cupric oxide, cuprous oxide, TiO_2 (anatase), and TiO_2 (rutile). The abscissa plots the interplanar spacing corresponding to each line; the height of the line is proportional to its intensity on the film. The strongest line in the pattern is assigned a relative intensity of unity. These data were taken from the Hanawalt card index.

If these data are to serve their intended purpose, not only must they be available but they must be arranged in logical manner to facilitate rapid identifications.

The method as developed by Hanawalt is dependent on two kinds of measurement: (1) interplanar spacings and (2) relative intensities of lines. How these data are tabulated may be seen in Fig. 24, which reproduces the index card for NaCl. The top left row lists d values for the three strongest lines as well as the value for the line of greatest spacing measured. The second row records the relative intensities of these lines,

---

* For further details the reader should write American Society for Testing Materials, 1916 Race Street, Philadelphia 3, Pennsylvania.

with a value of 100 assumed for the strongest line. If two lines appear equally strong, the one with larger d is given priority in the tabulation. Information on how the x-ray data were obtained, crystallographic and optical data, and the source of material or its method of preparation is recorded below the spacing and intensity figures. The chemical formula and name are given in the upper right-hand corner, and the structure if the compound is organic. The vertical columns record the full sequence of spacings, relative intensities, and Miller indices, where known. The black star in the right-hand corner signifies that the data are of highest reliability. The array of cards is arranged in decreasing order of interplanar spacings, as judged by the first d value.

5-0628

d	2.82	1.99	1.63	3.258	NaCl					⭐
I/I₁	100	55	15	13	Sodium Chloride		Halite			

Rad.Cu λ 1.5405 Filter	d Å	I/I₁	hkl	d Å	I/I₁	hkl
Dia. Cut off Coll.	3.258	13	111			
I/I₁ d corr. abs.?	2.821	100	200			
Ref. Swanson And Fuyat, NBS Circular 539, Vol. II, 41 (1953)	1.994	55	220			
	1.701	2	311			
Sys. Cubic S.G. O⁵ₕ – Fm3m	1.628	15	222			
a₀ 5.6402 b₀ c₀ A C	1.410	6	400			
α β γ Z 4	1.294	1	331			
Ref. Ibid.	1.261	11	420			
	1.1515	7	422			
ε α n ω β 1.5428 γ Sign	1.0855	1	511			
2V Dₓ2.164 mp Color	0.9969	2	440			
Ref. Ibid.	.9533	1	531			
	.9401	3	600			
An ACS reagent grade sample recrystallized	.8917	4	620			
twice from hydrochloric acid.	.8601	1	533			
X-ray pattern at 26°C.	.8503	2	622			
	.8141	2	444			
Replaces 1-0993, 1-0994, 2-0818						

Fig. 24. ASTM index card for NaCl.

In the Hanawalt procedure, the cards are subdivided by spacers so that the initial d listings fall into the 87 groups listed here. With this breakdown each of the 87 groups encompasses a region some ten times as great in width as the error in a careful measurement around that spacing. For instance, if the strongest line from an unknown sample came at 5.33 A. one could feel fairly certain that the associated card would be found in the 5.25-A. to 5.50-A. group and hence concentrate his attention on cards within this group. For convenience, the cards within any one group are usually sorted in terms of the middle d value.

Spacings and relative intensities are tabulated for the unknown pattern. One now turns to the card group which covers the spacing of the strongest line from the unknown and to that region within the group corresponding to the second line. If the unknown is a single substance and its pattern catalogued, a match for the third line should be immediately apparent. Once this is found, all spacings from the unknown are compared with the card listings. If agreement is found for every line, within an admissible error, and there are no extra lines, the identification may be considered complete.

Spacings (A.)	Divisions	No. of groups
20		1
20-18		1
18-16		1
16-14		1
14-12		1
12-11		1
11-10		1
10-6	In 0.5-A. divisions	8
6-5	In 0.25-A. divisions	4
5-3.50	In 0.1-A. divisions	15
3.50-1.00	In 0.05-A. divisions	50
1.00-0.80	In 0.1-A. divisions	2
0.8		1

Hanawalt (47) has found that when he employs molybdenum radiation, a cylindrical (quadrant) camera 8 inches in radius, and a cassette that has been calibrated against a standard material, the error in measurement increases from ±0.001 A. at 1 A. through ±0.01 A. at 3.5 A. to ±0.06 A. at 8 A. Since most of the information was secured under these conditions, one must realize that the card data may be in error by this amount. In comparing experimental values with card data, differences as great as twice the above error may be considered permissible.

When the unknown material contains two or more components, slight ingenuity must be exercised. One has to consider all combinations of, say, the first six lines, taken three at a time. In practice, this can be done very quickly. As soon as one component has been identified the remaining analysis is greatly simplified. In some instances, lines from two components may be superposed to further complicate matters. As examples of multicomponent identifications using the ASTM index cards we shall consider two cases: (1) Two-component "unknown" with no superimposed index lines. (2) Two-component "unknown" showing superimposed index lines.

1. Figure 25a is a plot of the d values and relative intensities from an "unknown" sample studied by Hanawalt (47). Three lines, D (2.94

A.), F (2.53 A.), and G (2.32 A.), appear with equal intensity. Starting with the largest interplanar spacing, D, we open the card index to the 2.95 to 2.90 group and search for a card with a middle index line around 2.53 A. No such card is found, so we next look for a middle spacing close to 2.32 A. in this same group. Again no such card is apparent, so we now turn our search to a card with a middle d spacing around 3.29 A. This time we are successful, since sodium chlorate exhibits a middle spacing of 3.29 A. The third strongest sodium chlorate line appears at 1.76 A., which is also present in the "unknown." Therefore, we compare the whole sequence of sodium chlorate spacings (Fig. 25b) with our

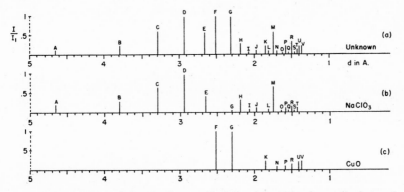

Fig. 25. (a) Plot of the d values and relative intensities for an "unknown" sample studied by Hanawalt. (b) Plot of pattern from sodium chlorate (data from ASTM index). (c) Plot of pattern from cupric oxide (data from ASTM index).

"unknown" pattern and find that every sodium chlorate spacing (with the exception of a very weak line at 1.89 A.) occurs in the "unknown." Except for lines at 1.58 and 1.50 A. all the matched lines have either the same or lower relative intensity than those in the sodium chlorate standard. There are several factors, such as large particle size and lattice imperfections, which may serve to weaken a line below the intensity listed in the standard pattern, but none which will materially increase its strength. We must now account for the unknown lines which do not match sodium chlorate, hoping too that the second phase will show lines at 1.58 and 1.50 A. and thus help to resolve our intensity difficulty. This time we turn to index group 2.55 to 2.50 and look for a second line around 2.32 A. (G). Cupric oxide is found to qualify here, and its third line is at 1.85 A., which could well be line K. When the standard pattern of cupric oxide (Fig. 25c) is studied, good agreement is found with all the remaining lines in the "unknown," and there are cupric oxide lines at 1.58 A. and 1.50 A. as required. Thus we conclude that the "unknown" comprises a mixture of sodium chlorate and cupric oxide.

2. Figure 26a plots the spacings and estimated relative intensities for a two-component "unknown" used by Smith and Barrett (92) as part of a laboratory exercise in chemical analysis by x-ray diffraction. Starting with the strong spacing at 3.03 A., all cards in the 3.05 to 3.00 group having a strong line near 5.9 A. or 2.8 A. were taken from the file. The three strong lines on each card were compared with data from the "unknown," and for only one card, $CaSO_4 \cdot \frac{1}{2}H_2O$, was agreement found. When the complete pattern for $CaSO_4 \cdot \frac{1}{2}H_2O$ (Fig. 26b) was compared

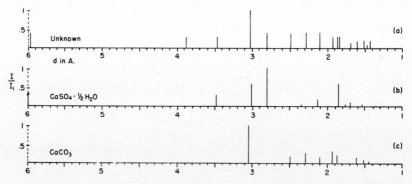

FIG. 26. (a) Plot of spacings and relative intensities for an "unknown" sample used by Smith and Barrett as a laboratory exercise in x-ray analysis. (b) Plot of powder pattern data from $CaSO_4 \cdot \frac{1}{2}H_2O$ (ASTM index). (c) Plot of powder pattern data from $CaCO_3$ (ASTM index).

with the "unknown" spacings, there was little doubt that one of the components had been identified. Before starting a search for the other constituent it was noted that, although the 3.03-A. line was by far the strongest line in the "unknown," it was only the second most intense line in the $CaSO_4 \cdot \frac{1}{2}H_2O$ pattern. This led to the suspicion that the second phase also possessed a strong line near 3.03 A. Again referring to the 3.05 to 3.00 card grouping selection was made of all cards showing a strong line at 2.48 or 2.28 A. Once more the three strong lines on each card were compared with the remaining "unknown" lines, and this pointed to the card for calcium carbonate. When the full complement of calcium carbonate spacings was examined (Fig. 26c), agreement with the residual "unknown" spacings was found to be satisfactory. All the lines in the unknown are accounted for by these two constituents. It is not too surprising that certain very weak lines from the standard patterns were missed in the "unknown." The relative intensities are also found to give rough agreement, so the identification problem is considered solved.

With a little practice one can become quite adept at unraveling multicomponent patterns. The beginner is referred to articles by Hanawalt et al. (47), Smith and Barrett (92), and Davey (31), where these and other examples covering various possibilities are treated in great detail.

It would not be proper to conclude this section without a word concerning the limitations and difficulties of the x-ray diffraction method as applied to chemical analysis. Obviously the scheme is confined to crystalline materials and applies only to substances catalogued in the index. The method is also limited in its ability to detect phases present in low concentration. The minimum detectable concentration will depend on the material in question and also on the other materials present. As a usual thing, however, the lower limit will be somewhere between 0.5 and 5% by weight. In addition, there are minor instances in which different materials give powder patterns of the same spacing and intensity to a first-order approximation and which therefore demand greater precision than is available here. Chief among these are compounds subject to isomorphism, solid solutions, mixed oxides of the perovskite (ABO_3) and spinel (AB_2O_4) types, and a few elements showing structural similarities. This emphasizes that what one obtains from x-ray diffraction patterns is *structures* and that on rare occasions these structures may not provide rigid chemical identification. The reader is referred to an article by Frevel (39) for a thorough discussion of the limitations outlined above.

6.2. Quantitative Analysis of Powder Mixtures

In the preceding section we considered the identification of crystalline components in a mixture. Usually, one also would like to know the percentage of each substance present, or at least the relative proportions of each. Quantitative analyses are not an outstanding feature of the x-ray diffraction method, but such determinations can be carried out with fair precision at some expenditure of effort.

Measurement of the amount of a crystalline constituent in a mixture via x-ray diffraction requires a precise knowledge of line intensities, and, as mentioned earlier, the diffractometer is clearly superior to the photographic method for obtaining this information.

Alexander and Klug (1) have investigated the problem of x-ray intensities diffracted by a small-particle-size flat powder specimen sufficiently thick† to give maximum diffracted intensities. This type of

---

† To satisfy the thickness condition, μs must be greater than 6.4, where μ is the linear absorption coefficient of the sample, and s is the maximum path length traversed by the x-rays in the sample.

sample is commonly employed in diffractometer work. For a uniform multicomponent mixture, they deduce the following general expression:

$$I_1 = \frac{K_1 x_1}{\rho_1[x_1(\mu_1{}^* - \mu_M{}^*) + \mu_M{}^*]} \tag{18}$$

where I_1 is the diffracted intensity for a chosen line from component 1; x_1, ρ_1, and $\mu_1{}^*$ represent the weight fraction, density, and mass absorption coefficient of the desired component; $\mu_M{}^*$ is the effective mass absorption coefficient of the matrix; and K_1 is a constant, being a function of the apparatus geometry and component 1.

In making practical use of the above equation, the authors consider three special cases, depending on the number of components present and the relative values of $\mu_1{}^*$ and $\mu_M{}^*$.

Case I. Mixture of n components: $\mu_1{}^* = \mu_M{}^*$. Here eq. (18) reduces to

$$I_1 = \frac{K_1}{\rho_1 \mu_M{}^*} x_1 = K x_1 = (I_1)_0 x_1 \tag{19}$$

which states that the diffracted intensity from component 1 is proportional to its concentration in the sample. Thus, all the prior calibration information needed is a line intensity measurement from a pure sample of 1 to fix $(I_1)_0$. Admittedly, there will be few practical cases where all components in the sample have equivalent absorption coefficients.

Case II. Mixture of two components: identifications known, but $\mu_1{}^* \neq \mu_2{}^*$. In this instance the intensity-concentration curve will not be linear, since the absorbing powers of the unknown and diluent are unequal. A calibration curve can be prepared experimentally from synthetic mixtures of the two materials, covering the full range of composition. Since the respective mass absorption coefficients can be obtained from reference to tables (e.g., "Handbook of Chemistry and Physics"), an equivalent calibration curve can be calculated from the expression

$$\frac{I_1}{(I_1)_0} = \frac{\mu_1{}^* x_1}{x_1(\mu_1{}^* - \mu_2{}^*) + \mu_2{}^*} \tag{20}$$

here $(I_1)_0$ is the line intensity from a pure sample of material 1. Figure 27 illustrates typical results for cases I and II.

Case III. Mixture of n components $(n > 2)$: $\mu_1{}^* \neq \mu_M{}^*$. In this case the absorbing power of the desired component differs from that of the matrix, the latter usually being unknown. Here one must resort to use of an internal standard. It can be shown that when a weight fraction,

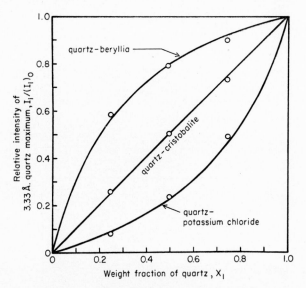

Fig. 27. Calibration curves to illustrate cases I and II (see text). Since quartz and cristobalite are polymorphs of silica, the criterion that $\mu^* = \mu_M^*$ is fulfilled, and a linear calibration curve results. The quartz-beryllia and quartz-potassium chloride examples correspond to case II. Here the solid lines were calculated from eq. (20), with $\mu^*_{SiO2} = 34.9$, $\mu^*_{BeO} = 8.6$, $\mu^*_{KCl} = 124$. The experimental points show the excellent agreement found for synthetic mixtures containing known weight fractions of quartz. Courtesy of Alexander and Klug (1).

x_s, of internal standard is added to the sample under analysis, the concentration of the desired component is given by

$$x_1 = \frac{K'}{1 - x_s}\left(\frac{I_1}{I_s}\right) \tag{21}$$

with I_1 and I_s being the diffracted intensities for a chosen line from component 1 and the internal standard, respectively.

$$K' = \frac{K_s \rho_1 x_s}{K_1 \rho_s}$$

Values of K_1 and K_s can be established from line intensity measurements $(I_1)_0$ and $(I_s)_0$ on the pure materials. Provided a constant weight fraction of internal standard is always added, eq. (21) simplifies to

$$x_1 = K''\left(\frac{I_1}{I_s}\right) \tag{22}$$

and a linear calibration curve of I_1/I_s versus x_1 results. A sample consisting of pure component 1 with the constant proportion of internal standard added suffices to establish K''. Figure 28 depicts the results obtained when 20% by weight of CaF_2 (the internal standard) was added to known mixtures of quartz and calcium carbonate. The intensities of the 3.34-A. quartz line and the 3.16-A. fluorite line were used to determine the ratio (I_1/I_s).

In order to attain reasonable precision and reproducibility in quantitative determinations careful attention must be given to sample preparation in addition to the usual instrumental factors. Clearly, preferred orientation of crystallites must be absent, and the crystallites must be

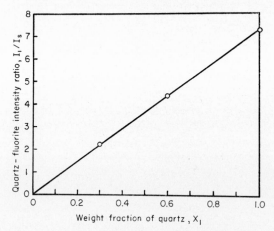

FIG. 28. Plot to illustrate case III, with 20% by weight CaF_2 as an internal standard. Each experimental point is the average of ten determinations from a sample containing a known amount of quartz. Note the linear relationship, thereby confirming eq. (22). Courtesy of Alexander and Klug (1).

sufficiently small that extinction (29) and microabsorption (17) effects are negligible. McCreery (68) has described an excellent sample preparation procedure for minimizing preferred orientation. Prolonged grinding of the sample to assure particle diameters $<10\ \mu$ and rotation of the flat sample about an axis normal to its face will aid greatly in the achievement of reproducible intensity measurements (10, 21a). With reasonable care these procedures will enable one to determine components present in amounts greater than 10% to an accuracy of $\pm5\%$ of the true concentration.

Prior to the availability of the diffractometer, considerable quantitative work was accomplished with the photographic technique (4, 25, 44). Here a microphotometer serves to measure line intensities. Interestingly enough for x-ray film, the optical density, $\log_{10}$ (incident light/transmitted light), from diffraction patterns turns out to be a linear function of exposure over the usage range (O.D. = 0.5 → 3.0). This is in contrast to the usual film behavior where the optical density is proportional to log exposure.

6.3. Chemical Analysis by Absorption of X-Rays

Mention should be made of a nondiffraction technique for achieving this end. This method is based on the absorption of an x-ray beam in traversing a sample which contains the material to be assayed. The problem is to choose an x-ray wavelength for which the sought-for component exhibits an absorption coefficient, μ, considerably in excess of that shown by any other component in the sample. The effect on absorption of a reasonable difference in μ is large, since this quantity appears as an exponential in the intensity equation (see p. 32). Since $\mu \propto Z^3$, the method is quite sensitive when the sought-for element is one of high Z (atomic number) and the remaining components consist of light elements. A case in point is the lead tetraethyl present in high-test gasoline. Sullivan and Friedman (96) claim an accuracy of 1% in analyzing such gasoline for lead. By using monochromatic radiation with a wavelength just below the K absorption edge of the desired constituent one can achieve a large specific absorption even when the atomic number spread present in the sample is not great. Engström (36) has described a technique for obtaining a range of monochromatic wavelengths using a single Machlett AEG 50 high-intensity x-ray tube (83). The primary radiation is allowed to fall on a particular target, fluorescent rays from the latter serving as the beam whose transmission through the unknown is measured. The most important consideration in all this work is measurement of the transmitted x-ray intensity. The usual photographic film-microphotometer combination is deficient in both accuracy and convenience for precise work. The General Electric Company manufactures an instrument which utilizes a fluorescent screen-electron multiplier arrangement for the intensity measurement (64). Sullivan and Friedman employed a special quantum-sensitive Geiger-Müller counter in their gasoline analysis.

7. Crystal System Identification and Unit Cell Determinations

7.1. Identifying Crystal System from Powder Pattern

In Fig. 29 are shown those diffraction lines obtained from the various kinds of cubic crystal, with the same unit cell size assumed for each. The expressions under the root sign are values of $h^2 + k^2 + l^2$, which allows one to deduce the reflections as specified. It is seen that in the range covered a simple cubic crystal shows a diffraction line for every possible value of $h^2 + k^2 + l^2$. Seven, fifteen, and twenty-three are absent because there exists no three integers the sum of whose squares yields these totals. In body-centered and face-centered cubic crystals certain additional lines are missing. This means there must be parallel planes containing an equal number of lattice points half-way between the set under consideration. When this condition exists, x-rays scattered by the adjacent planes are 180° out of phase and complete destruction results. For example, in Fig. 10 no first-order reflection would be expected for (100) planes ($h^2 + k^2 + l^2 = 1$), since there are (200) planes interspersed between this set. There are no lattice points between adjacent (200) planes and thus no chance of interfering planes. Consequently, a line would be expected from the

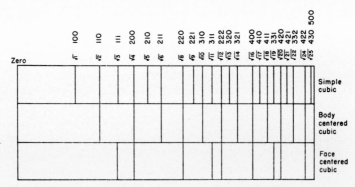

Fig. 29. Powder spectra expected from various cubic crystals, with the same unit cell size assumed. The figures under the root sign correspond to the sum $h^2 + k^2 + l^2$. The reflections hkl for each line are also listed.

(200) set ($h^2 + k^2 + l^2 = 4$), and Fig. 29 shows this to be correct. In fact, it is by the absence of certain spectra from the diffraction pattern that one makes crystal class identifications.

The following general statements can be made with regard to body and face-centered lattices. These statements hold true for all systems.

1. Body-centered crystals give reflections only when $h + k + l$ is an even integer.

2. Face-centered crystals yield reflections only for indices which are all odd or all even.

All crystals having the same type of cubic lattice give similar patterns. It must be remembered, however, that although the line *sequence* will be identical the actual positions will differ if the crystals have unit cells of different size. Likewise, the ratio of intensities from corresponding planes will not be the same for all lines of two different cubic crystals. These points can be illustrated by comparing the patterns from sodium chloride and potassium chloride. Both are face-centered cubic crystals. Yet their patterns as sketched in Fig. 30 differ on two counts. In the first place, corresponding lines from sodium chloride are spaced farther apart than those from potassium chloride. This tells us that potassium chloride has a larger unit cell. Then there are a few weak lines on the sodium chloride film that do not show up at all for potassium chloride. This happens because K^+ and Cl^- have practically the same scattering power. Complete interference results, and thus certain legitimate reflections show zero intensity.

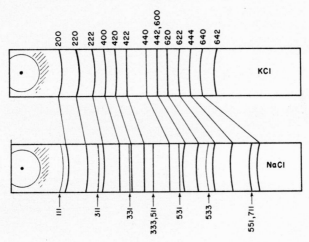

Fig. 30. Comparison of powder patterns from potassium and sodium chloride. ($a_{KCl} = 6.29$ A.; $a_{NaCl} = 5.64$ A.)

Suppose one wished to analyze a powder pattern having the following line sequence, moving outward from the central beam spot: A pair of lines in close proximity, a single line, another pair, a single line, a third pair, ... This would be strong evidence favoring a face-centered cubic structure. It would then require but a few minutes to index each line according to Fig. 29. Next, eq. (8) could be applied to give a value for "a," the lattice constant. If one obtained the same "a" using d and hkl values for every line, he could feel confident that his interpretation was correct.

Except for isometric (cubic) crystals this simple approach is not available to us. In general $a \neq b \neq c$ and $\alpha \neq \beta \neq \gamma$. Hence, there will be no unique line sequence, and the indexing poses a real problem. The situation is not too difficult for tetragonal, hexagonal, and rhombohedral crystals (rhombohedral crystals can be referred to hexagonal axes), since the angles are known, $a = b$, and one needs only a and the ratio c/a to index the pattern properly.* The procedure here has been greatly simplified by the publication of so-called Hull-Davey charts for the above systems (30).† The ordinate represents c/a, and the abscissa corresponds to relative d values (based on $a = 1$) plotted on a logarithmic scale. Various curves indicate how all hkl spacings within the range covered vary with c/a. All planes parallel to the Z-axis (hko) have a constant spacing, as would be expected. To use these charts one places a strip of paper along the calibrated base line and a mark opposite each d value calculated from a powder pattern of the unknown. In most of the plots the base line covers a spacing decade, i.e., .25 to 2.5 A., 2.5 to 25 A., etc. For any spacings that cannot be accommodated at a single setting, the strip is shifted along the scale one full decade, effectively extending the range another order of magnitude. Once all spacings are recorded, the strip is moved over the chart to various horizontal positions until the marks coincide with curves on the chart. This amounts to trying different c/a and "a" values until the predicted pattern matches the observed one. When this is accomplished the lines are identified as to hkl, and the lattice constants can then be calculated. For example, if we tested this technique using the d values obtained from a powder pattern of zinc metal we would find an excellent match on the Hull-Davey plot for the hexagonal system at a c/a value of 1.85. Furthermore we would see at a glance that the 2.47-A. spacing was a (00.2) reflection, the 2.29-A. spacing a (10.0) reflection, the 2.08-A. spacing a (10.1) reflection, and so on. We would now possess sufficient data to determine the unit cell dimensions for zinc.

7.2. Unit Cell Determination

Noting that the 2.29-A. spacing arises from the (10.0) set of planes, we use eq. (10) to find a. This gives

$$a = \sqrt{\tfrac{4}{3}}\, d = 2.66 \text{ A.}$$

Since $c/a = 1.85$, we know that

$$c = (1.85)(2.66) = 4.93 \text{ A.}$$

Thus the unit cell of zinc is completely determined.

* Lipson (67) has proposed an analytical procedure for indexing orthorhombic crystals which has been used by numerous workers with good success. Ito (53) has developed a method which can in theory be applied to any lattice. Though extremely ingenious, these techniques are rather involved, and a detailed explanation is beyond the scope of this review. One interested in becoming familiar with these methods should consult the original papers.

† C. W. Bunn has prepared a related series of four charts, two for the tetragonal system and two for the hexagonal (and rhombohedral) system. Copies of these charts can be secured from the Institute of Physics, 47 Belgrave Square, London SW 1, England.

7.3. Number of Atoms per Unit Cell

It is always prudent to check unit cell values by calculating the number of atoms or molecules per unit cell. A face-centered cubic crystal contains four equivalent points, a body-centered cubic crystal two points, a hexagonal crystal one point per unit cell, etc. The number of atoms (for elements) or molecules (for compounds) will be equal to or be some multiple of these numbers. If our calculations show this to be true, we may feel confident that our unit cell constants are probably correct. The number of atoms (molecules) per unit cell is determined as follows: The density of a body is

$$\text{Density} = \rho = \frac{\text{Mass of body}}{\text{Volume of body}} \qquad (23)$$

Consider a zinc unit cell. The mass it contains is

$$\text{Mass} = (n)(65.38)(1.66 \times 10^{-24}) \text{ g.}$$

where n is the number of atoms (molecules) in the cell, and 65.38 is the atomic weight of zinc (for a compound, the molecular weight is used); 1.66×10^{-24} is the mass in grams of unit atomic weight. The volume of a unit hexagonal prism is

$$\text{Volume} = \frac{\sqrt{3}}{2} a^2 c = (0.866)(7.12)(4.93) = 30.5 \text{ A.}^3 = 30.5 \times 10^{-24} \text{ cc.}$$

For zinc ρ is 7.14 g./cm³.

Putting the above figures into eq. (23) we find that $n = 2.02$. Thus we conclude that zinc contains two atoms per unit cell. This is consistent with the previous statement and is in fact what one expects for an element whose structure is close-packed hexagonal.

In general, merely finding the number of atoms per unit cell does not uniquely determine the structure, since there will be numerous ways to arrange this number of entities in the given volume. A knowledge of spectral intensities and the absence of certain reflections are usually required to make this final step. These data normally involve single crystal studies and will not be discussed here.

8. Crystallite and Particle Size from Powder Patterns

An important property of powders and metals is their *particle* or *grain size*. Since an x-ray powder pattern is markedly affected by the size of the crystallites* producing the pattern, diffraction methods can be applied to problems of crystallite size.

---

* A clear distinction should be made between particle and crystallite. A crystallite is taken to mean a small single crystal. A particle *may* consist of many crystallites in close contact. In metals terminology *grain* and crystallite are used interchangeably.

From an x-ray diffraction point of view the crystallite size (diameter) spectrum is divided into three ranges. (1) Above 10^{-3} cm. (2) 10^{-5} to 10^{-3} cm. (3) 0 to 1000 A.

8.1. Crystallite Size from Spottiness of Pattern

In region 1 each crystallite in diffracting position contributes a spot to the x-ray pattern. Such a pattern is depicted in Fig. 57b. If one has calibrated a camera by measuring the spots produced by samples of known crystallite size, he can use this procedure on unknowns to gain some idea as to the dimensions of their crystallites (23). As an alternative he can calculate the volume of sample exposed to the x-rays (transmission method) and count the number of spots on any diffraction ring. Then, allowing for the multiplicity of equivalent planes in the particular family giving rise to the ring, he can deduce an average crystallite size for the specimen (94). Microscope methods are to be preferred in this region because of their greater accuracy. For subsurface particles, however, or for measurements on the crystallite size of one component in a heterogeneous mixture, the x-ray method has a definite utility.

In range 2 (10^{-5} to 10^{-3} cm.) the x-ray pattern shows only smooth lines (see Fig. 57a), since the individual spots are no longer resolved on the film. Furthermore, the pattern is insensitive to size changes within this region. Hence region 2 represents a blind spot for the x-ray method.

8.2. Crystallite Size by Line Broadening (21)

Below 1000 A. (region 3) the diffraction lines begin to broaden because the minute crystals lack resolving powder. This phenomenon is quite analogous to the well-known optical case of diffraction maxima produced by line gratings. If the grating contains many lines to the inch the diffraction maxima are quite sharp, whereas a grating composed of but a few lines yields broad, ill-defined maxima. A crystal behaves as a three-dimensional grating toward a beam of x-rays, and the breadth of a resulting diffraction line will depend critically on the number of diffraction centers in each crystallite, i.e., the crystallite size. The broadening effect is very pronounced once the average crystallite diameter falls below 200 A. Since this is just where the electron microscope begins to lose sensitivity, there is real need for a method applicable to this region.

Many people have examined theoretically the problem of line broadening as a function of crystallite size (62, 79, 85). As long as one confines his attention to a size 200 A. and less, the average crystallite dimension is related to the line broadening by the formula

$$l = \frac{K\lambda}{B \cos \theta} \tag{24}$$

where l is the crystallite thickness normal to the (hkl) plane responsible for the diffraction line; λ the x-ray wavelength; θ the Bragg angle; B the angular broadening due to size of scattering units; and K a numerical constant. For normal three-dimensional crystals K is taken as 0.89. The value of B is normally computed from a photometer trace of the line in question, the width at half-maximum intensity divided by the camera radius being the desired quantity. Since all diffraction lines possess a finite width due to camera geometry, etc., B is more correctly given by

$$B = \sqrt{B_x^2 - B_s^2} \tag{25}$$

where B_s is the angular width at half-maximum for a line from a standard material known to fall in region 2. The standard may be mixed with the unknown so long as important lines do not overlap. B_x is the angular width for the unknown.

Figure 31 shows powder patterns (101) for magnesium oxide of different crystallite size. These samples were produced by heating magnesium carbonate in air at (a) 450°C., (b) 550°C., (c) 650°C., and (d) 800°C. The effect of crystallite size on line breadth is clearly shown. Figure 32 presents a plot (11) relating particle size in magnesium oxide samples with the heating period of magnesium carbonate at various temperatures. Here the sizes were determined by both x-ray broadening and the electron microscope. The two methods show good agreement in the region above 100 A.

At this point a word of caution should be injected. Line broadening can also arise from other factors, chief among these being lattice distortions within crystallites. These distortions are caused by internal stresses which are not uniform throughout the grain. Therefore, it is sometimes a problem to assign correctly the cause of the observed broadening. If the sample has been annealed and is known to be free of internal stresses, then one can assert with some assurance that the effect is due to particle size. This is also true when the broadening is quite large, as is the case for the 450°C. and 550°C. magnesium oxide samples of Fig. 31. Microstrains cannot induce such extreme broadening as this except under very special conditions (16). Thus the work by Biscoe and Warren (12) and Clark and Rhodes (26) on carbon blacks and that by Clark et al. (24) on nickel catalysts, to cite only a few cases, seem to be on a firm basis. In borderline cases where the broadening is not very marked one must be conservative in interpreting the observed results. Dehlinger and Kochendörfer (34) and Smith and Stickley (93), have endeavored to distinguish between particle size broadening and distortion broadening in metals, but neither group claimed very positive results.

Oftentimes crystallite sizes obtained by line broadening differ considerably from particle sizes for the same sample as observed in electron

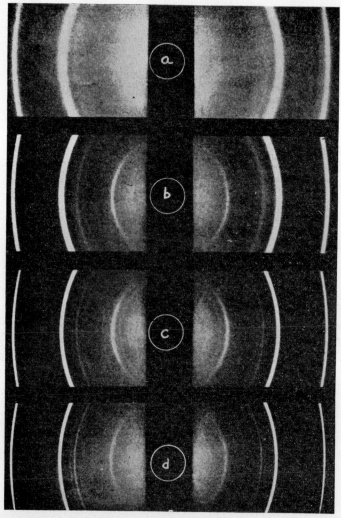

FIG. 31. Powder patterns from magnesium oxide showing the line broadening resulting from decreased particle size. Magnesium oxide specimens produced by heating magnesium carbonate at (a) 450°C., (b) 550°C., (c) 650°C., (d) 800°C. Average crystallite diameter: (a) 42 A., (b) 90 A., (c) 142 A., (d) 225 A. From Warren (101).

micrographs. There is a simple explanation for this apparent discrepancy. It hinges on the difference between a crystallite and a particle. As noted on p. 83, a discrete particle viewed in an electron micrograph may be composed of many crystallites in close contact. Thus there is no a priori reason why one should demand agreement between the two

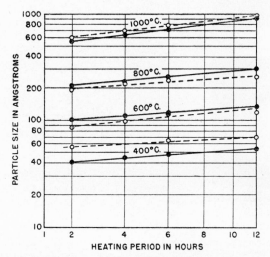

FIG. 32. Comparison of x-ray line broadening and electron microscope determinations on the particle size of magnesium oxide samples. —— X-ray line broadening. - - - Electron microscope. From Birks and Friedman, (11).

measurements. When agreement is obtained, as is the case in Fig. 32, it must mean that each particle is likewise a single crystallite.

8.3. PARTICLE SIZE BY LOW-ANGLE SCATTERING

In concluding this section we shall describe a new x-ray technique applicable to powder samples which gives results in terms of an effective particle size instead of crystallite size. When a beam of x-radiation traverses an inhomogeneous material, in addition to the ray scattered at relatively wide angles to form the usual diffraction pattern there will be intense scattering of rays at very small angle ($2\theta \approx 1°$). The manner in which this intensity varies with scattering angle is connected with the magnitude of the inhomogeneities within the sample and has been much studied in recent years. The physical reason for expecting such scattering is evident from Fig. 33a. An element of volume at A in the homogeneous sample will scatter radiation in all directions. Let us concentrate on that scattered in the direction AO. If we move along the incident x-ray wavefront it is possible to find some point B such that the path

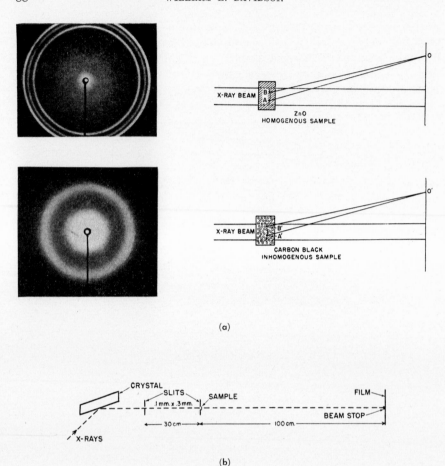

(a)

(b)

Fig. 33. (a) These sketches provide a simple explanation as to why one would expect low-angle scattering of x-radiation from inhomogeneous materials. The average particle size of the zinc oxide is about 10,000 A. The spaces between particles will be of the same magnitude, and so any low-angle scattering will remain hidden behind the beam stop. The carbon black, however, has an average particle diameter around 300 A. Consequently, we would expect considerable low-angle scattering out to 2θ angles of several degrees. (b) Experimental arrangement suitable for studying low-angle scatter phenomena. The x-ray beam should be monochromatized by reflection from a crystal. To reduce air scattering, the path between sample and film should be evacuated. Numerous experimenters in this field prefer to use a Geiger-Müller counter for recording the scattered intensity.

length BO will be $\lambda/2$ less than AO. Thus, destructive interference will occur, and there will be no resultant x-ray intensity at O. Since A is any arbitrary point, it is clear that cancellation will be general for all directions off the main axis. The situation is changed when we turn to a sample which is not homogeneous. Here an element of volume at A' will scatter as before, but it may well be that B' falls at a point devoid of matter. In this event the radiation scattered from A' will not be canceled, and a measurable intensity of scattered radiation will appear at small angles to the direct beam.

Figure 33b depicts an experimental arrangement suitable for low-angle work. The long specimen-film distance is necessary to cover scattering angles of a few minutes of arc. It has been found by numerous workers that x-rays monochromatized by reflection from a crystal should be employed for best results. In addition, it is preferable to place the entire camera in an evacuated enclosure because of the danger of film fogging from air scattering. The North American Philips Co. markets a low-angle scatter camera which can be attached to their Norelco diffraction unit. Some workers prefer the Geiger counter method of detection to photographic recording.

Biscoe and Warren (12) have shown that if monochromatic radiation is used and it is assumed that no scattering interference occurs between separate particles, the intensity of scattering at angle 2θ is given by

$$I = Ce^{-0.221k^2R^2} \tag{26}$$

where $k = (4\,\pi \sin\,\theta)/\lambda$; λ is the x-ray wavelength in A.; R is a length measured in angstroms which may be interpreted as an effective inhomogeneity radius (one may interpret $2R$ as the average particle diameter in the sample or conversely as an average void diameter); and C is a constant indicative of the kind and amount of scattering matter in the beam and the incident x-ray intensity.

If we take the logarithm of eq. (26) we find

$$\ln I = \ln C - 0.221k^2R^2 \tag{27}$$

If we plot $\ln I$ versus k^2 for a material having a uniform inhomogeneity size R, we would expect a straight line with intercept on the I-axis equal to $\ln C$ and a slope equal to $-0.221R^2$. Note that in reversing this process, i.e., calculating R from an experimental curve, only differences in $\ln I$ are important. This means that relative intensity values alone need be known, and, furthermore, sample thickness and time of exposure should not affect the final result. Figure 34 is intended to show how the curves will vary with different values of R. In general, any real sample will possess a continuous distribution of inhomogeneity sizes, and consequently the experimental plot will exhibit variable slope. Jellinek *et al.* (57), have published a graphical method for determining the contributions due to various particle size groups from the composite curve. In this manner they are able to construct a plot showing particle size

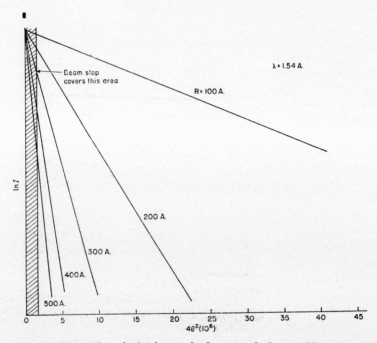

FIG. 34. These plots depict how a ln I versus θ^2 plot would appear for a material possessing inhomogeneities of a single size, R, when irradiated with monochromatic x-rays of wavelength 1.54 A. For a constant λ, k is proportional to θ, so this graph is equivalent to a ln I versus k^2 plot. For R values much in excess of 500 A. most of the scattered radiation lies within the shadow cast by the beam spot, thus limiting the method to about $R = 1000$ A. for apparatus with 0.1-mm. slits and a specimen-film distance of 1 meter.

distribution in the sample. A more elegant procedure has been introduced by Shull and Roess (89). The latter authors assume an analytical distribution function which contains two adjustable parameters. A theoretical scattering curve is then found which fits the experimental data. The values of the parameters which accomplish the match then serve to establish the peak and breadth of the particle size distribution. Usually, average particle size measurements by the low-angle scattering technique agree quite well with equivalent measurements by other methods. Figure 35 shows the correlation found by Shull and Roess between particle size (by low-angle x-ray scattering) and specific surface as measured by the B.E.T. gas adsorption method.

In addition to the work mentioned above, the reader is referred to studies by Fankuchen and Mark (37). Guinier (45), and Hosemann (48)

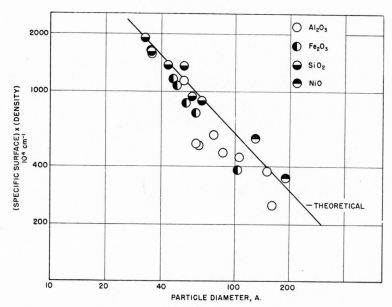

Fig. 35. Correlation between average particle diameters measured by low-angle scattering and surface areas measured on the same samples by the B.E.T. technique. In general, the experimental points fall rather close to the theoretical curve. A large error in low-angle scatter results might occur for a sample composed mainly of large particles ($>$ 1000 A.) with a sprinkling of small particles. In this case only the latter would contribute to the low-angle pattern, and one might mistakenly assume that this was representative of the whole sample. From Shull and Roess (89).

on plastics and fibers, and to Guinier (46), Elkin *et al.* (35), and Jellinek and Fankuchen (56) on catalysts.

9. Structure of Long-Chain Organic Compounds

One of the most interesting applications of x-ray diffraction has been to the study of long-chain organic molecules such as the paraffins, fatty acids, and soaps. The pioneering work of Müller (73, 74) proved that these materials are composed of long zigzag hydrocarbon chains which align themselves side by side and end to end. Crystals of these long-chain compounds consist of many such layers stacked one on top of the other as in a deck of cards. The lateral spacings remain fairly constant for a homologous series, but the spacing along the chain increases with increasing chain length. The zigzag chain leads to a difference in repeating distance, c, depending on whether the compound contains an even or odd number of carbon atoms. This also accounts for the well-known dif-

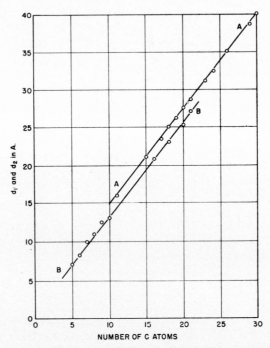

Fig. 36. Long spacing in crystals of the normal paraffin series varies with the number of chain carbons. The slope of either line is close to 1.25 A. Similar plots have been made for the fatty acids, soaps, etc. The acids crystallize with carboxyl groups facing one another. This leads to a chain repeating distance extending through two molecules and essentially doubles the spacings listed above. A similar situation holds for the soaps. From Müller (73).

ference in physical properties between odd and even members of the normal paraffin series. Once the number of carbon atoms per molecule increases beyond 20, this structural difference seems to disappear.

Figure 36 shows that the long spacing varies linearly with the number of carbon atoms in the compound, the two lines indicating two slightly different structures. The normal structure, A, is found at temperatures near the melting point, whereas the B form appears at lower temperatures. In the A modification the chains are perpendicular to the long spacing planes, whereas in the *B* form they are likely tilted at a slight angle to the normal. Figure 37 depicts the x-ray patterns from zinc salts of two fatty acids. The concentric rings near the center of the pattern represent first and higher order reflections from the long (001) crystal spacing. Calculations give 30.0 A. and 42.3 A. for the spacings from Figs. 37a and 37b, respectively. Reference to a curve similar to Fig. 36 but for the zinc salts of fatty acids identifies the samples as zinc laurate (a) and zinc stearate (b). This scheme can be used in identifying any member of a homologous series, although polymorphism and solid solution represent possible complications. As examples of this sort of x-ray analysis we may cite Piper's work on potassium salts (8), Patter-

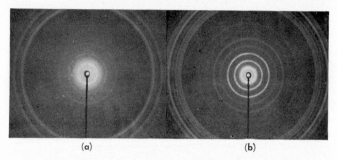

(a)   (b)

Fɪɢ. 37. (a) Powder pattern from zinc laurate. Three orders of the long spacing reflection are visible. $d = 30.0$ A. The outer rings represent lateral spacings and do not change materially with a change in chain length. (b) Powder pattern from zinc stearate. Seven orders of the long spacing reflection are visible on the original film. $d = 42.3$ A.

son's studies on phenyl-substituted fatty acids (78), and the researches of Clark and Smith on fractionated paraffin waxes (27).

10. Diffraction Effects from Noncrystalline Materials

Our apparent preoccupation with crystalline substances thus far might lead the reader to suppose that noncrystalline matter does not yield discernible diffraction effects. This is not correct. A certain degree of short range order exists in *liquids* and *gases,* since bond distances are fixed and no two atoms can approach each other closer than the sum of their radii. In addition to these regularities, the atoms in noncrystalline *solids* have permanent neighbors, tending to introduce still greater order. Thus, it is not too surprising that noncrystalline materials such as glasses, carbon blacks, elastomers, and many plastics do give diffraction patterns, even though the patterns appear vague and ill defined, usually consisting of one or more broad halos. Still, through detailed study of such patterns one can deduce considerable information concerning the spatial arrangement of the atoms comprising the specimen.

The theoretical base enabling one to glean radial distribution information from these broad halos was laid by Debye (32) and developed further by Zernike and Prins (105). According to their arguments, the intensity of x-rays coherently scattered (unmodified) from a noncrystalline material composed of one kind of atom, e.g., carbon black or rubber (with the H atoms ignored), should be given by the expression

$$I = Nf^2\left\{1 + \int_0^\infty 4\pi r^2[\rho(r) - \rho_0]\frac{\sin kr}{kr}\,dr\right\} \tag{28}$$

where N represents the number of atoms irradiated, f the atomic scattering factor for the element in question, $\rho(r)$ the number of atoms per unit volume at distance r from the reference atom, ρ_0 the average density

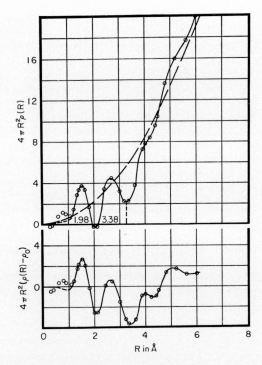

FIG. 38a. The upper curve is a radial distribution curve of neighboring carbon atoms about any selected atom in natural rubber. The dashed line (parabola) represents the average atomic distribution in the sample. The lower curve is a plot of the differential expression $4\pi r^2[\rho(r) - \rho_0]$. These results are compatible with the accepted molecular structure. Courtesy of Simard and Warren (91).

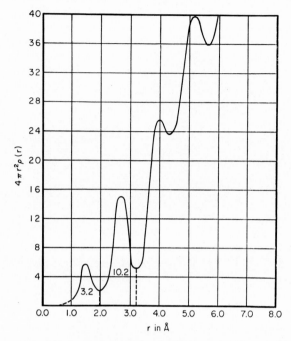

FIG. 38b. A radial distribution plot obtained by Warren (100) for a commercial carbon black. Note the existence of 3+ nearest neighbors at ≈ 1.4 A. and 10+ second nearest neighbors at an average distance of ≈ 2.7 A. This is in fair agreement with the atomic distribution to be expected around any carbon atom in a single graphite layer (see Fig. 38c).

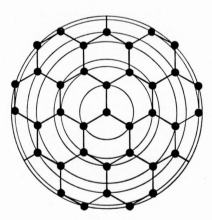

FIG. 38c

of atoms in the sample, and $k = (4 \pi \sin \theta/\lambda$, θ and λ having their usual significance.

Now $4 \pi r^2 \rho(r) \, dr$ is the number of atoms in a spherical shell of radius r and thickness dr. Clearly, the factor $[\rho(r) - \rho_0]$ is a measure of the difference in actual atomic density compared to the average density.

By means of the well-known Fourier integral theory the above intensity expression can be transformed to

$$4\pi r^2 \rho(r) = 4\pi r^2 \rho_0 + \frac{2r}{\pi} \int_0^\infty k i(k) \sin kr \, dk \qquad (29)$$

where $i(k) = (I/Nf^2) - 1$. The reader is referred to Klug and Alexander (60, Chapter 11) for a detailed explanation of the steps to be followed in going from the raw scattering data to a full tabulation of $k \, i(k)$ over the required range of k. Once this information is in hand one still has to evaluate the integral for many different values of r. This is best accomplished with a harmonic analyzer, although graphical or analytical methods can be employed at the expenditure of greater effort. Finally $4\pi r^2 \rho(r)$ or the differential expression $4\pi r^2 [\rho(r) - \rho_0]$ is plotted as a function of r.

Figure 38 depicts such plots obtained by Simard and Warren (91) from unstretched natural rubber and by Warren (100) from carbon black.

When more than one kind of atom is present in the sample, the above formulas must be modified and certain simplifying assumptions made to permit the Fourier transformation. Nevertheless, the same basic procedures obtain.

In many cases it is possible to derive worth-while information from the scattering halos without performing the detailed analysis outlined above. These scattering maxima correspond to particular interatomic distances in the noncrystalline material which occur with great frequency. For example, in high polymers the most frequent interatomic distance is the spacing between chains. Therefore, the interchain spacing derivable from the scattering maximum yielded by a polymer sample is an important attribute of that material.

A word of caution is in order. One cannot use the normal Bragg equation to relate d (here r) and θ, since the scattering centers here do not constitute an ordered three-dimensional lattice.

To find the appropriate relationship one can note from reference to eq. (28) that the intensity will normally be a maximum when $(\sin kr)/kr$ attains its greatest value. But this will be so when

$$\frac{d[(\sin kr)/kr]}{d(kr)} = 0 \qquad (30)$$

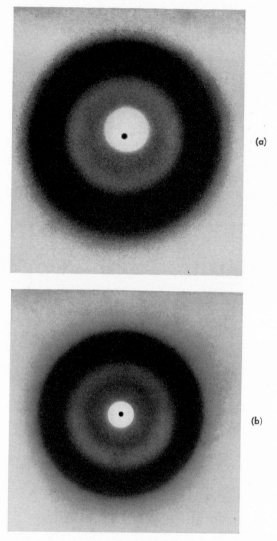

FIG. 39. (a) Scattering pattern from a polybutadiene sample. (b) Scattering pattern from polyisobutylene photographed under conditions identical to those used in (a). Note the smaller diameter halo in (b), indicating that the inter-chain spacing in polyisobutylene is considerably greater than that in poly-butadiene. This is understandable in terms of the molecular structures of the two polymers (see text).

or

$$\frac{\cos kr}{kr} - \frac{\sin kr}{(kr)^2} = 0 \tag{31}$$

which can be written

$$kr \cos kr = \sin kr \tag{32}$$

or

$$kr = \tan kr \tag{33}$$

Aside from a nonobservable match at $kr = 0$, the first value of kr satisfying this requirement is **7.72**.

Remembering that $k = (4\,\pi \sin \theta/\lambda)$, we find that this leads to

$$\lambda = (0.814)2r \sin \theta \tag{34}$$

which differs from the Bragg equation only by the factor 0.814. Stated another way, the true spacing corresponding to the halo maximum is 23% greater than one would deduce from use of the Bragg equation.

Figure 39 compares the scattering patterns from polybutadiene and polyisobutylene taken under identical conditions. Note the smaller halo diameter for the polyisobutylene sample, indicating a larger average interchain spacing. This is precisely what one would predict in view of the two pendant methyl groups attached to alternate chain carbons in polyisobutylene as contrasted with no side groups in the case of polybutadiene.

11. Metals

Metals constitute the sinews of modern civilization and, as such, richly deserve the great amount of scientific attention that has been devoted to them. It is the atomic structure and crystallite arrangement in a metal or alloy and not merely the chemical composition which determine in large measure the unique properties it may possess. Since x-ray diffraction methods reveal structures, it is not surprising that these techniques have contributed greatly to our knowledge of metals and their technological use (99).

11.1. Crystal Structure of Metals

A metallic crystal may be pictured as a lattice of positive ions submerged in a free electron gas. Such a model admirably explains many of the usual properties associated with metals and alloys, including their ductility, high thermal and electrical conductivity, ready combination in other than stoichiometric proportions, and closeness of packing. Judged by their large densities it is not too surprising that many metals

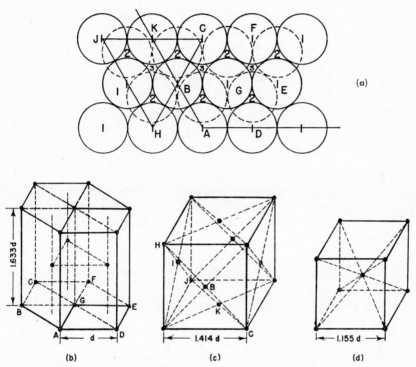

FIG. 40. (a) Diagram which illustrates the close packing of equal spheres. Those marked 1 form the first layer. The dotted circles (2) represent the second layer. The third layer can be formed in two ways either by placing spheres on position 1 or on 3. The first arrangement leads to (b), a hexagonally close-packed structure. The second plan yields (c), a face-centered cubic lattice; (d) represent a third common structure found in metals, the body-centered cubic lattice. (b) Two atoms per unit prism. Volume of unit prism equals $1.41d^3$. (c) Four atoms per unit cell. Volume of unit cell equals $2.82d^3$. (d) Two atoms per unit cell. Volume of unit cell equals $1.54d^3$.

crystallize so as to make the most efficient use of the space available. This leads to one of two lattice structures, the face-centered cubic or the hexagonally close-packed arrangement. The third common metal structure, body-centered cubic, is not quite so efficient in its use of space. The ideas underlying the efficient packing of equal spheres can be understood by reference to Fig. 40a. We start with a layer of spheres as indicated by the full circles. The second layer is formed by placing a sphere over each point marked 2. To complete a third layer we have two alternatives, to fill either those positions marked 1 or those labeled 3. If we choose the first course it is clear that spheres in the third layer are directly above those in the first, and the repeating sequence will be 1, 2, 1, 2, 1, 2, etc. If we adopt the second plan, however, the fourth layer is the first having positions which coincide with the initial layer, and the sequence becomes 1, 2, 3, 1, 2, 3, 1, 2, 3, etc. It can be seen that the first scheme fits the close-packed hexagonal arrangement depicted in Fig. 40b, whereas the second corresponds to the face-centered cubic (f.c.c.) cell shown in Fig. 40c. The labeled points in each cell correspond to similarly marked spheres in the bottom layer of Fig. 40a. This shows that, although the bottom layer forms the base of the unit hexagon, it is really the (111) plane in the f.c.c. cell. The body-centered cubic (b.c.c.) cell is shown in Fig. 40d. If it is assumed that each atomic sphere has a diameter d, the unit cell dimensions will be as indicated for the three modes of packing. Noting that the hexagonally close-packed (h.c.p.) unit prism contains two spheres, the f.c.c. cell four spheres, and the b.c.c cell two spheres, we easily see that 74% of the available space will be filled in the first two arrangements, and 68% in the third. It is important to us that most metals crystallize in one of these ways, because all three possess high symmetry. This means that we can usually deduce the unit cell of a metal from its powder pattern. Bulk metals and alloys are normally composites of extremely minute crystallites and can be induced to form large single crystals only with difficulty.

11.2. ALLOYS

If two metals are thoroughly mixed in the molten state and then allowed to cool, several things can happen.

1. They may separate as crystals of each metal. In this case, the x-ray diffraction pattern will exhibit the lines due to each component.

2. They may dissolve one in the other to form a continuous series of solid solution (alloys). Here a single pattern will be obtained, but the positions of the lines will be shifted to indicate a different size of unit cell.

3. Under the right conditions a special kind of solid solution, termed an intermetallic compound, may be formed. In the x-ray pattern the shifting of atoms to form an intermetallic compound will be evidenced by changes in the line intensities and the possible appearance of new lines.

4. Because of limited miscibility two distinct phases may exist side by side. Each phase will exhibit its own characteristic pattern on the diffraction film.

Which of the above possibilities actually occurs depends on several factors, including identity of the two metals, amount of each in mixture, heat treatment given mixture. For example, two metals will form a continuous series of solid solution only if they have the same lattice structure, have similar electronic configuration, and consist of atoms differing in size by no more than 12%. Au-Cu, Au-Ag, and Cu-Ni are examples of binary systems fulfilling these conditions. In such alloys, atoms of one kind replace at random atoms of the other at lattice points. Gold and copper are f.c.c. crystals having cube edge a equal to 4.07 and 3.61 A., respectively. Consequently, an alloy of gold and copper would be expected to show a f.c.c. pattern over the whole range. According to

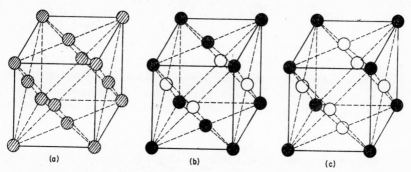

(a)   (b)   (c)

FIG. 41. (a) Gold-copper alloy in disordered state (quenched). There is equal chance of finding either atom type at any lattice point. (b) Gold-copper alloy in ordered state (super-lattice). ●—Au positions; ○—Cu positions. (c) Gold-copper alloy in ordered state. ●—Au positions; ○—Cu positions.

Vegard's law of additivity, the lattice parameter will be linearly related to the atomic percentage of one of the components. Though generally true, numerous exceptions to this law are found (69, 102). In any event, from x-ray patterns of known mixtures it is possible to establish a curve relating lattice constant to composition. It then becomes a simple matter rapidly to analyze unknown compositions of the alloy system by powder diffraction techniques. Trzebiatowski *et al.* (98) describe how this is done for chromium-molybdenum alloys.

This general behavior, which corresponds to event 2 above, is premised on an alloy quenched from the melt. If we should take a 50-50 (atomic percentages) gold-copper molten mixture and allow it to cool very slowly, a new phenomenon would result. The change is depicted in Fig. 41. Figure 41a represents the quenched condition, with an equal chance of finding gold and copper atoms at any lattice point. Slow cooling brings about the condition displayed in Fig. 41b. There are now gold atoms at the corners of each cell plus top and bottom face centers, with copper atoms at the center of the side faces (or vice versa). This structure is called a *superlattice* and is a natural consequence of the crystal's endeavoring to assume the state of lowest potential energy.

The change from (a) to (b) will be readily noted in the x-ray pattern. Line intensities will change, owing to a difference in scattering power of the layers. Because of the different radii of gold and copper atoms, the new lattice will not be strictly cubic and new lines will appear. The transition between states (a) and (b) is known as an order-disorder transformation. Johansson and Linde (58) were the first to make an extensive x-ray study of order-disorder transitions in the gold-copper system.

The geometry of the ordered 50% gold–50% copper configuration requires a 1:1 ratio for the number of gold and copper atoms. It is termed an *intermetallic compound*, although it depends for existence on geometrical and not on chemical considerations. Another indication that the word compound is not strictly applicable arises from the fact that this ordered phase is retained over a rather broad range of composition. In the neighborhood of 25% gold–75% copper, another such compound, $AuCu_3$, is found, with gold atoms at cube corners and copper atoms at the six face centers (Fig. 41c).

The system copper (f.c.c.)–zinc (h.c.p.) represents a combination of events 3 and 4 mentioned above. One would not expect a continuous series of solid solution here, and this is correct. Starting with pure copper one continues to get only a copperlike pattern (α-brass) until 38% zinc by weight has been added. Similarly, if one starts with zinc, 5% copper may be added before the hexagonal zinc lattice is seriously affected. Between these two limits one finds new patterns arising. For instance, a 60% copper–40% zinc alloy shows, in addition to the brass pattern, a second phase (β-brass) which exhibits a b.c.c. lattice. Normally the two atoms occupy any lattice point in random fashion. When equal numbers of each are present, however, an ordered stated state is possible consisting of copper atoms at cube centers with zinc atoms at the cube corners (or vice versa). Since each corner contributes one-eighth atom to the unit cell, this corresponds to a "compound," $CuZn$. Other phases in this system are γ-brass (cubic) and ϵ-brass (hexagonal), represented in their most ordered states by Cu_5Zn_8 and $CuZn_3$, respectively.

Numerous other binary systems are found to yield a similar sequence of β-, γ-, and ϵ-structures. Hume-Rothery (49) pointed out that the important condition governing each phase is ratio

$$\frac{\text{Number of valence electrons}}{\text{Number of atoms}}$$

For the β-phase this is $\frac{3}{2}$, for the γ-phase $2\frac{1}{13}$, and for ϵ $\frac{7}{4}$. Note that the copper (one valence electron)–zinc (two valence electrons) compositions fit these ratios. It turns out that the atomic structure possessed by an alloy is a more important criterion of its physical properties than

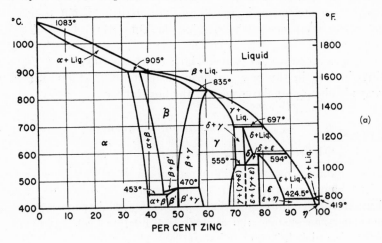

(a)

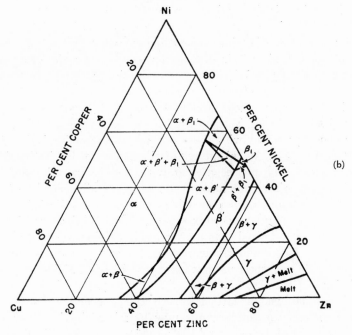

(b)

Fig. 42. (a) Constitution diagram for copper-zinc system. (b) Constitution diagram for copper-zinc-nickel system at 775°C. From "Metals Handbook," pp. 1367 and 1375, American Society for Metals, Cleveland, Ohio, 1939.

the atoms it contains. Therefore by studying the structure of a new alloy with x-rays one can predict its properties with considerable accuracy.

All the previous cases refer to "substitutional" solid solution. An alternate arrangement is known as "interstitial" solid solution. This takes place when one of the alloying elements (H, B, C, N) has a small atomic radius, it being possible for these to take up interstitial positions among the atoms of the solvent lattice. Above 800°C. 1% carbon dissolves in iron in this way to form austenite (70). Interstitial solution always leads to an enlargement of the host lattice.

12. Constitution Diagrams

12.1 Methods Used to Establish Constitution Diagrams

Information regarding the phases of an alloy as a function of composition and temperature can be presented most compactly in a "constitution" or "equilibrium" diagram. Figure 42a is such a diagram for the copper-zinc system, and Fig. 42b is a diagram for the ternary system copper-zinc-nickel. The complete ternary diagram is a three-dimensional plot. Shown here is the section corresponding to a temperature of 775°C.

Several methods can be used to establish these diagrams. They include: (1) Use of heating and cooling curves. (2) Dilatometric measurements. (3) Study of physical attributes such as resistivity and magnetic properties. (4) Microscopic examination of polished and etched surfaces. (5) X-ray diffraction patterns.

The last two methods are used most and supplement each other very well. When care is exercised, the x-ray method yields results in rather good agreement with those obtained by metallurgical techniques (66) (see Fig. 43). An advantage of the x-ray scheme is that it determines not only the phases present but also the crystal structures involved. Whereas both microscope and x-ray usually examine the specimen at room temperature, depending on quenching to lock in the high-temperature structure, special x-ray cameras have been used to study samples at the desired temperature. The high-temperature cameras developed by Goetz and Hergenrother (43) and by Hume-Rothery and Reynolds (51) may be considered as typical designs. The x-ray method is inferior to the microscope in finding phases present in small amount. Sometimes, because of lattice imperfections, a phase representing as much as 5% of the total sample may be missed in the x-ray pattern. On the other hand, Bradley and Lipson (13) by careful adjustments have found phases constituting less than 0.2% of the over-all sample. Conversely, the microscope method fails for crystallites of very small size.

12.2. Determination of Constitution Diagrams in Binary Systems Using X-Rays

There are two ways of using diffraction patterns to locate phase boundaries. They are the disappearing phase method, and the parametric method.

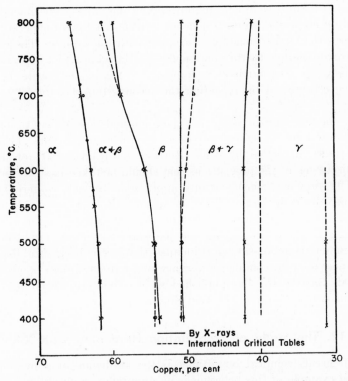

Fig. 43. Phase boundaries in copper-zinc system determined by x-rays and by metallurgical methods. In general, the agreement is satisfactory. From Lipson (66).

The first procedure depends on the fact that in a two-phase region the amount of each phase is proportional to the intensity of the diffraction lines from that phase. Hence, one takes x-ray patterns of several compositions in the two-phase region, quenched from a common temperature. The patterns are photometered, and from these data an *intensity versus composition* curve is plotted for one phase. Extrapolation to zero intensity will give the boundary for that phase at the quenching temperature. The boundary is extended by repeating the above, with a different quenching temperature.

The parametric procedure is based on the knowledge that lattice spacings usually vary smoothly with composition in a single-phase region, whereas within a two-phase area of a binary system (at any one temperature) the lattice spacings do not change with composition. Therefore one first establishes a *lattice parameter versus composition* curve by measuring several single (say α) phase samples quenched from a temperature that ensures complete solubility. Now one takes a specimen lying in the adjoining $\alpha + \beta$ region, quenches it from a known temperature, and measures the lattice constant associated with the α-phase. The composition corresponding to this parameter on the above plot represents the boundary for the particular temperature. Again the entire boundary may be established by repeating the second step at different temperatures.

It should be emphasized that these methods are subject to numerous errors, and extreme care is necessary for accurate results. The reader is referred to an article by Hume-Rothery and Raynor (50) for an extensive discussion of the precautions that should be taken in such work.

The previous considerations apply equally well to ternary alloy systems, although the possibility of added complications should be quite evident. Nevertheless, much effort has been devoted to ternary systems. Through use of certain properties associated with isothermal diagrams and numerous labor-saving principles that have been established, the work necessary to complete a ternary phase diagram can be greatly decreased. Barrett (5) has published an excellent discussion of methods used in determining constitution diagrams.

13. The Study of Precipitation Hardening with X-Rays

Of great technical importance is the hardening of alloys on aging. A good example of this behavior is an aluminum-copper alloy containing about 5% copper, studied by Fink and Smith (38). When this alloy is given a solution heat treatment followed by a quench, it exists as a supersaturated solution of copper in aluminum and initially shows a yield strength of approximately 25,000 p.s.i. As shown in Fig. 44, after aging at 160°C. for 2 weeks the yield strength has increased to 45,000 p.s.i. This hardening also proceeds at room temperature, though more slowly. With continued aging the yield strength decreases once more. When examined microscopically certain alloys, during aging show a definite growth of new phases along slip lines and grain boundaries. From this picture it was believed originally that the hardening was due to the keying of slip planes by particles precipitated from the supersaturated matrix. A major objection to this theory was the lack of evidence for any precipitate in aluminum-copper specimens aged at low temperatures and studied either with the microscope or with x-rays. It might be said that x-rays actually hindered the early development of aging theory, because improved metallographic technique finally enabled workers to observe microstructural alterations in certain alloys as soon as the hardness began to increase. The negative x-ray results are explained by the inherent insensitivity of the diffraction method to phases present in

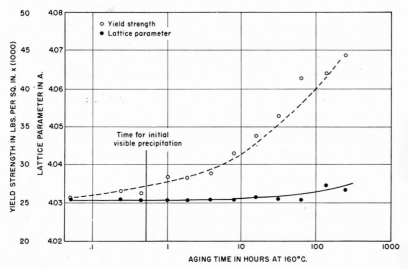

Fig. 44. Yield strength and lattice parameter vary with aging time at 160°C. for an aluminum-copper alloy (5.17% copper). It is apparent that the yield strength begins to increase and precipitation of a new phase occurs long before the lattice parameter shows a measurable change. From Fink and Smith (38).

minute amount. Precipitation can be well advanced in certain restricted areas while the general matrix is still largely unaltered. In this event the powder pattern may show no change. To avoid this difficulty several workers have resorted to the more sensitive Laue method involving single crystals. It is true that many alloys exhibit a uniform precipitation of particles throughout the grains, and here the lattice parameter deduced from powder patterns changes continuously during aging.

Once it had been appreciated that the x-ray powder method must be applied with prudence in aging studies, its value increased greatly. The method has now vindicated itself through numerous worth-while contributions to the theory of precipitation hardening.

As an example, let us review the work by Barrett *et al.* (7) on the

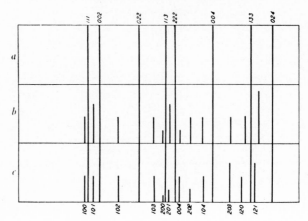

FIG. 45. Powder photograms of alloy of 20.2% silver in aluminum. (a) Spectrum of δ solid solution. As quenched from solution heat-treatment. (b) Spectra of δ + γ'. Quenched and aged 5 minutes at 387°C. (c) Spectra of δ + γ. Solution heat-treatment followed by cold-work; aged 16 hours at 175°C. From Barrett *et al.* (7).

alloy 79.8% aluminum–20.2% silver. They recorded powder patterns in a cylindrical camera at three different stages: (a) As quenched from solution heat treatment. (b) After 5 minutes' aging at 387°C. (c) After 16 hours' aging at 175°C. Figure 45 is a sketch of the patterns they obtained. The first plot shows a single f.c.c. δ-phase, typical of aluminum-silver solid solutions. The second pattern indicates that a new phase has formed, this one a h.c.p. structure which is called γ'. The third pattern still shows the h.c.p. structure but with slightly changed lattice constants. This phase is termed γ. A fact not evident in the plots is that the basal

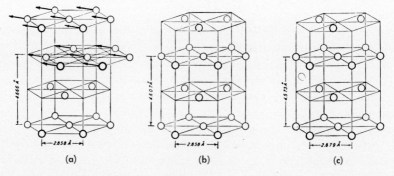

FIG. 46. Crystal lattice of phases present in aged alloys. (a) Structure of solid solution. (b) Structure of transition phase. (c) Structure of equilibrium precipitate phase. From Barrett *et al.* (7).

planes of the hexagonal crystallites showed the same orientation as the
(111) f.c.c. planes of the bulk matrix. All these facts are nicely explained
by the mechanism pictured in Fig. 46. Figure 46a represents f.c.c. δ-phase
prior to aging, although the cubic symmetry is not apparent from the
drawing. The layers pictured are (111) planes. At an early stage of
aging it is suggested the third and fourth layers shift as indicated. This

Fig. 47. Polycrystalline wire aged 25½ hours at 387°C. (× 2000). Precipitate is γ' + γ. Etched in 0.5% hydrofluoric acid. From Barrett *et al.* (7).

leads to pattern (b) and a h.c.p. lattice (γ'). As aging continues, more
and more planes make this shift, causing the thin precipitate layer to
grow. This sets up extreme stresses in the bulk matrix, since at each
interface the h.c.p. atoms must come into registry with the (111) planes
of the f.c.c. lattice. These stresses undoubtedly contribute greatly to
the hardening and are likely more important than any keying action
produced by the precipitate. Eventually the layer grows to such a
thickness that it is able to overcome the matrix stress. At this point

the precipitate breaks away and assumes the equilibrium γ-structure depicted in Fig. 46c. The interfacial stress is relieved, and softening of the alloy begins. The importance of this explanation lies in the far-reaching effects that are predicted from relatively trivial shifts in the atom layers. Figure 47 pictures $\gamma' + \gamma$ plates precipitated on the (111) planes of the aluminum-silver matrix.

14. Use of X-Rays in Explaining Magnetic Properties

The idea of a strained lattice is also used in explaining the unusual magnetic properties of certain ternary alloys. For example, Fe_2NiAl

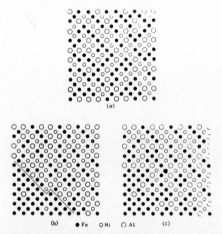

FIG. 48. Fe_2NiAl alloy after different heat treatments: (a) quenched, (b) slowly cooled, (c) special controlled cooling treatment. From G. L. Clark, "Applied X-Rays," p. 413, McGraw-Hill, New York, 1940.

gives a product having high coercivity and is thus useful as permanent magnet material. The optimum properties are secured not by quenching the melt or by slow cooling but through a special controlled cooling. Bradley and Taylor (14) utilized x-ray powder patterns to explain the mechanism accountable for this result.

At high temperatures, and hence in quenched samples, the alloy shows a single b.c.c. lattice. As pictured in Fig. 48a the nickel and aluminum atoms occupy definite lattice positions, with the iron atoms appearing at random, some replacing nickel units and others aluminum. If the melt is cooled slowly, a pattern showing two phases is obtained, both b.c.c. but differing in lattice constant by a small amount. What has happened is that a phase consisting almost entirely of iron atoms has

split off to form grains of essentially α-iron, as indicated in Fig. 48b. At
an intermediate rate of cooling the iron atoms start to segregate but
do not have time to form definite grains and are forced to assume a
lattice which fits that of the bulk material (Fig. 48c). This condition
gives rise to a single phase, but the x-ray lines are somewhat broadened.
Requiring these islands of iron atoms to conform with the dimensions of
the larger bulk lattice introduces large stresses within the alloy. These
are held to be responsible for the extraordinary magnetic properties of
the finished material.

15. Stress Measurement by X-Ray Diffraction

The measurement of residual stress is of considerable importance in
metals technology. Many schemes have been used including boring-out
techniques, sectioning methods utilizing strain gauges, and photoelastic
studies on plastic models. To these can be added x-ray diffraction.

This method is based on the fact that applied stresses produce corresponding strains in a material, the *elastic* portion of the strain revealing itself through a change in the lattice constants. When one is primarily
interested in surface stresses such as may be produced by grinding,
machining, or flame hardening, the x-ray method is especially applicable.
For these studies it is nondestructive. Thus changes resulting from
stress-relieving treatments or from service conditions may be followed
on a single specimen. The extremely small area of specimen that is sampled
is an additional advantage of the x-ray method. This is important when
high stress gradients are present, which is often the case. The time required for an x-ray stress analysis makes its use rather expensive, and
for this reason it is still primarily a laboratory tool.

To illustrate the method, suppose we desire to know the residual
stress on the surface of an iron bar near a welded joint. Regardless of the
actual stress configuration in an isotropic body, three mutually perpendicular axes can always be chosen so that the stress may be represented by components directed along the axes. These are called the princi-
ple stresses σ_1, σ_2, and σ_3. In our case we assume that σ_1 and σ_2 lie in the
plane of the surface. Then σ_3 will be zero, since a free surface cannot
support a stress perpendicular to that surface. It can be shown that
under these conditions the resultant strain perpendicular to the surface
is

$$\epsilon_\perp = \frac{-(\sigma_1 + \sigma_2)\nu}{E} \tag{35}$$

where ν is Poisson's ration and E is Young's modulus for iron. But by
definition

$$\epsilon_\perp = \frac{\Delta l}{l} = \frac{d_1 - d_0}{d_0} \tag{36}$$

where d_0 is the spacing of a set of atomic planes (in the unstressed state) parallel to the surface, and d_1 is the same spacing under stress.

Inasmuch as the spacing change will be very small at best, the back-reflection method is a necessity in this work. The setup is made according to Fig. 16. Here annealed gold or silver powder sprinkled on the iron surface serves as a calibration standard. Should we use Co K_α-radiation (see Table III) the (310) iron planes will reflect at a Bragg angle of $80\frac{1}{2}°$. If we choose this line, it means that we are measuring the spacing of planes almost but not quite parallel to the surface. For this reason our value of $\sigma_1 + \sigma_2$ will be too small by about 7% and can be corrected accordingly.

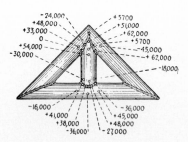

FIG. 49. Stresses in a welded triangle of steel tubing. ($\sigma_1 + \sigma_2$) in p.s.i. From H. Möller and A. Roth, *in* Barrett, C. S., "Structure of Metals," p. 282. McGraw-Hill, New York, 1932.

The problem of finding d_0 remains. We may anneal the specimen, or else cut out the small section examined above with a hollow drill. Either method will relieve the stress, and a new pattern of the same area will suffice to give d_0. Figure 49 illustrates results obtained by this method on a welded triangle of steel tubing (71). Note especially the large differences in stress for points in close proximity. These gradients would be difficult to detect by conventional methods.

The procedure described is weak in that it gives only the sum $\sigma_1 + \sigma_2$. A more elegant procedure has been devised which permits the determination of σ in any direction and furthermore does not require a measurement of d_0. It involves two x-ray exposures, one with the surface normal to the incident beam as above, the other with oblique incidence. The reader is referred to Barrett (6) for a discussion of this technique.

It should be pointed out that the x-ray method is applicable only to samples yielding sharp diffraction lines. An error of 0.0001 A. in interatomic spacing corresponds to roughly 2500 p.s.i. uncertainty in the stress, so diffuse lines cannot be tolerated. Since the surface layer penetrated by x-rays is small, extreme care should be taken in preparing the specimen for study. If this is not done, most of the diffracted image may arise from small projections which do not participate fully in the deformation of the underlying metal. Such a condition would lead to stress results far below the true values.

16. X-Rays as an Aid in the Processing of Metal

A mass of metal undergoes many physical operations between its extraction from the ore and appearance in a finished product. All these operations induce profound changes in its physical characteristics, and each change must be understood and controlled if efficient processing is to be achieved. X-ray diffraction has played a notable role both in explaining mechanisms involved and in supplying information leading to improved procedures(75).

16.1. Deformation

The first operation on a metal ingot is usually one of rolling, drawing, or extruding. The available evidence supports the contention that no matter how a single crystal may be deformed the general mechanism is the same. Since an ingot is a conglomerate of small single crystals, the picture here will be altered only in so far as neighboring crystals interfere with the motion of one another. The deformation mechanism within a crystal consists of slip or glide of thin lamellae parallel to certain atomic planes, the motion being in one particular crystallographic direction. A special method of deformation is distinguished when a thin layer within a crystal takes up such a position that its lattice is a mirror image of the rest. This process is known as *twinning*.

TABLE IV

Glide Components of Metal Structures

Structure	Glide plane[a]	Glide direction[a]
Face-centered cubic	(111)	[10$\bar{1}$]
Body-centered cubic	(112)	[111]
Close-packed hexagonal	(00.1)	[11.0]

[a] These really refer to the whole family of equivalent planes and directions. For example, the (111) form includes (111) ($\bar{1}$11) (1$\bar{1}$1) ($\bar{1}\bar{1}$1) and four other planes parallel to these. Similarly each plane contains three different directions of the form [10$\bar{1}$]. Thus there are twelve *slip systems* associated with (111) [10$\bar{1}$].

Normally the *slip plane* is the atomic plane most heavily populated with atom centers, and the slip direction is likewise that of closest packing. Hence both quantities will depend on the type of space-lattice present. Table IV gives the glide components for the common metal structures.

As a result of the movement of lamellae relative to one another, plus constraints induced by neighboring grains, many of the atoms lying near the slip planes no longer fit a perfect lattice arrangement. In other words, the lattice is distorted. Slip planes are no longer so well defined, and the grain shows increased resistance to further deformation. This behavior is known as *work hardening*.

X-ray diffraction is a valuable tool for revealing distortion within crystal grains (15, 59, 84). A specimen composed of perfect crystallites gives sharp diffraction spots on Laue photographs (white radiation), whereas distorted grains yield long radial streaks, a phenomenon termed asterism. This effect is clearly illustrated in Fig. 50, which shows patterns from two samples of transformer iron.

16.2. PREFERRED ORIENTATION

If further stress is applied, the deformed grains begin to break up into smaller entities. When the cold work is considerable, these fragmented grains assume perferred orientations. The appearance of sharp arcs in the x-ray pattern rather than smooth rings is evidence of preferred orientation of the crystallites.

The orientation in metals depends on the metal being worked and the method of working.

TABLE V

Ideal Preferred Orientations in Metal Structures

Structure	Drawing	Compression	Rolling	
			Direction	Plane
Face-centered cubic	$\begin{cases}[111]\\[100]\end{cases}$	[110]	$\begin{cases}[\bar{1}12]\\[111]\end{cases}$	(110) (112)
Body-centered cubic	[110]	$\begin{cases}[111]\\[100]\end{cases}$	[011]	(100)
Close-packed hexagonal	Variable	[00.1]	[10.0]	(00.1)

Table V lists the preferred orientations in several common metal structures for three types of cold work.

For drawn and compression (6, 8, 87) (uniaxial strains) it is neces-

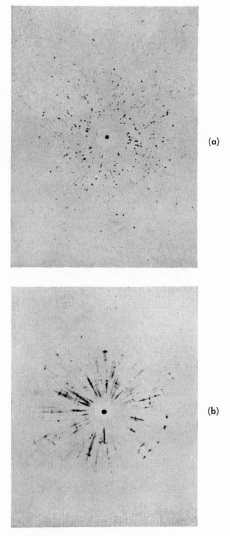

(a)

(b)

FIG. 50. Laue diffraction patterns (white radiation) of transformer iron. Sample giving pattern (a) is composed of perfect crystallites and will show good magnetic properties. Specimen giving pattern (b) contains distorted grains as shown by the asterism (streaks) present. This sample will have inferior magnetic properties. Courtesy of Picker X-Ray Corporation.

sary to specify only the crystallographic *direction* lying parallel to the direction of work, since the crystallites assume random orientations around this axis. For example, Fig. 51a is a powder pattern secured from a specimen of drawn aluminum wire, the sample being normal to the

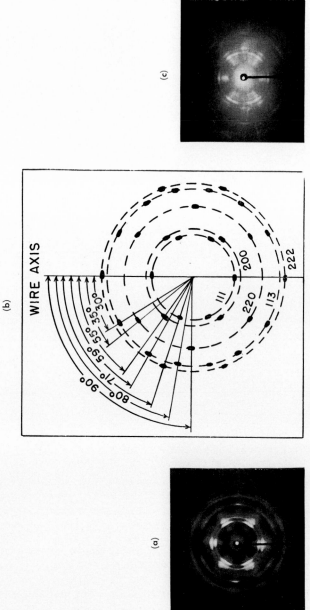

FIG. 51. (a) Powder pattern from aluminum wire using Mo $K\alpha$-radiation. The wire direction is parallel to the beam stop support. (b) Predicted pattern from aluminum wire, with all the crystallites assumed to be oriented with their [111] axis parallel to the wire direction. This is to be compared with the actual pattern shown on the left. Fairly good agreement is apparent. There is some evidence for a slight amount of [100] orientation, even though Table VII claims that aluminum normally shows, only [111] orientation. (c) Powder pattern from drawn copper wire (Mo $K\alpha$-radiation). Both [111] and [100] orientation are evident here, in agreement with the expected behavior listed in Table VII.

x-ray beam and wire direction as indicated. According to Table VII all the aluminum crystallites should be oriented with their [111] direction along the fiber axis. Let us now calculate the kind of pattern to be expected from a wire made up of f.c.c. crystallites with this orientation and see how well it agrees with that actually found.

In Fig. 52, AOX represents the x-ray beam, WW the aluminum wire, and F the photographic film. If a random arrangement of crystallites obtained, the family of planes represented by H could assume all directions in space and would thus produce a uniform diffraction ring R

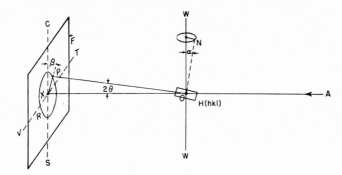

Fig. 52. Preferred orientations may be evaluated from the resulting diffraction pattern.

on the film. Since we are requiring that the [111] axis for all crystallites be parallel to WW, the planes H and plane normal NO can, at most, assume a position about WW wherein α remains constant. Only for specific positions will the Bragg conditions be fulfilled for H, and hence ring R will be replaced by a series of diffraction spots. Let us assume that with H as shown rays will be diffracted to P, which makes an angle β with the vertical CXS. Symmetry considerations require that a spot corresponding to P be found in each of the other quadrants on the film. Therefore, we need consider only the pattern formed in one quadrant such as CXT, utilizing the fact that CS and TV form lines of symmetry to fill in the remainder. Under the conditions cited the following relation can be shown to hold:

$$\cos \beta = \frac{\cos \alpha}{\cos \theta} \tag{37}$$

If relatively hard radiation (such as Mo K_a) is used, the Bragg angle θ for the most important reflections is small, and so $\cos \theta \approx 1$. To this approximation we see that $\beta = \alpha$. From the lattice geometry of cubic crystals one can deduce the following expression for the angle α between the normal NO to any set of planes (hkl) and any zone axis $[uvw]$:

$$\cos \alpha = \frac{uh + vk + wl}{\sqrt{u^2 + v^2 + w^2} \sqrt{h^2 + k^2 + l^2}} \qquad (38)$$

Since a knowledge of α gives us β directly, we are able to use eq. (38) to locate the angular positions of the spots on any diffraction line, assuming a particular crystallographic axis to be aligned with the wire axis.

Proceeding with the synthesis of our x-ray pattern from aluminum wire, reference to Fig. 29 for the face-centered cubic line sequence permits us to identify the planes responsible for the rings of the aluminum pattern. These are depicted in Fig. 51b. Table VI lists the angles α

TABLE VI

Angular Positions of Diffraction Maxima from Cold Drawn Face-Centered Cubic Materials

Reflection hkl	α (degrees)	
	$[uvw] = [111]$ parallel to wire axis	$[uvw] = [100]$ parallel to wire axis
111	0, 71	55
200	55	0, 90
220	35, 90	45, 90
113	30, 59, 80	25, 72
222	0, 71	55

(also = β) calculated from eq. (38) for these planes, with the fiber axis assumed to be [111]. Inasmuch as some f.c.c. crystals orient with [100] parallel to the wire axis we also include the angles expected in this instance. In Fig. 51b we have inked in spots at the calculated positions. This pattern shows good agreement with that displayed in Fig. 51a and

TABLE VII

Orientation Habit of Face-Centered Cubic Materials Subjected to Unidirectional Stress

Metal	Per cent crystallites showing [111] axis parallel to wire direction	Per cent crystallites showing [100] axis parallel to wire direction
Al	100	0
Cu	60	40
Au	50	50
Ag	25	75

thereby confirms the fibering habit of aluminum wire as being that originally assumed. Figure 51c is a diffraction pattern obtained from drawn copper wire, another f.c.c. metal. Note that in addition to the [111] *texture* there are spots indicative of a second type of orientation. The latter corresponds to the [100] texture mentioned previously. The amount of each type of orientation present varies from one metal to another as shown in Table VII (87).

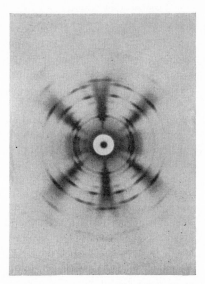

Fig. 53. Pinhole diffraction pattern of rolled aluminum sheet, showing preferred orientation. Courtesy of Picker X-Ray Corporation.

Samples that have been subjected to cold rolling present a more complicated type of preferred orientation (55, 76). Figure 53 shows the diffraction pattern obtained from a sheet of cold rolled aluminum. Comparison with Fig. 51a illustrates the fact that the preferred orientation is somewhat different in the two cases. For rolled samples, two indices are necessary to describe the situation: those specifying orientation in the rolling direction and those giving the crystal planes which lie parallel to the rolling plane. Drawing and compression yield a *true fiber* structure, whereas rolling leads to a so-called *limited fiber* structure. It should be emphasized that the data in Table V represent an idealized picture. Actually cold work never develops perfect orientation in a specimen but at best only approaches this condition. In practice, all gradations between complete randomness and perfect alignment occur. So, although it is true that the orientation occurring with greatest frequency can be described by one or two ideal orientations, the details of the scatter about these ideal alignments can be specified only by proposing a considerable number of less prominent, somewhat arbitrary orientations. It is of considerable technical importance, therefore, to possess a means

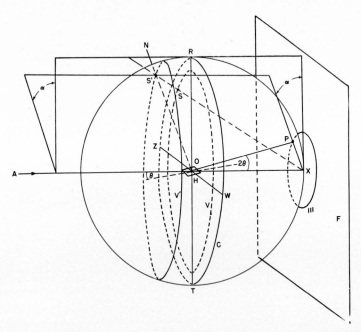

Fig. 54. Diagram to help elucidate the plotting of a pole figure. The plane of sheet specimen is mounted perpendicular to the incident beam of x-rays. *H* represents a concentration of (111) planes which satisfy Bragg conditions for reflection.

for quantitatively describing the true texture of any sample. This is achieved through the medium of *pole figures*.

16.3. POLE FIGURES

The construction and significance of a pole figure may be understood by reference to Fig. 54. Here the x-ray beam *AOX* intersects normally a thin flat specimen, *O*. A reference sphere of radius *OX* is drawn about *O* as center. Let us imagine the plane of the specimen to be extended, cutting the sphere in a great circle, *C*. This plane is to serve later as our projection plane. Assume now that plane *H* represents a concentration of, say (111) planes, which are in proper position to diffract. Thus a strong spot will be registered on film *F* at point *P*. We now desire to construct a normal to plane H from O to the point of intersection with the reference sphere. This can be done since it is clear that:

1. The incident beam, diffracted beam, and plane normal all lie in a plane tipped at an angle α to the vertical.

2. The plane normal must make an angle $90° - \theta$ with the incident beam.

From the diagram it is seen that the plane normal strikes the reference sphere at S'. S' is known as a *pole* for the (111) family of crystal

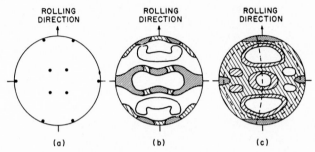

Fig. 55. (a) Pole diagram expected for the (111) plane of a rolled copper sheet showing perfect [Ī12] (110) alignment. (b) Actual pole diagram for a rolled copper specimen. From Iweronowa and Schdanow (54), *in* Barrett, "Structure of Metals," p. 398. McGraw-Hill, New York, 1943. (c) Pole figure for (110) poles of mild steel reduced 85% by cold rolling. Two reflection circles are indicated to show how the direction of the x-ray beam affects the orientation noted in the resulting pattern. From M. Gensamer and R. F. Mehl, *in* Barrett, "Structure of Metals," p. 162. McGraw-Hill, New York.

planes. In general, there will be several other spots on the (111) diffraction ring, and the pole for each is constructed in a similar manner. These additional poles will fall somewhere on circle V', since a line drawn to the circle from O makes a constant angle of $90° - \theta$ with the incident beam. The next step involves the stereographic projection of S' onto a sheet of paper coincident with the extended specimen plane. This is accomplished by viewing S' from point X, giving point S as the projection. The other (111) poles will fall somewhere on V, which is the projection of V' on the projection plane. V is termed the (111) reflection circle. V is concentric with C only when the incident beam is normal to the specimen plane.

The specimen is now rotated some 20° around RT (the projection plane and great circle C also rotate) and a second diffraction pattern secured. The poles for the (111) planes are again constructed and projected onto the same sheet of paper. This procedure is continued until the (111) reflection circle has moved across the projection plane. Even now there will be areas near R and T not covered. To fill in these regions

one restores the sample to its original position and then rotates about
ZW (which is mutually perpendicular to RT and AOX) in small increments, plotting the projections of the (111) poles as above. The finished
plot is termed a pole figure for the (111) family of planes. Similar plots
are made for two or three other planes having low indices. Taken
together they provide detailed quantitative information on the texture
of the specimen (33).

Figure 55 illustrates such a plot for the (111) plane of a rolled copper sheet. Had all the crystallites aligned themselves ideally, as recorded
in Table V, i.e., $[\bar{1}12]$ (110), the plot of Fig. 55a would have resulted. The
experimental results give Fig. 55b, the areas of greatest density representing the most favored positions of the projected poles. Although rough
agreement is found between the two plots, it is clear that there is by no
means a unique orientation of the (111) planes in the copper sheet.

Figure 55c depicts the pole figure for the (110) poles of mild steel
reduced 85% in thickness by cold rolling (41). The rolling plane is also
the projection plane, with the rolling direction as shown. Superposed
on the pole figure are two (110) reflection circles. The circle near the
periphery is that for a beam of x-rays normal to the rolling plane, and
the other is the reflection circle for a beam of radiation parallel to the
rolling plane. Note that the former circle nowhere passes into regions
of greatly differing pole concentration. This implies that the (110) reflection will show little evidence of preferred orientation when a pattern is
made with the beam normal to the rolling plane. Conversely, a pattern
taken with the beam parallel to the rolling plane should show strong
evidence of preferred orientation. This conclusion is vividly substan-
tiated by the patterns depicted in Fig. 56.

16.4. ANNEALING

In the oriented state a metal is quite anisotropic. For a few applications anisotropic qualities are desirable. For uses involving further forming operations, however, such qualities are highly detrimental. Therefore,
the next step is normally an annealing operation designed to restore the
original properties. This relieves residual stresses and brings about a
growth of the grains without affecting the external form of the material.
Figure 57 shows the effect of heating on worked metal. Figure 57a is a
pattern taken from a specimen of rolled brass strip. Figure 57b is from
the same strip after it was subjected to an anealing treatment. The recrystallization is very evident.

Often the grains of a recrystallized metal do not possess random
orientation but assume new orientations which may or may not be

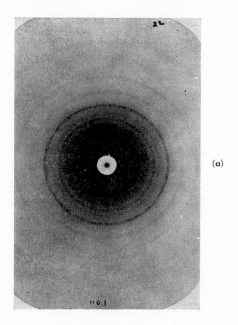

(a)

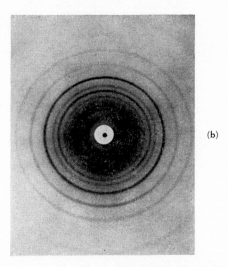

(b)

Fig. 56. Diffraction patterns of hot rolled steel strip used for making tin p'ate. Both samples were cut from the same strip but in such a way that the x-ray beam traversed the samples in different directions (see text): (a) taken with the beam normal to the specimen plane shows no appreciable preferred orientation; (b) taken with the beam parallel to the rolling plane indicates considerable crystallite alignment present. Courtesy of Picker X-Ray Corporation.

the same as those of the cold worked state. These are known as *recrystallization textures* (42, 88). The actual behavior again depends on the metal or alloy, the temperature of annealing, and the type of cold work originally employed. Here also diffraction patterns and pole figures constitute an important method of study.

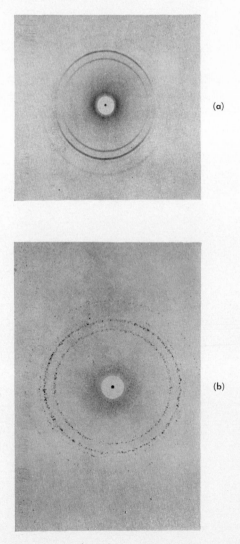

(a)

(b)

FIG. 57. Diffraction patterns from brass strip. (a) After rolling operation. (b) Rolled sample has been given an annealing heat treatment. Recrystallization is graphically demonstrated. Courtesy of Picker X-Ray Corporation.

17. Conclusion

In this chapter we have limited our discussion to the powder method of x-ray analysis, omitting the many basic techniques involving single crystals which include the Laue method, the Bragg method, and the rotating-crystal method. A refinement of the latter method is a procedure wherein both crystal and film move during an exposure. In omitting single-crystal methods we have also made no mention of powerful concepts such as the reciprocal lattice which are utilized in facilitating analysis by these methods. It is the author's opinion, however, that the average chemist will find the powder technique better adapted to his general chemical problems than the admittedly more elegant methods listed above, because of its versatility and basic simplicity. We have also neglected the field of electron diffraction (97) which differs from the x-ray case mainly in that it preferentially samples the structure of crystal surfaces or exceedingly thin films. Finally we have ignored, as being outside the scope of this chapter, the embryonic but promising field of neutron diffraction (103) made possible through the advent of atomic piles. The latter technique appears especially adapted to the location of hydrogen atoms in crystals (90), an accomplishment seldom obtainable with other diffraction tools.

References

1. Alexander, L., and Klug, H. P., *Anal. Chem.* **20**, 886 (1948).
2. Alexander, L., Kummer, E., and Klug, H. P., *J. Appl. Phys.* **20**, 735 (1949).
3. Arndt, U. W., *J. Sci. Instr.* **26**, 45 (1949).
4. Ballard, J. W., Oshry, H. I., and Schrenk, H. H., *U.S. Bur. Mines Rept. Invest.* **No. 3520** (June, 1940).
5. Barrett, C. S., "Structure of Metals," Chapter X. McGraw-Hill, New York, 1943.
6. Barrett, C. S., "Structure of Metals," Chapter XIV. McGraw-Hill, New York, 1943.
7. Barrett, C. S., Geisler, A. H., and Mehl, R. F., *Trans. Am. Inst. Mining Met. Engrs.* **143**, 134 (1941).
8. Barrett, C. S., and Levenson, L. H., *Trans. Am. Inst. Mining Met. Engrs.* **137**, 112 (1940).
9. Beers, Y., *Rev. Sci. Instr.* **13**, 72 (1942).
10. Birks, L. S., Naval Research Laboratory Report No. H-2517 (April 20, 1945).
11. Birks, L. S., and Friedman, H., *J. Appl. Phys.* **17**, 687 (1946).
12. Biscoe, J., and Warren, B. E., *J. Appl. Phys.* **13**, 364 (1942).
13. Bradley, A. J., and Lipson, H., *Proc. Roy. Soc.* **A167**, 421 (1938).
14. Bradley, A. J., and Taylor, G. I., *Nature* **140**, 1012 (1937).
15. Bragg, W. H., and Bragg, W. L., "The Crystalline State," Vol. 1. Macmillan, New York, 1934.
16. Bridgman, P. W., *J. Appl. Phys.* **8**, 328 (1937).
17. Brindley, G. W., *Phil. Mag.* **36**, 347 (1945).
18. Brown, O. E., *J. Appl. Phys.* **18**, 191 (1947).

19. Buerger, M. J., Buerger, N. W., and Chesley, F. G., *Am. Mineralogist* **28**, 285 (1943).
20. Cahn, R. W., *Acta Cryst.* **4**, 470 (1951); *J. Sci. Instr.* **30**, 201 (1953).
21. Cameron, G. H., and Patterson, A. L., *in* "Symposium on Radiography and X-Ray Diffraction," pp. 324-338. American Society for Testing Materials, Philadelphia, 1937.
21a. Champaygne, E. F., *Rev. Sci. Instr.* **17**, 345 (1946).
22. Chesley, F. G., *Rev. Sci. Instr.* **18**, 422 (1947).
23. Clark, G. L., "Applied X-Rays," p. 504. McGraw-Hill, New York, 1940.
24. Clark, G. L., Asbury, W. C., and Wick, R. M., *J. Am. Chem. Soc.* **47**, 2661 (1925).
25. Clark, G. L., and Reynolds, D. H., *Ind. Eng. Chem. Anal. Ed.* **8**, 36 (1936).
26. Clark, G. L., and Rhodes, H. D., *Ind. Eng. Chem. Anal. Ed.* **12**, 243 (1940).
27. Clark, G. L., and Smith, H. A., *Ind. Eng. Chem.* **23**, 697 (1931).
28. Cooke-Yarborough, F. H., *J. Brit. Inst. Radio Engrs.* **11**, 367 (1951).
29. Darwin, C. G., *Phil. Mag.* **43**, 800 (1922).
30. Davey, W. P., "Study of Crystal Structure and Its Applications." McGraw-Hill, New York, 1934.
31. Davey, W. P., *J. Appl. Phys.* **10**, 820 (1939).
32. Debye, P., *Ann. Physik* **46**, 809 (1915).
33. Decker, B. F., *J. Appl. Phys.* **16**, 309 (1945).
34. Dehlinger, U., and Kochendorfer, A., *Z. Krist.* **101**, 149 (1939).
35. Elkin, P. B., Shull, C. G., and Roess, L. C., *Ind. Eng. Chem.* **37**, 327 (1945).
36. Engström, A., *Rev. Sci. Instr.* **18**, 681 (1947).
37. Fankuchen, I., and Mark, H., *J. Appl. Phys.* **15**, 364 (1944).
38. Fink, W. L., and Smith, D. W., *Trans. Am. Inst. Mining Met. Engrs.* **122**, 284 (1936).
39. Frevel, L. K., *Ind. Eng. Chem.* **16**, 209 (1944).
40. Fried, S., and Davidson, N., *J. Am. Chem. Soc.* **70**, 3539 (1948).
41. Gensamer, M., and Mehl, R. F., *Trans. Am. Inst. Mining Met. Engrs.* **120**, 277 (1936).
42. Glocker, R., Kaupp, E., and Widmann, H., *Z. Metallk.* **17**, 353 (1925).
43. Goetz, A., and Hergenrother, R. C., *Phys. Rev.* **40**, 643 (1932).
44. Gross, S. T., and Martin, D. E., *Ind. Eng. Chem. Anal. Ed.* **16**, 95 (1944).
45. Guinier, A., *Ann. phys.* **12**, 161 (1939).
46. Guinier, A., *J. Chem. Phys.* **40**, 133 (1943).
47. Hanawalt, J. D., Rinn, H. W., and Frevel, L. K., *Ind. Eng. Chem. Anal. Ed.* **10**, 457 (1938).
48. Hosemann, R., *Z. Physik* **114**, 133 (1939).
49. Hume-Rothery, W., *J. Inst. Metals* **35**, 295 (1926).
50. Hume-Rothery, W., and Raynor, G. V., *J. Sci. Instr.* **18**, 74 (1941).
51. Hume-Rothery, W., and Reynolds, P. W., *Proc. Roy. Soc.* **A167**, 25 (1938).
52. Hume-Rothery, W., and Strawbridge, D. J., *J. Sci. Instr.* **24**, 89 (1947).
53. Ito, T., "X-Ray Studies on Polymorphism." Maruzen, Tokyo, 1950.
54. Iweronowa, W., and Schdanow, G., *Tech. Phys. U.S.S.R.* **1**, 64 (1934).
55. Jefferies, Z., *Trans. Am. Inst. Mining Met. Engrs.* **70**, 303 (1924).
56. Jellinek, M. H., and Fankuchen, I., *Ind. Eng. Chem.* **37**, 158 (1945).
57. Jellinek, M. H., Solomon, E., and Fankuchen, I., *Ind. Eng. Chem. Anal. Ed.* **18**, 172 (1946).
58. Johansson, C. H., and Linde, J. O., *Ann. Physik* **78**, 439 (1925).
59. Karnop, R., and Sachs, G., *Z. Physik* **42**, 283 (1927).

60. Klug, H. P., and Alexander, L. E., "X-Ray Diffraction Procedures for Polycrystalline and Amorphous Materials." Wiley, New York, 1954.
61. Korff, S. A., "Electron & Nuclear Counters." Van Nostrand, New York, 1946.
62. Laue, M. von, *Z. Krist.* **64**, 115 (1926).
63. Laue, M. von, Friedrich, W., and Knipping, P., *Ann. Physik* **41**, 971 (1913).
64. Liebhafsky, H. A., Smith, H. M., Tanis, H. E., and Winslow, E. H., *Anal. Chem.* **19**, 861 (1947).
65. Liebson, S. H., and Friedman, H., *Rev. Sci. Instr.* **19**, 203 (1948).
66. Lipson, H., *J. Inst. Metals* **69**, 3 (1943).
67. Lipson, H., *Acta Crysta.* **2**, 43 (1949).
68. McCreery, G. L., *J. Am. Ceram. Soc.* **32**, 141 (1949).
69. Mehl, R. F., *Trans. Am. Inst. Mining Met. Engrs.* **111**, 91 (1934).
70. "Metals Handbook." American Society for Metals, Cleveland, Ohio.
71. Möller, H., and Roth, A., *Mitt. Kaiser-Wilhelm Inst. Eisenforsch. Düsseldorf* **19**, 127 (1937).
72. Montgomery, C. G., and Montgomery, D. D., *J. Franklin Inst.* **231**, 447, 509 (1940).
73. Müller, A., *Proc. Roy. Soc. London* **A114**, 542 (1927); **A127**, 417 (1930).
74. Müller, A., and Saville, W. B., *J. Chem. Soc.* **127**, 599 (1925).
75. Norton, J. T., *in* "Symposium on Radiography and X-Ray Diffraction Methods," pp. 302-323. American Society for Testing Materials, Philadelphia, 1937.
76. Owen, E. A., and Preston, G. D., *Proc. Phys. Soc. (London)* **38**, 132 (1925).
77. Parrish, W., *Philips Tech. Rev.* **17**, 206 (1956).
78. Patterson, A. L., *Phil. Mag.* **3**, 1252 (1927).
79. Patterson, A. L., *Phys. Rev.* **56**, 978 (1939).
80. Pepinsky, R., Jarmotz, P., Long, H. M., and Sayre, D., *Rev. Sci. Instr.* **19**, 51 (1948).
81. Piper, S. H., *J. Chem. Soc.*, Part I, 234 (1929).
82. Pollard, E., and Davidson, W. L., "Applied Nuclear Physics," Chapter 3. Wiley, New York, 1951.
83. Rogers, T. H., Paper presented at 32nd Annual Meeting of the Radiological Society of North America, Chicago, December 1-6, 1946.
84. Sachs, G., "Handbuch der Experimentalphysik," Vol. V. Akademische Verlagsgesellschaft, Leipzig, 1930.
85. Scherrer, P., *in* "Kolloidchemie" (R. Zsigmondy, ed.). Otto Spamer, Leipzig, 1920.
86. Schiff, L. I., *Phys. Rev.* **50**, 88 (1936).
87. Schmid, E., and Wassermann, G., *Z. Physik* **42**, 779 (1927).
88. Schmid, E., and Wassermann, G., *Metallwirtschaft* **10**, 409 (1931).
89. Shull, C. G., and Roess, L. C., *J. Appl. Phys.* **18**, 295 (1947).
90. Shull, C. G., Wollan, E. O., Morton, G. A., and Davidson, W. L., *Phys. Rev.* **73**, 842 (1948).
91. Simard, G. L., and Warren, B. E., *J. Am. Chem. Soc.* **58**, 507 (1936).
92. Smith, C. S., and Barrett, R. L., *J. Appl. Phys.* **18**, 177 (1947).
93. Smith, C. S., and Stickley, E. E., *Phys. Rev.* **64**, 191 (1943).
94. Sproull, W. T., "X-Rays in Practice," p. 438. McGraw-Hill, New York, 1946.
95. Straumanis, M., and Ievins, A., *Naturwiss.* **23**, 833 (1935).
96. Sullivan, M. V., and Friedman, H., *Ind. Eng. Chem. Anal. Ed.* **18**, 304 (1946).
97. Thomson, G. P., and Cochrane, W., "Theory and Practice of Electron Diffraction." Macmillan, London, 1939.
98. Trzebiatowski, W., Ploszek, H., and Lobzowski, J., *Anal. Chem.* **19**, 93 (1947).

99. van Horn, K. R., *in* "Symposium on Radiography and X-Ray Diffraction Methods," pp. 230-281. American Society for Testing Materials, Philadelphia, 1937.
100. Warren, B. E., *J. Chem. Phys.* **2,** 551 (1934).
101. Warren, B. E., *J. Appl. Phys.* **12,** 374 (1941).
102. Westgren, A., and Almin, A., *Z. physik. Chem. (Leipzig)* **B5,** 14 (1929).
103. Wollan, E. O., and Shull, C. G., *Phys. Rev.* **73,** 830 (1948).
104. Wood, E. A., *J. Appl. Phys.* **18,** 929 (1947).
105. Zernike, F., and Prins, J. A., *Z. Physik* **41,** 184 (1927).

X-Ray Diffraction as Applied to Fibers

John A. Howsmon and Norman M. Walter

American Viscose Corporation, Marcus Hook, Pennsylvania

1. Characterization of Fibers

1.1. FIBER STRUCTURE

Successful application of x-ray diffraction to studies of high-polymer fibers, films, plastics, and rubbers requires a working knowledge of the concept of fiber structure and its derivation. All these materials consist of long-chain, linear macromolecules with a statistical distribution of lengths. Chemically, these molecules are composed of large numbers of identical or similar groups of atoms held together by primary valence bonds. The characteristically recurring group is called the chemical repeat unit. The volume, shape, and flexibility of any molecule are determined by the chemical composition and configuration of the repeat unit. Therefore, a large number of possible packing arrangements may exist for a polymer solid. The interchain forces, either weak van der Waals' or strong polar forces, tend to arrange the chains in fairly uniform three-dimensional arrays over regions of varying size and shape. The length of the molecules makes it reasonable that any one chain traced from one end to the other will pass through several regions of relatively high order and other regions of disorder (see Fig. 1). Therefore, it seems best to adopt a concept of regions of varying size and order adjacent to other regions of varying size and order (10). This picture is probably more realistic than the older concepts of crystalline and amorphous material in discrete regions such as micelles or crystallites.

When a fiber-forming polymeric material is deformed by extrusion through small holes and subsequent drawing, the macromolecules tend to align in a preferred way with the long-chain axis parallel to the axis of the fiber. The efficiency of alignment is dependent on the structure and treatment. Thus a "fiber structure" may be characterized by the varying amount of order-disorder, and the varying degree of parallel alignment.

This is not restricted to man-made fibers, for natural silk, wool, and cellulose fibers possess the same attributes.

1.2. Type of Polymers

Since all materials included in the general classification of fibers, plastics, and rubbers possess a certain amount of order-disorder structure owing to the linear form of the molecules, a more concrete designation

Fig. 1. Schematic representation of regions of high and low degrees of order in a fiber formed by long-chain molecules.

of class is necessary. A given polymeric material may be characterized by (1) the flexibility of its chains, (2) the strength of the forces between the chains, and (3) the distribution of interaction centers along the chains. For example, if all factors except chain flexibility are constant, that polymer with the most flexible molecule is most rubberlike. Or, for a given chain type, good fiber formers are marked by large interchain forces contributed by such hydrogen-bonding groups as hydroxyl, carboxyl, amino, or carbonyl groups. For a material to be used as a plastic it is best to have weaker interchain forces.

These forces may be weakened either by decreasing the number of highly polar groups per unit length or by increasing the interchain distances by addition of bulky side groups. Rubberlike properties of polymers are usually associated with weak van der Waals-type cohesive forces or a nonuniform distribution of attractive centers. A polymer of the latter type would probably be less rubberlike if the distribution of attractive centers were uniform. No attempt has been made to give a rigorous differentiation of polymers. It does, however, appear reasonable, and many articles have discussed the modifications involved (5-8). It must be recognized that an over-all similarity exists and that the x-ray diffraction characteristics of different polymers will be similar. Therefore, it is possible to use the same general techniques for all polymeric materials.

1.3. Characteristics of X-Ray Fiber Patterns

Typical x-ray fiber diagrams of a few very different polymer materials are shown in Fig. 2. Several distinct features are seen. First, the presence of sharp diffraction maxima indicate that there are regions of highly regular structure, which are perhaps as "crystalline" as sodium chloride. Second, there is diffuse scattering which indicates the presence of material with a very low degree of organization. And finally it is seen that only concentric arcs are present, instead of the complete rings of a normal powder pattern. This pattern is characteristic of a polycrystalline material in which the ordered regions are arranged in a preferred way, and it is quite similar to the pattern resulting from the rotation of a single crystal about a single crystallographic axis.

These fiber diagrams may be fully described by the following characteristics: (1) Number of diffraction maxima. (2) Distance of maxima from the center. (3) Relative intensity of each maximum. (4) Transformation of ring maxima into arcs (orientation). (5) Width or diffuseness of each maximum. (6) Diffuse scattering (disorder structure).

The first three factors are dependent on the structure and perfection of the ordered regions and will vary with the chemical nature of the polymer. The last three factors are directly associated with the fiber structure and will vary with treatment designed to change the alignment or perfection of this characteristic structure.

1.4. X-Ray Analysis Applied to Fibers of High Polymers

Basically there are two major fields in which x-ray diffraction techniques may be applied to films and fibers of high polymers. The first of these is the determination of the three-dimensional crystal structure of the ordered regions in a polymer. This work entails the determination of unit cell dimensions and atomic positions of the atoms. Much work has been done in this field, and excellent reviews are available (6, 30, 33, 38, 58, 78).

The second application is concerned with studies designed to determine the correlation between the form, arrangement, and relative amount
of ordered material in a fiber and the physical properties of that fiber.
For example, even though such celluloses as cotton, ramie, and wood

(a)   (b)

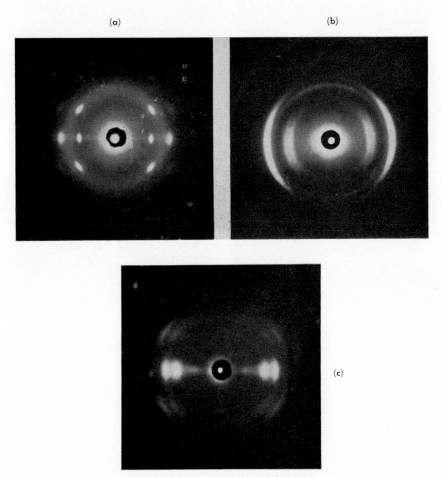

(c)

FIG. 2. X-ray fiber diagrams of (a) cotton, (b) stretched rubber, and (c)
Tussah silk.

all have essentially the same unit cell, they differ in the orientation,
size, and regularity of the ordered regions as well as in the relative
amounts of order-disorder and impurity content. It is factors such as
these that affect the fiber structure and give rise to variations in properties. X-ray diffraction techniques when used in conjunction with other

chemical and physical data on a polymer system can help immeasurably toward determining the nature of the changes which have taken place.

2. X-Ray Patterns of Fibers and Films of High Polymers

2.1. THE BRAGG EQUATION AND THE CONCEPT OF THE RECIPROCAL LATTICE

This chapter is not intended to be a detailed account of x-ray diffraction, but it is necessary to establish certain fundamental concepts of diffraction. The simplest expression of the principles of x-ray diffraction is embodied in the Bragg equation. A crystal is made up of atoms or molecules which may be thought of as being arranged about imaginary points in space. Each of these points is surrounded by the identical groups of atoms which surround all other points. Imaginary lines drawn between the equivalent points define a type of lattice. The lattice shape and dimensions will be determined by the arrangement of the primary groups of atoms or molecules surrounding each equivalent point. Further, it can be shown that many sets of parallel planes may be drawn through the points of the lattice such that for any family of planes all points in the lattice are lying on the planes with no points off the planes. One property of these planes is that they have different "interplanar" spacings. Depending on the symmetry of the crystal, different sets of planes may have the same spacing, but it is possible to determine which sets are equivalent.

Bragg's equation states that the interplanar spacing may be determined by reflecting a beam of x-rays from the set of planes. The direction, with reference to the incident beam in which the reflected beam proceeds, is in accordance with the equation

$$n\lambda = 2d \sin \theta \tag{1}$$

where n is the order of reflection, just as in the case of a grating spectrograph, λ is a monochromatic x-ray wavelength, d is the interplanar spacing of a given set of planes, and θ is the angle which the incident x-ray beam makes to the planes. Hence with a known wavelength it is possible to determine the various spacings in the crystal by measuring the diffraction angles.

Thus x-ray diffraction by a crystal may be regarded as reflection by sets of parallel planes in the crystal. When many planes must be dealt with simultaneously it becomes difficult to visualize the slopes of all these planes. The reciprocal lattice which utilizes the normal to the plane is a device for tabulating both the slope of the plane and the interplanar spacing. This reciprocal lattice concept is the basis for single-crystal x-ray techniques (19, 30).

A single-crystal reciprocal lattice is constructed in the following way. Vectors are drawn perpendicular to each family of planes in the crystal. The length of each vector is taken to be the reciprocal of the value of the interplanar spacing. Therefore, large values of d-spacing will give rise to vectors of short length, and small spacings will generate long vectors. If the ends of these vectors are then connected by straight

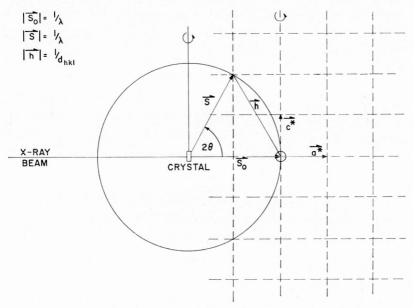

FIG. 3. Schematic representation of reciprocal lattice and sphere of reflection.

lines, a new lattice is derived which bears a definite relationship to the original crystal. Multiple orders of the same spacing occur along the same vector direction but of increasing length.

In order that this "reciprocal" lattice may help in visualizing the diffraction process, Ewald (see 19) linked it with the idea of a sphere of reflection. The relationship of these elements is seen in Fig. 3. The crystal is at the center of the sphere; the origin of its reciprocal lattice is at the point of emergence of the undiffracted beam and is fixed hypothetically to move in synchronism with its crystal. The radius of the sphere is the reciprocal of the x-ray wavelength. As the crystal and its reciprocal lattice rotate, the points will intersect the sphere of reflection and a diffracted beam will emerge in that direction, since the Bragg equation has been satisfied for that particular set of planes.

2.2. THE POWDER PATTERN

In a finely powdered crystalline material all possible orientations of the crystal are present. Therefore, there will always be some crystals in a position to diffract x-rays. The powder pattern can be thought of as being generated by the reciprocal lattice when a single crystal is rotated in the beam about the principal axes. Each time a point goes through the sphere a diffracted ray is produced. A flat film placed in a position corresponding to the origin of the reciprocal lattice and perpendicular to the x-ray beam intersects a series of cones which produce rings on the film. Each ring arises from a different interplanar spacing, and the intensity of each ring is dependent on the material. Every crystalline material has its own characteristic number of rings, ring diameters, and intensities. Hence, an unknown material may be identified by comparing its diffraction pattern with patterns of known samples (39). On the whole, the powder technique is confined to studies of inorganic materials and highly symmetrical, well-crystallized organic materials. The lower symmetry of polymers makes the powder pattern less useful than others for identification.

2.3. ROTATING-CRYSTAL PATTERNS

When a single crystal is placed in an x-ray beam, it is necessary to turn the crystal about an axis in order that all the planes may be brought into position for Bragg reflection to take place. A flat film is positioned at the origin of the the reciprocal lattice, a length called the specimen-to-film distance. As the crystal rotates about a principal crystallographic axis normal to the beam, a pattern of spots will appear, as shown in Fig. 4. The spots lie on a series of hyperbolae and are called layer lines. Had the film been placed in a cylinder around the sample, the layer lines above and below the so-called "equatorial" line would then appear on parallel layers across the film. If the crystal is rotated successively around the other two principal axes, the repeat distance can be calculated along the three directions, and hence the size and shape of the unit cell.

The repeat distance may be calculated from any spot on any layer line on a flat film from the equation

$$I = \frac{n\lambda}{\sin \alpha} \tag{2}$$

where I is the identity period, λ is the x-ray wavelength, α is the external angle of the cone of diffraction, and n is the order of the layer line (=1, 2, 3, etc.). When the proper values of n are used, the value of I is equal for all layer lines (7, 23, 33). When $n = 0$, the diffraction spots lie on the equator and are the reflections from planes parallel to the rotation axis of the crystal. It is not possible to explain all the features of rotating-crystal patterns, but the calculation of the identity period and the interplanar spacings of the various reflections, particularly the equatorial ones, is very important in the studies of fibers. Therefore, the following examples will illustrate the necessary calculations for flat-film rotating-crystal patterns.

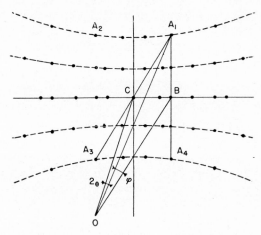

FIG. 4. Schematic representation of a rotation photograph of a single crystal.

Because of the geometry of the crystal and its reciprocal lattice, four equivalent spots will be recorded for nonequatorial reflections as the reciprocal lattice points pass in and out of the sphere of reflection. Equatorial planes will give only two equivalent points. Consider the four equivalent spots, A_1, A_2, A_3, A_4, on the second-order layer line and the calculation of the identity period from these maxima.

The sample position is at O, and the sample-to-film distance is OC. From eq. (2) we have

$$\sin \alpha = \frac{2\lambda}{I} \qquad \text{(for the second layer line)}$$

and from Fig. 4,

$$\sin \alpha = \frac{\overline{AB}}{\overline{AO}} = \frac{\overline{AB}}{(\overline{AC^2} + \overline{OC^2})^{\frac{1}{2}}}$$

Hence,

$$I = \frac{2\lambda \, (\overline{AC^2} + \overline{OC^2})^{1/2}}{\overline{AB}}$$

To calculate the d-spacing of the planes which give rise to the spots A_1, A_2, etc., we have

$$\tan 2\theta = \frac{\overline{AC}}{\overline{OC}}$$

and from eq. (1)

$$d = \frac{\lambda}{2 \sin \theta} = \frac{\lambda}{2 \sin \left[\frac{1}{2} \tan^{-1} (\overline{AC}/\overline{OC})\right]}$$

The necessary experimental values $\overline{AC}$ and $\overline{AB}$ are determined by measuring on the film the distances $\overline{A_1A_3}$ and $\overline{A_1A_4}$, which are $2\overline{AC}$ and $2\overline{AB}$, respectively.

2.4. Fiber Diagrams

Structurally many of the natural fibers occur with the long axes of the ordered regions lying parallel to the long axis of the fiber. The other two principal axes are oriented randomly about the fiber axis. The same type of orientation may be induced in other polymers by suitable mechanical means. This type of preferred orientation is known as uniaxial orientation, and as a consequence an x-ray pattern may be recorded which, when the beam is normal to the fiber axis, is equivalent to a single-crystal rotation pattern. It is not necessary, however, to rotate the sample about the fiber axis. This type of pattern has been termed the fiber pattern and is useful in structure studies of the ordered regions of the polymer system in question.

There are, however, differences between fiber patterns and true rotation patterns. These differences are basically attributed to the fact that the long axes of the ordered regions are not completely parallel to the fiber axis but assume a varying angular tilt to the axis. The first difference is that the reflections are recorded as circular arcs the lengths of which denote the amount of tilt. The limiting case would be complete circles as shown in the true powder pattern recorded on a flat film. Orientation and its measurement will be discussed later. The second characteristic difference between the fiber pattern and the rotation pattern is the presence of those reflections which are related to planes perpendicular to the fiber axis and hence parallel to the x-ray beam. Since these reflections could not occur if the planes were truly perpendicular, it is evident again that the ordered regions have an angular dispersion to the fiber axis. These reflections, if they appear, are at the vertex of the layer line hyperbola on a vertical line through the center. They are referred to classically as meridian reflections.

The meridian reflections from the diatropic planes (perpendicular to the fiber axis) are extremely useful, for they give an accurate measure of the identity period along the fiber. Under conditions of extreme parallelism there are no meridian reflections, and hence it is difficult to determine the position of the vertex of the hyperbola. In these cases the measurement is simplified by the use of a cylindrical film camera (see Section 5). The layer lines are then all recorded at the same height above the equator. A second possibility is to oscillate the fibers through a small angle centered on the angle θ which is the Bragg angle related to these planes (30, 58, 77). The geometry involved may be readily pictured when referred to the reciprocal lattice. By realizing that the reciprocal lattice is related to the sample in a definite manner, it is easier to determine the way in which a sample should be oriented in order to record particular reflections.

One of the chief uses for rotating-crystal techniques when applied to good single crystals is the determination of accurate unit cell dimensions, and the indexing of the various reflecting planes. An extremely regular polymer fiber or one with a large fraction of ordered regions makes it possible to determine unit cell measurements by means of rotating-crystal techniques (26, 28, 29, 33, 44, 74, 78, 87, 88).

Even though it may not be possible to determine uniquely the cell dimensions of a polymer material owing to lack of a sufficiently large number of reflections, it is possible to derive valuable packing information from limited data when they are coupled intelligently with other known chemical data. Many times it is only these data which give a clear insight into the relationships between properties and structure.

2.5. Fiber Repeat Distance

From the previous discussion, it is apparent that the identity period determined from a fiber diagram made with the fiber axis perpendicular to the x-ray beam is the distance required for the molecular pattern to repeat along the length of the polymer chain. In the simplest case, the identity period or the packing repeat unit will be the same length as the chemical repeat unit and will arise from planes which are perpendicular to the fiber axis. Other variations may occur as follows: (1) the identity period may be a multiple of the length of the chemical repeat unit; (2) the identity period length may be shorter than that required by the proper multiple of the chemical repeat unit; (3) the planes giving rise to the identity period may lie at some angle other than a right angle to the fiber axis; and (4) combinations of (3) may occur with other cases. These concepts are most easily seen from examples. The simplest long-chain molecule is the high-molecular-weight paraffin, polyethylene, whose fiber diagram is shown in Fig. 5. The chemi-

(a)   (b)

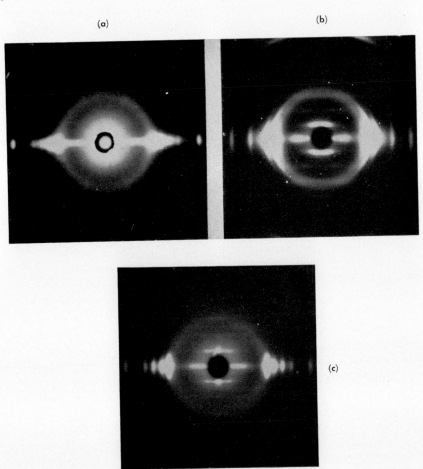

(c)

FIG. 5. Fiber diagrams of polyethylene (a), poly-ω-hydroxy undecanoate (b), and poly-ω-hydroxy decanoate (c). Diagrams (b) and (c) courtesy of W. O. Baker and N. R. Pape.

cal repeating unit is the —CH_2—CH_2— group whose length is 2.5 A., if the carbon-carbon bond length is assumed to be 1.5 A. and the tetrahedral angle of 109.5° for carbon. The identity period calculated from the x-ray pattern is also 2.5 A. (28), and the interference corresponding to this distance occurs on the pattern meridian; hence, the carbon atoms of adjacent chains must lie in horizontal layers perpendicular to the fiber axis, and the carbon atoms along a given chain are planar and zigzag according to the carbon tetrahedral angle. As part of the hydrogen atoms of the —CH_2—CH_2— group are replaced uniformly by another group, changes in packing arising from differences in polarity and size of hydrogen and the substituted group occur. The best examples of the packing variation with monomer composition are the vinyl polymers whose identity periods are listed in Table I.

TABLE I

Fiber Periods of Vinyl-Type Polymers

Polymer	Chemical repeating unit	Fiber period (A.)	No. of monomer units in repeating distance
Polyethylene	—CH_2—CH_2—	2.52	1
Polyvinyl alcohol	—CH_2—CHOH	2.52	1
Polyvinyl chloride	—CH_2—CHCl	5.0	2
Polyvinylidene chloride	—CH_2—CCl_2—	4.7	2
Polyisobutylene	—CH_2—$C(CH_3)_2$—	18.6	8

2.6. Vinyl Polymers

In the crystalline form both polyethylene and polyvinyl alcohol lie with the chains in the normal planar zigzag arrangement for which the identity period must be 2.52 A. In addition the hydroxyl groups of polyvinyl alcohol must approach a planar arrangement, as illustrated in Fig. 6, for otherwise geometric identity could not be established along the chain within one —CH_2—CHOH— group, and the identity period would have to be greater than the observed 2.5 A. (38). If a single chain of polyvinyl chloride is considered, the mutual repulsion of the C-Cl dipoles would be expected to bring the chain into a configuration in which each chlorine atom is at the maximum distance from its neighbors. That this tendency is carried over into the crystal packing is shown by the fact that the observed identity period along the chains is 5 A. This value requires a planar zigzag configuration for the chain carbon atoms but necessitates that every other chlorine atom be differently disposed along the chain. The probable arrangement illustrated in Fig. 6 is one in which the chlorines take up alternate positions above and below the plane of the carbon chain in agreement with repulsive forces between chlorine atoms (38). This repulsion between chlorine atoms is accentuated in polyvinylidene chloride (38) for which the fiber period of 4.7 A. shows a definite shortening compared to the planar zigzag arrangement which requires a period of 5 A. Such a shortening is obtained by rotating alternate pairs of chlorine atoms around the C-C bond so that each chlorine is the maximum distance from its neighbors

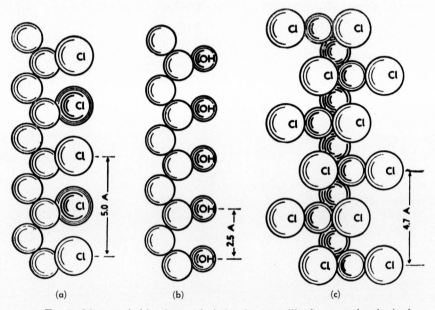

(a)   (b)   (c)

FIG. 6. Most probable shape of chains in crystallized areas of polyvinyl chloride (a), polyvinyl alcohol (b), and polyvinylidene chloride (c) (75).

and the carbon chain is distorted from the normal planar zigzag arrangement, as shown in Fig. 6. A similar helical chain arrangement due now to the size of the substituent groups instead of the repulsive forces between them is found in polyisobutylene (44), which has an identity period of 18.63 A. along the fiber axis. The large methyl groups do not allow a planar zigzag chain but force the chain into a helical form which requires eight —CH$_2$—C(CH$_3$)$_2$— groups to complete one coil. In this helix the effective length of the isobutylene unit is reduced from 2.5 A. to about 2.3 A.

Differences in longitudinal packing of chains such as those discussed above cannot be directly correlated to physical properties of the polymer, but general relationships do exist. For example, when the forces between chains are small and the monomer composition is such that the chains are incapable of restoring geometric identity along their length in a short distance, a tendency toward rubberlike properties results. This trend is apparent for the materials in Table I. Polyethylene crystallizes readily; polyisobutylene crystallizes only after stretching and behaves as a rubber.

Recent advances in the technology of polymerization have resulted in the production of stereoregular polymers (80). These polymers are marked by a low degree of chain branching and by the fact (1) that the side groups attached to the carbon chain of the polymer are all attached to the same hydrogen position in the monomer, or (2) that d- and l-monomer configurations alternate regularly along the carbon chain. Many polyolefins, such as polyethylene, polypropylene, and poly-4-methylpentene-1, have been prepared in linear or stereoregular forms. These are marked by high melting points and high degrees of crystallinity, but complete x-ray characteristics have not been established (80).

2.7. POLYESTERS

Another change in the chain molecule which does not appreciably affect its hydrocarbon nature is the introduction of polar groups at regular intervals along the chain, as in the synthetic polyesters (32, 39-43). The simplest case is a self-ester of a hydroxy acid which yields a chemical repeating unit as follows:

$$-COO(CH_2)_x-$$

Since the C—O bond distance approximates the C—C bond distance, and the C—O—C bond angle approximates a tetrahedral angle, this is essentially a paraffin chain in which an oxygen atom has replaced two hydrogen atoms of a methylene group at regular intervals along the chain.

By self-reacting ω-hydroxyundecanoic acid this change is carried out on every thirteenth carbon atom (39). The similarity of the fiber diagram of this polyundecanoate to that of polyethylene is apparent in the diagrams of Fig. 5. An additional layer line arising from planes containing the oxygen atoms added to the molecule occurs on either side of the meridian near the center of the diagram. These planes are inclined to the direction of the chains as is shown by the fact that the reflections do not coalesce on the meridian as they would if the planes were perpendicular to the chain axis. The observed fiber period is 15.0 A., and that calculated from accepted bond dimensions is 14.9 A. Therefore, the chains must have an extended planar zigzag arrangement, and the added dipoles have formed layers inclined to the fiber axis. This structure, shown schematically in Fig. 7, is typical of polyesters containing an even number of chain atoms. All the oxygen groups are on the same side of the chain, and the polar groups layer "head-to-tail" in the direction of the dipole vector of the ester group. If the oxygen atom is inserted on every twelfth carbon atom by self-reaction of ω-hydroxydecanoic acid, the structure shown in Fig. 7b results. It is evident that in this case the oxygen atoms must alternate from side to side on the chain. Now the dipole layers formed by the added atoms are perpendicular to the fiber axis, and the

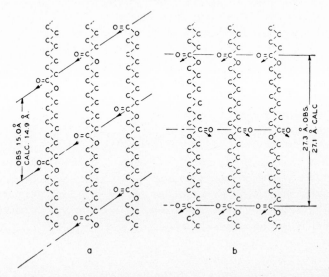

Fig. 7. Schematic formation of dipole layers: (a) with strong association in polyundecanoate (even number of chain atoms); (b) with weaker association in polydecanoate (odd number of chain atoms). Small arrows indicate dipole vectors. From Fuller and Baker.

new reflections from these layers will be exactly on the meridian line. These meridian reflections are shown in the diagram of polydecanoate in Fig. 5. As in the previous example, the observed fiber period (27.1 A.) agrees with that calculated (27.3 A.) from the model of Fig. 7b. In this case, however, the fiber period extends over two chemical repeating units instead of one. This second case is typical of polyesters containing odd numbers of chain atoms.

The layering of polar groups by dipole association is a general phenomenon for other series of polyesters (32, 39, 41-45), polyamides (11, 12, 40) and copolyesters (94). The planar zigzag arrangement of chains is not general, however, and the departure from such arrangement usually increases with increasing concentration of polar groups. Most polyesters have helical chain configurations as shown by the shortening of the actual fiber period under the calculated value. The effect of the different types of layering of polar groups, i.e., whether the layers are normal or tilted in respect to the chain axis, is apparent in the physical properties of the polymer, and general relationships between the type of layering and properties do exist. For example, polymers having the polar group layers tilted in respect to the chain axes have higher melting points than polymers having layers normal to the chain axis (39).

2.8. LATERAL PACKING OF CHAINS

After having considered the ways in which the fiber identity period may be used to give valuable information about the longitudinal aspects of the polymer chains, it now remains to point out ways in which the differences in the lateral arrangement of the chains may be characterized.

Those reflections associated with the lateral packing and arrangement will occur on the so-called equator of the diagram shown in Fig. 4. As the lateral packing of different types of polymer chain is studied, it is found that the intensity and position, or interplanar spacing, of the principal equatorial reflections are different for each polymer. For example, the spacings associated with polyethylene are characteristic of all long-chain paraffins. The intensities of equivalent reflections in each paraffin will be different from one another, but in general the same lateral spacings will occur. As the hydrogens are replaced by other groups the lateral distances will vary from those of the pure hydrocarbon because of (1) the size of the replacement group, (2) the number of such groups in each polymer unit, (3) the deviation of the chain itself from the planar zigzag arrangement with increasing substitution, and (4) the comparative ability of the substituted group to form hydrogen bonds and, hence, to alter the relative interchain forces. For example, polyvinyl alcohol which has the same fiber identity period has altered lateral packing because of the size of the hydroxyl group and its ability to form interchain hydrogen bonds. In polyisobutylene both the configuration of the chain and the lateral packing is altered so that all the factors are operative in producing the changes.

3. Qualitative Application of X-Ray Diffraction in Fiber Studies

3.1. POLYMER IDENTIFICATION

One of the most obvious applications of the data derived from studies of high-polymer fibers is that of identification. The x-ray pattern and the interplanar spacings of the lateral and longitudinal packing which are calculated from the pattern may be used to identify a polymer with much greater certainty, in many cases, than chemical methods. The existing file of reference standards for the identification of the x-ray powder patterns of inorganic and a limited number of organic crystals is the ASTM card file based on the Hanawalt index (see chapter by Davidson) (3). As yet, there is no comparable file existing for polymers. It is relatively easy to distinguish one polymer from another, however, when fiber diagram data of an unknown are compared with the fiber repeat distances and lateral spacing of standard polymer fibers. The x-ray method is one of the very few positive ways of identifying the different polymorphic forms which are encountered in such materials as cellulose, gutta-percha, cellulose acetate, and other synthetic polymer systems.

3.2. Chemical Reactions in Polymer Systems

X-ray methods have been used extensively to follow the course of chemical reactions in polymer systems. Even in the extreme case of the acid hydrolysis of cellulose during which no pronounced change in the x-ray diagram occurs, the lack of change indicates that only the regions of low order between the regions of three-dimensionally arranged chains are affected by the reaction. In other cases, the x-ray pattern is altered as the chemical reaction proceeds, and information about the mechanism of the reaction and the arrangement of the final reaction products is obtained. Among the many types of reactions which have been studied are those of substitution or derivative formation (12, 38, 94), copolymerization (12), and swelling (66). A typical substitution or derivative formation is that of the acetylation of cellulose in which it is possible to distinguish three fairly distinct phases: (1) In the early stages of the reaction, only the cellulose pattern is present; (2) the interferences of the reaction product are superimposed on the cellulose pattern; and (3) the cellulose lines disappear and only those of the reaction product remain.

3.3. Copolymers

A copolymer can be thought of as the product of a substitution reaction, and x-ray methods are applicable to studies of these systems. At the same time, these polymers serve as an illustration of the difficulties which may be encountered in attempting to identify polymers by their diffraction pattern as is done in the Hanawalt or ASTM file. Consider, for example, a copolymer which contains 80 mole % of $-CH_2-CHX-$ monomer and 20 mole % of a $-CH_2-CHY-$ monomer. There are several different ways in which this system might behave: (1) If the X and

Y groups are of about the same size and activity, then the copolymer may assume the packing of the pure polymer X, and complete identification cannot be made by inspection of the identity period and equatorial reflections. (2) If Y is larger than X, it may inhibit the crystallization of the polymer completely, and again identification is impossible by x-rays alone. And (3) an entirely different type of crystallization may be the preferred one for the system. This does not mean that x-ray methods are useless in these cases but only that the value of the technique is definitely greater for the study of known systems. For instance, in the above example with similar side groups, it is of interest to know that the two monomers are compatible in so far as packing is concerned.

3.4. SWELLING

One of the many general characteristics of fibrous systems which may be studied advantageously by x-ray diffraction is that of swelling. Swelling in fibers has been defined by Katz (66) as a process by which a solid takes up a liquid or vapor while at the same time (1) it does not lose its apparent homogeneity, (2) its dimensions are enlarged, and (3) the interchain cohesive forces are diminished. Under these conditions, two states may be obtained. The first is a penetration of only the disordered regions between the crystalline regions. There is no change in the ordered diffraction pattern, and the pattern of the amorphous liquid is superimposed on the pattern of the pure polymer. When the diffraction pattern of the crystalline polymer is altered by swelling, however, it may be definitely concluded that the liquid has penetrated the ordered regions of the polymer. These two states have come to be known as intercrystalline and intracrystalline swelling.

Intercrystalline swelling is illustrated by the effects of normal alcohols on cellulose. The intercrystalline swelling decreases as the molecular weight of the alcohols increases. On the other hand, benzene and its derivatives have the opposite effect in that the swelling increases with increasing dipole moment of the swelling liquid (99).

Intracrystalline swelling is further characterized by two different effects which are observed in the diffraction patterns. In the first case, the lateral dimensions of the unit cell increase in a continuous way as a function of the degree of swelling. The second type is characterized by the formation of a crystalline addition compound; i.e., the original crystalline fiber pattern decreases in intensity as a new crystalline pattern is formed. The first type is exhibited, in cellulose for instance, by the gradual spreading of the equatorial reflections into diffuse streaks through the origin as the fibers are swollen in strong sulfuric acid (72%) or phosphoric acid (85%). When, on the other hand, swelling compounds are formed, it is found that the molecules of the swelling agent arrange themselves throughout the expanded lattice in a definite geometrical pattern, and consequently there is a crystalline pattern characteristic of each swelling agent. This type of swelling may be illustrated by the action of diamines on cellulose (102). As shown in Table II the (101) spacing of

TABLE II

Effect of Diamines on the (101) Interplanar Spacing of Cellulose

Swelling compound	(101) Distance (A.)
Native cellulose	6.1
Hydrazine cellulose	10.3
Ethylenediamine cellulose	12.3
Tetramethylenediamine cellulose	14.6

the swelling compound increases as the length of the diamine molecule increases.

In the present discussion, we have considered in all cases that the crystals present were perfect and have ignored the fact that some fibrous materials are very difficult to crystallize. In fact, in cases like polyvinyl acetate it is practically impossible to produce any crystallized regions. Other materials, such as rubber, will crystallize only under stress or at low temperature. Such behavior is a manifestation of order-disorder phenomena involving the crystalline-amorphous character of fibrous systems emphasized in the introductory discussion. It is desirable then to extend x-ray methods not only to recognition of phenomena associated with the formation of crystals, but also to phenomena associated with forces tending to prevent crystal formation.

4. Orientation

4.1. Types of Orientation

In x-ray studies of polymeric materials, the term orientation is usually used in reference to the alignment of the ordered regions in respect to the fiber axis or to the surface of the specimen. It has no reference to the arrangement or orientation of the individual molecules within the ordered or crystalline regions. Therefore, it is theoretically possible to have a highly ordered material with random orientation or an amorphous material with parallel orientation, and, within limits, orientation and crystallinity may be varied independently. A highly oriented fiber can be considered to be more crystalline than an unoriented fiber

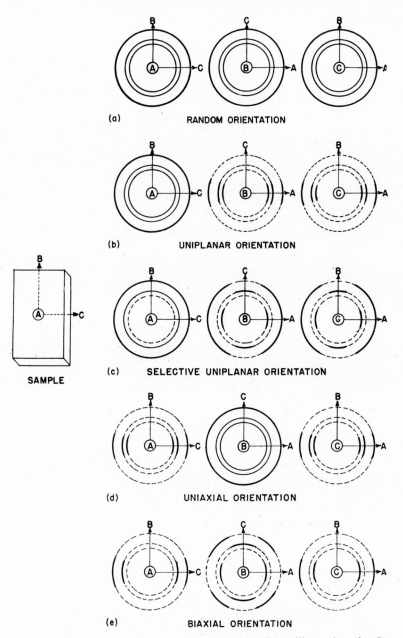

Fig. 8. Schematic x-ray diagrams of cellulose fibers illustrating the five general types of orientation.

only in the sense that the fiber as a whole possesses greater order in the fiber direction than in any other direction. Generally the term orientation refers only to the alignment of the long axis of the ordered regions in respect to the fiber axis, but other types are possible. The classification which follows was originally defined for native cellulose membranes (95) and has been extended to regenerated cellulose (93) and cellulose derivatives (1). It apparently is generally applicable. The various types of orientation are:

1. Random orientation. The crystallites lie in all possible directions (see Fig. 8a).

2. Uniplanar orientation. The b-axes of the crystals lie parallel to a plane. The direction within the plane is random, and all possible rotations around the b-axes are possible (see Fig. 8b).

3. Selective uniplanar orientation. The b-axes are again parallel to and arranged at random within a plane, but there is an added condition that some crystal plane has a selective orientation parallel to a plane which is usually the large surface of the specimen. In a fibrous sample, the large surface is the perimeter of the fiber. For cellulose, the selective plane is the (101) (see Fig. 8c).

4. Uniaxial orientation. The only condition is that the b-axes are oriented parallel to the fiber axis. This is the most common type of orientation occurring in natural and synthetic fibers (see Fig. 8d).

5. Biaxial or selective uniaxial orientation. The b-axes of the ordered regions are parallel to the fiber axis and a selective plane—for cellulose, the (101) plane—is parallel to a plane containing the fiber axis. This is a combination of uniaxial and selective uniplanar orientation and is not uncommon in fibrous materials (see Fig. 8e).

4.2. IDENTIFICATION OF TYPES OF ORIENTATION

The type of orientation present in a given sample must be determined from the appearance of the x-ray fiber diagrams. Consider a sample of native cellulose which crystallizes in the structure shown in Fig. 9a. The b-axis (direction of cellulose chains) is normal to the plane of the paper. The x-ray diagram (powder diagram) is shown in Fig. 9b. The concentric rings of increasing diameter in the diagram are the (101), $(10\bar{1})$, and (0.02), diffraction lines, respectively.

A sample of cellulose containing many small crystallites, each of which is packed as shown in Fig. 9a, is depicted in Fig. 8; A, B, and C are arbitrary references within the sample and represent the directions through which x-ray diagrams of the samples are made. If the orientation is random, the same x-ray diagram is obtained with the sample at any angle to the x-ray beam, and all the normal diffraction lines will be present in each diagram as illustrated in Fig. 8a. If the orientation is uniplanar and the b-axes of the ordered regions lie parallel to the A surface of the specimen, the x-ray diagram will be random with all lines present when plane A is perpendicular to the x-ray beam, but fiber diagrams will be obtained when the diagrams are made in either the B or C directions, i.e., with plane A parallel to the x-ray beam. These diagrams are illustrated in Fig. 8b. All the normal cellulose diffraction lines will be present in all the diagrams if the sample has pure uniplanar orientation. If the orientation is selective uniplanar, the (101) planes of the cellulose crystal will be selectively oriented parallel to the large or A surface of the specimen. With the x-ray beam perpendicular to this selective plane, a random diagram is obtained with the (101) line missing and the (10$\bar{1}$) present. With

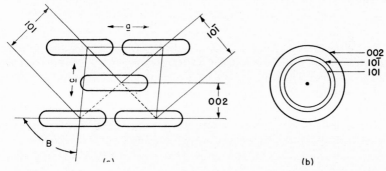

Fig. 9. Schematic representation of (a) the unit cell of native cellulose showing a, c, the angle β, and the (101), (10$\bar{1}$), and (002) planes and (b) the x-ray diagram of randomly oriented native cellulose.

the x-ray beam parallel to this plane, a fiber diagram is obtained in which the (101) line is present as a dense equatorial arc and the (10$\bar{1}$) line is present only as a faint arc on the meridian of the diagram. These diagrams are shown in Fig. 8c.

If the orientation is uniaxial and the b-axes of the ordered regions are arranged parallel to the B-axis of the sample, fiber diagrams with all lines present will be obtained when either the A or C face is perpendicular to the x-ray beam. A random pattern with all lines present is obtained when the x-ray beam is perpendicular to the B face, i.e., is parallel to the fiber axis. These diagrams are shown in Fig. 8d. This type of orientation is found in all modern rayons and other man-made fibers, and the term orientation, unless otherwise specified, usually refers to uniaxial orientation. For uniaxial orientation, the position and intensity of the lines will be constant at any sample position as long as the x-ray beam is perpendicular to the fiber axis. Biaxial orientation is marked in that fiber diagrams will be obtained with the x-ray beam either perpendicular or parallel to the fiber axis as shown in Fig. 8e. With the x-ray beam perpendicular to the fiber axis, all the lines may appear as intensity maxima, but the relative intensity of these lines changes if diagrams are made at various angles around this axis. For example, in the ideal case for cellulose in which the (101) and (10$\bar{1}$) planes intersect at slightly less than a right angle, the following condition would exist. If the selective plane is parallel to the x-ray beam, the (101) line will be present and the (10$\bar{1}$) absent. With the beam normal to the selective plane, the (10$\bar{1}$) line is present and the (101) line is absent. If the biaxial orientation is imperfect, both lines may appear in each diagram, but, even so, the relative intensities of the two lines will vary if the sample is rotated and diagrams are made at different angles around the fiber axis. In drawing the x-ray diagrams, considerable deviation from the preferred type of orientation is assumed, for a perfect orientation of any type is seldom if ever found in practice.

All types of orientation may be produced experimentally. Random orientation results when a sample is formed in such a way that no external tension or pressure reacts on the sample, and it is free to shrink in all directions. Uniaxial orientation results when a fiber is stretched and not allowed to relax. Uniplanar orientation may be obtained by pressing a film or by allowing it to shrink only in thickness during its formation and processing. Biaxial orientation results from conditions which allow elongation in one direction and rolling or pressing to produce a shrinkage in another direction.

After a given type or orientation is formed, it is possible in some cases to convert it to another type. For example, commercial cellophane sheets exhibit selective uniplanar orientation, which is changed to a uniaxial form if the sheet is stretched. This uniaxial orientation may then be converted to a biaxial form by rolling the stretched sheet without allowing it to relax. The effect of mechanical deformation on orientation has been discussed in detail for cellulose (92, 95), cellulose derivatives (7, 8, 10, 11), gelatin (101), keratin (9), and synthetic linear polymers (12).

4.3. MEASUREMENT OF ORIENTATION

The degree of a given type of orientation may be evaluated by several methods, such as microscopic study of visible fibrils, study of extinction angles, polarized light phenomena, and x-ray diffraction. Optical measurements are dependent on the orientation of both the crystalline and amorphous regions and are in that respect superior to the x-ray method, which gives only the orientation of the crystalline regions. The x-ray diagram gives reliable and complete information about the crystal orientation, however, whereas optical results are difficult to evaluate in absolute terms.

Uniaxial orientation is most common in fibrous materials, and therefore most of the reported work has been concerned with this type. With the advent of synthetic film materials such as cellophane and polyethylene, however, the uniplanar and selective uniplanar types have become increasingly important. For the present, uniaxial orientation will be stressed, keeping in mind at the same time that the technique is applicable to the others. All determinations of degree of orientation are based on the principle that the intensity of a diffraction ring around its circumference will be proportional to the number of planes contributing to the diffraction of x-rays at that angle. The x-ray patterns are taken with the fiber axis perpendicular to the beam, and for convenience the definitions are based on the intensity distribution of the equatorial reflections which correspond to planes parallel to the fiber axis. The length of the diffraction arc is thus a measure of the degree of orientation. For example, a short arc indicates a nearly perfect alignment of the ordered regions with the fiber axis. The intensity distribution around the arc gives some indication of the numerical frequency distribution of ordered regions over the angular range of the arc.

These effects are illustrated by the diffraction pattern of a highly oriented cellulose fiber in Fig. 10a, and, in Fig. 10b, a diffractometer trace made radially along the equator of this diagram. If several radial traces are made at small angular intervals to the equator or, more simply, if a direct azimuthal scan of a given reflection is made, a curve relating the intensity to the angular distance from the equator is obtained. A trace of this type, shown in Fig. 10c, is the basis for x-ray measurement of crystallite orientation in fibers. In the measurement a correction for the diffuse scattering on which the diffraction maxima are superimposed is necessary. A large number of methods of applying this correction have been reported (52, 54, 61, 68, 97), but no general agreement on method has been established. Whatever method is chosen for this correction, it is important that it be applied consistently before results are compared.

The actual measurement of intensity is carried out on film with a densitometer or microphotometer; the problems involved have been discussed in detail in the literature (68, 86, 98). Whenever possible, the rapid technique of direct measurement with a diffractometer and proportional counter is to be preferred (2).

4.4. Orientation Parameters

In order to have some index for comparison of degree or amount of orientation a number of useful parameters are given as follows:

1. The half-maximum angle (54, 61)—the angular length in degrees of the measured interference at half-maximum intensity, after correction for background intensity. This parameter is illustrated in Fig. 11. The angular length may actually be measured at any other convenient fraction of the maximum intensity. For example, most orientation studies of cotton utilize the angular length at 40% of the maximum intensity (20).

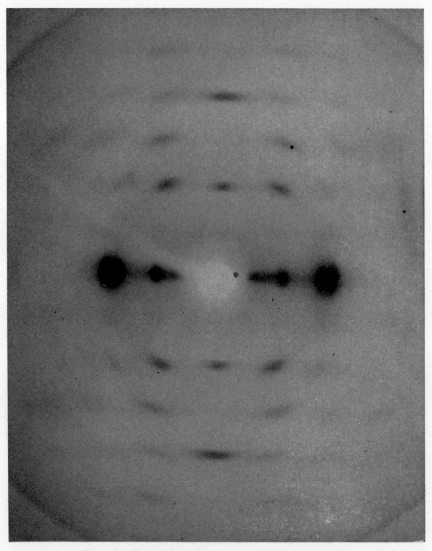

Fig. 10a. Precession photograph of Fortisan fibers.

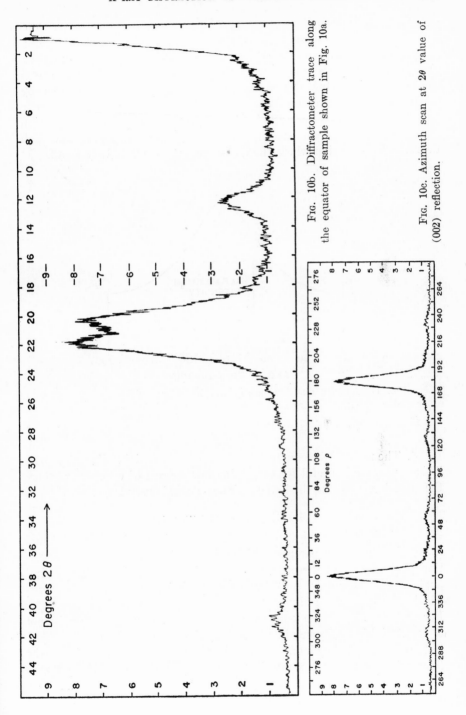

Fig. 10b. Diffractometer trace along the equator of sample shown in Fig. 10a.

Fig. 10c. Azimuth scan at 2θ value of (002) reflection.

2. The ratio 180/A (61), where A is the half-maximum angle. This provides a parameter which increases with increasing orientation.

3. Distribution curves. The angular distribution of the interference around the fiber axis is obtained by calculating the fraction of the total interference occurring at each angle (54, 97). This is simply done by dividing the measured intensity of the interference line at a given angle by the total intensity over 180° of the diffraction circle. The distribution curve is most useful in studying small orientation differences and high degrees of orientation where the half-maximum angle is very small.

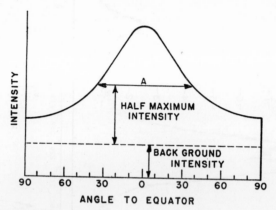

Fig. 11. Angular distribution of intensity around diffraction arc of a fiber diagram showing orientation measurement by half-maximum intensity method.

4. The ratio of the equatorial to the polar or meridian intensity (61). This parameter is useful for expressing low degrees of orientation where the error in measuring the half-maximum angle is very large.

4.5. SPIRAL ORIENTATION

Deviations from the types of orientation discussed above are found in certain cases. For example, native cellulose fibers may possess orientation of the b-axis of the ordered regions either parallel to or at a spiral angle to the fiber axis. A cotton fiber consists of many smaller fibrils which are arranged spirally around the fiber axis at an angle of about 30°. For such a structure the x-ray diagram would be expected to consist not of equatorial intensity maxima but of two intensity maxima at about 30° to the equator of the diagram. With the x-ray beam perpendicular to the fiber axis, however, the x-ray diagram of cotton does exhibit equatorial intensity maxima, because the x-ray diagram actually represents the projection of the spiral fibrils into a plane. Therefore, the intensity distribution around the diffraction ring is always shifted toward the equator because of the cylindrical form of the fiber (91), and the x-ray diagram may not indicate a spiral angle even though one is present. The x-ray diagram will show a spiral structure only when the spiral angle is large and the deviation from the spiral angle is small (96).

4.6. Effects of Orientation

The physical and chemical properties of a fiber depend on both the type and degree of orientation. The role played by the type of orientation on the properties of a polymeric material may be illustrated by the effect of rolling a sheet of a cellulose ester to 50% of its original thickness. The orientation, which was essentially random before rolling, has now assumed a uniplanar or selective uniplanar type with the long axes of the ordered regions parallel to the plane of the sheet. Consequently, the tear resistance of the sheet increases, since it is more difficult to tear across the long chains of molecules than it is to disrupt them laterally (10). In the same manner uniaxial orientation requires that the breaking strength will be much greater in the direction of the preferred axis than in any other direction. Ultimate uses of textile fibers require these directional properties, and, therefore, most synthetic fibers are produced with uniaxial orientation.

A summary of the effects of orientation of the chemical and physical properties of fibers is given in Table III. The effects of orientation which

TABLE III

Effect of Increasing Orientation on Some Fiber Properties

Increases	Decreases	Little or no effect
Tensile strength	Elongation	Water vapor sorption
Young's modulus	Longitudinal swelling	Elastic limit
Rigidity	Eye sorption rate	
Transverse swelling	Plasticity	
Refractive index	Crease resistance	
Luster	Chemical reactivity	
Recovery after stretching		

have been listed are applicable in all systems of polymeric materials within reasonable limits. The correlation of orientation and properties within a given system may be very difficult, however. The relationship of orientation to tensile strength and elongation for two experimental rayons are shown in Fig. 12. One yarn was spun into a bath containing only acid and sodium sulfate, the other into a bath containing acid, sodium sulfate, and zinc sulfate, and the orientation changed systematically by varying the amount of stretch applied during spinning. The curves for the two types of yarn have the same form and slope, and each shows that tenacity increases and elongation decreases with increasing orienta-

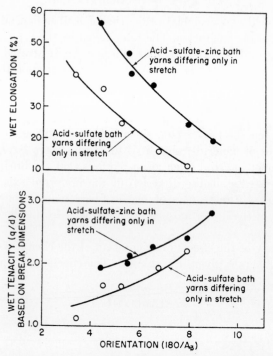

FIG. 12. Relation of wet tenacity and elongation to orientation for experimental rayons. From Ingersoll (61).

tion so that the general statements of Table III are upheld. For a given orientation, however, the yarns spun into an acid-zinc sulfate bath have both higher strengths and higher elongations. This displacement of the two curves must be due to variables other than orientation. As a general rule, a physical property such as tensile strength, which increases with orientation, may be correlated with orientation only when the tensile strength values have a definite correlation with some other property such as elongation, which decreases with increasing orientation. For example, if a fiber having a low tensile strength does not have a high elongation, then the low strength is probably due to factors other than orientation.

Other than orientation of the ordered regions the most important factors in determining physical properties are the degree of crystallinity and the lateral order distribution within the sample. It is possible to explain the displacement of curves in Fig. 12 on the basis of variations in these factors at constant orientation. In general, the physical properties may be correlated with fiber structure only when the orientation and relative degrees of lateral order are known.

5. Instrumentation and Sample Preparation

In the preceding sections the fiber pattern and other x-ray diffraction characteristics of fibers have been discussed. In order that the geometry of the experimental system might be more easily understood, the concepts of the reciprocal lattice and the sphere of reflection were introduced. It now remains to review the types of experimental equipment currently available, as well as to point out the best ways of obtaining x-ray data for study of fibers.

Basically, the instrumentation required for the study of fibers and polymers is not too different from that used in studies of highly ordered systems. The principal difficulties encountered in x-ray studies of polymer systems arise from the fact that imperfectly ordered fiber structures yield only diffuse x-ray diagrams which contain relatively few reflections. Any of the standard x-ray diffraction generators such as those made by the General Electric Company and Philips Electronics, Inc. (Norelco) are suitable for fiber study. Fiber study requires special auxiliary equipment, however. Some of this special equipment is commercially available, but in many cases it must be designed and built to specifications required by the particular study undertaken.

5.1. RADIATION

Since organic materials are more efficient in scattering short-wavelength radiation than inorganic materials, the use of monochromatic radiation for fiber study is usually desirable. A number of methods for obtaining monochromatic radiation are known. The simplest method employs an absorption filter which has its K absorption edge between the K_β and K_α-wavelengths of the radiation to be used. The transmitted x-radiation consists primarily of the K_α-doublet. This type of monochromatization is sufficient for most work. To reduce fluorescence from the filter material the filter itself is usually placed between the tube and the collimator, as shown in Fig. 13. The proper choice of filter materials for different radiations is discussed in the chapter by Davidson.

The most accurate method for monochromatization employs the

radiation reflected from a single crystal. The intensity of the reflected monochromatic radiation is quite low, however, and great care in selection of the crystal and the reflecting plane and in bending or grinding the reflecting plane for focusing effects is usually necessary to avoid extremely long exposure times. The use of crystal monochromators has been reviewed in detail (68, 85).

The development of proportional detector-counters has made possible the electronic selection or rejection of detected radiation. With these instruments the wavelength range detected may be restricted to a reasonably small wavelength interval. When used with a β-filter, the mono-

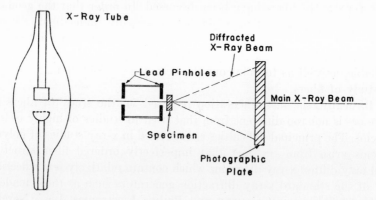

Fɪɢ. 13. Diagram of the monochromatic pinhole or fiber x-ray method.

chromatization obtained by a detector is appreciably better than that obtained from the filter alone, since a filter alone does not absorb shorter wavelength components as efficiently as it absorbs K_β (82, 83). These short wavelengths can be rejected by the proportional detector-counter.

5.2. FLAT-FILM TECHNIQUE

The simplest arrangement of sample and film for x-ray diffraction studies is illustrated in Fig. 13. If a single pinhole is used, an image of the x-ray target will be recorded on the film. Therefore, a collimator consisting of two pinholes separated by a fixed distance is used. The resolution of the pattern may be increased either by increasing the distance between the two pinholes or by decreasing the size of the pinholes. Both of these factors increase the time of exposure, however, and a compromise between time and sharpness of pattern is frequently necessary. Normally the collimator length is about 3 inches and the pinholes are 0.025 inch in diameter. The x-ray diagrams obtained by this flat-film technique are generally useful in fiber research and are particularly suited to the study of samples showing preferred orientation.

5.3. Cylindrical-Film Techniques

Cylindrical-film cameras are useful for fiber research because the layer lines are recorded as straight rows across the unrolled film instead of as hyperbolae as shown in Fig. 4. This arises from the geometrical relationship between the reciprocal lattice of the sample and the film. Fiber bundle samples are equivalent to a crystal rotating about a unique axis, and the projection of the spots as they intersect the sphere of reflection will be recorded on the film as a straight line which is the locus of intersection between the cone of reflections and the cylindrical film. Since the distance between the straight layer lines can be easily measured, the fiber identity period can be measured with greater accuracy than is possible with flat film. In addition the cylindrical camera permits the recording of data at much higher values of 2θ than the flat-film camera.

5.4. Moving-film Techniques

Two moving-film cameras, the Buerger precession camera and the Weissenberg camera, have unusual characteristics which are valuable in recording fiber x-ray data (27, 81). The precession camera is more useful and has the unique property that an undistorted reciprocal lattice may be recorded on a flat film. This is achieved by a compound motion of the film in relation to the sample and the use of a screen with an annular opening between the sample and film so that diffraction maxima are recorded only when the film is in the proper position. The fiber bundle is also oscillated about an axis perpendicular to the long bundle axis, and as a result the diatropic planes are recorded in their proper position with respect to the rest of the fiber pattern (60). In the Weissenburg camera, the film is transported on a line parallel to the axis about which the sample is rotated, and the fiber axis of the sample is mounted in a plane perpendicular to the beam. Since the film is shielded and its motion is tied to the rotation of the fibers, the pattern is distorted. The Weissenburg camera, however, gives the integrated intensities necessary for structure determinations and allows recording of the diatropic reflections.

5.5. Diffractometer Techniques

Diffractometers with electronic detection of individual x-ray photons allow the measurement of the intensity and angular position of a diffraction maximum directly without the use of film. Instruments of this type have been perfected by Philips Electronics and the General Electric Company and are now being adapted to the specific problems of polymer film and fiber study.

Basically the diffractometer is arranged as shown in Fig. 14. By use of slits and collimators the radiation is detected only when the sample is at the proper angle θ to the beam and the detector arm is at the angle 2θ to the direct beam. Just that radiation which is in the plane of the circle is detected. Normally for a powder sample the intensity is distributed in the rings so that only a proportionate amount of the total intensity is detected. If the sample has any preferred direction of alignment, then it is necessary to be able to move the sample with respect to

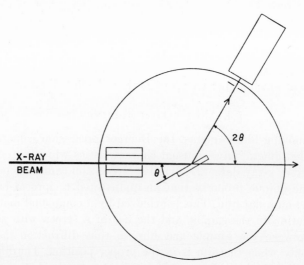

FIG. 14. View of diffractometer geometry. Detector located on circle at varying angle of 2θ with respect to the direct beam.

the beam and detector in such a way that the intensities in different directions may be measured.

By referring to the reciprocal lattice it can be seen that in a sample oriented with the fiber axis perpendicular to the plane of the circle only those planes which are parallel to this axis can be detected when the sample is mounted for transmission studies. Hence the axis of the fibers must be rotated into the plane of the circle, around an axis lying in the circle, in order that those planes which are at angles to the fiber axis will be detected. The combination of these two angular rotations—θ of the diffractometer, and ρ of the sample—make it possible to record almost all the useful diffracted data from polymer films and fibers. Sample holders have been reported in the literature for the Philips diffractometer (62).

With these holders it is possible to make azimuth scans to determine the degree of orientation directly. First, the diffractometer is rotated to the angle 2θ at which the desired reflection is detected, and then with the diffractometer stationary the sample is rotated. A curve as shown in Fig. 10 and discussed in Section 4.3 results. The azimuth drive is synchronized with the chart drive on the recorder, and consequently this technique is much more rapid than film recording.

The geometry is exactly the same as that of the precession camera. Therefore, preliminary precession film recording provides the required angles necessary to set the sample for direct recording of intensities.

5.6. Optimum Sample

The preparation of samples for x-ray examination is not difficult, nor is the form critical so long as all samples for a given study have the same physical form. The size of the sample is not too critical over limited ranges, and it is easy to show that for maximum diffracted x-ray intensity the optimum sample thickness is $1/\mu$, where μ is the linear absorption coefficient of the sample. For any given chemical compound, ABC, μ may be calculated from the relation

$$\mu = d\left[A\left(\frac{\mu}{\rho}\right)_A + B\left(\frac{\mu}{\rho}\right)_B + C\left(\frac{\mu}{\rho}\right)_C\right] \tag{3}$$

where d is the density; A is the proportion of A in the compound; B of element B, etc.; and μ/ρ is the mass absorption coefficient of the elements for the particular wavelength being used. These coefficients are listed in various handbooks and tables (51).

The mass absorption coefficients of organic materials are very small, however, and use of the $1/\mu$ relationship frequently indicates larger sample sizes for optimum intensity than are desirable for reasonable line resolution. Therefore, the ultimate sample size will be that which is sufficient to give a reasonable diffracted intensity and yet not so large as to give poor resolution. The type of study will determine the form and size of sample, and in general a sample thickness of about 0.5 mm will give a good diffraction diagram for most fiber samples.

5.7. Sample Preparation and Manipulation

The most general form of polymer sample is that of a powder. Polymer powders are handled in exactly the same manner as samples of inorganic or highly crystalline organic powders. It is not necessary to discuss the techniques and interpretations applied, since it has been done thoroughly in the chapter by Davidson and many texts (85). The powders in many cases may be molded for ease in handling, or if the material is already molded, such as a thermoplastic or resin, a section of the proper thickness may be cut out.

The simplest way in which fibers may be examined is in the form of a small cylindrically shaped bundle. These bundles are obtained by combing out, or in some other way rendering parallel, the fibers or filaments. The fibers are then clamped between the V-block clamps of a simple winding device. One clamp is free to slide back and forth, and in order that the crimp may be taken out of the fibers a small weight is attached.

The bundle of fibers is then rotated and bound together with a fine fiber such as hard silk. The amount of silk is negligible compared to the volume of the sample, so it gives no detectable pattern during normal exposure times. Sometimes the crimp in fibers returns when tension is released. Therefore, it is best to keep the fibers under tension by mounting them on some sort of spring clip arrangement during exposure. If a whole series of fibers are to be compared it is advisable to make all the bundles of the same volume as nearly as possible. This will ensure that the same amount of radiation will be scattered by each sample.

In research work concerned with the effect of a process variable on the structure and properties of a polymer material it is frequently inconvenient or impossible to evaluate a finished product. In many cases the effect desired may be studied by making a series of films in which one process variable is changed for each film in the series. The structural differences of each film may be evaluated, and by analogy the effect of the variable on the finished product is determined. Films of thermoplastic materials may be made by dipping glass plates into the melted polymer, and the supported film may then be treated by further exposure to heat, solvent vapors, or swelling agents (2, 13). Films of soluble polymers may be obtained by spreading the solution on a glass plate and then removing the solvent by evaporation or by use of a suitable coagulating bath. Another alternative is to allow the film to spread over the surface of a liquid and solidify as the solvent is evaporated. The film may then be removed from the surface of the liquid by means of glass plates or loops of wire. The sample for x-ray examination is prepared by building a block of the desired thickness from several layers of film. Samples prepared in this fashion may have a characteristic film orientation unlike that usually found in fibers or plastic products. In most cases, however, this orientation may be evaluated and controlled by the proper mechanical manipulation of the samples.

5.8. Microbeam Techniques

Normal beam dimensions used in x-ray diffraction give a pattern characteristic of the total volume irradiated, and it is impossible to see local inhomogeneities which can be shown to exist by other techniques such as microscope, dyeing, and birefringence.

Since the ordered regions of most fiber samples are of small dimensions, it is helpful to study just a small amount of material at one time. This may be accomplished by using a fine capillary tube as a collimator. This technique has been applied by a number of investigators, particularly for studies of the orientation in necked fibers or spherulite formation (25). Unfortunately the exposures are extremely long, and alignment of the fine capillaries, samples, and film is very difficult. There are now available, however, commercial microfocus units which produce an extremely intense x-ray beam of only a few hundredths of a millimeter in area. The Hilger Company of England makes such a unit, and it has met with some degree of success in the study of fibers.

5.9. SPECIAL TECHNIQUES

The order-disorder structure of fibers is very sensitive to environmental conditions such as moisture or temperature, and in many cases structural variations may be detected by varying the environment of the sample during x-ray exposure. Therefore, fiber cameras equipped with conditioning accessories are widely used. There are relatively few commercial cameras or other accessories built specifically for fiber study, so it is the usual practice to build one to specifications demanded by the data desired.

For example, stretching frames consisting of one fixed and one movable clamp have been widely used for elongating fiber bundles in incremental steps and making x-ray exposures at different elongations. Such frames are quite common in the study of rubber and rubberlike polymers. Bunn and Alcock (31) obtained high-temperature data by fitting a sample powder camera with pancake heaters above and below the specimen. Other investigators have used heated gas streams or have mounted the sample in a jacketed copper block around which oil at the desired temperature is circulated (37). Low-temperature studies may be conducted simply by allowing a fine stream of liquid air to flow over the sample. Moisture condensation may be objectionable, so it is best to use a closed system from which moisture may be excluded.

Studies concerned with the effects of humidity, swelling, pH, or solvents may be carried out by enclosing the sample in a thin-walled glass capillary. Presently available capillary tubes have extremely thin walls and give a relatively low halo intensity of their own. When the amount of liquid is large relative to the amount of sample, it is always advisable to take blank patterns with no sample in order that the background may be evaluated. Enclosed cameras of the vacuum type may be converted to humidity-conditioning cameras merely by passing air with the proper moisture content through the camera. A camera should be selected, however, in which the film is separated from the vacuum section by a screen of aluminum or other moisture-impermeable film. This will prevent the emulsion from swelling owing to moisture absorption during exposure.

In many cases when accessory sample holders such as those described above are used, it is difficult to determine the sample-to-film distances. When such a situation exists, a standard crystalline material whose lattice parameters are accurately known may be dusted on the surface or incorporated within the sample. The sample-to-film distance is then calculated from the x-ray diagram by using a known lattice dimension of the internal standard and the Bragg law. Finely ground sodium chloride is commonly chosen as a standard material for dry samples. Hermans (53) used insoluble molybdenum disulfide (molybdenite) as a standard for wet cellulose samples. The ASTM card file now contains sufficient data on common crystals so that an internal standard for most solvent and sample conditions may be easily found.

5.10. Selection of Samples

This introduction to the methods employed shows the actual experimental technique to be fairly straightforward, but the fact remains that the sample itself is the most difficult experimental variable to control. It implies that the x-ray study of high polymers is not simply a matter of obtaining x-ray diagrams of random samples. The order-disorder structure of any polymer solid will depend on the manner in which that solid was formed, chemical reactions, solvents, coagulation, heat treatment, mechanical deformation, and many other factors to which the sample has been subjected. It is impossible by x-ray or other methods to determine in absolute terms the order-disorder structure present in any given system. It is possible, however, to evaluate the changes in the order-disorder structure which accompany variations in the conditions to which the polymer has been subjected. Therefore, the value of x-ray diffraction studies of fibers can best be realized by a study of samples for which the history is known and has been carefully controlled.

6. Order-Disorder

The definition of the order-disorder structure of polymers by x-ray diffraction is confined to direct interpretation of the ordered structure which yields a definite diffraction pattern and to an indirect interpretation of the disorder structure. In preceding sections we have dealt with the ways in which x-ray diffraction may be applied to studies of the atomic arrangement in regions of extreme regularity. Sections 2 and 3 encompassed general features of the structural configurations, and Section 4 was concerned with the determination of the orientation of the ordered regions. There are at least two other fields of qualitative application. These are: (1) the determination of the amount of the highly ordered material, and (2) the investigation of the size of the highly ordered regions. The importance of these fields is indicated by the fact that many of the mechanical properties of polymers depend on both the quantity of material which is ordered in a three-dimensional way and the size and shape of the regions in which the extreme regularity exists.

6.1. Proportion of Ordered Material

In many cases, a measure of the amount of ordered material in a polymer may be obtained directly from x-ray methods. In principle, an x-ray method for determining the percentage of ordered material can be devised for any system for which the total radiation scattered by either the ordered or the disordered material can be measured and compared with the total radiation scattered by either completely crystalline or completely amorphous samples. The x-ray scattering by ordered material is strongly dependent, however, on the size, shape, and degree of perfection of the ordered regions, and on the crystal structure of the ordered regions; and it may be complicated by the presence of two polymorphic forms within a given sample. In any event, it is difficult to evaluate in terms of crystallinity alone, and it is seldom possible to obtain a completely ordered sample for use as a reference. The radiation scattered by disordered material is free of size and shape effects, and in the general case completely amorphous samples can be prepared for reference. Therefore, the most useful methods for determining the proportion of ordered material are based wholly or in part on the evaluation of the x-ray scattering by the disordered material.

Gehman and Field (46), in their studies of rubber, pioneered work of this type. Unstretched rubber gives an x-ray diagram consisting only of a halo characteristic of amorphous polymers. As rubber is stretched, crystalline areas are formed at the expense of the amorphous phase, and, as a result, the intensity of the halo decreases while the intensity of the crystalline fiber diagram increases (see Fig. 2). Gehman and Field obtained a first approximation of the amorphous content by simply relating the halo intensity to the sample thickness. Then for a partially crystallized sample the halo intensity is lower than would be expected from a completely amorphous sample of the same thickness but would correspond to the halo intensity expected from a thinner sample. From the measured thickness of the sample and the effective thickness of the amorphous material as indicated by the measured halo intensity, the per cent crystalline material in the sample was calculated.

Later workers have extended and refined the principles used by Gehman and Field and have developed methods for such diverse materials as polyethylene and cellulose. Matthews *et al.* (76) and Aggarwal and Tilley (1) determined the amorphous content of polyethylene by plotting the intensity of the scattered radiation versus diffraction angle and then resolving this curve graphically into radiation scattered by the amorphous material and that scattered by the (110) and (200) planes of the crystalline regions. The weight ratio (W_A/W_C) of the amorphous and crystalline material is then obtained from the relation

$$\frac{W_A}{W_C} = K \frac{I_A}{(I_{110} + I_{200})} \tag{4}$$

where K is a constant related to the relative scattering efficiencies of amorphous and crystalline material whose value is essentially unity, and I_A, I_{110}, and I_{200} are the total radiation scattered by the amorphous material, the (110) plane, and the (200) plane, respectively.

According to Krimm and Tobolsky (72), the best index of the quantity of amorphous material in polyethylene is the integrated intensity of the scattering from unoriented amorphous regions. Samples were compared at constant scattering mass with a completely amorphous sample obtained by heating the polymer above its melting point. The percentage of amorphous material was obtained by dividing the coherent amorphous scattering between 2θ values of $2°$ and $30°$ at a given temperature by the coherent amorphous scattering for the sample at $120°C$.

None of these relatively simple methods is generally applicable to crystalline polymers. In the general case, the x-ray diagram of the polymer has the scattering from crystalline centers superimposed on the scattering from the amorphous regions. In the x-ray diagrams of some polymers, such as rubber and polyethylene, in which there are no crystalline peaks superimposed on the amorphous halo or only one sharp crystalline peak superimposed on the amorphous halo, graphical resolution of the scattering into amorphous and crystalline components is relatively simple. Such graphical solutions are usually based on the assumption that both the amorphous halo and the crystalline peaks are symmetrical in the vicinity of the maximum.

For other polymers, such as cellulose, broad crystalline peaks occur on both sides of the amorphous halo, and exact evaluation of the radiation scattered by amorphous regions becomes difficult. Hermans and Weidinger (56) studied various cellulose fibers, however, and devised a method in which both the maximum intensity of the amorphous halo and the total integrated intensity of the radiation coherently scattered by ordered material could be estimated. The maximum halo intensity was assumed to be a measure of the disordered material, and the integrated intensity of the crystalline peaks a correct measure of the crystalline portion.

Although the principles used in all these methods for determining the amount of ordered material in various polymers are generally applicable, each different polymer must be treated individually. Modification of the method of evaluation of the scattered intensity in terms of ordered or disordered material must be made for each case. In cases where the x-ray spectra are unusually complicated, other methods of determining crystallinity (e.g., density, moisture regain, heat of fusion, infrared, or nuclear magnetic resonance) may be preferable to x-ray methods.

6.2. Size of Ordered Regions

Measurement of the size of the ordered regions in polymers is based on the fact that highly ordered regions possess the characteristics of optical diffraction gratings. That is, the regularly arranged lines, rows, and planes of atoms will diffract x-rays in the same manner as the ruled lines of an optical grating. When the number of ruled lines is very large, the diffraction maxima are sharp and clearly resolved. As the number of lines is decreased, however, the maxima broaden in extent until finally they merge into an almost continuous background; and in polymers the diffraction lines from ordered regions smaller than about 1000 A. are significantly broadened by these crystal size effects. The basic assumptions in the development of the theory of the relationship existing between diffraction line broadening and particle size were made by Scherrer (89), von Laue (73), and others (65, 79, 84, 103). Excellent reviews may be found in texts by Klug and Alexander, (68) as well as that of Peiser et al. (85). All treatments generally arrive at one equation of the form

$$D = \frac{K\lambda}{\beta \cdot \cos \theta} \tag{5}$$

where D is the extent of the particle or its diameter in a direction perpendicular to the family of planes corresponding to the measured line, λ is the wavelength of the radiation used, θ is the Bragg angle; K is a constant, and β is the line broadening. The value of the constant K depends on the methods used for measuring the line breadth as well as the assumptions used in the derivation of the formula. Values have been found to vary between 0.9 to 1.1, but since other experimental errors are usually greater a value of unity may be assumed (3). Since there are factors other than particle size which will effect the line broadening, it is necessary to correct for instrumental variables in the evaluation of β. A working approximation of sufficient accuracy for β is

$$\beta = (B_m{}^2 - B_0{}^2)^{\frac{1}{2}} \tag{6}$$

where B_m is the width, in radians, of the broadened diffraction from the small particles, and B_0 is the broadening from particles of sufficient extent to be called infinite. The factor B_0 is known as the instrumental broadening, for it is dependent on the experimental conditions.

In application of the method, a circular camera fitted with a pinhole system as used in the Scherrer powder method is required. The value B_m

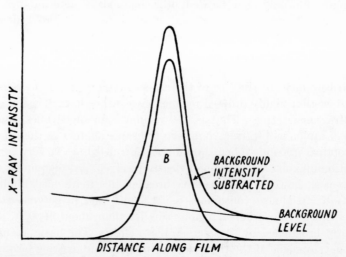

FIG. 15. Intensity distribution of a diffraction arc showing breadth of arc at half-maximum intensity. From Bunn (30).

is usually measured as the width of the diffraction line in radians at half-maximum intensity. Figure 15 represents the photographic density or intensity of the diffraction line as measured on a microphotometer plotted against the distance along the film on either side of the diffraction maximum. The total intensity is composed of the background intensity and the line intensity, and the curve may be unsymmetrical because of the difference in the background level on either side of the line. If at several points along this curve the background intensity is subtracted from the total intensity and these points are replotted, a symmetrical curve representing only the line intensity and illustrated by the lower curve in the figure results. In such a diagram, the intensity at the center of the peak will drop to half its value at two points on either side such as those joined by the line B. The "half-maximum" breadth, B_m, is the angle in radians subtended by the distance B. If the camera is cylindrical, $B_m = B/r$, where r is the camera radius. The value of B_0 is determined in the same way, with a reference material such as graphite as a sample (47), or metals such as copper or molybdenum whose particle size is known to be of the order of 0.2 μ so that there is no line broadening due to small particle size. If a diffractometer is used instead of a film camera it is a simple matter to measure the resulting recorder trace without the need for a densitometer reading of the film (see Fig. 10c).

Although eq. (5) was originally derived for a point specimen and crystals of cubic form in random orientation, later work by Seljakow (90), Brill (24), and von Laue (73) shows that the method may be simply used to indicate the particle shape for systems other than cubic. If B is determined for the diffraction from the planes ($h00$), ($0k0$), and ($00l$), it will give, respectively, the extension of the crystalline particles in the direction normal to these planes. Shape indications for the ordered regions in polymers may be obtained in this way even though the x-ray diagram has not been indexed and the (hkl) values are not known for a given diffraction spot. By measuring on the fiber diagram the widths of the meridian interferences from planes normal to the fiber axis and of the equatorial interferences from planes parallel to the fiber axis, values for both the length and width of the ordered regions may be determined.

Typical values which can be considered only as a lower limit for the size of the ordered regions are shown in Table IV.

TABLE IV

Estimated Size of Crystalline Regions of Fibrous Materials

Fiber	Width (A.)	Length (A.)
Ramie (64)	50	500
Rubber (raw) (64)	180 × 530	600
Rubber (vulcanized) (58)	64 × 300	
Polythene (27)	100 − 300	—

6.3. SIZE DETERMINED FROM INTEGRAL BREADTH

Unfortunately, line broadening can be produced by factors other than particle size. The most likely factor in polymeric systems is non-uniformity of size, for actually in polymers the size of the ordered regions varies over a wide range. This heterogeneous size distribution with a significant number of small crystals present usually results in a large broadening at the base of the intensity peak, which is not considered in the determination of particle size from the half-maximum breadth.

Von Laue (73) defined an "integral breadth" as the breadth of a uniform line having the same maximum intensity and the same total intensity as the actual line; that is

$$B_m = \frac{I d\Psi}{I_{\max}} \tag{7}$$

where B_m is the integral breadth I is the intensity, and Ψ is the angle between the primary beam and the diffracted ray. This value is obtained from the same type of curve as the half-maximum breadth, and in Fig. 15 the integral breadth would be the total area under the lower curve divided by the maximum intensity. This definition of line width is preferable to the half-maximum breadth because it gives more consideration to the presence of small ordered regions. Taylor (100), and Gehman and Field (47) have also defined the broadening, B, to take into account the size distribution factor according to the expression

$$B_r = [(B^2{}_m - B_0{}^2)^{0.5}(B_m - B_0)]^{0.5} \tag{8}$$

where B, B_m, and B_0 have the same significance as in eq. (6) except that all are expressed as integral breadths. Gehman and Field consider this value for B best for calculation of particle size where values of B_0 are available by calibration with large particles.

6.4. Low-Angle Scattering Techniques

Diffuse scattering at very small angles has long been recognized in fiber diagrams, especially in equatorial streaks. In recent years, the interpretation of such scattering has received much attention, and the mathematical treatment has been rapidly developed, especially by Guinier (48), Hosemann (59), Debye (34), and Warren (22, 104). This scattering occurs at angles of the order of minutes of a degree and may assume one of two forms: (1) scattering of low intensity which has a maximum at zero or a very small angle and decreases steadily as the angle of scattering increases, and (2) scattering giving specific sharp lines at low angles similar to those obtained at wide angles by normal techniques. In small-angle scattering of the first type for randomly distributed spherical particles, the diameter of which is large compared to the wavelength, the size of the particles causing the scattering can be related to the intensity of the scattered radiation. The relationship is best approximated by the expression

$$I = Ke^{-0.221 k^2 R^2} \tag{9}$$

where I is the intensity of the scattered radiation, K is a constant proportional to the difference in scattering of the particles as compared with that of the medium in which they are embedded, k is $(4\pi \sin \theta)/\lambda$, and R is the radius of the particle.

From this equation it is possible to calculate as a function of R the angle at which the scattered radiation diminishes to half its value at $\theta = 0$. According to Fankuchen and Mark (35), for Cu K_a-radiation the scattered intensity from particles of 50-A. radius will diminish to half its value at $\theta = 0$ at an angle of 31.5 minutes, and from particles of 400-A. radius at an angle of 3.9 minutes. Since it is practically impossible to measure the intensity at zero angle and calculate the value of R in this way, most workers use the method of Biscoe and Warren (22) in which $\log_e I$ is plotted against k^2 or against r^2, where r is the distance in millimeters of the scanning slit used to measure I from the center of the primary x-ray beam (63). The intensity may be measured from film with an ordinary densitometer or directly by means of a counter such as that employed on the diffractometer, and since only the logarithm of intensity is involved it may be expressed in arbitrary units. For uniform particles, this graph yields a straight line whose slope is characteristic of the value of R. For eq. (9), a plot of $\log_e I$ against k^2 will give a line whose slope is $-0.221R^2$ or, on conversion to Naperian logarithms, $-0.096R^2$. The slope of the plot of $\log_{10} I$ against r^2 may similarly be evaluated as a function of R.

When the particle size is not uniform, however, the curve is no longer a straight line, and it becomes necessary to find a distribution function for the sizes. One possible way to obtain the distribution function is through the use of Fourier transformations. The evaluation is rather complex and cumbersome for general use (15). A graphical approach has been developed by Jellinek et al. (64) for use with γ-alumina and carbon black. Even with its limitations it would appear that this approach would merit further consideration and evaluation for use with nonspherical particles.

6.5. Low-Angle Scattering by Fibers

In all the above cases of random particles, the observed low-angle scattering will be symmetrical in respect to the center of the diagram, and measured intensities will be the same in all directions from the center. But for fibrous high polymers consisting of rodlike particles oriented parallel to the fiber direction, this scattering loses its symmetry and appears as scattering on the equator and meridian of the diagram and is characteristic of the width and length of the rods, respectively. If perfect parallel orientation of particles whose centers are randomly distributed in space is assumed, the equatorial scattering approximates the following form:

$$I_{eq} = Ke^{-0.221k^2a^2} \tag{10}$$

where $2a$ is the width of the particle. The meridian scattering assumes the form

$$I_{mer} = Ke^{-0.221k^2l^2} \tag{11}$$

where $2l$ is the length of the particle. The evaluation is the same as that presented for spherical particles.

A number of highly oriented polymers which yield the continuous-type small-angle scattering have been investigated. In most cases, the meridian scattering is weak and occurs at such small angles that one can conclude only that the ordered regions are greater than 500 A. long. The equatorial scattering is more pronounced, and average widths of the ordered regions have been determined. The observed widths in typical cases are shown by the data of Fankuchen and Mark in Table V.

TABLE V

Width of Crystalline Areas in Fibers (Fankuchen and Mark, 35)

Substance	Average width of crystallized area (A.)
Tobacco mosaic virus	150
Fibrous asbestos	200
Stretched rubber	80
Drawn nylon	200
Highly oriented viscose rayon	50-200

Low-angle scattering of the second type, in which specific diffraction maxima occur, has been found in both equatorial and meridional scattering of oriented preparations. This type of scattering has been taken as evidence of a crystalline-like arrangement of fairly large uniform particles. In such cases, the interplanar period may be calculated for the observed diffraction lines by the Bragg law; and for meridional scattering "identity" periods in the fiber direction may be calculated by the methods used for wide-angle scattering. Equatorial scattering consisting of sharp lines has been observed only for such materials as tobacco mosaic virus (21) and chrysotile (36), but meridian scattering of this type is quite common in natural proteins (4, 16, 17, 50) and has also been found in synthetic materials such as polyamides and polyesters (57, 67). Some representative values are listed in Table VI.

TABLE VI

Large Fiber Periods of Fibers from Small-Angle Scattering

Substance	Fiber axis period (A.)	Large lateral spacing (A.)
Collagen	640	
Feather keratin	95	34
Porcupine quill keratin	198	83
Clam muscle	725	325
Drawn nylon	90	

The investigation and interpretation of such data are still in a rather fluid state, but several interesting conclusions can be drawn on present work which should lead to a better understanding of fiber structure. Bear (17, 18) had shown that the large fiber period of collagen varies with the treatment to which the fiber has been subjected, and that these variations may or may not be accompanied by changes in the wide-angle periods of the normal fiber pattern. Apparently only a fraction of the better ordered regions contribute to wide-angle diffraction, whereas larger structures embracing a number of smaller regions of all kinds contribute to small-angle diffraction. As the chemical complexity of the structure increases, the normal wide-angle patterns deteriorate and the structures responsible for low-angle scattering increase in size. Astbury (5, 8) has shown that fibrous proteins can be classified according to their wide-angle diffraction pattern, and Bear (17, 18) concludes that the small-angle pattern also permits such classification. For example, Astbury's keratin myosin class is recognizable from scattering at low angles by the possession of both longitudinal and lateral large spacings, but the collagen class lacks a large lateral spacing even though the longitudinal spacings are quite evident. The lateral spacing data are also shown in Table VI.

Neither silk protein (fibrous) nor unannealed nylon shows any distinct small-angle diffractions. This negative result seems interesting in view of the fact that silk fibers are formed by a rapid spinning process in contrast to the slow formation of collagen, keratin, and muscle fibers in the body. It may be that sufficient "crystallization" time is lacking for the production of structures capable of giving large spacings in silk. Similarly, the nylon large spacing appears only in highly oriented fibers which have been internally relaxed or "crystallized" by a swelling agent or heat. This behavior seems to support the crystallization time explanation (18).

Probably the best summary and bibliography available on the subject of small-angle scattering by fibers and other materials is that by Guinier *et al.* (49). The treatment is thorough and points up the many shortcomings of the present theory.

6.6. EXPERIMENTAL PROCEDURE FOR LOW-ANGLE STUDIES

The experimental techniques for small-angle scattering are rigorous and still undergoing improvement, but basically the method is the same as that outlined in Fig. 12. The pinholes are replaced by slits which are usually from 0.15 to 0.30 mm. wide and 2 or 3 mm. long. The slits are mounted in a collimator tube about 180 to 350 mm. long, depending on the angular resolution desired. The specimen-to-film distance should be kept at the minimum to reduce exposure times. The smallest adequate distance is determined by the smallest angle for which measurement is desired, the accuracy, and the effectiveness of the collimating system. For example, with slits 0.3 mm. wide a collimating system 180 mm. long will allow resolution of 240-A. distances with a 100-mm. sample-to-film distance; and with slits 0.15 mm. wide a system 300 mm. long will allow resolution of 600- to 700-A. spacings at a 300-mm. specimen-to-film distance (17). Monochromatic radiation is required, but usually the moderate monochromatization by a nickel filter for Cu K_a-radiation is sufficient. Most studies can be carried out with sufficient accuracy in air; but with large sample-to-film distances for resolving large spacings the system should be enclosed and evacuated during exposure. Detailed descriptions of apparatus have been given by Bear (17) and by Jellinek (63). A Geiger counter for registration of the scattered intensity (64) offers many advantages over film methods but this method has not as yet been widely used.

Kratky *et al.* (69-71) have shown that small-angle scattering can be accentuated by immersing the fiber samples in liquids of distinctly different x-ray scattering power or by depositing heavy metal atoms into the disordered regions of the fiber. For example, swelling cellulose fibers in benzene reduces the scattering power of the disordered zones as compared to the ordered zones and intensifies the low-angle scattering considerably. This technique may be extremely useful in cases where intensities of scattering are very weak.

There are many difficulties of registration and interpretation of low-angle diffraction effects. Even after assuming monochromatic radiation and elimination of slit and air scattering, the x-ray beam may be affected by such factors as absorption, the Compton effect, thermal scattering, and fluorescent radiation as well as by individual particle size effects. The method is, however, relatively free from differences within the ordered regions themselves as described under "lateral order" and can be utilized with correct choice of conditions so that all effects except that of size are small. Continued work on this method will undoubtedly lead to a better understanding of the particle size and distribution in polymeric systems.

6.7. LATERAL ORDER

The successful application of the line broadening technique for the determination of the extent of ordered regions has been principally in colloidal systems. Its validity, however, is unquestioned only when there are no other factors present which may affect the line width. For example, strain within crystals will produce characteristic broadening of the lines in metals (14), as will the presence of foreign atoms.

Another important cause of line broadening which has been evaluated in recent years is associated with random "faulting" either in growth or through deformation. Warren's (105) work in the β-brass system is an excellent illustration of this phenomenon whereby whole rows or planes of atoms randomly assume alternative positions, and hence the diffraction pattern of the original material is changed in a systematic way. This faulting is conceivably the easiest mechanism to account for the observed layer line streaking characteristic of fiber patterns. Since polymers present an even more complex system than those of metals or other organic materials, it becomes increasingly more difficult to evaluate the observed diffraction effects. This difficulty may be emphasized by the following: (1) the literal use of the terms "particle" or "crystallite size" for the ordered regions is unfortunate; (2) the shape of these regions is unknown exactly, but they are generally long and rodlike as confirmed by much cooperative work between x-ray and electron microscopy laboratories; (3) the size of these regions is subject to speculation, since with high-molecular-weight materials chain length is sufficient to be shared by a number of ordered regions; (4) in passing from one ordered region to the next, varying degrees of order may be encountered and fringe amorphous regions must exist, and, because of the large number of possible ways of packing, each ordered region will be slightly different from the others. Thus a fiber of a polymeric material represents a complex assemblage of crystal sizes and conformation in which the differences between the crystalline and amorphous regions are only a question of degree. Consequently, it is impossible to evaluate all these factors individually, since they will be contributing to a varying degree. In order partially to offset the inability to obtain unique measures of crystal size distributions and shapes in fibrous materials it seems advisable to develop useful criteria based on logical interpretations of the complex systems involved. A good starting point for this approach is the concept of lateral order of Baker and Fuller (12). This concept is based on the use of x-ray patterns and distinguishes between regions which show (1) crystalline order with the monomer units arranged in a three-dimensional array; (2) mesomorphic order in which the fiber repeat units are parallel to the fiber axis and corresponding groups are opposite along the chains but are randomly rotated about the chain, or mesomorphic order in which the units are simply parallel to the chain direction; and (3) no molecular order or amorphous regions. Certain subclasses of mesomorphic order exist for linear polymers which may be classified as follows:

1. Lateral disorder of chains of uniform composition; i.e., the chains contain only one kind of repeating unit. Lateral disorder implies that the individual chains are rotated at random around the long-chain axis in the polymer solid and is independent of the gross orientation discussed in Section 4. The best examples of this class are cellulose, cellulose triesters, and polyamides.

2. Longitudinal disorder in chains of nonuniform composition. The chains may include repeating units of different lengths so that equivalent chain sections such as polar linkages do not come together in adjacent parallel chains. Most copolymers exhibit longitudinal disorder.

3. Steric disorder from side groups in either uniform or nonuniform chains. The side groups may not occur frequently enough or may be too large to permit regular packing of the chains. Vinyl polymers, cellulose partial esters, and natural proteins show this disorder.

These three classes of order do not and are not intended to classify the organization of the chains in a given fibrous material, but they do show the varieties of chain configuration and packing which must be considered. These types of disorder are sometimes difficult to distinguish and may occur singly or in pairs. For example, steric disorder frequently leads to lateral disorder. These possibilities are treated more fully in the investigations of Fuller, Baker, and co-workers (10, 12, 13, 40).

6.8. MEASUREMENT OF LATERAL ORDER

After the existence of the various possible states of order is recognized, the primary objective of most studies is to determine the degree of order which exists. Perhaps the best way to approach the problem is to assume that the observable intensities and their distribution are sufficiently related so that the value of specific intensity ratios and line breadths will give a reasonably useful parameter. For example, if a diffractometer trace of the equatorial reflections of a fiber (as seen in Fig. 10) or a photometric trace of a film is made, the degree of lateral ordering which has taken place on the planes parallel to the fiber axis and in a direction perpendicular to the fiber axis is determined from the intensity and the radial widths of the maxima. An increase in lateral order will appear as a strengthening of the reflections as well as a decrease in the reflection half-width. These effects are shown in the two x-ray diagrams of terylene (condensation polymer of ethylene glycol and terephthalic acid). When the lateral order is low, the pattern in Fig. 16a results, but by heating at 100°C. ordering is allowed to take place and the pattern in Fig. 16b results.

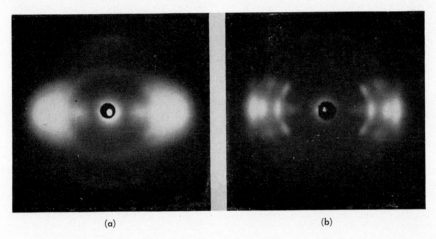

(a)   (b)

Fig. 16. X-ray fiber diagrams of terylene of (a) low lateral order and (b) high lateral order.

Several parameters useful for evaluating lateral order are as follows:

1. Interference width. The radial width of the interference is measured as outlined for Scherrer line broadening.

2. The reciprocal interference width is convenient, for it gives a number which increases with increasing lateral order.

3. The absolute intensity of an interference increases with increasing lateral order.

4. An intensity ratio is more reproducible than the absolute intensity. Ingersoll (61) showed that the ratio $[(I_1-I_m)/I_1]100$ increases with increasing lateral order in cellulose fibers. I_1 is the intensity of the (101) interference, and I_m is the minimum intensity between the (101) and (10$\bar{1}$) interferences of the cellulose diagram. In some cases a similar set of parameters may be evolved for the reflections associated with the meridional or repeat distance reflections for the determination of longitudinal order.

All these parameters are dependent on experimental conditions, and comparisons are valid only when sample preparation, x-ray exposure, and development conditions are controlled. Small orientation differences have little effect, but large differences change background corrections, interference intensities, and shape of intensity curves so that the order parameters are comparable only when the samples have the same orientation. The obvious way to correct for orientation differences involves comparison of the lateral order of randomly oriented samples or samples which have been randomized by cutting or grinding them to a powder. Caution is necessary, as cutting or grinding of polymer samples sometimes decreases the lateral order so that large errors can be introduced in this manner (55, 61). The best method is to rotate the sample (61) or film during exposure with subsequent evaluation of the powder-type diagram obtained. Rotation of the sample does not completely correct for large differences in orientation so that comparisons should be made whenever possible for samples of approximately constant orientation.

6.9. Results of Lateral Order Studies

None of these methods has been generally applied and their applicability to any given system is limited, for the results obtained are only relative and their meaning is in many cases somewhat obscure. Certain generalizations can be made, however. The effect of increasing lateral order on certain physical properties of fibers is shown in Table VII.

TABLE VII

Effect of Increasing Lateral Order on Properties of Fibers

Increases	Decreases
Tensile strength	Elongation
Young's modulus	Moisture sorption
Hardness	Swelling
Dimensional stability	Dye sorption
Density	Toughness
	Chemical reactivity
	Flexibility

7. Summary

X-ray diffraction analysis of fibers has two large fields of application. The first is the determination of the crystalline structure of the ordered regions. The second involves the study of the form, arrangement, and relative amounts of the ordered regions in the fiber structure. Details of methods for crystal structure analysis of fibers have purposely been limited in this discussion, for they have been discussed in detail in many texts on crystallography. Primary emphasis has been placed instead on the evaluation of the secondary structure of fibers because, in the author's opinion, it is these features that are most helpful to the chemists and physicists engaged in fiber research. The secondary structure features of orientation, crystal size, and degree of crystallinity are most important in determining the physical properties of the fiber; and in making possible even qualitative evaluation of these features, x-ray diffraction has been invaluable in evaluation of fiber structure and has contributed strongly to fiber improvement through control of these factors.

References

1. Aggarwal, S. L., and Tilley, G. P., *J. Polymer Sci.* **18**, 17 (1955).
2. Arndt, U. W., Coats, W. A., and Riley, D. P., *Proc. Phys. Soc. (London)* **66B**, 1009 (1953).
3. American Society for Testing Materials, Powder Diffraction Card File.
4. Astbury, W. T., *Trans. Faraday Soc.* **28**, 232 (1932).
5. Astbury, W. T., *Trans. Faraday Soc.* **34**, 377 (1938).
6. Astbury, W. T., "Fundamentals of Fiber Structure." Oxford Univ. Press, London, 1953.
7. Astbury, W. T., "Textile Fibers under the X-rays." I.C.I. Monograph, Kynoch Press, Birmingham, 197/2011/940.
8. Astbury, W. T., and Dickenson, S., *Proc. Roy. Soc.* **B129**, 307 (1940).
9. Astbury, W. T., and Sisson, W. A., *Proc. Roy. Soc.* **A150**, 533 (1935).
10. Baker, W. O., *Ind. Eng. Chem.* **37**, 246 (1945).
11. Baker, W. O., and Fuller, C. S., *J. Am. Chem. Soc.* **64**, 2399 (1942).
12. Baker, W. O., and Fuller, C. S., *J. Am. Chem. Soc.* **65**, 1120 (1943).
13. Baker, W. O., Fuller, C. S., and Pape, N. R., *J. Am. Chem. Soc.* **64**, 776 (1942).
14. Barrett, C. S., "The Structure of Metals." McGraw-Hill, New York, 1943.
15. Bauer, S. H., *J. Chem. Phys.* **13**, 450 (1945).
16. Bear, R. S., *J. Am. Chem. Soc.* **64**, 727 (1942).
17. Bear, R. S., *J. Am. Chem. Soc.* **66**, 1297 (1944).
18. Bear, R. S., *J. Am. Chem. Soc.* **66**, 2043 (1944).
19. James, R. W., "The Crystalline State," Vol. II. Bell, London, 1945.
20. Berkley, E. E., and Woodyard, O. C., *Ind. Eng. Chem. Anal. Ed.* **10**, 451 (1938).
21. Bernal, J. D., and Fankuchen, I., *J. Gen. Physiol.* **25**, 111 (1941).
22. Biscoe, J., and Warren, B. E., *J. Appl. Phys.* **13**, 364 (1942).
23. Bragg, W. L., "The Crystalline State," Vol. I. Bell, London, 1955.
24. Brill, R., *Z. Krist.* **75**, 217 (1930).
25. Brown, A., *J. Appl. Phys.* **20**, 552 (1949).
26. Buerger, M. J., "X-Ray Crystallography." Wiley, New York, 1942.
27. Buerger, M. J., American Society for X-Ray and Electron Diffraction Monograph No. 1 (1944).
28. Bunn, C. W., *Trans. Faraday Soc.* **35**, 482 (1939).
29. Bunn, C. W., *Proc. Roy. Soc.* **A180**, 40, 67, 82 (1942).

30. Bunn, C. W., "Chemical Crystallography," p. 364. Oxford Univ. Press, London, 1945.
31. Bunn, C. W., and Alcock, T. C., *Trans. Faraday Soc.* **41**, 317 (1945).
32. Carothers, W. H., and Hill, J. W., *J. Am. Chem. Soc.* **54**, 1559 (1932).
33. Clark, G. L., "Applied X-Rays," 3rd ed. McGraw-Hill, New York, 1940.
34. Debye, P., *Physik. Z.* **31**, 348 (1930).
35. Fankuchen, I., and Mark, H., *J. Appl. Phys.* **15**, 364 (1944).
36. Fankuchen, I., and Schneider, M., *J. Am. Chem. Soc.* **66**, 500 (1944).
37. Field, J., *J. Appl. Phys.* **12**, 23 (1941).
38. Fuller, C. S., *Chem. Revs.* **26**, 143 (1940).
39. Fuller, C. S., and Baker, W. O., *J. Chem. Ed.* **20**, 3 (1943).
40. Fuller, C. S., Baker, W. O., and Pape, N. R., *J. Am. Chem. Soc.* **62**, 3275 (1940).
41. Fuller, C. S., and Erickson, C. L., *J. Am. Chem. Soc.* **59**, 344 (1937).
42. Fuller, C. S., and Frosch, C. J., *J. Phys. Chem.* **43**, 323 (1939).
43. Fuller, C. S., and Frosch, C. J., *J. Am. Chem. Soc.* **61**, 2575 (1939).
44. Fuller, G. S., Frosch, C. J., and Pape, N. R., *J. Am. Chem. Soc.* **62**, 1909 (1940).
45. Fuller, C. S., Frosch, C. J., and Pape, N. R., *J. Am. Chem. Soc.* **64**, 154 (1942).
46. Gehman, S. D., and Field, J. E., *J. Appl. Phys.* **12**, 23 (1941).
47. Gehman, S. D., and Field, J. E., *J. Appl. Phys.* **15**, 371 (1944).
48. Guinier, A., Thesis, Series A, No. 1854, University of Paris, 1939; *Compt. rend.* **204**, 1115 (1937).
49. Guinier, A., Fournet, G., Walker, C. B., and Yudowitch, K. L., "Small Angle Scattering of X-Rays." Wiley, New York, 1955.
50. Hall, C. E., Jakus, M. A., and Schmitt, F. O., *J. Am. Chem. Soc.* **64**, 1234 (1942).
51. "Handbook of Chemistry and Physics," Chemical Rubber Publishing Company, Cleveland, Ohio.
52. Hermans, P. H., "Contributions to the Physics of Cellulose Fibers." Elsevier, Amsterdam, 1946.
53. Hermans, P. H., *J. Colloid Sci.* **1**, 185 (1946).
54. Hermans, P. H., Kratky, O., and Treer, R., *Kolloid-Z.* **96**, 30 (1941).
55. Hermans, P. H., and Weidinger, A., *J. Am. Chem. Soc.* **68**, 1138, 2547 (1946).
56. Hermans, P. H., and Weidinger, A., *J. Appl. Phys.* **19**, 491 (1948).
57. Hess, K., and Kiessig, H., *Naturwissenschaften* **31**, 171 (1943).
58. Hill, R., "Fibers From Synthetic Polymers." Elsevier, Amsterdam, 1953.
59. Hosemann, R., *Z. Physik* **113**, 751 (1939); *Z. Elektrochem.* **46**, 535 (1940).
60. Hughes, R. E., and Walter, N. M., to be published.
61. Ingersoll, H. G., *J. Appl. Phys.* **17**, 924 (1946).
62. Irvin, B., Breazeale, S. B., *Rev. Sci. Instr.* **24**, 627-31 (1953).
63. Jellinek, M. H., and Fankuchen, I., *Ind. Eng. Chem.* **37**, 158 (1945).
64. Jellinek, M. H., Solomon, E., and Fankuchen, I., *Ind. Eng. Chem.* **18**, 172 (1946).
65. Jones, F. W., *Proc. Roy. Soc.* **A166**, 16 (1938).
66. Katz, J. R., *Trans. Faraday Soc.* **29**, 279 (1933).
67. Kiessig, H., *Kolloid-Z.* **98**, 213 (1942).
68. Klug, H. P., and Alexander, L. E., "X-Ray Diffraction Procedures for Polycrystalline and Amorphous Materials." Wiley, New York, 1954.
69. Kratky, O., and Schossberger, F., *Z. physik. Chem.* (*Leipzig*) **B39**, 1451 (1938).
70. Kratky, O., Sekora, A., and Treer, R., *Z. Elektrochem.* **45**, 587 (1942).
71. Kratky, O., and Wurster, A., *Z. Elektrochem.* **50**, 249 (1944).
72. Krimm, S., and Tobolsky, A. V., *J. Polymer Sci.*, **7**, 57 (1951).

73. Laue, M. von, *Z. Krist.* **64,** 115 (1926).
74. Lotmar, W., and Meyer, K. H., *Monatsh.* **69,** 115 (1936).
75. Mark, H., *in* "Chemistry of Large Molecules," p. 33. Interscience, New York, 1943.
76. Matthews, J. L., Peiser, H. S., and Richards, R. B., *Acta Cryst.* **2,** 85 (1949).
77. Meyer, K. H., "Natural and Synthetic High Polymers." Interscience, New York, 1942.
78. Meyer, K. H., and Misch, L., *Helv. Chim. Acta* **20,** 232 (1937).
79. Murdock, C. C., *Phys. Rev.* **35,** 8 (1930).
80. Natta, G., *Angew. Chem.* **68,** 393 (1956).
81. Norman, N., Ph.D. Dissertation No. 219, Phys. Institute, University of Oslo, Norway.
82. Parrish, W., and Kohler, T. R., *Rev. Sci. Instr.* **27,** 795 (1956).
83. Parrish, W., and Kohler, T. R., *J. Appl. Phys.* **27,** 1215 (1956).
84. Patterson, A. L., *Phys. Rev.* **56,** 972 (1949).
85. Peiser, H. S., Rooksby, H. P., and Wilson, A. J. C., "X-Ray Diffraction by Polycrystalline Materials." The Institute of Physics, London, 1955.
86. Robertson, J. M., *J. Sci. Instr.* **20,** 175 (1943).
87. Sauter, E., *Z. physik. Chem.* (Leipzig) **B36,** 405, 427 (1937).
88. Sauter, E., *Z.* physik Chem. (Leipzig) B36, 427 (1937).
89. Scherrer, P., "Göttinger Nachrichten," July 26, 1918; cf. R. Zsigmondy, "Kolloidchemie," 3rd ed., p. 394. Otto Spamer, Leipzig, 1920.
90. Seljakow, N., *Z. Physik* **31,** 439 (1924).
91. Sisson, W. A., *Ind. Eng. Chem.* **27,** 51 (1935).
92. Sisson, W. A., *J. Phys. Chem.* **40,** 343 (1936).
93. Sisson, W. A., *Textile Research* **7,** 425 (1937).
94. Sisson, W. A., *Ind. Eng. Chem.* **30,** 530 (1938).
95. Sisson, W. A., *J. Phys. Chem.* **44,** 513 (1940).
96. Sisson, W. A., "Cellulose and Cellulose Derivatives," p. 239. Interscience, New York, 1943.
97. Sisson, W. A., and Clark, G. L., *Ind. Eng. Chem.* **5,** 296 (1933).
98. Sproull, W. T., "X-Rays in Practice," pp. 185-186, 432-434. McGraw-Hill, New York, 1946.
99. Stamm, A. J., *Ind. Eng. Chem.* **27,** 401 (1935).
100. Taylor, A., *Phil. Mag.* **31,** 339 (1941).
101. Trillat, J. J., *J. Chem. Phys.* **29,** 1 (1932).
102. Trogus, C., and Hess, K., *Z. physik. Chem.* (*Leipzig*) **B14,** 387 (1931).
103. Warren, B. E., *J. Chem. Phys.* **2,** 551 (1934).
104. Warren, B. E., *Phys. Rev.* **49,** 885 (1936).
105. Warren, B. E., *Acta Cryst.* **8,** 483 (1955).

Spectrophotometry and Absorptimetry

WALLACE R. BRODE AND MARY E. CORNING

National Bureau of Standards, Washington, D.C.

1. Introduction

A spectrum is an orderly arrangement of electromagnetic radiation by wavelength or frequency. The radiations are generally limited by γ-rays at the short-wavelength end (about 0.01 A.) and by microwaves at the long-wavelength end (10 cm.) (Fig. 1a). There is a natural sub-division of this broad range into specific regions because of the various methods and techniques for producing, detecting, and measuring radiation. For example, the 0.01-μ to 1-mm. range is subdivided into the ultraviolet region (0.01 to 0.4 μ), the visible (0.4 to 0.7 μ), and the infrared (0.7 μ to 1 mm.) (Fig. 1b).

A fundamental relationship exists between the properties of a substance and the interaction of radiation with a substance; or, in other words, there is a relationship between the basic chemical structure and electronic configuration of the atom or molecule and the specific absorption or emission of radiation. There is also a fundamental charac-

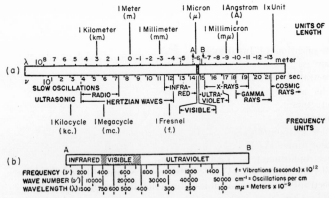

FIG. 1. Graphic indication of the spectral distribution of radiant energy.

teristic of radiant energy attenuation by absorption which is described by the same laws and equations throughout the spectrum of radiant energy.

An atom, which can be described in the simplest of terms as a nucleus surrounded by electrons arranged in energy levels, can be excited by an arc, spark discharge, or heat. This energy of excitation causes an electron to move from one electronic energy level to another one further removed from the nucleus. This excited state is unstable, and hence on removal of the source of excitation the electron will return to its normal level with a release of energy. The change in energy associated with this return of the electron is the radiation which is emitted by the atom. Thus, each spectral emission line represents energy lost by an atom, and it is specific and quantized:

$$E_2 - E_1 = \Delta E = h\nu$$

where ΔE is the change in energy, h is Planck's constant, and ν is the frequency of emitted light. Because this energy is quantized, the process may be reversed. The atom may be irradiated by radiation of this same emission wavelength, and this radiation will be absorbed by the atom. A spectral absorption line will thus be obtained by use of a continuous radiation source. This is a spectrum in its simplest form, that of an atom. It is a line spectrum, sharp and well defined.

The spectrum of a diatomic or polyatomic molecule, radical, or complex, however, is much more complicated and is a band rather than a line spectrum. The energy of a molecule consists not only of electronic but also of vibrational and rotational energy. In the simplest of terms, these energies can be described as follows: A molecule can rotate as a whole about an axis passing through the center of gravity and perpendicular to the internuclear axis, and the energy required is called rotational energy. Also, the atoms can vibrate relative to each other along the internuclear axis, and this is the energy of vibration. As in the case of energy changes in an atom, these changes in the energy content of a molecule are also specific and quantized, and they can be measured in terms of the wavelengths of radiation emitted or absorbed. The complexities of molecular spectra arise from the fact that any change in electronic level of the electron is usually accompanied by a change in vibrational level because each electronic level consists of a number of vibrational levels. In the same fashion, each change in vibrational level is accompanied by a change in rotational, because each vibrational level consists of a number of rotational changes. If there is a change in only the rotation of a molecule, this energy change is of the order of magnitude of 0.005 ev. and would therefore occur in the infrared region of the spectrum. A change in the vibration of the molecule is of the order of 0.1 ev., and this would occur in the near infrared region. Infrared spectra are not a part of our discussion and are treated in detail in another chapter. Changes in energy required to raise an electron from one electronic level to another are of the order of magnitude of 2 to 10 ev., however, and for this reason these spectra are found in the visible and ultraviolet regions; they consist not of sharp lines as atomic spectra but of broader bands with some fine structure superimposed (Fig. 2).

The purpose of producing and studying spectra is to obtain basic information on the fundamental structure of atoms and molecules. From infrared studies, data on internuclear distances, vibrational frequencies, force constants, and energies of dissociation can be obtained. With polyatomic molecules, which are of concern to us, there are complications. There are more than one internuclear distance, and a number of force constants and dissociation energies. However, visible and ultraviolet spectra are characteristic of each molecule, and these spectra provide a very

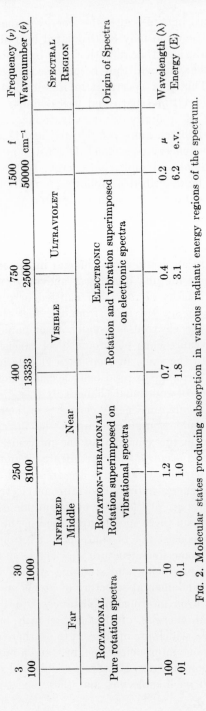

Fig. 2. Molecular states producing absorption in various radiant energy regions of the spectrum.

important tool to the chemist, both from the analytical point of view and for such purposes as kinetic studies, ionization constants, stereoisomerism, steric hindrance, color, and chemical constitution.

We are concerned in this chapter not with theoretical studies but rather with applications; and hence our discussion will be limited to nomenclature, terminology, methods and instruments for producing, observing, and recording spectra, and the treatment and applications of the data.

A single bond, a multiple bond, or a group containing an atom with an unshared pair of electrons will absorb radiation to produce a *spectrum*. The amount and kind of energy absorbed, however, depend on the nature of the absorbing structure; therefore, the absorption region can

TABLE I

Organic Chromophores

(a) Simple

$\diagdown C{=}C \diagup$ Ethylene

$\diagdown C{=}O$ Carbonyl

$-N{=}N-$ Azo

$-N{=}O$ Nitroso

$\diagdown C{=}S$ Thiocarbonyl

$\diagdown C{=}N-$ Azomethine

$\diagdown S{=}O$ Sulfoxide

(b) Complex (involving two or more simple chromophores)

$-N\diagup^{O}_{\diagdown O}$ Nitro

$\overset{O}{\underset{}{\parallel}}$
$-N{=}N-$ Azoxy

$\diagdown C{=}C{=}O$ Ketene (cumulative unsaturation)

$O{=}C\diagup^{C{=}C}_{\diagdown C{=}C}\diagdown C{=}O$ Quinone

$\diagdown C{=}C{-}C{=}C{-}C{=}C\diagup$ Divinyl ethylene (conjugated unsaturation)
(polyethenylene)

Fulvene (branched conjugation)

Benzene (cyclic conjugation)

occur at various wavelengths in the visible and ultraviolet region. The electrons in a single bond are very tightly held and require a great deal of energy to excite them. Hence the absorption of alkanes would occur in the vacuum ultraviolet region or below 1600 A. Multiple-bond compounds such as alkenes would absorb below 2400 A., and a compound with an unshared pair of electrons such as ammonia would absorb below 3500 A. The term chromophore is used to designate that linkage or group which will absorb radiation to produce a discontinuous or absorption spectrum. If the chromophore absorbs in the visible region, then a color is produced. Changing the environment of the chromophore by conjugation or substitution can shift the absorption to different wavelengths and is one means of obtaining more information on the structure of a molecule. Table I gives a listing of some of the common organic chromophores. They will be discussed in more detail in the treatment of spectrophotometric data.

2. Spectral Absorption and Transmission

Fundamental to the study of absorption spectra are two basic laws: Bouguer's law (also termed Lambert's law) and Beer's law. The combined term Bouguer-Beer law refers to the combination of these two laws. Bouguer's law essentially states that the absorbance of radiant energy of a specific wavelength by an absorbing medium will vary directly as the thickness of the absorbing medium is varied. Beer's law states that the absorbance of radiant energy by an absorbing material in a solution will vary directly as the concentration of the absorbing material is varied in a sample of unit solute thickness.

About a century ago Bunsen and Roscoe outlined the theory of the absorption of radiant energy as it concerned chemical analysis and identification. They presented an equation which is generally known as the Bunsen absorption equation:

$$I = I_0 \cdot 10^{-A} = I_0 \cdot 10^{-kcd}$$

where I = intensity of transmitted light or radiant energy at single wavelength.

I_0 = intensity of incident light or radiant energy.

A = absorbance = kcd.

k = specific absorbance.

c = concentration.

d = thickness.

The equation for the Bouguer-Beer law is also represented by this Bunsen absorption equation. Where the concentration is constant or unity (as in the case of a pure substance), the concentration factor becomes a part of the absorbance constant, and the equation represents Bouguer's law, which equates change in absorbance as a direct function of length of the absorption path.

In a similar manner, maintaining a constant thickness and changing concentration of the absorbing substance will generally produce a corresponding change in absorbance. When this change is directly proportional the absorbing substance conforms to Beer's law.

Absorbance, indicated in the equation as kcd, is generally indicated by the symbol A and is the absorption value which is usually recorded and plotted. Adjustment of this observed absorbance, A, is made to

TABLE II

Relation between Absorbance and Transmittance Terms

I_0 = incident intensity; I = transmitted intensity. Note that for absorption spectra of solutions these values are usually corrected for solvent absorption so that I_0 is the transmitted intensity through the solvent and I is the transmitted intensity through the solution (solvent + solute).

I/I_0 = transmittance = T. When transmittance is corrected for solvent, the relative transmittance is called transmittancy.

$T \times 100$ = per cent transmittance = $\%T$.

$I = I_0 \cdot 10^{-kcd}$, where c = concentration in grams per liter, d = cell or sample thickness in centimeters, and k = specific absorbance (also known as specific extinction).

A = absorbance = $\log I_0/I = kcd$ (also indicated by E and called extinction). Absorbancy indicates relative absorbance.

k = specific absorbance = A/cd = absorbance per unit concentration and unit thickness as defined above.

Log A = log absorbance (also indicated by log E = log extinction).

ϵ = molar absorbance = $k \times$ molecular weight (also called molecular extinction.)

$\dfrac{kcd}{1000} = E_{\text{cm.}}{}^{\text{p.p.m.}}$ = extinction (absorbance) in parts per million.

$kcd \times 10 = E_{1\text{cm.}}^{1\%}$ = extinction (absorbance) in per cent concentration.

Specific reference, standard, and observed values for special concentration and thickness are often used for special analysis methods; for example, the use of $E_{1\text{cm.}}{}^{1\%}$ 328 mμ in the determination of vitamins in natural oils, or the use of $E_{1\text{cm.}}{}^{\text{p.p.m.}}$ when it is desirable to express the concentration in units in relation to known standards of equivalent concentration.

$$A = \log I_0/I = -\log I/I_0 = -\log T = \log \frac{1}{T} \qquad \text{where} \qquad T = I/I_0$$

Density, optical density, extinctancy, extinction, and extinction coefficient are terms sometimes used for absorbance and absorbancy.

Absorbance values A (or E), k, and ϵ are often recorded as exponential or power values, especially where the units become large or difficult to present graphically. For example: $k \times 10^3$, log A (or log E), $\epsilon \times 10^5$, log ϵ, etc.

There is some confusion in the literature over the value of c, which in some cases may be given as grams per cubic centimeter or g. per 100 cc. rather than grams per 1000 cc. as defined above.

specific absorbance, k, by conversion to unit thickness and unit concentration. Absorbance A can also be changed to molar absorbance, ϵ, by conversion to unit thickness and molar concentration. The specific or molar absorbance values are often used in standard data presentations for comparison of specific molar properties.

For qualitative identification of chemical substances and for the description of color it is often desirable to record the per cent of radiant energy transmitted rather than absorbance. The per cent transmittance has been widely used in the presentation of infrared absorption spectra; but with improved quantitative procedures of observation there is an increase in the use of absorbance so as to permit direct quantitative estimation. In addition to ease of quantitative estimation by direct measurement of absorbance values, this method of recording permits direct addition and subtraction of absorbance values to determine the nature of impurities or mixtures. For this differential absorbance measurement, a known pure substance is used in the solvent cell of a double-beam instrument, and the unknown in the solution beam is the same compound with an unknown quantity of impurity. The differential spectrum thus provides a direct measurement of the impurity present.

Intercomparison of terms for transmission and absorption are given in Tables II and III.

TABLE III

Conversion of Absorbance, A (Extinction or Optical Density), to Transmittance, T
(Note: $A = \log 1/T$; $T \times 100$ = per cent transmittance)

A	T	A	T	A	T
0.0	1.00	0.5	0.32	1.0	0.10
0.1	0.79	0.6	0.25	1.1	0.08
0.2	0.63	0.7	0.20	1.2	0.063
0.3	0.50	0.8	0.16	1.3	0.050
0.4	0.40	0.9	0.125	1.4	0.040

Note that, since A is a reciprocal logarithmic function of T for each successive decimal range, i.e., from unit to tenths, to hundredths, etc., there is a corresponding increase in the characteristic of the A value for 0 to 1, to 2, and every fourth consecutive extinction value such as 0.0, 0.3, 0.6, or 0.4, 0.7, 1.0, etc.; will have corresponding transmittance values which are one-half the preceding value, i.e., 1.0, 0.5, 0.25 for the first example, and 0.40, 0.20, 0.10 for the second series. Hence the entire table can be constructed from the first three values of A, 0.0, 0.1, and 0.2, and the corresponding transmittance values of 1.00, 0.794, and 0.631.

One important item to be noted in the equation which included the Bouguer-Beer law effects is that it is not the actual value of the intensity but rather the relative value of I_0/I which is significant. In the case of solutions the Bouguer-Beer law applies only when there is no change in the solute molecules (i.e., no chemical interaction between the solute and the solvent). Thus, it is desirable to check to see whether a solution obeys Bouguer-Beer law. Conformance to this law is indicated when a plot of absorbance values at a selected wavelength against concentration yields a straight line.

Apparent or real deviations from the Bouguer-Beer law may be caused by a number of factors which can be classified as either instrumental or solution variables. Instrumental characteristics such as the degree to which the radiant energy is monochromatic, slit width effects, and stray light all are determining factors. Solution variables influencing the absorption spectra and the conformance to Bouguer-Beer law are concentration effects with accompanying association between solute molecules or between solute and solvent molecules, dissociation or ionization, solvent, temperature, pH, and irradiation. These observed discrepancies, however, enable the observer to learn more of the reactions and equilibria of some of these solutions. These will be discussed in detail later in the section on spectral data. It should be noted here, however, that because of these considerations spectral data should always include name and model of instrument, solvent, concentration of solution, thickness of absorption cell, temperature and slit width, as well as absorbance values at various wavelengths.

3. Nomenclature and Terminology

The subject of nomenclature and terminology in spectrophotometry has been investigated by numbers of workers in the field, and nearly as many proposals have been made, but no one system has been adopted. The problem can be approached from the physical view, the chemical view, or one which tries to bridge the gap between the two with a terminology common to both fields. Far-reaching recommendations have been made by the Photometry and Colorimetry Section of the National Bureau of Standards, the Joint Committee of the American Society for Testing Materials and the Society for Applied Spectroscopy, and the Colorimetry Committee of the Optical Society of America. In a broad sense, most of these recommendations follow a physical rather than a chemical approach, and the ASTM-SAS committee's nomenclature would be particularly useful for the applied physical spectroscopists. The nomenclature and terminology in this chapter represent a compromise between these reports which lends itself for chemical applications. It maintains the physical basis for the phenomena but does not go into all the detailed rigors; however, it is accurate and precise for the demands of chemical investigations of absorption spectra and electronic and molecular configurations.

In general it would seem desirable to use (1) the ending "-ion," as in transmission, absorption, conduction, etc., to indicate a process or effect, (2) the ending "-ance," as in transmittance, absorbance, conductance, to indicate a measured property of material, and (3) the ending "-ancy," as in transmittancy or absorbancy, to indicate a relative property. The use of the two endings of "-ance" and "-ancy" will be more or less equivalent in much of the published literature and in the application of absorption spectra data. The term absorbance is generally used to indicate either total or relative absorption, and the actual significance may be determined by the method of observation and character of the data recorded.

The measurement of radiant energy intensity involves some concept of the wavelength of the radiant energy region. This may be a broad, inclusive spectral region, a narrow band width of known wavelength values, or a specific wavelength, depending on the method of measurement and the instrument. For nearly all substances whose absorption spectra are desired, the values measured are of energy transmitted, but the data depicted in graphical form usually represent the energy absorbed.

The nature of absorption spectra data is such that, except for the few cases of unhindered vapor resonance or of protected structures at low temperatures in protective solvents (e.g., the vapor spectra of benzene or the rare earths in solution), absorption spectra bands are broad and not too sharply defined so that the accuracy of wavelength determination of the effective maxima is seldom greater than 1.0 mμ (or 10 A.). For this reason the use of the millimicron (mμ) as the numerical form of recording absorption spectra data is logical because the number of significant figures is consistent with the accuracy normally obtained.

Comparing the various wavelength and frequency forms of data recording (Table IV), we find that the fresnel is a correspondingly satisfactory form of indicating frequency. In fact, the limits of the visible spectrum in wavelength are usually given as from 400 to 750 mμ, and, by coincidence, the limits of the visible spectrum in frequency are from 750 to 400 fresnel units (vibrations per second $\times$ 10^{-12}). The wave number system is also used instead of wavelength or frequency. This is defined as the number of waves per centimeter, or cm.$^{-1}$. It has been proposed that the name kayser should be given to cm.$^{-1}$ and abbreviated as K. This has not as yet been universally accepted, however.

TABLE IV

Relation of Wavelength, Frequency, and Wave Number Systems of Spectral Notation

Wavelength:
Standard unit of length = Cd red line = 6438.4696 angstrom units (A.)

Angstrom, A.:

$$A = \frac{1}{6438.4696} \text{ of the wavelength of Cd red line}$$

Other symbols used for angstrom include IA, Å, AU.

Millimicron, mμ:

$$m\mu = 10^{-9} \text{ m.} = 10^{-7} \text{ cm.} = 10 \text{ A.}$$

Micron, μ:

$$\mu = 10^{-6} \text{ m.} = 10^{-4} \text{ cm.} = 1000 \text{ m}\mu$$

Wave number,[a] $\bar{\nu}$ (other symbols used for wave number include v'):

cm.$^{-1}$ = waves per centimeter = kayser = K.
cm.$^{-3}$ = waves per centimeter $\times$ 10^{-2} = waves per 0.01 cm.

Frequency,[b] ν

Fresnel, f.

$$f. = \text{vibrations per second} \times 10^{-12}$$

Interconversion of above units:

$$\frac{1}{\lambda} = \bar{\nu} = \frac{\nu}{c}; \qquad c = \text{speed of light} = 3 \times 10^{10} \text{ cm./sec.}$$

Example of interconversion and relation of units:

$$1/\lambda \text{ in m}\mu \times 10^7 = \bar{\nu} \text{ in cm.}^{-1}; \qquad \bar{\nu} \text{ in cm.}^{-1} \times 3 \times 10^{-2} = f.$$

E.g.,

$$400 \text{ m}\mu = \tfrac{1}{400} \times 10^7 \text{ cm.}^{-1} = 25000 \text{ cm.}^{-1} = 25000 \times 3 \times 10^{-2} \text{ f.} = 750 \text{ f.}$$

---

[a] For data in the visible and ultraviolet, wave numbers are often recorded as cm.$^{-3}$; i.e., the visual spectral region at the blue end (400 mμ) has a wave number value of 25000 cm.$^{-1}$ or an equivalent 250 cm.$^{-3}$.

[b] Frequency is often used as a measure of radiant energy character and is specifically defined as the number of radiant energy wave cycles passing a set point in a unit time.

In grating instruments wavelength values are essentially linear throughout the observing range, and hence errors of reading and slit width settings are reasonably constant. In prism instruments the dispersion rate of quartz and glass is such that the resulting spectra are much more nearly linear on a frequency than on a wavelength basis of observation.

There are many technical reasons for utilization of wave number, wavelength, or frequency systems of recording spectral data, and one should be conversant with the three systems and capable of converting one system to another (Table V).

TABLE V

Conversion Table of Wavelength—Wave Number—Frequency

Wavelength (mμ), λ	Frequency (f.)	Wave number (cm.⁻¹)	Wavelength (mμ), λ	Frequency (f.)	Wave number (cm.⁻¹)
1000	300.0	10,000	430	697.7	23,256
975	307.7	10,256	420	714.3	23,810
950	315.9	10,526	410	731.7	24,390
925	324.3	10,811	400	750.0	25,000
900	333.3	11,111	390	769.2	25,641
875	342.9	11,429	380	789.5	26,316
850	352.9	11,765	370	810.8	27,027
825	363.6	12,121	360	833.3	27,778
800	375.0	12,500	350	857.1	28,571
775	387.1	12,903	340	882.4	29,412
750	400.0	13,333	330	909.1	30,303
725	413.8	13,793	320	937.5	31,250
700	428.6	14,286	310	967.7	32,258
675	444.4	14,815	300	1000.0	33,333
650	461.5	15,385	290	1034.5	34,483
625	480.0	16,000	280	1071.4	35,714
600	500.0	16,667	270	1111.1	37,037
575	521.7	17,391	260	1153.8	38,462
550	545.5	18,182	250	1200.0	40,000
525	571.4	19,048	240	1250.0	41,667
500	600.0	20,000	230	1304.3	43,478
475	631.6	21,053	220	1363.6	45,455
450	666.7	22,222	210	1438.5	47,619
440	681.8	22,727	200	1500.0	50,000

(Column headings: λ or $\nu \rightleftharpoons \nu$ or λ ; $\nu \rightleftharpoons \tilde{\nu}$)

Note that wavelength and frequency have inverse relationship in that any value in the wavelength column, λ (in mμ), is equivalent to the indicated value in the frequency column, ν (in f.); or the λ and ν headings of the column may be reversed; for example, 750 mμ = 400 f., and correspondingly 750 f. = 400 mμ.

A correction is generally made in emission spectra studies involving standard wavelength values in their conversion to frequency values for use in theoretical calculations. This correction is for the change of the speed and refraction of light in the medium of observation, i.e., air to vacuum. Such a correction, however, need not be made in recording absorption spectra data in frequency.

4. Presentation of Data

It is obvious that with a choice of different systems for both ordinate and abscissa presentation of absorption spectra there will be many combinations in the published literature. In some cases the direction of machine recording will determine the presentation form.

The data obtained from spectrophotometric studies can be treated and plotted in a number of ways, depending on the investigator and the application in which he is interested. A person interested in chemical studies usually prefers a plot of absorbance as ordinate and wavelength as abscissa. For the visible and ultraviolet regions, the choice of the unit is usually the millimicron. This is consistent with the accuracy and precision of the instruments commercially available.

Persons interested in color studies and the specification of color usually use transmittance or reflectance. This is because the calculation of color specification can be made directly from such data (Fig. 3).

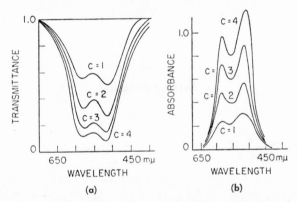

FIG. 3. Comparison of two systems for graphic presentation of absorption spectra. (a) Transmittance $= T = I/I_0$. (b) Absorbance $= A = \log I_0/I = kcd$.

In the intercomparison of spectra of compounds, a plot of $\log k$, $\log A$, or $\log \epsilon$ is more useful if the spectra of both compounds show weak and strong absorbance values. If $\log A$ is plotted ($\log \log 1/T$), the curves all have the same shape regardless of thickness or concentration.

In the interest of uniformity and ease of interpretation it is recommended that when plotting wavelength the higher numerical values be plotted on the left, and for wave number frequency the higher numerical values be on the right. This will maintain red on the left and blue on the right as far as the visible spectrum is concerned (Fig. 4.).

We have discussed the production of spectra, the relationship between the amount of absorption and the wavelength, and the terminology and nomenclature for describing these spectral quantities and relationships. Next we shall consider the instrumentation involved.

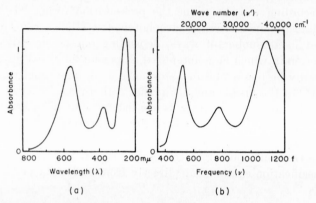

Fig. 4. Recommended systems of recording absorption spectra data: (a) in wavelength; (b) in wave number or frequency. Note change in curve shape when the same absorption spectrum is recorded in the two systems.

5. Instrumentation

Basically, the following component parts are necessary to investigate spectral absorption: (1) source of radiation; (2) spectral isolation of region of radiation; (3) sample and cell through which radiation will pass; (4) detector for transmitted radiation; and (5) measuring device. Variation and modification of these component parts divides instrumentation into various groups. These are not necessarily sharp and well-defined classifications, because historically terminology has developed which is not consistent with current trends. We shall now define our terms, and, although they may appear a little arbitrary, it will help in our discussion to set these limits.

5.1. Classification of Instruments

The earliest means of utilizing the fact that a substance absorbs visible radiation and hence exhibits color was to match the color intensity of a known and an unknown solution and to use this as a technique for estimating what and how much of a colored substance was there.

This procedure of chemical analysis by color has long been called colorimetry, primarily by the chemists. Today, however, colorimetry has an entirely different meaning to the physicist. The physics definition of colorimetry relates to the measurement and specification of color in terms of luminance or luminance factor (appropriate photometric quantity) and chromaticity (chromaticity coordinates, or dominant wavelength and purity). It is this physics definition which we shall accept here. Thus, some instruments commonly called colorimeters are not strictly speaking colorimeters, and we shall use the terms color comparator and absorptimeter to describe more exactly such instruments for chemical analysis. The color comparator is based on a visual comparison, and the absorptimeter on the measurement of the radiant energy by photoelectric rather than visual methods.

The color comparator is an instrument for the matching of intensity of color by the eye as an estimation of what and how much of a substance is present. The eye is a very sensitive light-measuring device, but it possesses a nonlinear (nearly logarithmic) response to intensity changes and provides little indication of wavelength value. Thus any visual color comparator would be limited by the method of detection. The technique has become refined, however, and with it the method has undergone several modifications, namely, narrowing the wavelength region produced to a smaller band and detecting it with a more suitable detector. The separation of wavelengths or bands of wavelengths then belongs to what is termed absorptimetry (absorptiometry), filter photometry, and spectrophotometry. An absorptimeter is an instrument for the photoelectric measurement of the absorption of a substance over a relatively broad or narrow region of wavelengths. It is often called a filter photometer or an abridged spectrophotometer if the dispersing element is a filter. With the use of a filter, the isolation of spectral energy is not by specific wavelengths but rather by a comparatively narrow or relatively broad band of wavelengths, depending on the filter. The spectrophotometer is an instrument for the precise relative measurement of radiant energy as a function of wavelength. The spectrophotometer uses either a prism or a grating, or both in conjunction. Here the radiant energy is dispersed according to wavelength, linearly in the case of the grating, and nonlinearly with a prism.

Thus, in the measurement of radiant energy and its relationship to the structure of molecules there are several classifications of instruments currently available commercially to fit the various needs and requirements of the chemist. All these instruments—color comparator, absorptimeter, filter photometer, and photoelectric spectrophotometer—may be used for qualitative and quantitative analysis of solutions. They differ, however, in precision and accuracy. Also the filter photometer and to a much greater extent the spectrophotometer are not limited to chemical analysis by color but may be utilized for kinetic studies, reaction mechanisms, and electronic configuration of molecules. The various basic components of an instrument are determining factors in the precision and accuracy of the measurement and will first be considered as separate entities.

5.2. SOURCES

In general, sources can be classed as either discontinuous or continuous. Discontinuous sources are nonhomogenous and provide radiant energy which is limited to certain wavelength values of the spectrum. The mercury arc is a good example of a discontinuous source. A continuous source is one which may have a maximum or minimum in intensity over a broad range, but it does not have an abrupt change in intensity with wavelength. The continuous source with high intensity over the visible and ultraviolet regions is most desirable for use in absorption spectrophotometry studies in these regions. The tungsten filament lamp is an excellent source for the visible (and also the near infrared). When heated to incandescence, it provides continuous radiation in the range of 350 to 1000 mμ. The hydrogen discharge lamp is the most suitable source of continuous spectrum in the ultraviolet (200 to 400 mμ). Because glass absorbs ultraviolet radiation, the tube must either be made of special ultraviolet-transmitting glass or be constructed with a quartz window. The tube contains two electrodes and is filled with hydrogen gas at a pressure of about 5 to 10 mm. of mercury. When the hydrogen is bombarded, electrons absorb energy in collision, and when they return to their normal energy levels there is a continuous spectrum emitted.

5.3. SPECTRAL ISOLATION

In the earlier discussion it was shown that spectrophotometric data are usually given in terms of absorbance values per wavelength. Hence in the actual instrumental measurement it is necessary to determine the absorption of a material at a particular wavelength. Therefore, some means must be devised for spectral isolation. The three primary procedures for spectral isolation in the visible-ultraviolet region are filters, prisms, and gratings. These elements may also be combined to produce the most effective and efficient system. At this point in our discussion, we shall consider their individual characteristics and properties and include the combination discussion under the pertinent instrument.

5.3.1. Filters. Essentially, a filter will prevent the transmission of certain wavelengths and transmit a selected band of wavelengths. The two broad classifications of filters are absorption and interference.

Absorption filters may be solid, liquid, or gas. There are many colored glass filters made by such concerns as Corning Glass, Eastman

Kodak, and Jena Optical Works. These filters are available with a listing of their characteristics from the companies (Fig. 5). Filters may also be gelatinous with the filtering material absorbed, or the filtering material may be adsorbed on plastic or cellophane. Gelatin filters are usually unstable to heat or moisture, whereas glass filters are more stable. A good absorption filter transmits a narrow and high intensity band of radiation.

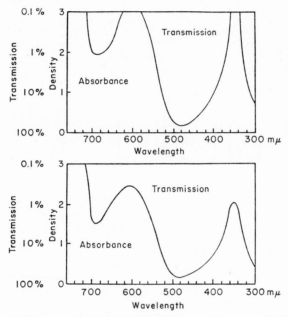

Fig. 5. Absorption spectra of Eastman-Wratten filters. Example of data as supplied by manufacturer (Eastman Kodak). Upper graph, No. 59 projection green; lower graph, No. 59A projection green (light).

Interference filters are made by depositing on a glass plate two metal films which are separated by a transparent spacer film of non-absorbing material. These films are then covered by protecting glass covers. Interference arises from multiple reflections between the metallic films, and the thickness of the spacer film determines the wavelength position of the band pass and therefore of the transmitted light. In this way maximum transmission is obtained at particular wavelengths, and on each side of this the transmission goes nearly to zero. These filters have a narrow band pass. There is a wide selection of filters available from Baird-Atomic, Bausch and Lomb Optical Company, and Farrand Optical Company.

Filters serve two main purposes. They are an integral part of instruments such as the filter photometer or abridged spectrophotometer because they serve as the spectral isolation component. Even in photo-electric spectrophotometry, however, where prisms or gratings are the components for spectral isolation, filters are often used to reduce stray light and enhance the accuracy of the instrument. There is a variation in the sensitivity of the eye and the photosensitive cells to different wave-length regions of radiant energy (Fig. 6), and hence some spectral

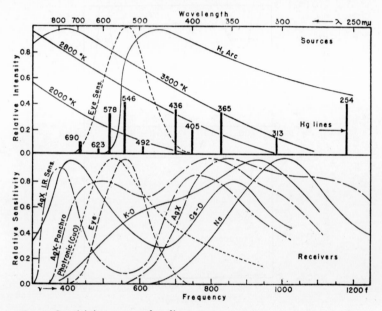

FIG. 6. Sensitivity range of radiant energy receivers and relative intensity of radiant energy sources. Receivers are indicated as (a) photoelectric (solid line); (b) photovoltaic (barrier layer or photronic photocell) (dotted); (c) photographic emulsions (dash-dot); and (d) human eye (dash).

measurements will fall in these regions of low sensitivity. In regions of low sensitivity stray light may have the same wavelength to which the receiver is highly sensitive, and this will become a major factor in the errors of measurement. For this reason it is desirable in both the visual and photoelectric instruments to introduce band-pass filters into the optical path even though the optical system includes a well-designed spectrometer or monochromator of fairly high dispersion (Fig. 7).

The use of blue filters when working in the blue region of low visual sensitivity, and of red filters when working in the red regions of low visual sensitivity, materially increases the accuracy of observation and this same principle may be applied to photoelectric instruments. For example, the accuracy of the readings on the Beckman visible and ultraviolet instrument is considerably improved in the region of 800 to 1200 mμ by the insertion of a Corning 254 filter which eliminates the visual regions of transmission and thereby removes stray light of the wavelength of the maximum sensitivity of the photocell. Blue filters also improve the near-ultraviolet sensitivity of this instrument. The accuracy of observation is improved by the use of monochromatic radiation, and

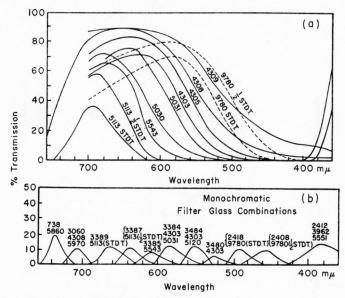

FIG. 7. Absorption spectra of Corning Glass filters: (a) group of available blue filters, and (b) combinations for band-pass filters, as given in Corning filter catalog.

it is suggested that the mercury green line, 546.1 mμ, which can be easily isolated by filters, is ideal for visual and certain photoelectric instruments.

The use of filters is also essential with certain grating instruments in order to remove higher or lower orders of spectra in those regions where the grating orders may overlap.

5.3.2. *Properties of Filters.* If filters are to be used as the means of spectral isolation, it is necessary to know the relationship between the properties of a filter and the color of the solution.

The color of a solution often indicates the maximum of transmission. As an absorption center is moved across the visual spectrum from blue to red (as a result of increasing weight or complexity of the chromophore producing the absorbed colors), a change in hue occurs known as color deepening. The order of color deepening takes place with the colors appearing successively as clear, yellow, orange, red, purple, blue, and green, with a corresponding position in the spectrum of the absorption band as ultraviolet, violet, blue, green, yellow, orange, and red. This color change is described as a bathochromic effect. The colors thus produced are not true spectral colors but instead are a summation of all spectral colors from which a limited amount of radiant energy (determined by the width and intensity of the absorption band)

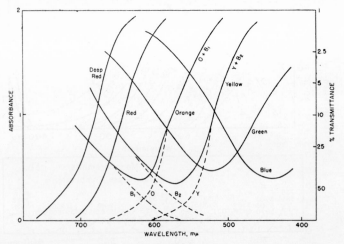

FIG. 8. Absorption curves for a set of color filters (broken-line curves indicate separate filters of the combination).

has been removed. Yellow will thus be white light from which only the blue end has been removed, leaving the green, yellow, orange, and red spectral colors. From Fig. 8, the blue, green, and red glasses transmit a limited or narrow band-pass spectral region as limited by the absorption bands of the filter and the response curves of the eye or photoreceiver.

The choice of a filter or light source transmitting or supplying yellow light would be of no use in the measurement of the intensity of the yellow solution. Light of the wavelength of maximum absorption should be used for this comparison. Hence blue light or blue transmitting filters should be used for observation of yellow solutions, red light for blue solutions, purple light for green solutions.

The choice of a filter complementary to that of the absorption band of the measured material is generally the best procedure. Where the measured material shows more than one band with wide separation of peaks, as in green nickel solution, it may be sufficient to choose a transmitting filter that passes light only of the wavelength of the absorption band of the unknown at which the receiver cell is most sensitive.

5.33. Combination of Filters. In the application of filters to color comparison analyses, we can measure the absorbance of a substance by means of interference filters, band-pass filters, or cutoff filters. Interference filters are replacing the combination of a series of absorption filters because they produce such a narrow band of wavelengths. Many times, however, it is not possible to obtain an interference filter for

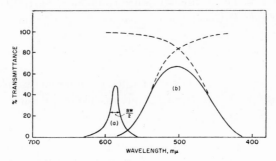

Fig. 9. Band-pass filters: (a) interference filter (half band width indicated as width of the transmission band at half its maximum transmittance), and (b) combination filter (separate parts indicated by broken lines).

exactly the desired range, and hence a frequent technique is to combine filters. This may be done in two ways: cutoff filters and band-pass filters. By cutoff filters we mean the differential transmission values of two filters of different wavelength cut off but cutting in the same direction. The yellow and orange filters (dotted lines) include a wide band pass (Fig. 8). By comparison of the transmitted intensities of the yellow, orange, and red filter with and without the measured substance, however, one may by a method of difference obtain the relative transmitted intensity for that narrow band pass represented by the difference between the absorption band edges of the compared filters. By band-pass filters one can obtain nearly monochromatic or narrow band-pass illumination of essentially the same wavelength as the absorption band of the substance. This is done by using two filters in combination with the same cutoff but cutting toward each other so as to produce a band-pass filter. Of these two procedures the band-pass type is preferable if suitable combination can be found. Where one filter, such as a copper blue type, may not absorb enough to produce a symmetrical narrow yellow transmission band, the combination of a copper blue (red-absorbing) filter with yellow and with orange filters will produce a band-pass filter, a yellow and orange band pass in this case, with an improvement in the accuracy of observation.

The combination of long-wavelength and short-wavelength transmitting filters to produce an efficient band-pass filter requires that the two cutting edges be steep or sharp and that the summation of the extinction curves produce a filter with sufficient transmitted intensity to be capable of giving a reasonable instrument response in the photometric observing device. The over-all efficiency may be indicated as the half band width (i.e., band width at one half its height as observed on a transmission basis). The absorbing substances are assumed to have a smooth cutting edge without evidence of fine structure component parts (Fig. 9).

5.3.4. Prisms. Prisms made of glass are restricted to use in the visible region because glass absorbs ultraviolet radiation. Quartz prisms, however, may be used for both the visible and ultraviolet regions. White light is broken up into its individual wavelengths by a prism and dispersed according to wavelength. These energies of different wavelengths travel at different rates in traversing the prism. Therefore each wavelength is emitted at a different angle of deviation, and the wavelength dispersion is nonlinear. In order to achieve constant deviation, there are various arrangements for the optical system of a spectrophotometer. We shall discuss only those used in the instruments to be described later. A constant deviation monochromator has its entrance and exit slits fixed in one position, and the prism is rotated so that the spectrum always falls on the exit slit. The Littrow arrangement combines the prism and the mirror. A 30° prism is mirror-coated on the back face. The beam is therefore refracted along the path of the incident and is brought to focus by the same lens that collimated the incident beam. This is termed autocollimating. In instruments employing this type of arrangement, the entrance and exit slits are close together, which makes a compact arrangement, but it is difficult to eliminate stray light because of the single dispersion.

The Féry system is similar to the Littrow except that there is no separate lens required because the prism surfaces are ground and polished spherical instead of plane.

5.3.4. Gratings. Another element for dispersion of light is the grating. This is more generally used in infrared instruments, but it is incorporated into the design of several instruments we shall be discussing later. Diffraction gratings may be either transmission or reflection. The diffraction grating consists of a large number of close equidistant slits or diffracting lines. The transmission diffraction grating is a transparent plate with diffracting lines; and the reflection diffraction grating is a mirror or aluminum-coated glass with a number of lines. The basic process involved in all these types is that light diffracted from a grating undergoes constructive interference, and when it is focused a pattern is produced which consists of groups of spectra arranged in what are termed orders.

An echelette grating is one whose lines have been ruled so that radiation of a given wavelength is largely concentrated in one order. A detailed discussion of these gratings and their theory is not necessary here but can be found in a standard book on optics.

5.4. Cells and Sample Concentration

The sample for use in colorimetry or spectrophotometry should be homogeneous in character. If it is not, the entire unknown should be properly sampled, which can be done by mixing and removing an aliquot part characteristic of the unknown. The use of unusually small samples should be avoided, but, if there is no alternative, microtubes of a smaller diameter may be used to produce a longer liquid column with a smaller cross-sectional area. The intensity of absorption is a function of the cell thickness rather than of the cell diameter. Solutions with high chromophoric character require a microthickness cell which may be obtained by special ground recessed openings or by use of wafer spacers of platinum or other metal foil (Fig. 10).

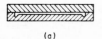

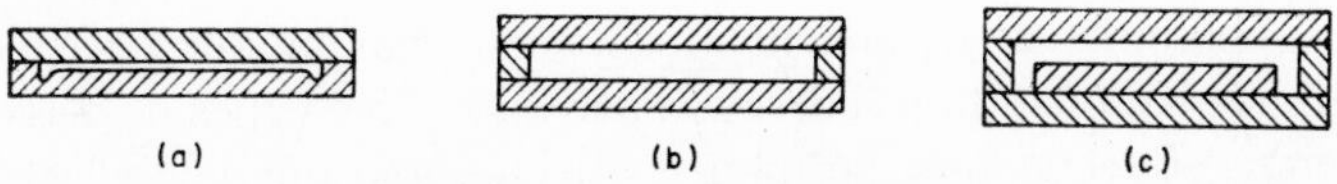

(a)   (b)   (c)

FIG. 10. Thin cells produced by (a) ground indentation, (b) wafer spacer, and (c) nonabsorbing insert.

Samples of low tinctorial value may require extra-long cells. Such measurements are almost certain to suffer from solvent absorption effects and should be avoided where possible. For routine measurements a thickness of 0.5 to 4 cm. is desirable, although thinner cells may be conveniently used providing the cell thickness can be determined with an increased accuracy. Error in cell thickness determination may easily become the greatest observational error, especially in the use of low values in a variable cell system (Duboscq color comparator type).

The concentration of sample and cell thickness are two factors which can be varied in all available instruments. The combination of these two factors (thickness, d, and concentration, c) determines the absorbance, A, of the sample in accordance with the Bouguer-Beer law:

$$kcd = A = \log I_0/I$$

where k, the specific absorbance, is a characteristic constant of the compound for the wavelength observed. It is desirable to adjust either the concentration or the thickness, or both, so as to bring the measured values into the most efficient range of the instrument. In general this range will lie between 0.6 and 1.6 absorbance units (25% and 2.5% transmittance). Absorbance values determined from transmittance observation above 80% transmittance or below 0.5% transmittance are difficult to determine with the usual instruments and should be avoided where possible.

The presence of colloidal or other general obstruction due to turbidity, which is not selective in absorption in a given spectral region, may be in part corrected by measurement of the absorbance at the wavelength or region of maximum transmission and subtraction of this value from the determination observed at the wavelength of maximum absorption.

The nature of the liquid in the comparison beam is not too critical where aqueous solutions are used and there is no absorbing material present other than that which is being measured. It is, however, essential that a compensating solution be measured in a similar cell to obtain a proper matching when the solvent itself is colored or has some absorption.

5.5. Detectors

After the radiation has passed through the sample, there must be some means of detecting and measuring the relative intensity of the radiation. The photometer component of a spectrophotometer measures this relative intensity of radiant energy. There are three types of detectors of interest to us: the eye, photographic emulsions, and the photoelectric type of receptor (see Fig. 6). The eye is very sensitive to gradations of light and dark, and to gradations of chromaticity, when comparisons can be made in a suitable two-part photometric field. However, it fatigues readily and cannot give a numerical evaluation except through an auxiliary optical device. Its combined speed and precision are much inferior to photoelectric devices and it is, of course, useless outside of the visible spectrum. Photographic emulsions vary in sensitivity over the spectral range, and in the far ultraviolet regions a special emulsion is required. The photoelectric type of receptor is most effective for investigations in the visible-ultraviolet regions. Photoelectric cells may be divided into three main classifications: photoconductive, photovoltaic, and photoemissive.

5.5.1. Photoconductive Type. This type of cell is based on the fact that a number of substances have different ohmic resistance on being irradiated, and the change in resistance depends on the intensity of the incident radiant energy. Materials such as lead sulfide, selenium, and thallous sulfide are all suitable, but because they exhibit a slow response and high temperature coefficient this type of detector is more suitable for the infrared region.

5.5.2. Photovoltaic Type (Barrier Layer or Photronic Photocell).

This cell consists of a conductor in contact with a semiconductor; for example, a layer of selenium is placed on a steel backing, and a metallic film of gold or platinum is deposited on the selenium. When this is illuminated, the selenium releases electrons to the metallic film, and an electric current is set up that is proportional to the illumination. This type of cell is sensitive over the whole visual range, but has the disadvantage of fatigue effects; that is, the current output falls off with increasing exposure time of light. This type of cell is often used in filter photometry, however, because it has comparatively simple circuitry.

5.5.3. Phototube (Photoemissive Type). A photosensitive cathode is used, such as cesium oxide on a metal base. On exposure to radiation, this surface emits electrons; the number of electrons per lumen is directly proportional to the intensity of incident radiant energy, and the maximum velocity of the electrons is directly proportional to the frequency of the incident radiant energy. The anode is at a positive potential with respect to the cathode, and this is maintained by an external battery or power supply. The two electrodes are in an evacuated bulb; the electrons emitted by the cathode are attracted to the anode, and an electric current is set up in the external circuit. This current is small, but the internal resistance of the tube is high. The advantages of this type are that amplifications can be made, it does not suffer from fatigue, cathodes with sensitivity to the various spectral regions can be obtained, and it has linearity and speed of response. One possible source of error is the "dark current"— stray electrons due to the potential difference across the electrodes when the tube is not illuminated. This should be compensated for in design of the instrument.

A modified version of this basic design is that of the electron multiplier tube, where there are a number of electrodes each at a successively higher potential, and secondary emission is obtained. The amplified photocurrent is measured by a deflection-type meter or the null point method with a potentiometer.

A single photoelectric detector may be used if it is alternately exposed to two beams, or if the electrical signal from each beam of light is distinguished by frequency or phase modulation. Two detectors may also be used for the two beams of radiation, but either the detectors must then be matched or any differences in characteristics must be compensated by some method incorporated into the system.

6. Instruments

Instruments will be considered in terms of their design and applications and hence will fall into three main classes: color comparators, absorptimeters (including filter photometers), and spectrophotometers.

6.1. Color Comparators

This type of instrument is based on the comparison, usually visual, of the color of an unknown with a standard to determine how much is present. The technique may vary: The unknown (liquid or solid) can be

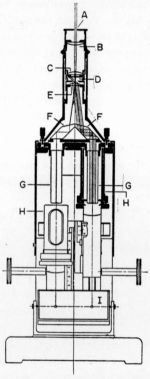

Fig. 11. Schematic diagram of the Duboscq color comparator (Bausch and Lomb), illustrating path of light rays. Light is reflected from mirror I, passes through glass bottom comparison tubes H, one containing the unknown and the other the reference solution. G is a glass cylinder with fused end plate. Tubes H are raised or lowered so that viewing depth of colored solutions is varied. Light beams then pass through biprisms F and E, slit D and lenses C and B. Eye views in split field light transmitted and adjusts cylinders until intensities match.

compared with a set of standards until an intensity match is obtained; the color of an unknown can be reproduced by starting with a known amount of the same reagents until the color is duplicated; an unknown solution can be diluted until it reaches the same color intensity of the known solution; or the unknown can be compared with a known by a balancing technique which varies the depth of the solutions viewed.

Color comparators formerly were standard equipment for analysis, but because the visual color-matching procedure is being replaced in most instances with direct photoelectric measurement we shall cite only one instrument as a typical example of this type of color analysis. The Duboscq comparator has been selected because it is one of the best known; it has been in use for some time and subsequently modified in numerous ways. This instrument is an example of the balancing type of mechanism. Figure 11 shows the basic schematic diagram. As in all color comparison methods, the Bouguer-Beer law is the basis for relating the color to the concentration of the material present. Conformance with this law then is a necessary prerequisite for this method to be useful. As shown in the schematic, this instrument is equipped with a plunger-type mechanism (G) which varies the depth of the unknown viewed until a color match with the known is achieved. Then, from the Bouguer-Beer law,

$$\log I_0/I = kc_1d_1 \qquad \text{for the known solution}$$
$$\log I_0/I = kc_2d_2 \qquad \text{for the unknown solution}$$

Because $\log I_0/I = \log I_0/I$ at all wavelengths, then $c_1d_1 = c_2d_2$; we know d_1, d_2 and c_1, and so can calculate c_2.

6.2. Absorptimeters

The absorptimeter differs from a color comparator in that it has a dispersing element in its optical system and the measurement of the absorption of the substance is generally done photoelectrically. The most common element for dispersion in the absorptimeter is a filter, or a series of filters, and the most common element for detection is the barrier-layer photocell. The absorptimeter may have one cell which requires that the measurement be made in two steps. The detector is often calibrated directly in terms of transmittance and/or absorbance. The detector must be adjusted for a transmittance of 1 for the blank, and then the intensity is determined for the solution under investigation. This method is easy and simple, but it does not have the accuracy of a two-cell absorptimeter. In a two-cell absorptimeter the two detector cells operate on a null principle so that the relative amount of absorbing material is measured directly. The balancing of these cells may be done electrically, by an optical diaphragm, or by angle of incident light. The concentration or intensity is indicated by scales on these resistances, diaphragm, or angle of incident position.

An absorptimeter (often called absorptiometer) which is really a filter photometer is the Hilger-Spekker instrument. The source is a projection lamp, filters serve as the dispersing element, and the detector is two barrier-layer photocells operating on a null point mechanism. The schematic is given in Fig. 12.

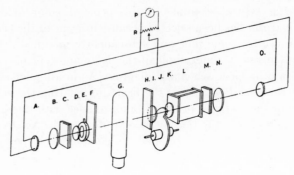

FIG. 12. Schematic optical diagram for the Hilger-Spekker Absorptiometer and its photocell circuit. Light from lamp G illuminates two photocells, A and O. Light from G passes through heat-absorbing filter H, window I, shutter J, and lens K before passing through sample L. Transmitted light then passes through another filter M and lens N before reaching photocell O. Light from lamp G passes through heat absorbing filter F, iris diaphragm E, lens D, spectrum filter C, and window B before reaching photocell A. Cell A is used as compensating cell and is connected to O through a bridge circuit consisting of spot galvanometer P and sensitivity control R.

An absorptimeter which is quite different in design from the standard filter photometer is the Spectronic 20 of the Bausch & Lomb Optical Company (Fig. 13). This has a diffraction grating as the monochromator, an

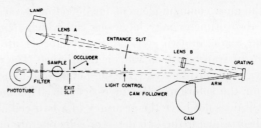

FIG. 13. Schematic optical diagram for the Bausch & Lomb Spectronic 20. Light from lamp is focused by lens A on the entrance slit, refocused by lens B on the grating. Monochromatic light from the grating passes through the exit slit, falls on the sample, and then on the phototube. A cam is used to rotate the grating so that light of desired wavelength can be selected.

effective band width of 20 mμ, covers the range 375 to 650 mμ, measures optical density and transmission, and has a phototube instead of the usual photocell for a detector. Because of its design the instrument can also be used for spectrophotometric purposes, although the measurement would be quite slow and tedious because the present design has room for only one absorption cell at a time in the compartment.

6.3. SPECTROPHOTOMETERS—VISIBLE REGION

Examples of spectrophotometers commonly in use in the visible region are the Beckman Model B, the Unicam SP. 600, and the General Electric recording spectrophotometer. Table VI gives a comparison of the basic

TABLE VI

Comparison of Visible Spectrophotometers [a]

	Nonrecording		Recording
Component	Beckman B	Unicam SP. 600	General Electric
Range	320-1000 mμ	360-1000 mμ	380-700 mμ
Source	Tungsten lamp	Tungsten lamp	Tungsten lamp
Monochromator	Féry glass prism	Littrow glass prism	Double, 2 glass prism
Photometer	Null point system	Null point system	Flicker system, optical null method
Cells	1-50 mm.	1-40 mm.	
Band width	5 mμ or <	<3 mμ	10 mμ
Detector	Two phototubes, one red-sensitive, one blue-sensitive	Two vacuum photocells, one red-sensitive, one blue-sensitive	Z-1454 phototube
Scale	% transmittance	Absorbance (log) % transmission (linear)	% transmission % reflectance
Stray light	<1.5%, filter in 320-400-mμ region	<1%, filter	negligible
Accuracy			
Wavelength			1.0 mμ
Absorbance			0.5%
Reproducibility			
Wavelength	0.5 mμ		
Absorbance			0.2%

[a] Data describe basic instrument design and represent information from manufacturers' catalogues.

component parts and characteristics of the three instruments. Schematics for them are given in Figs. 14, 15, and 16, where the design and tracing of the beam through the system are clearly given. The Beckman Model B's counterpart instrument in England is the Unicam SP. 600, and comparable instruments exist in Germany and Russia. The Beckman B and

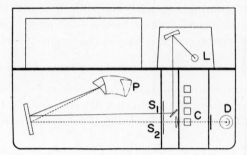

Fig. 14. Schematic optical diagram of the Beckman Model B. Light from a tungsten lamp (L) is dispersed and imaged by a Féry prism (P). The surfaces of the prism are curved so that the light imaged is automatically focused. The light passes out through the exit slit (S_2), through the sample (C), and onto a phototube (D).

Unicam SP. 600 use the autocollimation principle in design, although the Beckman has a Féry glass prism and the Unicam a Littrow arrangement. Both the instruments are manually operated and utilize the null point photometric system.

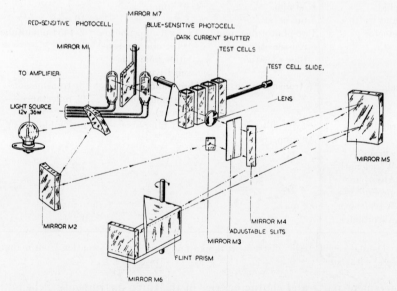

Fig. 15. Schematic optical diagram of the Unicam SP. 600. Light from a tungsten lamp is imaged and directed through the lower half of the slits to a collimating mirror, then to a glass prism and Littrow mirror which disperses the radiation. On the return path, the light beam passes through the upper half of the slits and through the absorption cell to the photocell.

The General Electric recording spectrophotometer is substantially different in design. It is an automatically recording instrument; and, whereas the other two instruments give readings of transmittance (or absorbance), the General Electric can be used not only for transmission measurements but also for reflection measurements. For this reason, the

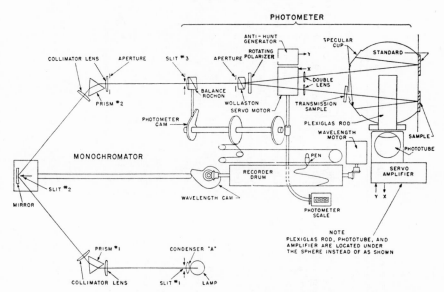

Fig. 16. Schematic optical diagram of the General Electric recording spectrophotometer. Light from a projector lamp is dispersed by prism 1. The slit and mirror select a band of light about 10 mµ wide. This band of light is further dispersed by prism 2 and trimmed by slit 3 for spectral purity. The monochromatic beam then is plane polarized by a Rochon prism and divided by a Wollaston prism into two divergent beams, one polarized horizontally which falls on the sample, and one polarized vertically which falls on the standard. The Rochon prism rotates the plane of polarization of the light and varies the ratio of intensities of the two beams emerging from the Wollaston prism. A polarizing filter flickers the two beams so that when one beam is transmitted at maximum intensity the other beam is extinguished. The two beams pass into an integrating sphere, where each varies alternately from maximum to zero on the sample and standard. The phototube is located below the sphere and receives light through a transparent plastic rod (Plexiglas) from the ceiling of the sphere. If the intensity of the light reflected from the sample and that from the standard are not identical, a phototube signal is amplified, applied to a servo system which drives a motor, which is connected through the photometer cam to the analyzing Rochon prism. The Rochon prism is rotated until there is equal reflectance from the sample and the standard, and the angle position of the Rochon prism is a measure of reflectance of the sample in terms of the standard. The photometer cams control the movement of the recorder pen.

TABLE VII[a]

Comparison of Visible-Ultraviolet Nonrecording Spectrophotometers

Component	Beckman DU	Unicam SP. 500	Hilger Uvispek	Zeiss PMQ II
Range	220-1000 mμ	200-1000 mμ	200-1000 mμ	200-1000 mμ
Source	Interchangeable tungsten lamp and hydrogen discharge tube	Interchangeable tungsten lamp and hydrogen arc	Interchangeable tungsten lamp and hydrogen discharge lamp	Interchangeable tungsten lamp and hydrogen lamp
Monochromator	Littrow quartz prism	Littrow quartz prism	Littrow quartz and glass interchangeable prisms	Littrow quartz prism
Photometer	Null method	Null method	Null method	Null method
Cells	1-10 mm.	1-40 mm.	1-40 mm.	5-50 mm.
Band widths	0.5 mμ		<1 mμ	
Detector	Two phototubes, photoemissive type, one red-sensitive, one blue-sensitive	Two vacuum photocells, one red-sensitive, one blue-sensitive	Two photocells, one red-sensitive, one blue-sensitive	Photoelectric multiplier cell
Scale	Absorbance % transmittance	Absorbance % transmission	Absorbance Transmission	Extinction (absorbance) Transmission
Stray light	<0.1%, filters can be used in 320-400 mμ			220-1000 mμ, 1% with filter
Reproducibility				
Wavelength	0.05 mμ	0.1 mμ		0.05 mμ
Transmittance	0.1%			

[a] Data describe basic instrument design and represent information from manufacturers' catalogues.

instrument is extremely useful in obtaining spectrophotometric data for colorimetric calculations—that is, the measurement, analysis, and control of color. In reflectance measurements, the sample is measured against a standard white. The international color standard is freshly prepared magnesium oxide. For a working standard, white vitrolite prepared by the National Bureau of Standards can be used. For transmission measurements and color comparison work, magnesium carbonate blocks can be used.

6.4. Spectrophotometers—Visible-Ultraviolet Nonrecording Instruments

Table VII gives a comparison of the component parts of the instruments commonly used for absorption spectra studies in both the visible

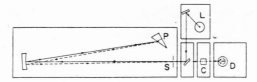

Fig. 17. Schematic optical diagram of Beckman Model DU. Light from a tungsten lamp or a hydrogen discharge lamp (*L*) is dispersed by a Littrow crystal quartz prism (*P*), passes through the exit slits located above the entrance slit, through cell (*C*) and onto phototube (*D*).

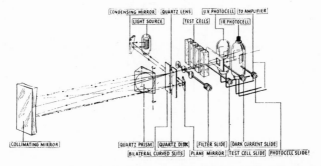

Fig. 18. Schematic optical diagram of the Unicam SP. 500. An enlarged image of the light source is focused by an aluminized condensing mirror and plane mirror onto the entrance slit, which is the lower of the two slit openings placed vertically with respect to each other. Light passing through the slit is made parallel by a collimating mirror and directed toward the Littrow quartz prism. The spectrum produced is focused by the collimating mirror in the plane of the slits, and light of a particular wavelength goes through the slit, through the quartz lens, and absorption cell to the photocell.

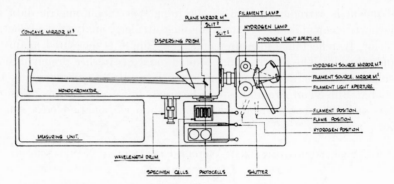

Fig. 19. Schematic optical diagram of the Hilger Uvispek spectrophotometer. Light enters the monochromator slit, is dispersed by a quartz or glass dispersion prism, passes through the second slit, through the absorption cell, and onto the photocell. The output of the photocell (proportional to the radiation received) passes to an electronic measuring unit where it can be balanced by an opposing electromotive force from a calibrated potentiometer.

and ultraviolet regions. The Beckman DU, Unicam SP. 500, Uvispek, Zeiss PMQ II, and the Russian counterpart instrument, all follow about the same general design (Figs. 17 to 20). The Littrow prism is used for creating an autocollimating system; in the Uvispek a quartz or glass

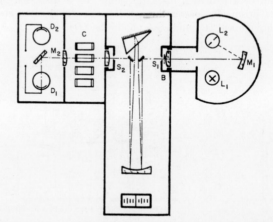

Fig. 20. Schematic optical diagram of the Zeiss spectrophotometer PMQ II. Light from either a tungsten lamp (L_1) or a hydrogen lamp (L_2) is imaged on the entrance slit (S_1) by means of a tilting mirror (M_1). The chopper diaphragm (B) in front of the entrance slit modulates the light. Approximately monochromatic radiation leaves the exit slit (S_2) of the monochromator and traverses one of the four shiftable cells (C) and falls via a tilting mirror (M_2) onto the radiation detector, D_1 for near infrared region and onto D_2 for ultraviolet visible region.

prism can be interchanged for usage in the special regions. All operate on the null point reading system. Numerous attachments have been devised for these instruments, such as for fluorescence and reflection measuring as well as recording devices.

6.5. Spectrophotometers—Visible-Ultraviolet Recording Instruments

A comparison of the component parts of the automatically recording instruments for visible and ultraviolet regions is given in Table VIII. There is considerable variation in the monochromators of the various instruments. An excellent way to increase the spectral purity of the radiation beam is to use the exit energy from one monochromator as the source of energy for another monochromator. This system is followed in the Cary Models 11 and 14. The Cary model 11 utilizes two phototubes and a split-beam system so that light separately traverses the sample and reference cell. The phototubes must be matched pairs, and the photometric system

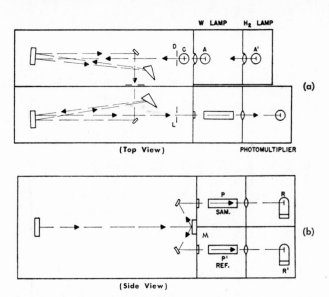

Fig. 21. Schematic optical diagram of the Cary Model 11. Radiation from the source A or A' passes through the entrance slit (D), through the double monochromator, and out the exit slit (L) as monochromatic radiation. A shutter (C) driven by a synchronous motor modulates the entrance radiation at 60 c.p.s. A beam splitter (M) divides the exit radiation into two equal collimated beams arranged one over the other. These beams pass through the reference and sample cells (P' and P) and fall onto the reference and sample phototubes (R' and R). The two photocurrents are measured and compared by the photometric system.

TABLE VIII[a]

Comparison of Visible-Ultraviolet Recording Spectrophotometers

Component	Cary 11	Cary 14	Beckman DK-2	Perkin-Elmer 13-U	Spectracord Model 4000
Range	200-800 mμ	186 mμ-2.6 μ	200 mμ-3 μ	190 mμ-2.5 μ	200 mμ-2.8 μ
Source	Interchangeable tungsten lamp and hydrogen arc	Interchangeable tungsten lamp and hydrogen arc	Interchangeable tungsten lamp and hydrogen arc	Interchangeable Nernst glower and hydrogen arc	Interchangeable tungsten lamp and hydrogen arc
Monochromator	Double, two quartz prisms	Double, fused silica prism, echelette grating	Single, quartz prism	Single-pass Littrow, fused silica prism	Double mono, 30° quartz prism
Photometer	Double-beam system, null balance system	Flicker beam	Split flicker beam system	Double beam, direct ratio using phase discrimination placed before monochromator system	Double beam
Cells	Micro-100 mm.	Micro-100 mm.	1-100 mm	Micro-100 mm.	1-100 mm.
Detector	Dual multiplier phototubes, multipot zero compensation	Single multiplier phototube 1P28, multipot zero compensation	Single	Single photomultiplier 1P28	Two photomultipliers
Recorder	Strip chart	Strip chart, dual pen 0-1, 1-2	Built-in file-size papers, 11 × 17 inch	Strip chart	Drum type, 11 × 17-inch chart
Scanning speed	1-125 A./sec., variable	0.5-500 A./sec., variable		Ultraviolet, 2.5, 5, 10, 20, 40, 80, 160 min. Visible 1, 2, 4, 8, 16, 32 min.	90 sec.-12 min.

TABLE VIII—Continued

Component	Cary 11	Cary 14	Beckman DK-2	Perkin-Elmer 13-U	Spectracord Model 4000
Scale	Linear λ, linear A, in two ranges, 0-2.5 1-3.5, linear T	Linear λ, linear A, in two ranges, 0-1.0, 1.0-2.0	Nonlinear λ, linear A, linear T	Nonlinear λ, linear T	Nonlinear λ, Linear A, linear T
Stray light	<0.0001%	<0.0001% (210 mμ-1.8 μ)		Ultraviolet, negligible, <1% at 210 mμ Visible, <2% at 400 mμ, at 650 mμ	Maximum 0.01% between 220 mμ and 1.5 μ
Accuracy Wavelength	Ultraviolet, 5.0 A. Visible, 10.0 A.	Ultraviolet, 4 A. Visible, 4 A.			Ultraviolet 5 A. Visible 10 A.
Absorbance			0.01 A	T, 0.5%	T, 0.5%
Reproducibility Wavelength	Ultraviolet, 0.5 A. Visible, 3.0 A.	Ultraviolet, 0.5 A. Visible, 0.5 A.			Ultraviolet, 1A. Visible, 2A.
Absorbance	0.012		0.001 A	T, 0.5%	T, 0.2%

a Data describe basic instrument design and represent information from manufacturers' catalogues.

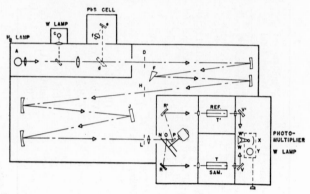

FIG. 22. Schematic optical diagrams of the Cary Model 14. Radiation from the hydrogem lamp (*A*) or tungsten lamp (*C*) enters the double monochromator through slit *D*, is dispersed by the prism (*F*) and the grating (*J*). Monochromatic radiation leaves through slit *L* and is sent alternately through the reference cell (*T'*) and the sample cell (*T*) by means of a rotating semicircular mirror (*O*). Light pulses of the beams from the reference cell and the sample cell are out of phase with each other, and thus the photocell receives light from only one beam at a time. The photocell signals are measured and compared in the photometric system of the instrument.

operates on a null balance principle. Null balance is achieved before the sample signal passes through the amplifiers (Fig. 21). The Cary Model 14 also has a combination of dispersing elements; a fused silica prism is

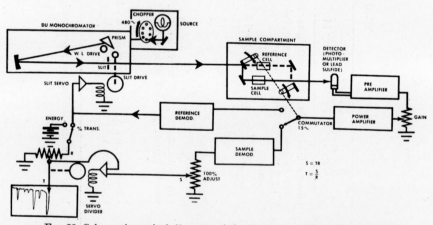

FIG. 23. Schematic optical diagram of the Beckman DK-2. This instrument uses the Beckman DU monochromator. The source light is chopped mechanically at 480 c.p.s. The chopped beam is then switched fifteen times a second from reference to sample cell and then to the photoreceiver. This results in a double-beam ratio recording instrument with a simple audio-type electronic amplifier, equivalent to the double-beam optical principle.

combined with an echelette grating. These are used to obtain the advantages of both systems: the high optical efficiency and low scattered light of the prism with the high resolving power and low temperature coefficient of the grating. The detector is a single multiplier phototube. The optical and electronic system is such that the receiver measures and compares the radiation transmitted through first the sample and then the reference cell. This eliminates any errors due to variations in the characteristics of two phototubes (Fig. 22).

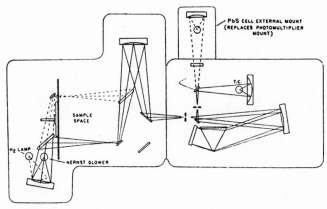

FIG. 24. Schematic of the Perkin-Elmer Model 13-U Universal. Radiation is split into two symmetrical beams of radiation, chopped 90° out of phase, and brought to focus at the sample and reference beam positions in the sample compartment. The two beams are then recombined and imaged on the entrance slit of the single-pass Littrow-type monochromator equipped with a fused silica prism. After dispersion, the radiation passes through the exit slit and is focused onto the photomultiplier detector.

The Beckman DK-2 uses the single monochromator of the Beckman DU but has a split double-beam system and a single photodetector (Fig. 23). The Perkin-Elmer Model 13-U chops radiation which passes through reference and sample before it is recombined and goes through the Littrow-type monochromator equipped with a fused silica prism (Fig. 24). The passage of the radiation through the sample before it goes to a monochromator might cause in some instances the effect of phototropism, if the material is susceptible to these certain wavelength radiation effects. The Spectracord 4000 (Fig. 25) is a combination of a double monochromator with the Warren Spectracord unit. The latter is often used as an attachment for single monochromators in order to render them automatically recording. The Model 4000 employs a double-stage Littrow-type monochromator with a beam splitter and chopper at the exit slit of the monochromator to give modulated double-beam performance. This is designed to give good dispersion, resolution, and less scattered radiation.

The modern advance in electronic and automatic instrumentation of absorption spectra instrumentation is probably as dramatic as the similar advance in computer instrumentation. The history of absorption spectra instruments evolves from the earlier Hartley-Baly-Hantzsch devices using arc sources, plate spectrographs with photographic emulsions and vari-

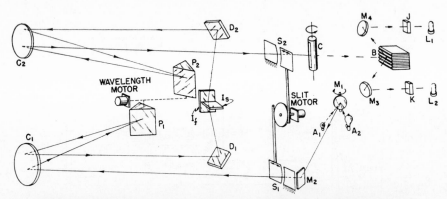

FIG. 25. Schematic optical diagram of the Model 4000 Spectracord. Radiation from source A_1 (tungsten lamp) or from A_2 (nester lamp) is focused by mirror M_1, entrance mirror M_2, passes through extrance slit S_1 into double monochromator. Double monochromator consists of first stage collimator C_1, prism P_1 and diagonal D_1; interstage slit jaw I_s, flat mirror I_f; second stage diagonal D_2, collimator C_2, prism P_2. Radiation leaves monochromator through exit slit S_2, passes through chopper C, and divided by beam splitter B into two beams—one of which passes through collimating mirror M_3, reference cell K, and reference detector L_2; the other, through collimating mirror M_4, sample cell J, and sample detector L_1.

able-thickness cells, sector spectrophotometers, wedge cells, and step cells. These earlier devices required careful photometry and tedious plate reading and plotting, a process which could provide a point-by-point curve in about an hour or two at the least. Photoelectric multipoint instruments not only reduced the time to 10 or 15 minutes but also improved accuracy and reduced the noise and inconvenience associated with spark sources and photographic procedure. Concomitant with this increase in speed and accuracy there was a reduction in instrumental cost which led to much wider usage. With about ten thousand Beckman DU instruments in use as compared with the probable one hundred or so sector spectrophotometers, it is hardly worth while describing this earlier method. Although the nonrecording Model DU type is very useful and popular, there has been an increasing tendency to modify this instrument with automatic recording devices and to design new instruments which have high speed in recording and greater precision. In modern industry and research, where many curves are to be observed, it is actually more economical to employ the higher speed recording instruments. Such recording instruments will, in the future, supplant most nonrecording instruments except for teaching and casual observation purposes.

6.6. CALIBRATION

There are two kinds of calibration required on a spectrophotometric instrument: wavelength and photometric. Wavelength calibration is the comparison of the experimentally determined wavelength with the known value of a standard. This standard may be a monochromatic source, such as the green mercury line (546.1 mμ) or hydrogen line (656.3 mμ) ; a filter, such as didymium glass for the visible region; or the spectrum of a liquid, such as the benzene for the ultraviolet. Selection of a glass or a liquid as a standard must be based on the fact that their spectra consist of sharp, well-defined bands, so that the maximum can be determined with accuracy and precision.

The photometric calibration is based on the comparison of experimentally determined absorbance or transmittance values with the known values of standard colored glasses or solutions which have broad maxima and minima. In the photometric calibration, narrow bands are not desirable because then the slit width and wavelength become critical. Calibration glasses are available from the National Bureau of Standards; and solutions such as potassium chromate and potassium nitrate can be used.

The calibration of instruments and their performance data are of interest to the worker in the field. There have been a number of intercomparisons made of instruments of the same and different manufacture to determine the reliability and precision of spectrophotometers. In general, these results have been very encouraging so that the worker can feel relatively secure in the precision of the spectral data presented.

7. Color Analysis of Solutions by Absorption Methods

As has been previously indicated, the determination of concentration of colored solutions can be easily accomplished by the measurement of the absorbance at the maximum of absorption and comparison with known standards or absorbance data. As an example we may refer to the data involved in the colorimetric analysis of cobalt, copper, and nickel nitrate solutions. Figure 26 indicates the absorption of pure standard solutions of cobalt, copper, and nickel nitrates in aqueous solution. For the analysis of an unknown copper solution it is essential to choose a filter with a transmission band corresponding to the absorption band of copper. From Fig. 27, it can be seen that an orange filter would be satisfactory for this purpose, although the maximum of the absorption band of the copper solution is beyond the region of the visual sensitivity and a red filter would actually be preferable. An unknown solution of copper nitrate

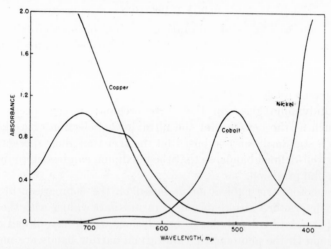

FIG. 26. Absorption spectra of cobalt, nickel, and copper nitrate solutions: concentrations are Co = 12.7, Ni = 25.4, and Cu = 13.3 g/l. of water.

gave a density or absorbance reading of 0.875 as compared with the absorbance of 0.623 for the copper standard solution which contained 6.58 g./l. Hence the concentration of the unknown can be easily calculated as 6.58 × 0.875/0.623 = 9.25 g./l. A similar consideration on an unknown cobalt solution would show that a desirable filter for this measurement would be the G filter, since its band pass at about 520 mμ is essentially that of the wavelength of the absorption band of cobalt nitrate. An unknown cobalt nitrate solution having an absorbance of 1.04 would thus be shown to have a concentration of 1.04/0.776 × 5.07 = 6.78 g./l. By applying this data to a mixed solution of cobalt and copper nitrates, it can be seen that, since the absorption bands of each of the two components are in quite separate spectral regions and do not overlap, the above measurements can be made on mixtures so as to determine each of the components. In binary examples involving copper and nickel or ternary mixtures of copper, nickel, and cobalt it can be seen from the data in Fig.

26 that the absorption bands overlap and the colorimetric analysis involves the determination of the sum of the absorbance values of the copper and nickel. The determination of the absorbance and concentration of the nickel alone by means of its absorption in the blue, the calculation of the absorbance due to nickel in the red, and the subtraction of this absorbance value from the total observed absorbance gives the absorbance due to copper (sample 2 in Table IX).

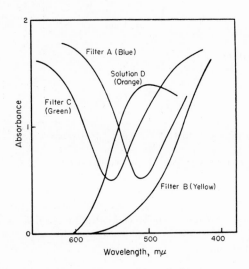

FIG. 27. Use of band-pass filters with colorimeter to measure solution absorption. Satisfactory filter, A, for the measurement of solution, D. Maximum of filter transmission is at the same wavelength as maximum of absorption of observed solution, and the filter band is sharp enough to give little or no transmittance of spectral region where observed solution has little or no absorption. Unsatisfactory filters, B and C for measurement of solution D. Filters transmit considerable radiation at spectral regions where the observed solution has little or no absorption.

A ternary mixture of copper, nickel, and cobalt (sample 5 in Table IX) can be analyzed by determination of the cobalt concentration at a wavelength of 520 mμ (at this wavelength copper and nickel show practically no absorption). The absorbance of cobalt in the blue (430 mμ) can be determined from the observation on a known standard (sample B in Table IX); and from the total observed absorbance of the unknown as 430 mμ the absorbance and concentration of nickel can be determined. A similar treatment of the summation absorbance of the copper and nickel in the red (640 mμ) permits the calculation of copper as indicated in Table IX.

TABLE IX

Example of an Absorptimetric Analysis of Copper, Cobalt, and Nickel Nitrate Unknowns by Use of Band-Pass Filters (Fig. 27)

(Note that A and k values are for band-pass filters and agree only in relative amount with calculated values from spectrophotometric curves; see Fig. 26)

(a) Known Standards

Sample	Solution	A, 1 cm.			Concentration	k		
		Filter			Metal, g./l.	R	G	B
		R (660 mμ)	G (520 mμ)	B (430 mμ)				
A	Copper nitrate	0.41	0.011	0.008	6.58	.0623	.0016	.0012
B	Cobalt nitrate	0.002	0.393	0.210	5.07	.0004	.0776	.0412
C	Nickel nitrate	0.226	0.015	0.155	5.00	.0451	.0030	.0310

(b) Unknown Solutions (known concentration given in last column)

Sample	A, 1 cm.			Elements	Calculated conc. (absorptimetric) (g./l.)	Known conc. of prepared samples (g./l.)
	Filter					
	R	G	B			
1	0.498			Cu	8.10	8.20
2	0.520		0.170	Cu	5.94	6.00
				Ni	5.56	5.50
3	0.318			Ni	7.05	7.20
4		0.471	0.251	Co	6.08	6.18
				Cu	4.45	4.40
5	0.405	0.255	0.240	Ni	3.40	3.45
				Co	3.30	3.40
				Cu	4.03	4.00

In this ternary mixture the calculations have been simplified by assumption of zero absorption where the absorbance values are less than 0.05. It is possible by means of simultaneous equations to solve for all three components and to take into consideration the observed absorbance of each of the components at each of the chosen wavelength values.

The example given above, based on the nitrates of cobalt, copper, and nickel, was chosen merely to present the problem of a multicomponent mixture. In routine analysis it is possible to use an indicator or test reagent such as dipyridyl, thiocyanate, ammonia, or other color-enhancing reagent so as to increase materially the chromophoric character of the ion to be measured and thus increase the accuracy and sensitivity of the method.

8. Absorption Spectrophotometric Studies

The absorption spectrum of a molecule in the visible and ultraviolet regions is complex but is characteristic of the molecule, and it is often a criterion for the identification of the compound. As indicated earlier, the basic group responsible for this absorption is termed a chromophore, and it may be an unsaturated linkage, a radical, or a grouping with an unshared

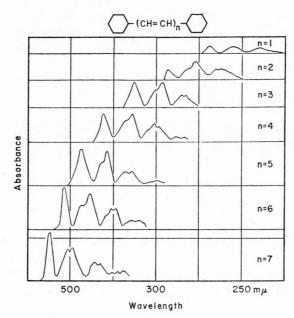

FIG. 28. Effect of increasing the number of conjugated chromophoric groups on the spectra of diphenyl polyenes.

pair of electrons. Materials which absorb radiation in the visible range usually exhibit a color to the eye. In general, if there is a change in the chromophoric structure of the molecule, any or a combination of the following color effects may be observed:

1. Hyperchromic, an increase in the absorbance value of the absorption band. The intensity of the color increases.

2. Hypochromic, a decrease in the absorbance value of the absorption band. The intensity of the color decreases.

3. Bathochromic, a shift of the absorption band toward the red (lower frequency). The color deepens (i.e., a change from yellow, to red, to purple, to blue, to green).

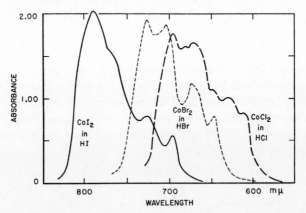

FIG. 29. Absorption spectra of cobaltous halides in their corresponding halogen acids.

4. Hypsochromic, a shift of the absorption band toward the blue (higher frequency). The color lightens (i.e., a change from green, to blue, to purple, to red, to yellow).

Figure 28 shows the resultant spectra of a series of diphenyl polyenes where the length of the conjugating linkage is increased. In the simplest compound, where $n = 1$, there are two absorption bands occurring in the region 250 to 300 mμ. With an increase in the number of conjugated linkages, the absorption band shifts toward the visible spectrum, and there is an increase in the intensity of the long-wavelength band; that is, the spectrum shows bathochromic and hyperchromic effects. This illustrates that there is a smaller difference in the energy content of the ground state and the first electronic level in the longer chain molecule.

There are inorganic as well as organic chromophores. The chromophoric character is due to the electronic structure of the atom with incomplete energy levels in such compounds as the cobaltous halides. The difference in weight of the chromophoric group as the halide varies from chloride → bromide → iodide causes a shift in the spectra to longer wavelengths (Fig. 29), or a bathochromic effect. When there is more than one chromophoric center in a molecule, investigation of the spectrum often leads to better understanding of the degree of conjugation, interaction, or transmission of resonance effect through the various linkages.

We shall discuss in more detail in a later section the systematic study of some dyes and their substituted derivatives which serve as an excellent example of the relation between chromophores, their environment, and the resultant absorption spectra.

But first, we should like to emphasize the need to specify the conditions under which the spectra are obtained, because temperature, nature of the solvent, pH, irradiation, and changes in concentration may influence the reproducibility of the data.

8.1. THERMOCHROMIC EFFECT

The thermochromic effect is defined as a change in color on heating or cooling, and the reaction is reversible. The resultant change in absorption spectra may be one of intensity or an actual change in the wavelength of absorption. An intensity change implies simply a change in the association state of the dye, whereas a change in the absorption wavelength signifies a change in the molecular configuration of the dye.

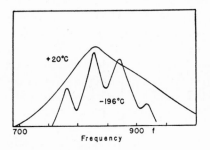

FIG. 30. Influence of temperature on the resolution of component structure in absorption bands. Absorption spectrum of dodecapentanoic acid in ether-alcohol. (Lewis and Calvin.)

A substantial decrease in temperature will tend to sharpen an absorption band and increase the resolution. A decrease in temperature limits the molecular motion of a molecule which broadens an absorption band but does not restrict the atomic or electronic changes (Fig. 30).

Figure 31 shows the absorption spectra of thionine and the modification in the spectra on changes in temperature and concentration. Dilution and elevation of temperature produce the same change in the aggregation state of thionine.

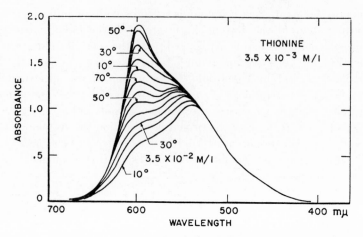

FIG. 31. Influence of concentration and temperature change on the absorption spectra of thionine. Lower concentration (3.5×10^{-3} mole/l.) in 10-cm. cell; higher concentration (3.5×10^{-2}) in a 1-cm. cell.

8.2. SOLVENT EFFECT

Substances such as water, alkali and alkaline-earth hydroxides, halides, sulfates or carbonates, and many compounds such as the simple hydrocarbons, heptane, hexane, isoöctane, cyclohexane, ethanol, hydrocarbons, ethers, carbon tetrachloride, and benzene show no selective absorption in the visible region. For this reason they are often used as solvents for absorption spectrum studies because they do not exhibit a spectrum which interferes with that of the material under study. It is very possible, however, that even these solvents may influence the spectrum of a material, because they may modify the configuration, structure, or state of polymerization of the material under investigation either by an induced effect or by direct chemical reaction. Polar solvents such as water, alcohol, acids, or bases tend to react with the substance being investigated. Nonpolar solvents such as carbon tetrachloride, benzene, and isoöctane do not, but they are not so universal a solvent. Solvents must be of high-grade purity because a trace impurity may change the spectrum considerably.

A change in absorption spectra as a result of reaction between the material under investigation and the solvent is demonstrated in the absorption spectra of phenylazophenol. Derivatives of phenylazophenol are formed in hydrochloric acid, aqueous sodium hydroxide, and 95% alcohol (Fig. 32).

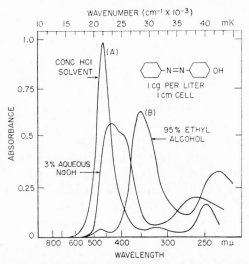

Fig. 32. Absorption spectra of phenylazophenol in alcohol, concentrated hydrochloric acid, and aqueous sodium hydroxide.

8.3. pH Effect

A solution may be very susceptible to changes in pH and undergo a change in the visual color. This type of substance is used as an indicator in acid-base titrations. This indicator effect is interestingly illustrated by

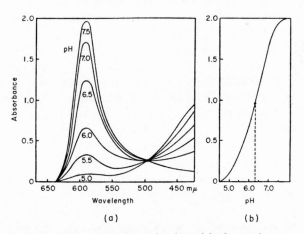

Fig. 33. Spectrophotometric determination of hydrogen-ion concentration. (a) Absorption spectra of bromocresol purple at the indicated pH values; note isosbestic point at 498 mμ. (b) The dissociation curve calculated from the absorbance at 580 mμ and the pH values in (a). Dotted line in (b) indicates dissociation constant for the indicator.

a study of the absorption spectra of the indicator at various pH values. The maximum absorption band of the compound does not gradually shift across the spectrum, but rather there is a decrease in the intensity of one absorption band and an increase in another as the pH of the solution changes. The reaction is a reversible one, depending simply on the change in pH. The absorbance value at one point in the spectrum as the pH is changed remains constant. This is known as the isosbestic point, a fulcrum for changes in the absorption curve where absorption remains constant at various pH values, and it is a characteristic of the material under investigation. Figure 33 shows the change in absorption spectra with pH and the isosbestic point which occurs at 498 mμ, the point of equal absorbance; this demonstrates that there is an equilibrium existing between the acid and basic forms of the substance. From the isosbestic point, the amount of the indicator present can be determined regardless of the acidic or basic conditions of the solvent.

8.4. IRRADIATION EFFECTS

Some compounds are susceptible to radiation, and their absorption spectra can be consequently changed. This may be irreversible in those cases where oxidation or decomposition may occur. A reversible reaction may also be stimulated by exposure to radiation, however, and this is called a phototropic effect. This reversible reaction occurs when a compound can exist in two or more isomeric forms which have different absorption spectra and energy content. Irradiation of one isomer at its wavelength of absorption tends to activate the molecule to an excited state in which it reverts to the other isomeric form. There is thus an increase in the amount of the nonactivated form. This process can be reversed by irradiating the solution with the wavelength of absorption of the second isomer. A good example of irradiation effect is that shown by the cis and trans isomers of thioindigo (Fig. 34). Each isomer has reasonable stability, with little interference from steric forces or hydrogen bonding. Exposure of thioindigo solution in chloroform or benzene to yellow light produces a yellow solution (cis), and an exposure of this latter solution to blue light produces a bluish solution (trans). This absorption spectrum also has an isosbestic point, indicative of an equilibrium between the two isomers and independent of the equilibrium ratio.

In the investigation of material spectrophotometrically, the absorption curve should be determined under a variety of conditions because a study of these factors and their influence on the absorption spectra will give additional structural information. A solution is said to follow Bouguer-Beer's law if by dilution or an increase in concentration the change in absorbance is proportional to the change in concentration.

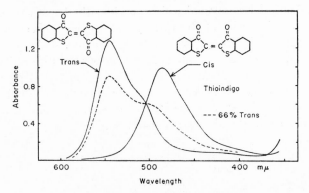

FIG. 34. Change in absorption spectra of thioindigo due to irradiation. (Note isosbestic point produced by common intercept of separate curves.) *Trans* curve produced by irradiation with blue light; *cis* curve produced by irradiation with yellow light.

9. Molecular Configuration of Dyes

A study of a series of investigations of the spectra of dyes illustrates the manner in which absorption spectra can clarify some structural and configurational problems. Dyes are of such high color intensity that a very small quantity will suffice to produce absorbance values in the range desired for accuracy and reproducibility, i.e., a few hundredths of a gram per liter of solvent. The molecular weight of dyes ranges from about 100 to 1000, and therefore one would estimate that the monomeric form should predominate in this concentration range.

Because dyes are such complex molecules and have a number of unsaturated linkages which provide them with their chromophoric characteristics, the resonance effect is a very important factor. The configuration which a molecule assumes or the configuration which contributes most to the make-up of a molecule is that which is most stable and is thought to be coplanar. In other words, it is the configuration which has the greatest resonance stabilization. Thus substitution in a dye structure which promotes or stabilizes the coplanarity of the structure will either increase the intensity of the absorption and enhance the color or shift the absorption toward longer wavelength and produce color deepening. Substitution which interferes or destroys coplanarity will change the absorption spectra considerably.

Both position and geometrical isomerism changes are reflected in absorption spectra. A simple case illustrating the position isomerism is the resonant structure dimethylaniline and its monochlorinated derivates

(Fig. 35). The *p*-Cl compound which provides the longest resonant path has the greatest intensity of absorption, whereas the *o*-Cl compound illustrates a hypochromic effect, thus indicating that there is interference with the electron cloud of the Cl— and the methyl group. It is not possible to have both the chlorine atom and the methyl radical in the same plane; therefore, the $(CH_3)_2N$ group undergoes a rotation out of plane. This destroys the resonance transmission between the N and the ring and hence the change in the absorption spectrum.

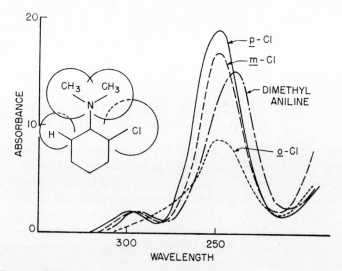

FIG. 35. Influence of position of substitution on absorption spectra of monohalogenated dimethylanilines (Remington).

This influence of steric effect which is illustrated so well in some of the relatively simpler compounds is also a very important factor in dye structure and is, therefore, very closely involved in the hue and also in the tinctorial strength of a dye. For example, if 1-aminoanthraquinone is methylated, the dimethylamino derivative has a different spectral intensity and is not so strong a dye as the mono because of steric inhibition with the adjacent carbonyl.

A brief discussion on several different families of dye structure will serve to show the usefulness of absorption spectra studies in determining the molecular configuration of dyes.

9.1. Azo Dyes

The simplest of the monoazo dyes is phenylazobenzene, more commonly known as azobenzene:

Phenylazobenzene can exist in two isomeric forms, *cis* and *trans:*

trans   *cis*

If the solution were measured spectrophotometrically, the curve obtained would be primarily the *trans* form because this is the more stable

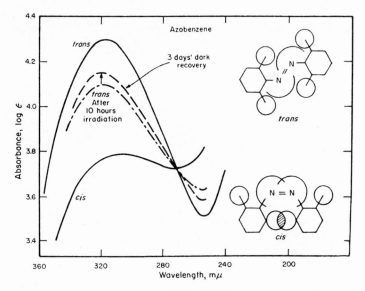

Fig. 36. Absorption spectra of *cis*- and *trans*-azobenzene. *Trans* form irradiated with ultraviolet light (360 to 300 mμ) produces *cis* form.

isomer. If the *trans* form is irradiated with radiation of the same wavelength as absorbed, however, it can be converted into the *cis* or labile isomer. The Cary spectrophotometer has been modified by means of a beam interrupter system in which the sample is irradiated and measured successively 1800 times a minute. In this way it is possible to observe exceedingly fugitive or labile dye systems. This apparatus (light chopper

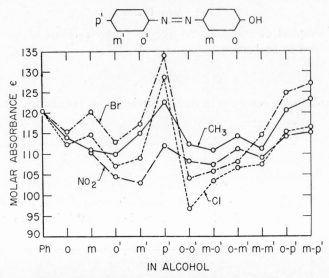

FIG. 37. Effect of substituents in phenylazophenol, as shown by shift of band intensity (alcohol solution).

adaptation) permits irradiation by light beams of selected radiant energy content and therefore can relate the change in the molecule to the wavelength of the radiation beam (Fig. 36).

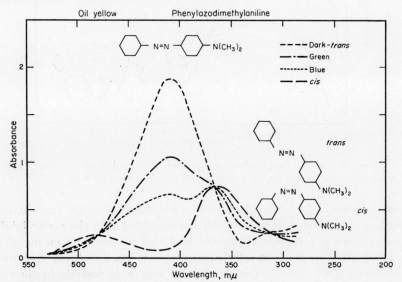

FIG. 38. Influence of irradiation on the absorption spectra of 4-dimethylaminophenylazobenzene.

This *phototropic effect* is influenced by substitution on the ring. If an hydroxy group is in the *ortho* position, there is hydrogen bonding between the N and H. This would create a stabilized *trans* configuration not susceptible to a phototropic effect.

The effect of NO_2, Br, CH_3, and Cl as substituents in various positions in phenylazophenol is shown in Fig. 37. This illustrates the effect of position isomerism on absorption spectra.

The spectrum of a substituted azobenzene, 4-dimethylaminophenyl-azobenzene, is shown in Fig. 38. Compared to the azobenzene spectrum, it absorbs at a longer wavelength owing to the increase in the length of the resonant system and polarity of the molecule.

The *para*-substituent effect is demonstrated in a study of the dye phenylazo-*p*-cresol. An increase in the size of the substituent in the para position causes a small bathochromic effect and a change in the relative intensity of the component bands (Fig. 39).

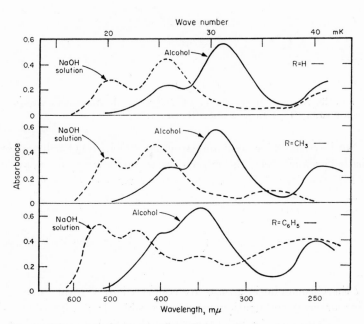

FIG. 39. The *para*-substituent effect. Increase in the size of the *para* substituent causes an increase in the relative intensity of the long-wavelength component of double-component absorption bands.

9.2. DISAZO DYES

A systematic study of dyes produces information on the combination, configuration, and interaction of chromophoric groups. In Fig. 40 there are a number of spectral curves for some disazo dyes. The lower curve represents the individual azo dye; the top curve represents an entirely different compound which can be considered as two molecules of the azo dye linked by an ethenylene linkage (—CH=CH—). This group provides a conjugating linkage; that is, it transmits the resonating effect, and

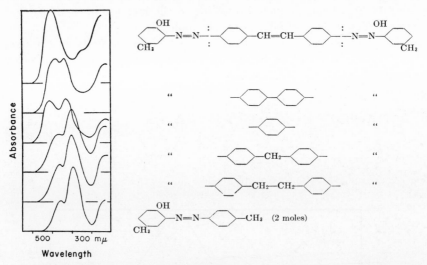

FIG. 40. Absorption spectra of disazo dyes indicating a varying degree of conjugation (top) to separation (bottom).

hence we have a larger resonant structure which shows a hyperchromic and bathochromic effect. In between these two extreme curves are examples where the linkage between the two azo parts of the molecule varies in terms of its ability to serve as a conjugating structure. The ethylene linkage (—CH₂—CH₂—) is a better insulator than the methylene (—CH₂—), and the phenylene $\left(-\bigcirc-\right)$ does not transmit as well as the $-\bigcirc-\bigcirc-$ group.

If the chromophoric groups are connected by certain linkages, conjugation or cross-conjugation may be possible. It is also of equal importance to consider the influence of one chromophore on another where there is no conjugated linkage. Chromophoric groups with strong ionic attraction forces should either attract or repel other strongly ionic groups or chromophores, and such a combination or repulsion may result in enhancement or reduction of chromophoric character. This kind of conjugation is not a complete conjugation because the absorption spectrum is actually a composite of the monoazo and the disazo dye. A truly conjugated linkage such as —CH=CH— between two azo dyes gives a spectrum of an apparently larger resonant group with both of the azo dye components combining to act as a single unit. The spectrum would thus

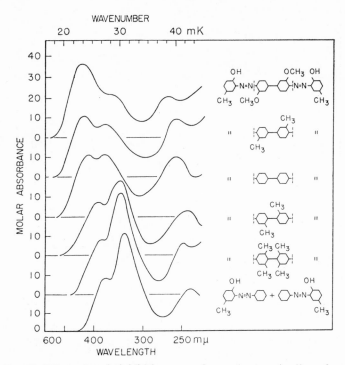

FIG. 41. Effect of steric inhibition on coplanar structure in disazo benzidine dyes.

be changed by both bathochromic and hyperchromic effects. There is one other kind of linkage of chromophores which is not illustrated specifically in the graph and can be termed cumulative or cross-conjugation. A linkage such as a triphenyl between the two azo units would give a situation where there would be competition between the various resonant systems.

We have seen that the diphenyl group serves as an excellent conjugating linkage. The disazo benzidine dyes with various substitutions made on this stilbene linkage illustrate the effect of steric inhibition on the coplanar structure of the disazo benzidine dye. The lowest spectral curve in Fig. 41 is that of the azo dye; the top spectral curve is the disazo benzidine dye with —OCH₃ substituted in 3,3'-positions. This latter substituent tends to stabilize the molecule in a coplanar state.

The substitution of CH₃— instead of —OCH₃ in the 3,3'-position also promotes coplanarity through its electronic effect but is not quite so effective as the —OCH₃. The third curve from the top is typical of the intermediate stage between a stable coplanar configuration (top curve)

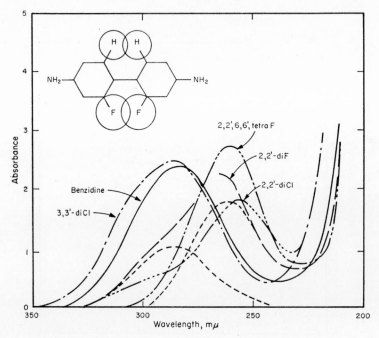

FIG. 42. Absorption spectra of halogenated diphenyl derivatives.

and the separate azo dye. The dye (second curve from bottom) with four methyl groups in the 2,2',6,6'-positions gives an absorption spectrum very similar to the separate azo dye, indicating that these provide almost complete insulation between the two ends of the molecule. The dimethyl-substituted molecule (2,2') provides some insulation, and hence the resultant structure must be composed of both monoazo and disazo components.

Steric effect is a very important factor in the study of the coplanarity of benzidine and its derivatives. If benzidine is fluorinated in the 2,2',6,6'-positions, this is sufficient to put the two phenyl rings out of plane, and the resultant absorption spectrum is very much like that of aniline. 2,2'-Difluorobenzidine exhibits an absorption spectrum intermediate between the coplanar benzidine and the noncoplanar 2,2′,6,6′-tetrafluorobenzidine. This would indicate both coplanar and nonplanar configurations contributing to the resonance structure of 2,2′-difluorobenzidine (Fig. 42).

On irradiation of the disazo benzidine dye which has substituents in the 2,2′,6,6′-positions, *cis* and *trans* modifications are obtained with different absorption spectra and a single sharp isosbestic point. In equilibrium between two forms, these separate characteristic spectra have a

AX$_2$-AXY-AY$_2$

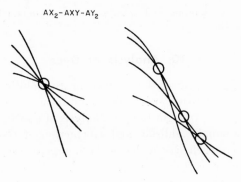

FIG. 43. Portion of absorption spectra of phototropic disazo dyes showing fixed isosbestic point (left) and moving points (right) as produced when the chromophoric centers (X and Y, corresponding to *cis* and *trans* forms) are insulated through the connecting group A (fixed) or conjugated through A (moving). The moving point involves a three-component system.

crossing point which is common to all equilibrium ratios. This point is termed the isosbestic point. When the rings are coplanar, however, the dye acts as a single chromophoric structure.

Then on irradiation there will be three possible compounds: a *trans-trans*, a *cis-cis*, or an intermediate *cis-trans*, each with its characteristic spectrum. In this three-component equilibrium there will be a definite end product with characteristic maxima, but the intermediate product may not be so easily recognized. Unless the spectra are markedly separated there will be an isosbestic line between the points (Fig. 43).

9.3. INDIGO

Indigo should exist in both *cis* and *trans* forms; however, only absorption spectrum of the *trans* form is observed. This indicates that the configuration of indigo is stabilized in the *trans* form by hydrogen bonding (Fig. 44). This same effect is also demonstrated in the acid-thioindigo solutions. The stabilizing effect of the hydrogen bond is destroyed in acetylation of indigo, and both the *cis* and *trans* isomeric forms are obtained, representing the isosbestic points formed by the end products and the intermediate state (Fig. 45).

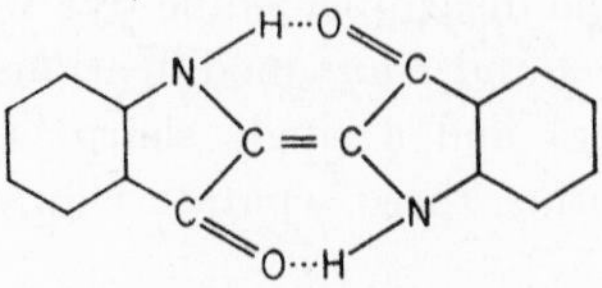

FIG. 44. Indigo, showing hydrogen bonding to maintain *trans* form.

10. Analysis of Dyes

One interesting aspect of the analysis of dye solutions is that not all dyes which may exist together in dilute solution will give a true summation curve. It was first thought that an analysis of a mixture of dyes could be made by the simple addition and subtraction of absorbance values. This requires that each dye molecule be a separate entity in solution. There are, however, certain dyestuffs which, even in these very dilute solutions, tend to react with other molecules of the same dye or different

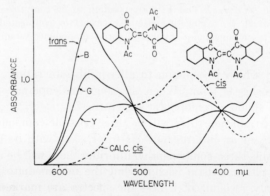

FIG. 45. Phototropic effect of irradiation as shown by absorption spectra of diacetyl indigo. Blue light, *B*; green light, *G*; yellow light, *Y*.

dyes. This association between dyes exists not only between colored dyes but also between a colored and a colorless dye—that is, an optical bleaching agent. Dispersoids such as a polyethylene oxide condensation product can be used to prevent aggregation of dyes.

The dye Chrysophenine G does not by itself exhibit association tendencies in a solution because its spectrum is not substantially changed on the addition of a dispersoid. The spectrum of Sky Blue FF with a dispersoid shifts about 10 mμ toward the red and shows a reduction in absorbance of about 0.5 absorbance unit in a shift from 0.65 to 0.60. A mixture of the two dyes shows marked association; the mixture curve shows a decrease in intensity as compared with the summation curve (Fig. 46).

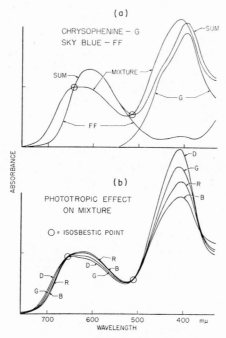

FIG. 46. Chrysophenine G and Sky Blue FF. (a) Sum and mixture curves. (b) Irradiation effect on mixture of the two dyes.

Treatment with heat or solvents (pyridine) causes a change in the absorption curve toward the summation curve with well-characterized isosbestic points. Irradiation of the mixture results in a change in the spectrum and a shift of the red portion of the curve to simulate the summation curve, and a pair of well-characterized isosbestic points are obtained (see Fig. 46). These isosbestic points indicate quite definitely that a specific compound is produced as a result of this association. At first observation one might assume that the change in absorbance in the far red portion of the spectrum as a result of irradiation implies a transfer of energy from the blue to the red portion of the spectrum, but a more reasonable view would seem to be that irradiation of the Chrysophenine G produces an isomeric form which does not associate and whose spectrum adds normally rather than associating and producing an anomalous mixture curve.

Further proof of this separate compound produced by association is found in the addition of an excess of Chrysophenine G to Sky Blue FF. As one adds the yellow dye there is a definite isosbestic point about which the curve appears to rotate to derive the curve of the new complex. After the concentration of Chrysophenine G has reached a certain value, however, the curve no longer follows the isosbestic point but produces an isosbestic line similar to a salting-out process.

The particular effects which are worthy of note are the proof of molecular combination as evidenced by isosbestic points and the polymeric shift in size as evidenced by the lack of an isosbestic point in salt effects and excess addition of one reagent dye. Also only certain dye configurations induce association or dimerization, and certain structures may prevent this association.

We cannot specify the exact association or interaction (although we know it is capable of being dissociated by heat, solvent, or dispersoid), yet it appears to be a reaction of strongly charged resonance structures in an adhesion to each other which is probably closely akin to adhesion to fibers or other isoelectric charged materials. This is just one example of many instances where absorption spectra studies are extremely useful in determining electronic structure, configuration, and properties of a substance.

11. Colorimetry

Colorimetry, as defined earlier in this chapter, is the measurement of color in terms of luminance and chromaticity and is not a method of chemical analysis. Spectrophotometric reflectance data are used, however, to compute color specifications. Color has been defined by the committee on Colorimetry of the Optical Society of America: "Color consists of the characteristics of light other than spatial and temporal inhomogeneities; light being that aspect of radiant energy of which a human observer is aware through the visual sensations which arise from the stimulation of the retina of the eye." The characteristics of light which constitute color are specified in terms of (1) an appropriate photometric quantity (luminance or luminance factor) and (2) appropriate chromaticity numbers (chromaticity coordinates, or dominant wavelength and purity). Colorimetry is a field distinct from chemical absorption spectrophotometry, and instruments and techniques are available for color measurement and specification directly without relying completely on the conversion of spectrophotometric data.

12. Summary

A survey of the fields of spectrophotometry and absorptimetry has been given, with description of the fundamental phenomena, the production of spectra, the nomenclature and terminology, the measurement of spectra, and its applications. This spectrophotometric field of utilizing a physical method for chemical needs, whether it is for analysis or for fundamental chemical research on electronic and molecular configuration, is dynamic with continuing advances. The changes in techniques, the refinements of the instruments, and the mechanization of the methods increase the potential of absorption spectra studies in the applied and the research laboratory. The characterization of a substance currently often includes a description of its absorption spectra. Many of the scientific journals, such as *Analytical Chemistry, Journal of the American Chemical Society, Journal of Chemical Physics, Journal of the Chemical Society (London), British Bulletin of Spectroscopy, Photoelectric Spectrometry Group Bulletin, Comptes Rendus, Optik y Spektroskopie,* contain consistently a number of absorption spectra studies. The enormous number of spectral curves available today has initiated activity to produce the same sort of punched card system for the ultraviolet region that is now in progress for the infrared field.

References

No attempt has been made to cite specific references to research publications. For additional information in this field, the following texts are recommended as well as the catalogs and publications of the manufacturers of the equipment used in this type of work.

Biffen, F. M., and Seaman, W., "Modern Instruments in Chemical Analysis." McGraw-Hill, New York, 1956.

Boltz, David F. (ed.), "Selected Topics in Modern Instrumental Analysis." Prentice-Hall, New York, 1952.

Braude, E. A., and Nachod, F. C., "Determination of Organic Structures by Physical Methods." Academic Press, New York, 1955.

Brode, W. R., "Chemical Spectroscopy," 2nd ed. Wiley, New York, 1943.

Brode, W. R., *in* "Advances in Enzymology" (F. F. Nord and C. H. Werkman, eds.), Vol. IV. Interscience, New York, 1944.

Brode, W. R., *in* "Major Instruments of Science and Their Applications to Chemistry" (R. E. Burk and Oliver Grummitt, eds.). Interscience, New York, 1945.

Charlot, G., and Gauguin, R., "Dosages Colorimétriques. Principes et Methodes." Masson, Paris, 1952.

Delahay, Paul, "Instrumental Analysis." Macmillan, New York, 1957.

Gibb, T. R. P., Jr., "Optical Methods of Chemical Analysis." McGraw-Hill, New York, 1942.

Gillam, A. E., and Stern, E. S., "An Introduction to Electronic Absorption Spectroscopy." Edward Arnold, London, 1954.

Hardy, A. C., "Handbook of Colorimetry." Technology Press, Cambridge, Massachusetts, 1936.

Harley, John H., and Wiberley, Stephen E., "Instrumental Analysis." Wiley, New York, 1954.

Harrison, G. R., Lord, R. C., and Loofbourow, J. R., "Practical Spectroscopy." Prentice-Hall, New York, 1948.

Heilmeyer, L., "Spectrophotometry in Medicine." Adam Hilger, London, 1942.

Hershenson, H. M., "Ultraviolet and Visible Absorption Spectra: Index for 1930-1954." Academic Press, New York, 1956.

Judd, D. B., "Color in Business, Science and Industry." Wiley, New York, 1952.

Kilching, H., "Klinische Photometrie." Stuttgart, Wissenschaftliche Verlagsgesellschaft, 1951.

Kortum, G., "Kolorimetrie, Photometrie und Spektrometrie," Vol. II. Springer, Berlin, 1955.

Lange, P. W., "Kolorimetrische Analyse." Weinheim, Verlag Chem., 1952.

Lothian, G. F., "Absorption Spectrophotometry," 2nd ed. Macmillan, New York, 1958.

Meyer, F. X., and Luszczak, "Absorptions-Spektralanalyse." de Gruyter, Berlin, 1951.

Mehl, J. W., "Manual of Clinical Procedures for Beckman Spectrophotometers, Models B and DU." Beckman Instruments, South Pasadena, California, 1953.

Mellon, M. G. (ed.), "Analytical Absorption Spectroscopy." Wiley, New York, 1950.

Mellon, M. G., "Colorimetry for Chemists." G. Frederick Smith Chemical Co., Columbus, Ohio, 1945.

Miller, E. S., "Quantitative Biological Spectroscopy," Vol. 1. Burgess, Minneapolis, Minnesota, 1940.

Morton, R. A., "The Application of Absorption Spectra to the Study of Vitamines, Hormones and Co-enzymes," 2nd ed. Adam Hilger, London, 1942.

"Munsell Book of Color." Munsell Color Co., Baltimore, Maryland, 1939.

Optical Society of America, Committee on Colorimetry, "The Science of Color." Crowell, New York, 1953.

Sandell, E. B., "Colorimetric Determination of Traces of Metals." 3rd Edition Interscience, New York, 1959.

West, W. E., "Technique of Organic Chemistry," Vol. IX, Chemical Applications of Spectroscopy. Interscience, New York, 1956.

MANUFACTURERS

(See also catalogs of general laboratory supply houses)

American Optical Co., Buffalo, New York.
Applied Physics Corporation, Pasadena, California.
Bausch & Lomb Optical Co., Rochester, New York.
Beckman Instruments, Inc., Fullerton, California.
Corning Glass Works, Corning, New York.
Eastman Kodak Company, Rochester, New York.
General Electric Co., Schenectady, New York.
Hilger & Watts Ltd., London, England.
Perkin-Elmer Corporation, Norwalk, Connecticut.
Unicam Instruments, Ltd., Cambridge, England.
Carl Zeiss, Oberkochen, Wurtt, Germany.

Emission Spectrography*

J. SHERMAN

Philadelphia Naval Shipyard, Philadelphia, Pennsylvania

1. Introduction

The discussion in this section will be devoted to the problem of obtaining qualitative and quantitative chemical analyses of materials by means of their emission spectra. The spectra are excited in air, and the region usually considered is contained between 2000 and 4000 A.

At present there is no precise rational physical basis for "spectrographic" procedures in the sense that, given a material of a certain

---

* The opinions expressed in this chapter are those of the author, not of the Navy Department.

composition and a mode of exciting, dispersing, and recording the spectra, it is not possible to compute, even approximately, the relative intensities of the emitted spectra associated with the elements present in the specimen.

Accordingly, there are two interesting problems in the field of spectrographic analysis: (1) an investigation of the physical bases for the relation between intensities of emission spectra and composition, and (2) an application of the spectra to chemical analysis, under close empirical control, deriving whatever advantages this method has over others. We shall be mainly concerned with the latter problem.

In general it is a simple matter to make a few chemical analyses by spectrographic means when no great demands are laid on speed or precision. After the purely mechanical process of preparing a spectrographic plate has been learned, the analysis is merely a matter of the evaluation of the relative blackness of some appropriate lines in the spectrum of the material to be analyzed compared to the corresponding lines in the spectrum of a standard, i.e., a specimen similar in general composition to that under consideration but one whose analysis is known. The process is about as involved as the simpler of the more empirical colorimetric comparisons. When, however, it is required that the samples be analyzed for many elements, say five to ten, with a precision and accuracy at least as reliable as those of other procedures, the wet chemical ones in particular, in a total elapsed time of the order of several minutes per sample, and with a work load per man day from ten to twenty or more times that permitted in any wet chemical laboratory, then the problem of the control of spectrographic procedures is lifted from the trivial to the domain of the difficult.

The use of spectrographic methods for routine chemical analyses is especially advantageous when it is necessary to consider speed or volume of work, or when only a small amount of sample is available, or when the more conventional wet chemical methods are particularly difficult or involved, a condition usually resulting whenever extensive separations are necessary. As far as the commercial aspects of these problems go, they may all be condensed into the matter of speed. It is this factor, more than anything else, that has led to such a phenomenal increase in the number of spectrographic laboratories during the last few years. Hence, particular attention will be paid to the organization and function of a laboratory engaged in the routine quantitative analysis of large numbers of samples divisible into relatively few classes or types where time and precision requirements are to be met at a low cost per analysis rather than at a low initial cost of equipment.

The following discussions may properly be divided into the following parts:

1. The spectrographic laboratory.
2. Equipment and instrumentation.
   (a) External to the arc and exercising no influence on it.
   (b) Directly connected to the arc.
3. Procedures.

For reference to historical and some current practices the reader should consult (2, 19a, and 27).

2. The Spectrographic Laboratory

2.1. COMPARISON OF SPECTROGRAPHIC AND CHEMICAL PROCEDURES

The function of the spectrographic laboratory to be considered is, as was stated in the Introduction, to furnish quantitative chemical analyses of materials (metals). The analyses are of a special ultimate nature in that they are concerned only with estimates of the concentrations of the metallic elements in the specimen. This restriction is due to the nature of emission spectra produced by the usual arc or spark in air and should be assumed to be part of the conditions of the general spectrographic procedure.

Spectrographic procedure	*Chemical (gravimetric) procedure*
1. Similarities	
(a) Arc phenomena	(a) Chemical reaction
(b) Spectrograph (dispersion and resolution)	(b) Chemical separation
(c) Photographic processing	(c) Preparation of precipitates
(d) Densitometer (measurement of radiant energy)	(d) Balance (measurement of weight or mass)
(e) Analysis (plate calibration and analytical curve)	(e) Stoichiometrical relations (gravimetric factors)
2. Differences	
(a) Common method for all analyses with only minor variations	(a) Multiple methods with no apparent connection between them
(b)	(b) Distinction between difficult and easy method
(c)	(c) Essential difficulty of separations
(d)	(d) Contamination due to reagents
(e) Complex and specialized instrumentation	(e) Simple instrumentation
3. Scientific basis	
(a) Empirical	(a) Rationalized

A spectrographic laboratory is thus similar to an analytical chemical laboratory in function and results. The differences are only those of the methods involved. Much has been written on the rather obvious differences between the spectrographic and the classical or wet chemical methods of analysis, but it is instructive to consider the similarities as well. A general comparison from the point of view of a chemical analyst is presented in the table.

In a certain sense the spectrographic procedure is physically more fundamental in that colligative properties of the radiant gas in the arc (i.e., of the sample) are used.

The chemical analyst will appreciate the simplicity of the spectrographic procedure in that it involves one reaction with a uniform separation procedure and treatment of reaction products. The equation of the "spectrographic reaction," the equilibrium constants, and anything resembling rational stoichiometrical relations are almost completely unknown, however. Hence arises the necessity of the strict empirical control of arc conditions. It is reasonable to suppose that this control is, at least in part, haphazard in that essential factors may be overlooked because they are unknown while considerable attention may be paid to minor or trivial conditions. Only a successful theoretical solution of arc or spark mechanism under normal excitation conditions will place spectrographic procedures on a rational basis. All operations or instruments not directly connected with the arc, such as the spectrograph, plate processing, and the densitometer, may be considered as purely mechanical devices, and improvement in their uniformity of response presents only the usual instrumental difficulties. The empirical control of spectrographic procedures has reached a point, however, where the resultant analyses may be considered at least as precise or accurate as those obtained by good routine wet chemical methods. And, because of the inherent great advantages, spectrographic procedures, in common with other physical methods, are rapidly replacing older chemical methods of analysis wherever applicable in industry.

2.2. Economics

Probably the most important factor in the accelerated development and expansion of spectrographic laboratories is the economic one, considering the saving in elapsed time to complete an analysis as well as the cost. A comparison between chemical and spectrographic methods as observed in one laboratory is given in tabular form. This table does not quite evaluate the actual gain in using spectrographic procedures, since most of the difficult and time-consuming chemical determinations such as Sn or Pb in stainless steel, Ag in storage battery lead, Cd in pure

Metal Analyses
(Fe, Al, Mg, Pb, Zn, Cu alloys)

Period (26 weeks)	I		II	
	Spectro-graphic	Chemical	Spectro-graphic	Chemical
Ratio, steel to total	38%		44%	
Samples per week	650		1510	
Determinations per sample	9		9	
Men per day	3.5	7.8	10	38
Determination per man day	284	14	238	25
Elapsed time per sample (in days)	1.25	3	1	3

zinc, or As in ingot copper are considered only in the spectrographic columns.

Since the usual spectrographic procedures involve no chemical separation and exhibit no distinction between chemically difficult or easy analyses, occasions may arise where the difficulties of chemical procedures may become the deciding factors for the use of spectrographic methods. For example, Scribner and Mullin (23) describe a method for the estimation of thirty-three elements in uranium base material at concentrations as low as a fraction of a part per million. The difficulty and time requirements of the complex chemical methods make them impractical procedures for any sort of urgent routine methods. Spectrographic methods are practically the only solution to the control of such material.

Generally speaking, a work load of twenty samples with five determinations per sample to be completed in one day should be considered a sufficient minimum to warrant a spectrographic installation. The saving is estimated to be three men per day.

Current prices are at a high level, but in any recent market the cost of primary spectrographic equipment, i.e., spectrograph, excitation sources, microphotometer, pellet press, darkroom accessories, etc., could easily amount to over $50,000, depending on quality and power. The equipment for available direct reading units may cost well over $50,000, exclusive of installation.

2.3. INSTRUMENTS AND PROCEDURE

The analytical routine or flow sheet for the quantitative analysis of metals may be analyzed as follows:

A. Material (Sample) Preparation
  1. Preparation of samples into selected electrode forms by grinding, machining, use of pellet press, etc.

B. Spectrography
   2. Excitation—arc or spark source
   3. Spectrograph
   4. Photographic processing
C. Analysis
   5. Densitometer: measurement of optical density of selected lines
   6. Plate calibration: conversion of density measurements into estimates of intensity
   7. Analysis: interpretation of intensity estimates in terms of chemical analyses

The analytical procedure to be discussed is known as the internal standard method. The routine is as follows:

1. A specimen, assumed to be representative of the material to be analyzed, is prepared in the selected electrode form. This may be either (1) two rods, each about $\frac{1}{4}$ inch in diameter and 2 inches long, (2) a flat surface about 1 inch square, or (3) briquetted chips, each briquette about $\frac{1}{4}$ inch in diameter and $\frac{1}{4}$ inch long. The dimensions are indicative, not restrictive. The top of the rods may be made flat or slightly conical (included angles about 150°). One prominent laboratory prefers to grind a spherical top on the rods. A counter electrode is to be used with flat plane specimens the material of which may be either the matrix element (iron for steel analysis, copper for brass, etc.) or graphite.

2. The specimen is then placed in a suitable clamp or holder and made the electrode of a selected arc or spark excitation. The excitation source may be a high- or low-voltage d.c. arc, a high-voltage a.c. arc, or a high-voltage condensed spark which may be controlled by a synchronous interrupter or a series spark with an air blast. The spark circuits are usually equipped with adjustable resistance, inductance, and capacitance elements. The arc time may be automatically or manually controlled.

3. The radiation from the arc is passed through a spectrograph, and a selected portion of the spectrum, usually in the range of 2300 to 3500 A., is recorded on a photographic plate with selected emulsion response characteristics.

4. The plate is developed and processed under controlled conditions.

5. The densities of a selected pair of lines, one of the matrix and one of the element sought, are measured.

6. The densities are converted to log I (i.e., log intensity) by using a prepared plate calibration.

7. The analysis is completed by using an analytical curve, i.e., a curve which correlates delta log I, i.e., [log I (element line) − log I (matrix line)] and concentration of the element, usually expressed in terms of log per cent. This curve in delta log I × log per cent coordinates

is usually a straight line always with positive slope. It is prepared by applying the analytical procedure to previously analyzed specimens.

It can be seen that the greatest economy will be effected by uniformity of procedure in (1) sample preparation, (2) excitation conditions, including single exposure, and (3) plate processing, since various specialized fixture and adapters can be prepared. It is suggested in this connection that the reader consider the daily output, arbitrarily chosen to be sixty samples, as the unit rather than the individual analyses. Average time estimates for steel analysis, using rods, are as listed (per sample), with an over-all efficiency of about 75%. Thus a second exposure

1. Sample preparation	1 minute
2. Exposure	$\frac{1}{2}$ to 1 minute
3. Plate processing	10 minutes per plate
4. Densitometer	20 seconds per line
5. Computation	$\frac{1}{2}$ minute per element

per sample means about 1 hour per day for the spectrograph alone. It is a simple arithmetrical procedure to evaluate different procedures from this point of view but nevertheless an important one, particularly under heavier work loads.

2.4. ORGANIZATION OF A LABORATORY

Particular care should be taken to arrange a spectrographic laboratory so that there is minimum friction or obstruction in the usually heavy traffic of samples. It is difficult to suggest specific floor plans, owing to the diversity of equipment, and also because a laboratory is usually built into a space rather than the other way round.

In general, there are two types of industrial laboratories—(1) producers and (2) consumers. A laboratory in a producer industrial plant is usually concerned with the rapid analysis of each sample as it is received, since the samples may represent heats still in the furnace. Some of the larger laboratories in steel plants are equipped with pneumatic tube systems directly to the furnaces. These systems may well cost more than the laboratory. A laboratory associated with a consumer industrial plant is usually part of an inspection system. There is less pressure for the analysis of a single sample, the emphasis being rather on the daily output.

A large central inspection laboratory will have many details to consider. It may well happen that the clerical and stenographic work involved in the recording, numbering, and assorting of incoming samples and the checking and preparation of outgoing reports will take more

effort in man-hours or time than the actual analyses unless special carefully prepared systems are used.

The director of a laboratory should be aware of the necessity of
maintaining an organization to ensure the proper performance of the
various operations of sample preparation, exposure, darkroom procedure,
readings on the densitometer, checking of analyses with specifications,
determining the need of check analyses, reporting analyses, etc. One of
the most important functions is that of instrument and equipment maintenance. A fixed procedure should be established to locate and adjust
any source of trouble at the first sign of malfunction. The writer has
found the highest efficiency, measured by work output, to result from a
sharp delineation of function. Thus, the individual operating the excitation source should have the samples brought to him, or her, properly arranged and with indications of the procedure to be used. After excitation
the samples should be removed from time to time. Similar concentration
of effort is applied to the preparation of samples, reading of spectra, etc.
The investigative and production aspects of a laboratory should be kept
distinct and if possible be made the work of different individuals.

3. Spectrographs and Densitometers

The spectrograph and densitometer, or microphotometer, are as a
rule commercially procured instruments.* They are not directly associated
with the arc. Hence, after certain criteria of satisfactory performance
are satisfied, further refinements are apt to be vacuous in so far as improvement in precision and the speed of routine analyses are concerned.
Spectrographs and densitometers are expensive, and manufacturers attempt to make them as versatile and flexible as possible. The selection of
proper instrumentation for any given laboratory is then not so much a

---

Note: Descriptions of commercially available equipment are valid only as of
the time of writing. There is a high rate of change, almost always in the direction of
improvement, in equipment provided by an instrument maker and in addition equipment is offered by more manufacturers. At present the changes can be seen from
year to year. For example, the Bausch and Lomb medium prism spectrograph has
been discontinued and their large spectrograph is offered in a prism-grating combination with a continuous wave length selection. The two-lens Wadsworth mounting
spectrograph supplied by the Gaertner Scientific Corporation is apparently not
available any more. As for direct reading spectrographs, not only are the number of
suppliers increasing, including those from foreign sources, particularly from Germany
and Italy, but the domestic suppliers change and improve their instruments almost
from month to month. Under these circumstances, the descriptions in the text are
to be considered only as illustrative. Certainly, anyone contemplating the acquisition
of a spectrographic system should investigate the equipment available at the present
time, and for good measure, those instruments planned for the near future.

problem of evaluating the quality of an optical instrument as one of choosing equipment with the most appropriate mechanical or optical features for the specific purpose intended. Specialization is incompatible with versatility, and the proper compromise between them is a matter of judgment with no readily applicable hard and fast rules.

The spectrograph and densitometer are quite independent of each other except for two items: (1) the use of a common photographic element, i.e., glass plates of a certain size or 35-mm. or cut film, and (2) slit or line width on the plate, for some densitometers require wider lines than others.

Frequent use will be made of the terms complex and simple spectra by which are meant spectra with many or few lines per unit length of plate. Steel, particularly stainless or high-speed tool steel (containing high amounts of W, V, Cr, Mo, or Ni) will exemplify complex spectra; aluminum alloys will represent simple spectra; and copper alloys such as manganese bronze will be considered an intermediate class. Thus the phrase "a spectrograph suitable for steel analysis" does not indicate a qualitative connotation peculiar to steel but rather a spectrograph capable of resolving and dispersing the steel spectrum well enough to be used for analysis.

3.1. Spectrographs

3.1.1. General Characteristics. A spectrograph is a complex optical instrument with many possible essential variations in design and construction. The reader interested in the various optical details and theories should consult the references, particularly ref. (22). As far as the industrial laboratory is concerned the spectrograph is a packaged instrument and a satisfactory spectrograph is one that adequately fulfills the following requirements: (1) optical: speed, linear dispersion, and resolving power; and (2) mechanical: minimum simple and reproducible adjustments.

Essential optical properties such as sharp focus and low level of scattered light and mechanical properties such as rigidity and sturdiness may be considered as satisfactory in any of the better commercial instruments. The major portion of metallurgical analyses is based on the use of lines in the region 2500 to 3300 A. with practically all work confined to the region 2300 to 3500 A. Hence the consideration of the characteristics of the spectrum will be limited to that region. All optical transmission elements must necessarily be quartz. Although there is no necessary optical connection between linear dispersion on the plate (angstroms per millimeter), resolving power (minimum difference in wavelength distinguishable between two lines, usually expressed as $\lambda/\Delta\lambda$), and optical speed, the three factors may be considered mutually dependent in the comparison of available commercial instruments, i.e., a higher linear dispersion (fewer angstroms per millimeter) is to be associated with higher resolving power on the plate (separation of two lines closer together in wavelength) and lower optical speed (longer exposure to obtain a given density).

Steel analysis requires a dispersion of about 3.5 to 4. A./mm. or about 14 inches for the region 2300 to 3500 A. Since the usual spectrograph uses 10-inch plates, multiple exposures on one sample may be involved, and the mechanical manner in which different portions of the spectrum are adjusted should be considered. Analyses involving simple spectra such as aluminum or magnesium alloys should be performed on spectrographs that record the entire usable spectrum on one 10-inch plate. The higher optical speeds of the lower dispersion spectrographs reduces exposures to the neighborhood of 10 seconds. Not merely is there a saving of time, but the uncontrollable chemical changes in the electrodes due to the heat of the arc are not so great.

The commercially available spectrographs may be classified according to: (1) type of dispersing element (prism or grating), (2) high or medium dispersion, and (3) optical arrangement or mounting. The type of mounting is of minor functional importance and is reflected in the size of the spectrograph. Although laboratory space is an important factor, it is a static one, similar to consideration of the cost, in the sense that no compromise or improvement is possible. If the space or money is not available it is useless to discuss a choice based on quality or efficiency of performance.

Available spectrographs of high and medium dispersion are:

A. Prism
   1. Littrow (high) and Babinet-Bunsen (medium) mounting supplied by Bausch & Lomb Optical Co., Rochester, New York; Adam Hilger, Ltd., London, England
   2. Two-lens modified Wadsworth mounting supplied by Gaertner Scientific Corp., Chicago, Illinois
B. Grating
   3. Eagle mounting (3 meter and 2 meter) supplied by Baird Associates, Cambridge, Massachusetts
   4. Paschen-Runge mounting (first and second orders) supplied by Applied Research Laboratories, Glendale, California
   5. Wadsworth mounting (21 feet 10 inches and 480 cm.) supplied by Jarrell-Ash Co., Boston, Massachusetts

Prism spectrographs produce single stigmatic spectra with curved lines and nonuniform dispersion. Absorption by the quartz combines with the nonsensitivity of the photographic emulsion to result in a much lower sensitivity or transmission of light at wavelengths lower than 2400 A. The curvature of the lines (22) produces lines approximately parabolic in shape with the horns toward the shorter wavelength. Although this effect is not particularly disturbing on the larger spectrographs when short lines are used, the curvature will be troublesome if longer lines, particularly the narrower ones, are employed in an effort to increase the precision or accuracy of density measurements by using a larger area of plate, since the densitometer slits are straight. The nonuniform dispersion may be considered annoying in extended qualitative analysis, since the determination of wavelength becomes a more involved and local procedure. The differences in dispersion over the extended spectrum are greater with the smaller instruments, but even in the large Littrow the dispersion at 2300 A. is 1.75 A./mm., whereas at 3300 A. it is 5.65 A./mm. It is true that routine analyses use the same lines, whose positions and patterns are quickly learned, but the crowding of the lines at the longer wavelengths may and usually does result in an inefficient use of the spectrum, in that the criterion of sufficient dispersion is necessarily that of the longest wavelength region necessitated. This results in too much space being taken up by the shorter wavelength portion of the spectrum and hence may necessitate multiple exposures, if 10-inch plates are used. The spectra are stigmatic, and therefore mechanical exposure modifiers such as sector disks may be used at any setting between the slit and source. Prism spectrographs in general are sturdy optical instruments and require almost no maintenance of optical parts.

Grating spectrographs produce multiple spectra (different orders) with straight lines and practically uniform dispersion in any order. The lines are astigmatic, except for the Wadsworth mount, and hence step section disks must be appropriately placed (at the vertical focus). Lines of overlapping multiple orders may sometimes introduce difficulties in qualitative analysis, but the position and pattern of frequently used lines, as in routine quantitative analysis, is soon learned. The astigmatism of the lines helps to make the lines uniform throughout their length, even though there is a loss of intensity due to the fact that a line is lengthened. This loss of intensity may be disregarded as of only minor importance. The uniform dispersion is conducive to an efficient use of plate space. The focal curvature of small instruments becomes too great for the use of photographic plates of normal thickness, and X-thin plates or film are needed. Differences in line contour, i.e., density of a line as a function of linear distance across the line width, between prism and grating spectra may be disregarded as nonsignificant. Ghosts may be disregarded as nonsignificant disturbances in the use of lines for routine quantitative analysis. Many gratings show a marked loss of intensity of lines lower than 2400 A. in the first order. Commercial spectrographs of comparable average dispersion in the range 2300 to 3500 A. have comparable optical speed, and differences are usually nonsignificant. The grating instruments in effect "open" the longer wavelength portions of the spectrum, and more widespread use of these instruments may result in greater flexibility in choice of lines for metallurgical analysis. There is a marked difference in the effect of prism and grating spectrographs on plate contrast; this will be treated in the discussion on plate calibration.

In general it is more satisfactory to choose spectra with the minimum dispersion that will separate the necessary lines, since this will increase optical speed and hence decrease the necessary exposure time. After the dispersion has been decreased to the level where the entire usable spectrum is contained within one plate, however, further reduction may be nonsignificant.

There is an optical difference between the Littrow and Eagle mountings and the others in that the light practically retraces its path in the former arrangements as opposed to the "through" path in the others. Accordingly greater care must be taken by the manufacturers of the Littrow and Eagle arrangements to minimize the fogging of the plates by scattered light. The disturbance due to this effect may be considered sometimes significant.

3.1.2. Commercial Instruments. (a) The large Littrow spectrographs have ample dispersion and resolving power for the analysis of all but a few elements in unusual amounts, for example, traces of zinc in steel (including stainless and high-speed tool steel). The spectrum from 2300 to 3500 A. is about 14 inches long. Since the instruments are equipped for 10-inch plates, multiple exposures may be necessary. The focus adjustments are subject to seasonal variations. The Bausch & Lomb* instrument is provided with ten discontinuous spectrum region positions, whereas the Hilger has a continuous change mechanism. Certain automatic features may be added by the user, such as a motor-driven plate-racking device and an air or hydraulic piston, electrically controlled, to effect a rapid change from one spectrum region to another. It is advisable to obtain spectrographs using the full aperture of the prism or lenses, with no opaque stop in the middle section to minimize scattered light. The obliquity of the cassette to the optic axis to ensure good focus and the angle of the collimator lens to minimize scattered light are problems for the manufacturer, not the user of spectrographs.

The medium quartz spectrograph is readily suitable for aluminum and magnesium alloys. Although the longer wavelength portion of the

---

* See note to p. 256.

spectrum is quite crowded, most, if not all, of the necessary lines are in the lower wavelength portion. Ten-inch plates are used.

(b) The large two-lens modified Wadsworth mounting prism spectrographs have a somewhat lower dispersion than the other comparable Littrow prism instruments. The large and intermediate sizes are equipped to use plates 14 inches long, with adapters in the cassettes for 10-inch plates. The large instrument will record 2200 to 3400 A. on a single 14-inch plate. The changes in wavelength region are continuously controlled by one adjustment, similar to the Hilger Littrow. The intermediate size will record 2100 to 3500 A. on a 10-inch plate and has thus a 40% greater dispersion than the usual medium-size quartz spectrograph with the spectrum still contained on one plate.

(c) The Eagle mounting is similar in principle to the Littrow prism mounting in its optical arrangement. It is the most compact arrangement. The 3-meter size has a dispersion of 5.6 A./mm. in the first order. The second order, 2.8 A./mm. is an open spectrum practically for all steels but will only record 700 A. on the 10-inch plate for which the instrument is designed. Three adjustments, controlled by electric switches, are necessary to change from one wavelength region to another. These adjustments cannot be made quickly. The focus adjustments appear to be independent of seasonal temperature variations. The 2-meter size has a dispersion of 8 A./mm. in the first order. The second order will cover about 1000 A. per 10-inch plate, and hence multiple exposures may be necessary. The dispersion in the second order, 4 A./mm. is sufficient to analyze all but the most complex steels. The curvature is too great, however, to allow ordinary glass plates to be used. Extra-thin glass or film is necessary, with consequent microphotometer difficulty.

(d) The Paschen-Runge mounting instruments have a dispersion of about 7 A./mm. in the first order. The radius of curvature is about 150 cm. It is not practical to arrange for ready mechanical means to select spectrum ranges, but multiple ports, each with its own slit and optical bench, may be provided. The usual range in the older type of instrument is 2380 to 4600 A. It is understood that a new version of this instrument with a 2-meter radius and with a port arranged to produce spectra in the second order is in construction. On account of the high curvature, this instrument is equipped for 35-mm. film. The newer model is planned to have a provision for variable lengths of film up to its full capacity.

(e) The Wadsworth mounting produces stigmatic spectra. The 22-foot model, with a 15,000-line-per-inch grating, has a dispersion of 5.0 A./mm. It differs in its cassette arrangement in that two plates, each 10 inches long and placed side by side, may be exposed simultaneously.

The entire usable spectrum in the second order may then be obtained in one exposure. Various portions of the spectrum may be exposed on a single 10-inch plate by moving the cassette along the back of the spectrograph. The slit and cassette are at opposite ends of the spectrograph, a construction that should facilitate the arrangement whereby the cassette is loaded directly in the darkroom. The intermediate size, with a dispersion of 7 A./mm. in the first order, requires film or extra-thin plates.

Recent developments have been in the direction of improving instrumentation and techniques rather than investigations into the fundamentals of the spectrographic process. The changes in spectrographs have been in greatly improved speed and resolution and in the introduction of combination (interchangeable) prism and grating elements. The changes may be outlined as follows:

The Jaco-Ebert Plane Spectrograph. A special feature of this spectrograph is the order sorter, a low-dispersion, direct-vision, achromatic illuminator mounted on the accessory bar with its lens against the slits in place of the usual quartz condensing lens. The order sorter arranges the orders one above the other so that they are recorded simultaneously on the same plate. This ordered series shows normal spectra at a high magnification, making the lines in a complex spectrum even easier to identify than those in a spectrum of normal dispersion.

The Bausch & Lomb Echelle Spectrograph. This combination of two dispersing elements was devised by G. R. Harrison. Radiation, collimated by the objective, is first dispersed in the plane of the optical axis by a 30° prism and then falls on the echelle which reflects it back through the prism after dispersing it in a plane perpendicular to that of the optical axis. The two dispersing elements are mounted so that the vertical dispersion of the echelle is superimposed on the horizontal dispersion of the prism. The latter serves now solely to separate the "free spectral ranges," the echelle providing the high dispersion and resolution characteristic of the combination. The "free spectral range" referred to is defined as the spectrum interval between successive orders of a given wavelength. If the prism were not used in the echelle spectrograph, the vertical (echelle) dispersion would persist. There would be no horizontal spread, however, and the multiple echelle orders (several hundred in the visible region above) would be piled one on top of the other in confusion. The echelle-prism combination is necessary to eliminate this confusion, and the resultant spectrum is a two-dimensional echellogram.

The high revolving power of the echelle (100,000 to 300,000) makes it possible to study hyperfine structure. Similarly in the new and expanding field of isotope analysis the echelle is an extremely useful tool. In this field it is well known that for certain lines of many elements isotope shifts of 0.05 A. or more are seen for the hyperfine structure components for the different isotopes.

The *spectral range* has also been extended. A commercial vacuum instrument (Applied Research Laboratory) is now available which will enable the spectrum to be extended into the deep ultraviolet.

3.1.3. The Illuminating System. The illuminating system to be discussed here is that part which is external to the spectrograph, i.e., the parts between the slit and source.

The slit usually provided by the manufacturer is of the adjustable bilateral type. Although this is a flexible device, current versions are too unstable and not reproducible enough for precise routine use. The slit is an important element in the control in the over-all optical density of the spectrum (see ref. 22). At narrower widths the density increases as the logarithm of the width until a certain critical value, and then the line merely becomes broader with increasing slit width. It is advisable, for stable routine operation, to use a slit width above the critical point when small changes in slit width will not materially influence the density of the lines if the dispersion or focal properties of the spectrograph will permit that width. Consequently, the use of fixed slits, of varying width if necessary, is recommended. Appropriate fixtures are to be provided so that the slits may be readily interchanged. Usable slit widths, most likely not the optimum, for the various spectrographs are as follows: medium quartz spectrograph, 25 to 30 μ; Littrow spectrograph, 25 to 35 μ (wider slits will destroy line quality); Paschen-Runge mounting (150 cm.), 60 μ; and Eagle mounting (3 meter), 40 to 100 μ. It is to be observed that wider slit widths may be used on grating spectrographs. The significance of wider lines will be discussed under densitometers.

The most stable illumination is obtained by focusing the image of the arc on the grating or on the collimating lens by means of a weak quartz lens mounted immediately adjacent to the slit and external to it, i.e., the coherent mode. Experience has shown that external condensing lenses, or right-angle reflecting prisms, are sources of instability. The spectrum line is a diffraction rather than a geometrical image of the slit; a theoretical discussion of illumination may become quite involved, and complete agreement has not been reached (22). Intensification or diminution of intensity of radiation can be effected in a stable and reproducible manner by moving the source closer to or farther away from the slit. This change may be effected without altering exposure conditions or reaction at the arc and is equivalent to the use of a condensing lens. The slit cover lens should be changed to compensate for about every 10 inches of motion.

The usual optical bench supplied by the manufacturer is rarely rigid or stable enough for continued use. It is usually designed to act as repository or holder of many lenses and sectors. A sturdy rigid bench on which the source may be freely moved and stationed in a reproducible manner is a much more desirable arrangement. It may be necessary not to attach the bench directly to the spectrograph but to construct it independently as a rigid piece of apparatus. A scale should be appropriately attached to indicate the position of the arc relative to the slit.

Numerous exposure modifiers other than condensing lens, both optical and mechanical, are available. Some of these are ruled step slits, evaporated step wedges, screens, rotating sectors, step sectors, and log sectors. They all have their place but not in a routine quantitative laboratory. Although the qualitative use of a rotating sector or wedge to attenuate an exposure may not be harmful, the dependence of quantitative results on step ratios or transmission ratios of mechanical or optical devices is not to be considered a stable procedure. A theoretical discussion of the disturbances that may be introduced by the use of optical devices on flat plates before the slit is to be found in ref. (25). Difficulties due to intermittency, reciprocity, and stroboscopic errors introduced by rotating sectors, together with the extreme difficulty of illuminating a long slit uniformly, all combine to make the use of such devices questionable.

There are many kinds of electrode holders, each apparently designed to hold as many different forms of electrodes in as many ways as possible. A more desirable electrode holder for routine use is one which will hold the standard electrode form as firmly in the desired position and with as little contact resistance as possible. The holders should be massive to conduct the head of the arc as rapidly as possible; in certain applications water cooling may become necessary. It is desirable to arrange the mechanical devices around the holders so that the electrodes are practically in proper position when they are in place, for instance, with appropriately designed forceps, with only a minor adjustment using an arc-width gauge or separator. Optical devices for centering and locating electrodes are to be considered too flexible and subject to too much error for routine use. For example, the electrode clamps used by the writer are designed to hold rods from $5/32$ to $9/32$ inch in diameter, and a wider diameter, say $11/32$ inch, will throw the image of the arc off the collimator lens. This is a deliberate feature of the design, since it was found that the high-voltage a.c. arc on the wider electrodes under standard conditions did not yield consistent results.

Any device in as important a position as in the illuminating system should be scrutinized to see not how well it should function but how easily or badly it may introduce unexpected and undesirable deviations or errors.

3.2. DENSITOMETERS

The densitometer or microphotometer is analogous to the balance in the chemical methods of analysis. Although a good densitometer is a necessary condition for precise spectrographic analysis, it certainly is not sufficient. With care in the choice and use of the instrument, the densitometer error may be made a nonsignificant part of the total error.

In its present form the densitometer is a complex optical and electrical instrument designed for rapid and precise determination of the light-absorbing properties of a small area (spectrum line) on a photographic plate or film. The usual functions of light attenuation are defined as follows: Let $I_0 \equiv$ intensity of incident light, and $I \equiv$ intensity of transmitted light. Then optical density $(D) \equiv \log_{10} (I_0/I)$; transparency $(T) \equiv (I/I_0)$; and opacity $(O) \equiv (I_0/I)$.

Subjective instruments—that is, those instruments depending on the eye of the observer to match the line to be measured with a portion of a standard or calibrated gray scale—will not be considered here. The discussion will be limited to those devices in which the light is converted into electrical energy by a phototube or photocell (barrier layer cell) and the electrical output measured by some appropriate means. Although some older and foreign instruments made use of the bolometer or other thermoelectric device, present-day instruments measure the photocurrent either by passing it directly into a sensitive galvanometer and measuring the deflection of the reflected spot on a scale, or by amplifying the current electronically and either measuring it on a microammeter or putting it into a bridge circuit and measuring the unbalance. The details and difficulties involved in the design and construction of suitable densitometers are essentially problems for the instrument makers, and the laboratory should properly be concerned only with the packaged instrument and how well it answers the analytical needs. Perhaps it is a tradition carried over from older types of instruments used in spectroscopic or astronomical research that densitometers should be made with some secondary function, such as a comparator by juxtaposing a mapped reference spectrum, or an interval or wavelength measurer by correlating the motion of the plate or film between lines with some linear scale; but it need hardly be emphasized that the function of a densitometer is to yield precise density measurements with as few adjustments and as rapidly as possible and that other applications are of minor importance.

3.2.1. General Characteristics. The currently available densitometers differ widely in construction and applicability to special purposes. They all have devices to align the slit and the spectrum line, contain rheostat or aperture regulation to control the indicator for maximum light or deflection (I), and provide means for scanning almost the entire plate or film. There are significant differences, however, that concern the analytical laboratory. Some of the more important general characteristics may be listed as follows:

1. Type of photographic element.
   (a) Plates 4×10 inches or smaller.
   (b) 35-mm. film. No instrument is specifically adapted to use cut film. Home-made adapters, unless carefully designed and constructed, are usually not satisfactory.
2. Ease in locating a line.
   (a) A sufficiently large portion of the plate or film should be made easily visible by projection so that the spectrum pattern is apparent.
   (b) The spectrum line being measured should remain in full view during measuring process.
   (c) The spectrum line being measured should be clearly indicated.
   (d) The line is scanned or stationary during the measurement.
3. Fixed focus.
   (a) The plate or film should be in focus when placed into the instrument without visual adjustment from plate to plate.
   (b) The entire plate or film should be in focus without special adjustment.
4. Minimum scattered light.
   (a) The density of a line whose (projected) width is sufficient to cover the densitometer slit should be independent of its width.
   (b) The resolving power of the instrument should be equal to that of the lines on the plate or film.
5. Housing. The instrument should be housed so that it can be operated in a normally lighted room.
6. Disturbance.
   (a) Special precautions are necessary to guard against mechanical vibration.
   (b) Special precautions are necessary to guard against electrical pickup.
7. Slit. The slit should be adjustable in width from 5 to 50 μ and in length from 0.5 to 5.0 mm. in order to average out plate nonuniformity.
8. Speed. It should be possible to measure from 3 to 5 lines per minute over an extended period (2 to 3 hours) without undue fatigue.

9. Range in density. Almost all instruments have a linear response, and the conversion to density units may become only an arithmetic process. The measurements should be precise over a range from 0.05 to 1.25 in density.

10. Precision. The precision should be such that the total error or at least the repetition error or variance should be nonsignificant at the 95% probability level.

11. Maintenance.

   (a) The instrument should not present a significant maintenance problem.

   (b) The instrument should operate on line current or storage batteries.

3.2.2. Commercially Available Densitometers. Complete information about the commercially available densitometers is not available. Statements in manufacturers' catalogs give detailed design or constructional features and are undoubtedly sincere in claims of performance, but objective studies on significant precision or maintenance difficulties, for example, are not to be readily found.

Some characteristics of the commercially available densitometers, arranged in the alphabetical order of the manufacturer's name, as follows:

1. Applied Research Laboratories, Glendale, California. A comparator is incorporated with the densitometer. The 35-mm. film is standard, but modifications may be made for 4×10-inch or 2×10-inch plates. A $\frac{3}{8}$-inch-square portion of the spectrum is projected on the screen at $10\times$ magnification. For measurement of density, the desired line is moved manually to an indicated portion of the screen, and a button is pressed which depresses a shoe containing a slit, 0.012×1.1 mm., over and in contact with the line. A motor scans the line across the slit, and during the measuring operation the spectrum is completely obscured. The photocurrent is electronically amplified and indicated on a microammeter or as a taut suspension galvanometer deflection on the panel or screen. Owing to the mode of construction the line is always in focus, and there is no scattered light. The instrument requires a semidarkened room for best operation. It is necessary to shield against electrical pickup from the spark excitation, for example. The scale is calibrated 0 to 100. Speed requirements are adequate.

2. Baird-Atomics Associates, Cambridge, Mass. The 4×10-inch plates are standard, although smaller plates may be used. Almost the entire area may be used. The light from the source is divided into two trains, both interrupted at 150 c.p.s. but 180° out of phase with each other. The projection train is brought through the spectrum plate and onto the viewing screen. In the measuring train a circular step diaphragm graduated in density steps of 0, 1, 2 is provided for shifting the density range. The measuring element is a logarithmic aperture calibrated in density from 0.0 to 1.0. The photoelectric tube alternately picks up the light transmitted by the two optical paths, and equality is indicated by a "magic eye." The line is not scanned. The speed of reading is considerably less than in the other instruments. A

much wider line must be used on the plate; hence it is doubtful whether plates made on the medium spectrograph could be used.

3. Hilger, Ltd., London, England. The spectrum should be on a glass plate which may be up to 6×10 inches. The plate is manually adjusted so that the desired line moves across the projected image of a lamp filament. A second objective images the beam on a slit in the center of a screen above the instrument. Normally only the small area of the plate illuminated by the filament area is clearly seen on the screen. To permit a larger area to be viewed, another lens may be inserted into the beam and a larger area illuminated. The photoelectric element is a barrier layer cell. Storage batteries are necessary for the scanning lamp. In place of the usual galvanometer a "galvascope projector" may be used. This is essentially an optical lever; thus, although the galvanometer may deflect through only a small angle, the resultant sensitivity is about the same as the usual high-sensitive current galvanometer, namely about a microampere per radian. A scale is the moving element on the galvascope screen. The merit of the galvascope is that it occupies a space about 2 square feet and is so insensitive to mechanical vibration that it may be placed directly on a desk. This is quite an advantage over the Julius mounting for sensitive galvanometers.

4. Leeds and Northrup Co., Philadelphia, Pennsylvania—Knorr-Albers recording microphotometer. This instrument is constructed in two parts—a plate stage and a Speedomax recording unit. The plate stage holds a 4×10-inch plate in an exposed vertical position. Mechanical adapters are provided for smaller glass plates. The filament of an electronically controlled light source is focused on the emulsion, and the desired line, which may be viewed through a simple lens, is motor-driven across the filament image at a selected speed. The image of the light source at its maximum is about 0.015×2 mm. The photocurrent is electronically amplified and fed into a bridge circuit in the Speedomax unit, the unbalance of which drives a pen across a moving strip chart, effectively 9 inches wide. The plate and spectrum are in full view at all times, but it is necessary to look through a lens or lens assembly to see the line being measured. Each plate must be focused, and the mechanical stage is not so rigid that the entire plate is quite in focus at one time. The scattered light is extremely small, probably less than with the other types of densitometer, and the resolving power is equal to that of the lines on the plate. The instrument may be used in a normally illuminated room. It must be shielded against electrical pickup. The effective slit, i.e., the filament image, may be increased in width by a defocusing procedure, but that is not a reproducible operation. The speed of operation would not be too high if a few lines were to be measured at frequent intervals, as in a producers' laboratory. When a 4×10-inch plate has about twenty spectra of similar material imposed on it, however, it is a rapid and simple procedure to read the same line on each spectrum by racking the plate, and the speed for the whole plate is well within the previously indicated lower bound. The electrical precision is stated to be within "0.2% of the full deflection." The density range is effectively 0 to 1.5 with an extension (amplifier switch) to 2.3. It operates entirely on 110-volt a.c. In common with similar electronic instruments, the maintenance problem should be considered. It is not difficult to make repairs or adjustments; it is only difficult to locate or determine the source of trouble. The manufacturer has developed a recent model of the Speedomax recorder unit that is self-adjusting and hence may be more trouble-free, but it has not yet been applid to the microphotometer.

5. Leeds and Northrup Co., Philadelphia, Pennsylvania—Sawyer and Vincent

densitometer. This instrument operates on a principle similar to that of the Hilger densitometer. The image of a lamp filament is brought through the plate and focused on a small screen containing a slit, behind which is a barrier layer cell. The photo current is passed through a galvanometer, and the deflection is measured in the usual lamp and scale arrangement. The galvanometer is of the high-sensitive type, i.e., 1 to 2 μa. per radian, with a period of 1.5 to 2 seconds. A proper critical damping resistance is supplied, and the overshoot is quite small. The instrument requires the use of plates 4 $\times$ 10 inches. The focus is fixed and is maintained over the entire plate by placing the plate in the holder. There is some scattered light which is kept at the minimum by the use of coated optical elements. The resolving power is not equal to that of the lines on the plate but is satisfactory. The instrument should be operated in at least a semidarkened room. The galvanometer usually has to be mounted in an external Julius suspension about 6 feet away from the densitometer, although a newly introduced taut suspension galvanometer should minimize vibration troubles. The scanning is manually controlled by fast and slow traverse knobs. The speed is well within the lower limit. The scale is 500 mm. long, and the usable range of deflection should be retained between 50 and 400 mm. The instrument is precise and should present practically no maintenance problem other than that implied by the use of storage batteries to regulate the voltage on the scanning lamp. The batteries may be connected on floating charge (21).

3.3. Direct Reading Equipment

Recent developments in nine-stage photomultiplier tubes (numbers 931, 931A, 1P21, 1P28) have opened a new approach to measuring intensities of spectrum lines (4, 7, 20). The spectrum line is allowed to fall directly upon the sensitive element of the photomultiplier tube. Owing to the high internal amplification of the photocurrent, about 300,000, it is possible to construct external stable amplifying circuits to measure the output of the tube as a whole. It is thus possible to eliminate the photographic emulsion and the densitometer.

Various schemes have been proposed and used in the last 2 or 3 years. One of them (20) isolated the spectrum lines by means of reflecting mirrors and prisms. The light is then brought into the slit of the phototube housing. The electrical circuit is so designed that the photocurrent is stored in a condenser, which alternately stores the energy liberated by line plus background and discharges the energy due to the background. At the end of the sparking cycle, 20 seconds, the remaining energy is measured by an integrating circuit (time to discharge a condenser). The total time to analyze a magnesium alloy for about five quantitative determinations is about 40 seconds. The equipment has been operated satisfactorily for about 2 years under routine conditions.

Another system, for instantaneous comparisons of spectrum intensities, is described in ref. (7). The relative output of the phototubes one to represent the matrix element and the other to represent the element sought, is instantaneously compared by means of the Leeds and Northrup flight recorder modified to serve as an intensity ratio recorder, or an indicating system may be constructed by feeding the output of the phototubes into a two-gun oscillograph. The mechanical system is so arranged that the lines are scanned in any desired order. Mirrors to divert the spectrum lines are not necessary.

The Applied Research Laboratories instrument, called the Quantometer, applies the output of the phototubes, after sparking cycle, to operate an integrating record in the form of drums upon which are placed, in a properly calibrated form, numbers to represent the concentration of the particular element represented by the selected line.

It can thus be seen that the trend through direct reading equipment is to replace the only chemical reaction in spectrographic analysis—namely, that involved in the development of the latent image in the photographic emulsion—by a physical process involving phototubes. Although it is true that the photographic emulsion for measurement of developed lines is one of the uncontrollable sources of error in the spectrographic analytical process, it is believed that this error is significantly less than the error or variance introduced by the lack of understanding, hence lack of control, of the arc reaction.

The use of direct reading equipment, at present, involves a complex electronic setup with its maintenance problem to retain stability. As a routine production procedure it may decrease the analysis time perhaps by a relatively significant amount but of course nowhere near the decrease in time due to the change from the wet chemical to the photographic spectrographic process. The intricate and time-consuming task of adjusting the phototubes to receive the exact lines means that a spectrograph and its accessory equipment must be reserved for the analysis of a particular material for a selected group of elements using fixed lines. The expected gain is in the reduction of the error variance due to the photographic emulsion and densitometer, and, what is perhaps more important, in the lifting of the conditions with regard to the measurable upper density limit and the use of practically monochromatic line pairs imposed by the photographic emulsion. Owing to the nature of the envelope of the phototube it is necessary to restrict the usable lines to those having wave lengths greater than about 2600 A.

It is believed that the significant immediate benefit of direct reading equipment will be derived from well planned studies of the arc reaction, i.e., the effects of the variations in the excitation source, electrode form, and temporal effects in the arcing period. After the arc reaction is well understood, even in an empirical manner, it will be possible to make a real evaluation of the components of the spectrographic procedure.

Analysis of recent developments indicates that the gain in precision obtained with direct reading equipment is in large measure due to the ease with which the equipment is adjusted for drift of the analytical calibrations. It becomes a matter of only a minute or so to run a high and low standard, for example, and then to adjust the analytical scales accordingly. Extensive analyses of analyses made by means of photographic plates indicate that the major contribution to the error is not the scatter of the analytical values around their mean, or true value, within the plate, but rather the drift, either in slope or in translation, or in both, of the analytical curves between plates. It can be estimated that if such a drift correction or adjustment could be made as expeditiously for plates as for direct reading indicators then the difference in precision between the two procedures might even become nonsignificant. These considerations hold, of course, only for those conditions or line pairs suitable for use with photographic plates and do not reflect on the much greater flexibility of the direct reading process due to the extension of the usable intensity and wavelength differences of the element and matrix lines.

In spite of their high cost (up to $70,000 per instrument), the number of direct reading spectrographs has increased to a remarkable degree. There are now a half-dozen or so domestic models available. Most of them require some sort of air-conditioning for optimum operation, but one model (Spectromet, Baird Atomics Associates) is constructed with a sealed electronics compartment.

The advantages of a direct reading spectrograph, compared to a photographic instrument, have to be experienced in order to be fully appreciated. The increased efficiency and facility of operation are most significant.

4. Excitation Sources

The equipment directly concerned with the arc and influencing its action includes the excitation sources and the electrode systems. Proper control of the arc is the central problem in quantitative spectrography. It is indeed the preoccupation with this problem that is the distinction between spectrography for chemical analysis and what is usually understood by spectroscopy. The concern of spectroscopy is the theoretical analysis of spectra after they are produced, whereas that of spectrography is essentially that of the physical production of spectra.

Discontinuous bright-line spectra, which are the concern of emission spectrography, almost without exception are radiated from atoms in a gaseous or vapor state which store up energy in some manner and then radiate it as luminous energy. Sources differ in the manner by which energy is supplied to the atoms and in the amount which can be absorbed before radiation. Atoms may receive energy by absorption of radiation, as kinetic energy from atomic collisions, or by thermal excitation. Simple thermal excitation is found in flame and arc spectra. The actual processes involved in these cases are, no doubt, a mixture of other modes of excitation, the energy which the colliding electrons, atoms, or molecules possess being provided by the kinetic energy of thermal agitation. When the supplied energy is high enough, the atoms in the gas or arc space will become ionized and radiate spectra characteristic of the elements present in the arc. It is known that the amount of radiation corresponding to a certain line of a certain element is linearly proportional to the number of atoms present, the transition probability from one energy level to another, i.e., the exact partition of the energy among the various lines of the element, and exponentially proportional to the absolute temperature.

Accordingly, the problem of the control of the arc may be divided into two parts: the first is to devise some source of excitation that will generate and maintain a precisely reproducible radiating arc (of the same temperature), and the second is that the distribution of the relative intensities of the spectra of the elements present in the arc should be simply correlated with the concentration or distribution of the elements in the electrodes. The problem is a difficult one and is made more so by the lack of any rational theoretical physical basis that would indicate the manner or type of its solution. The mechanism of transfer of the atoms from the cold solid electrodes to the hot radiating gas, which is clearly the central theme, is particularly obscure. The trend of modern development appears to be in generating periodical bursts of radiating gas in small amounts and at a high temperature, allowing the arc to be extinguished and the vapors removed from the reactive zone between each period. The assumption is that if one were able to begin anew at each period—that is, with the same initial conditions in the gap with barely altered electrodes—the character of the radiation would remain reasonably constant and reproducible for a given electrode system. It is known that continued arcing will melt the electrodes or superficial patches of them, thus promoting fractional distillation of the elements and chemical reaction with the oxygen in the air, which will enhance whatever selective action the arc (or spark) may have on the surface of the electrodes. Thus the arc would, in general, behave as a very hot, small cylindrical furnace, and that is admittedly difficult to reproduce or control.

Most excitation sources are electrical in nature. This has caused many discussions of the electrical circuits involved, the assumption being that a reproducible and stable circuit from the usual electrical point of view will result in a reproducible radiating arc. This condition appears physically necessary, but it is not known whether it is sufficient. The chances probably are that it is not. In any event, an arc is a non-linear circuit element, and the resultant mathematical analysis is difficult. The various analyses that have been published appear to have introduced simplifying linearizing assumptions too early in the solution, so that, although solutions under the assumptions have been approximated, they have not successfully approximated the physical findings in the laboratory.

The usual electrical source is made for the purpose of generating arcs or sparks in air and at atmospheric pressure. A brief description will now be given of arc and spark history (15, 16).

The arc discharge is characterized and distinguished from other types of discharge by its exceptionally low cathode fall of potential and its high current densities. Its cathode falls run about one-tenth or less of those in the glow discharge, and arc currents are measured in the order of amperes per square centimeter in place of microamperes per square centimeter. The primary mechanism at the cathode of the arc is believed to be thermionic in nature. Through intense concentration of current, enough heat is poured into localized areas to raise the local temperature to the point of some sort of thermionic emission, in sufficient strength so as to maintain the discharge. The difficulty appears in the definition of the concept of temperature to the microscale of occurrences which take place at the cathode.

Arcs exist either at high or low pressure, in the ambient gases or in the vapors of their own volatilized electrodes. They are initiated either by a glow or spark discharge, or by a contact between two electrodes that are separated. As the contact breaks, the heavy current through the electrode fuses and vaporizes the last small point of contact, leaving a metal vapor discharge which can change to an arc if the external resistance is low so that the rush of current is not limited. Owing to the high temperature in arcs, potential measurements are not too satisfactory. The potential change is linear with distance from the cathode except in the immediate vicinity of the electrodes. The characteristic anode and cathode falls probably occur in distances of only a few electron free paths, which at atmospheric pressure and arc temperature are of the order of 10^{-3} to 10^{-2} cm. The magnitude of the potential drop at the cathode in truly hot arcs is of the order of only one to two times the ionizing potential of the vapor. At the anode the fall may be somewhat greater than the cathode fall, depending on the anode material and temperature. The concept of temperature in the ordinary sense is probably meaningless when referred to the cathode or anode. Indications are, however, that the anode temperature may be equal to or greater than the cathode temperature. Thus in the carbon arc the values are of the order of 4000° and 3600°K., respectively. The anode temperature of certain metals, such as Zn, Al, and Mg in air, may be much greater than their melting temperature. This is due to the formation of oxide layers. At atmospheric pressure, diffusion of the positive column is small, so that the column behaves like a self-contained cylindrical furnace without walls.

Ionization in the arc most probably proceeds by means of collisions between atoms rather than by means of electrons and atoms. The electrons ionize indirectly by raising the temperature of the column. That is, in any small section of arc column, at the cathode end a heavy current density of electrons is generated and flows through the column toward the anode. At the anode end a small current density of positive ions is generated which flows toward the cathode. The electrons move quickly, the positive ions slowly. The resistance by the gas atoms and molecules to the passage of these charged carriers produces heat which in a stable column must just balance the radial and axial heat loss by radiation and conduction produced by the various mechanisms. The added electrical energy must also compensate for the loss of ions from the column by ambipolar diffusion and recombination. The rate of loss of ions from the column by ambipolar diffusion and the energy loss by radiation and conduction have not been worked out. It is estimated, however, that the radiation from the positive column, for a carbon arc operating at about 10 amp., is about 1.5%. The radiation is small, owing to the fact that the emission of the light proceeds only from the lines of atomic or band spectra, which are narrow wavelength intervals with large nonradiating gaps between. The large energy loss is by means of heat conduction, in the kinetic theory sense, at high temperature with, however, an effective transfer by means of excited higher vibrational and rotational states as well as of metastable states and ions. The core of the arc, i.e., the true column, is thus surrounded by a considerable mantle of hot gas. Convection plays an important part in the cooling of arc columns in free gas spaces. The voltage-current characteristics of d.c. and a.c. arcs have been extensively studied. An empirical formula for the metal arc of the following form has been suggested:

$$V = A + Bi^{-n}$$

where V = volts, i = current, and A, B, and n = constants. For d.c. arcs the Ayrton equation may be written as

$$V = \alpha + \beta l + \frac{\gamma + \delta l}{i}$$

where l = length of arc, and α, β, γ, and δ = constants. The characteristic may thus have negative derivatives (which have the dimensions of resistance). This has certain marked consequences as concerns stability and initiation of oscillations, for the negative resistance of an arc may neutralize the damping resistance of the rest of the circuit.

If the arc length is too short for a given potential, a hissing arc will develop. This is due to oscillations in the vapor mass of the arc and appears to be due to excessive evaporation at the anode because of the high current density required by the high potential and short path. The generation of the vapor cloud cools the arc, reduces the fall of potential at the anode, and so increases the current. As soon as the current exceeds the value fixed by the stability conditions, it drops back and the cycle repeats. The asymmetry of the conditions at the cathode and anode of the arc, which has a high current-carrying capacity, may favor the formation of the arc in one direction and impede it in the opposite. Hence in an arc with electrodes of different metals or different rates of cooling, one may expect an asymmetry in radiation close to the electrodes. There is obviously a transport of positive ions from the anode to the cathode. Furthermore, the higher speed of the electrons would leave positive ions behind so that one would expect an enhancement of metallic radiation from the portion of the arc near the electrodes, particularly the cathode. Such an enhancement, of the order of 5 to 1, does occur and is the basis of the "cathode layer" method of analysis. This is particulary applicable for qualitative analysis of very small amounts of sample (26).

The streamer theory of spark formation may be summarized as follows. One may begin by considering a gap in which the cathode is illuminated by ultraviolet light or other means of ionization, perhaps residual, so that at least one free electron is present in the cathode area. The potential across the electrodes is assumed to be sufficiently high (over 30 kv./cm. in dry air for plane parallel electrodes). The electron starts across the gap, quickly acquiring an average random energy of some $E = \frac{1}{2}mC^2 = 3.6$ ev. and a drift velocity in the field direction of about 2×10^7 cm./sec. As it moves it creates new electrons, so that at the distance x its progeny amounts to $e^{\alpha x}$ electrons, where $\alpha =$ the rate of formation, forming what is called an electron avalanche. Therefore, $e^{\alpha x}$ positive ions have been left behind by the electron group, virtually where they were formed, since the mobility of positive ions is of the order of 10^{-2} to 10^{-4} that of the electrons. As the electron avalanche advances, its tip spreads laterally, owing to the random diffusive movement of the electrons. Some experimental results have indicated that under certain conditions $\alpha = 17$, so that, for a 1-cm. gap, at 0.04 cm. from the anode there are 1.2×10^7 ions. Most electrons will be drawn to the anode except for some that are bound by the positive ions, making a sort of conducting discharge plasma in the avalanche path. Such a distribution of ions does not make a conducting filament of charges across the gap, however, and hence in itself an avalanche that has crossed does not constitute a breakdown of the gap. Accompanying the cumulative ionization there is produced by the electrons from four to ten times as many excited atoms and molecules. Some are excited beyond the ionizing potential of some of the atoms and molecules present. These excited atoms emit radiation of very short wavelength in some 10^{-8} second, and this ultraviolet radiation is highly absorbed in the gas and leads to further ionization. In fact, the whole gas and the cathode as well are subjected to a shower of photons of all energies traveling from the region of dense ionization with the velocity of light. Thus nearly instantaneously in the whole gap and from the cathode new photoelectrons are liberated which almost at once begin to ionize cumulatively. The photoelectrons created at points in the gas and at the cathode at any great radial distance from the avalanche axis will merely create other avalanches. Those photoelectrons created near the space-charge channel of positive ions, however, and especially near the anode, will be in an enhanced field which exerts a directive action drawing them into itself. If the space-charge field is of the order of magnitude of the imposed field, this action will be very effective; in addition the values of α will be enhanced. The electrons from the intense cumulative ionization of such photoelectron avalanches in the combined fields which are drawn into the positive space charge feed into it, making it a conducting plasma which starts at the anode. The positive ions they leave behind will therefore extend the space charge toward the cathode. In this fashion the positive space charge develops toward the cathode from the anode as a self-propagating positive space-charge streamer. As the streamer advances toward the cathode, it produces a filamentary region of intense space-charge distortion along a line parallel to the field. The conducting streamer of a plasma consisting of electrons and ions extending to the anode makes a very steep gradient at the cathode end of the stream tip. As this advances toward the cathode, the photoelectron avalanches produced by radiation at the cathode begin to produce an intense radiation near the cathode, and positive ions created there may increase the secondary emission. Thus, as the space-charge streamer approaches the cathode, a cathode spot is forming which may become a source of visible light. When the streamer reaches the cathode there is a conducting filament bridging the gap. As the streamer tip reaches the cathode, the high field produces a rush of electrons toward the end of the streamer. This, if followed by a current of electrons, gives a high potential wave which passes up the preionized conducting channel to the anode, multiplying the electrons present by a large factor. The channel is thus rendered highly conducting. If the metal can emit a copious supply of electrons because of the formation of an efficient cathode spot, then the current of electrons continues up the channel, maintaining its high conductivity and even increasing it. This current, unless limited by external resistance, will then develop into an arc. It is, however, the intense increase in ionization by the potential wave which gives the highly conducting channel characterizing the spark. The velocity of propagation of the returning wave of ionization up the preionized channel may be exceedingly great, reaching up to 10^8 to 10^9 cm./sec. Once the arc has been initiated, it will proceed in its history as previously described unless the voltage is cut off or some similar disturbing event is initiated.

It may thus be seen that the entire process depends on the presence of some initial electrons (ionization) near the cathode. If a sparking potential is applied to a given gap, it will be observed that the spark discharge may occur at almost any interval of time after the gap has acquired that potential. The delay may be exceedingly short or very long (10^{-5} second to 30 minutes), provided inadequate ionization exists near the cathode. The time interval between the application of the potential and the occurrence of the spark is called the spark time lag. It is quite unpredictable, and modern treatments of this phenomenon have resorted to statistical methods. The spark time lag may be decreased by overvoltage at the electrodes. Modern spark sources have been designed to compensate, as far as possible, for fluctuations due to this effect.

The above brief discussion of phenomena within the arc or spark column, taken essentially from the book by Loeb and Meek (16), is intended to illustrate the extreme complexity of the reactions involved and to indicate the difficulty of analyzing the events to derive stoichiometrically quantitative relations between the number of atoms (in the electrodes or in the column) and the relative intensity of their radiations.

4.1. OXYACETYLENE FLAMES OR LUNDEGÅRDH SOURCE (17)

This mode of excitation is induced by burning a stream of acetylene, aspirated through the solution to be analyzed, in oxygen. Only the simplest spectra of the strongest lines, of low ionization potential, are emitted. Most of the spectrum is in the visible region, i.e., between 4000 and 7000 A. The simplicity of the spectra, and of the source, may be advantageous in cases where it is convenient or desirable to use solutions, as in the analysis of biological liquids for the alkali metals. Although the precision of analysis is strongly dependent on the gas pressures involved, it is stated to be adequate for clinical laboratories.

The equipment, including nozzles, solution chambers, and gas pressure regulators, may be obtained from commercial instrument manufacturers.

4.2. THE ELECTRIC ARC

The electric arc between electrodes of the material to be analyzed or between graphite electrodes, at least one of which is provided with the material to be analyzed, is a widely used source, probably the most popular. It is sensitive in the sense that the most minute traces of elements are made detectable. It may be used on metallic specimens as well as on nonmetallic ones. Nonconductors may be analyzed if supported on graphite or other conducting rods or mixed with graphite powder. In its simpler forms it is one of the easiest types of excitation unit to construct, no equipment being necessary other than an insulated holder for the electrodes and some sort of series resistor for current control, since the current may be part of the plant supply.

It is a difficult source to control in a quantitative sense, however, for two reasons. The electrodes and the gap become extremely hot, the specimen is fused, and there is danger of selective or partial distillation; i.e., low-boiling elements are distilled out of the sample before the spectrum may be recorded, or else the time rates are dependent on the sample size. For example, with a 0.5-g. sample of steel containing 0.5% molybdenum, in a d.c. arc of 5 amp., it is not uncommon to find that all the molybdenum has disappeared after about 1 minute of arcing. One expedient to avoid this error is to start with a predetermined weight of material and to burn it to completion. The precision would still be inadequate for the stricter demands of the metallurgical industry even if the relatively longer exposure times did not retard the output too severely. Another source of variability arises from the "wandering" of the cathode spot. This spot, small and intensely hot, is the source of most of the electron emission which maintains the discharge. It is inclined to wander irregularly, from one part of the electrode surface to another, which for some reason or other becomes a preferred emitter at that moment. Resultant large and inverse fluctuations of current and voltage accompany this wandering, for the arc has a negative characteristic for part of its history. As a result, there are large fluctuations of the discharge temperatures, which, in turn, cause variations in the relative intensities of the emitted spectra. Further results of these fluctuations are variations in the volume and density of the arc column, particularly if the electrodes contain a volatile element, such as zinc, which, together with the temperature fluctuations, leads to variable self-reversal in the arc lines. Attempts to restrict this wandering have been made by shaping the electrodes, by using narrower counterelectrodes in order to increase current density, and by the use of the "globule arc." Discussions of these features will be reserved for the section on electrodes.

The usual arc circuit is one of the four combinations of high voltage (2200/4400 volts) or low voltage (110/220/440 volts), and direct or interrupted (pulsating) direct or alternating current.

The argument for the variations of the simple 110-volt d.c. arc may be stated as follows. The parameter to be controlled is the current through the gap. Since unavoidable fluctuations in gap conditions are bound to occur, it is felt that a high series resistance (1500 to 2000 ohms) would exercise a strong balasting effect and help stabilize the current; hence the high voltage. (Some resistance is necessary even in low-voltage arcs to keep the current from increasing beyond safety bounds.) The use of a.c. establishes a symmetrical gap, and with reignition each half-cycle causes a re-establishment of the cathode spot on both electrodes for every cycle. In addition, the random wandering of the spot, since it lasts only for part of a half-cycle, will act in a manner to "sample" the electrode surface in a more representative manner. Besides it is easier to provide high-voltage alternating than direct current. Some manufacturers of equipment regulate the high-voltage a.c. by means of a variable iron core in the transformer. This is not so stable a regulation as the use of resistors, but it is considerably cheaper to build. Interrupted high-voltage d.c. may be considered a variant of the high-voltage a.c. that may have some advantages in certain special instances, for example when counterelectrodes are used. The use of a.c. and interrupted d.c. sources are examples of the trend to the use of periodic arc bursts. The interruption of the d.c. may be accomplished either by a mechanical rotating switch or by some electronic device, using thyratrons, for example. Low-voltage arcs may range from 2 to 25 amp. (or even up to 100 amp. in the analysis of massive tungsten rods); high-voltage currents may range from 1 to 5 amp.

High-voltage a.c. or interrupted d.c. arcs are usually initiated by means of a Tesla spark for a short period. Low-voltage a.c. arcs are maintained, i.e., reignited, by a low-capacity spark continued throughout the arcing period. This type of spark, although it does not emit any appreciable spectrum, will provide an ionized path for the arc itself. Low-voltage d.c. arcs are usually initiated by contact, either of the electrodes themselves or by means of a graphite rod.

Little may be done in the way of finer electrical control of the circuit. The use of a coil in the circuit to provide an inductive reaction against rapid current charges has been reported, but no marked improvement was claimed.

In spite of its shortcomings, the arc is a simply constructed, expedient source almost universal in its applications. It is difficult to see how it can be replaced for the analysis of minute traces or of refractory materials such as minerals, ceramics, pigments, and ash of plants.

4.3. THE ELECTRIC SPARK SOURCES

Electric high-voltage condensed spark excitation sources are more flexible in power and control than arc sources. In addition, the higher excitation generates spectra with lines due to more highly ionized energy states of the atom. Although spark spectra are not so sensitive for detection of minute traces of elements as arc circuits, control features render them much more reproducible. The high precision and accuracy of modern spectrographic analyses in the higher concentration ranges (1 to 20%) would be impossible to reach if one had to depend on arc sources. The following discussion will be restricted to spark sources for use with metallic electrodes. Other electrode forms, such as sparking from solution, are not considered to be of sufficiently important industrial application.

At first glance, the spark seems to satisfy all the criteria of a stable excitation. A condenser is charged by an a.c. supply to a definite voltage and energy and then discharged between the electrodes in the analytical gap. The spark will be extinguished when the condenser voltage has dropped below the breakdown value of the gap only to be reignited at the next cycle. Hence the arc is generated in periodic bursts of constant energy with high current density (the current through a spark path or streamer is of the order of 10^3 amp.) for such a short time (microseconds) that the gross heating effect on the electrodes is small.

Closer investigation, however, indicates a complicated mechanism, and, since high precision is at stake, continued effort to clarify the essential spark mechanism will be necessary. The investigation will have to consider not merely spark formation but the distribution of energy among the positive ions which are torn off the electrodes and which radiate the spectra, so that the relative intensities of the spectra may be proportional in some simple manner to the concentrations of the corresponding elements in the electrodes.

In view of the above requirements it is not surprising that an entirely satisfactory statement or analysis of the electrical requirements of the circuits involved has not yet been made. Thus, at present one may choose, apparently in an arbitrary manner, between low or high voltage, low or high capacity or inductance, low or high frequency, weakly or strongly damped, and controlled (interrupted) or uncontrolled sources. Since a condenser discharge is usually of an oscillating type and at rather high frequency, it is still a matter of dubious choice whether it is better to record the initial radiation corresponding to the first high-voltage surge or to effect a kind of integration over the entire train of oscillations.* It may appear that it would be better to use the initial burst of radiation, since after this the gas behaves in an arclike fashion with all the thermal disturbing effects of the low-voltage arc and a strong dependence on gap geometry or configuration.

In spite of the lack of complete understanding of the requirements of the ideal source, however, the following conditions are fairly well agreed on: namely, the supply to the electrodes should be uniform in time and in energy as far as possible, and independent or undisturbed by the inevitable local small changes in the configuration of the analytical arc space. For this reason, control gaps are put in series with the analytical gap, the argument being that since the control gap is not disturbed with change of samples (electrodes) it should have a stabilizing effect on the entire discharge circuit. In addition, the added gap by itself, even without the use of additional means, would have a stronger quenching effect on the circuit. This is considered desirable. On the other hand, care must be taken to prevent an unpredictable or random exchange of energy between the gaps, for this may result in the cure being worse than the disease.

A little consideration should be given to the mathematics involved in the analysis of the usual circuit. For a more complete discussion the reader is urged to consult refs. (12, 13, 14, 19). The investigation is usually begun by considering a circuit, similar to that in the figure, but simplified (without a filter, for example), that contains lumped R, L, and an arc A, in series and C parallel with A (where $R \equiv$ resistance, $L \equiv$ inductance, $C \equiv$ capacitance, $A \equiv$ arc element). The charging cycle is the simpler portion. The arc element, A, is considered as an open circuit, and the equation is

$$L \frac{d^2q}{dt^2} + R \frac{dq}{dt} + \frac{q}{c} = E_0 \cos{(\omega t + \psi)}$$

with the usual initial conditions, at $t = 0$, $q = 0$ (t is time, q is the instantaneous charge on the condenser, and ω and ψ are the angular frequency

* It is suggested that the direct reading photomultiplier tube equipment may be put to good use in this connection. Thus, if the output of two tubes, placed on a determined pair of lines, were to be fed to the plates of a two-gun oscilloscope, with no x-gain, then moving pictures, taken sufficiently rapidly, of the fluorescent screen would indicate initial emission corresponding to the first high-voltage breakdown of the spark. And if, at the same time, the spectra were to be recorded on a photographic plate, which effects an integration of the entire light output, then a proper comparative study of the results should throw some light on the problem.

and phase angle, respectively, of the driving voltage, E_0). There may be
a little disturbance due to q not being exactly equal to 0 at $t = 0$, since
the previous discharge would have ceased when the voltage on the condenser dropped below that necessary to maintain the arc, but that trouble
is not too bad. This equation may be solved, with the aid of Laplace
transforms, under the assumption that L, R, and C are constants. Both
the charging current and the voltage are shown to be nonsinusoidal;
hence low-frequency rms meters will not give true readings except when
measuring the total applied voltage.

The discharge cycle is more difficult, however, and too involved to be
treated so simply. The "resistance" of the gap, A, is not independent
of the current, and hence the equation becomes nonlinear. In addition,
the voltage-current characteristic of the arc may have both positive and
negative derivatives (resistances).

Kaiser (13) approximated the circuit by assuming the arc voltage to
be of the same sign and to be representable by a symmetrical square
wave; i.e., the voltage is constant in absolute value during the discharge
period and changes sign each half-cycle. Since his discussion is based
on an analysis of the Feussner circuit (see below), many factors are
omitted deliberately by the author in order to simplify the computations.
Some of these factors are, referring to the arc element, the change of
voltage with current, the change of voltage with the change of length of
gap, and the initial rise and final decay of voltage for each train. The
resultant model, or equivalent circuit, is amenable to computation.
The situation is even more complicated, since experimental verification or
validation of the approximation depends on measurement of instantaneous secondary current; and, since galvanometer or thermocouple
ammeters (r.f. ammeters) measure mean values of the integrals with
respect to time of the absolute value of the current and the square of the
current, respectively, even the verification involves approximation. A
limiting relation, for decreasing external resistance, is derived, showing
that the secondary current indicated by a thermocouple ammeter is
proportional to $L^{-\frac{1}{4}}$, whereas it is well known that the inductance enters
much more strongly into the physical findings. It is also pointed out
that circuits with the same readings on the ammeter may be obtained with
quite different values of the various parameters but the circuits show
quite different behaviors as a light source. Hence, it is concluded that the
secondary current, as indicated, is not too conclusive or decisive a measurement.

Enns (1) assumed in his approximation that $V = \alpha + \beta l$, where α
and β are constants, and l is arc length.

It is known, however, that currents in the spark discharge range from zero up to about 1500 amp. (instantaneous values). Under these conditions the arc characteristic, dV/di, changes from negative to positive (1a). The differential equation of the circuit, as given above, becomes definitely nonlinear, and the classical mathematical analysis as given in (10a) is invalid and must be considered only as an approximation. It is the opinion of workers in the field of nonlinear differential equations that the approximations should be made after the solution is obtained, not before. It is meaningless at this stage to consider conclusions obtained from the solutions of a nonlinear circuit equation containing R and L in series and C in parallel to a nonlinear element, namely the arc, since the solutions have as yet not been obtained. Whether the classical

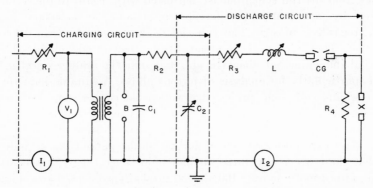

Fig. 1. Diagram of Feussner circuit.

approach is entirely invalid, as far as spectrographic interests are concerned, or whether it is only a matter of a minor error in approximation is difficult to determine at present. The classical approach has not solved the problem of determining the essential elements of a suitable excitation source; whether the nonlinear considerations will do any better remains to be seen. The mathematical aspects are quite complex, as the reader may note by referring to the references (1a, 5a, 9, 10a, 14, 19), and a solution to the problem is not anticipated in the immediate future.

Modern high-voltage spark circuits are usually provided with controlling or interrupter gaps as shown in Fig. 1. With reference to the figure, R is the primary resistance. Adjustment of this value affects the rate at which the main, oscillating condenser, C_2, is charged. T is a high-voltage step-up transformer, 220/33,000 volts, and may be rated at 5 or 15 kw. $C_1 - R_2$ is a filter combination to protect the transformer windings from transients. R_2 had been recommended to be in the range of 1000 ohms, but the indicated higher value, 25,000 ohms, appears to be more desirable in that it offers more protection and increases the current

in the tank circuit. R_3 and L_3 are the adjustable resistance and inductance, respectively. R_4 is a leakage resistor to ensure that the control gap
fires first. Part of C_2 may be arranged as a capacity voltage divider
(0.002 μf. and 1 μf.), and the low voltage across the high capacity and
ground may be used as a signal on the vertical plates of a cathode-ray
oscilloscope.

The control gap may be actuated in two ways, with a synchronous
motor (Feussner circuit) or with an air blast at constant pressure. The
usual arrangement of a Feussner circuit, with 60-cycle a.c., employs a
three-phase synchronous motor at 1800 r.p.m. A disk provided with four
discharge points on the rim, $\frac{3}{16}$-inch tungsten rods projecting about $1\frac{1}{2}$
inches from the rim synchronously adjusted with regard to the secondary
voltage by means of an oscilloscope, interrupts the secondary at each
peak, regardless of sign. The value of C_2 is usually between 0.004 and
0.020 μf. The value of L is about 40 μh.; usual rigid circuits have a
residual inductance of about 10 μh., and some laboratories add a little
more, particularly for analysis of ferrous alloys. A suitable inductor is a
space-wound coil; some prefer edge-wound flat copper strip, wound on a
9-inch mandrel with $\frac{1}{2}$ inch between turns. The usual addition is about
10 turns. It has been found that the continued addition of more than 30
turns has little noticeable effect for the other parameters as indicated
so that there are really three distinct inductance ranges, about 10 μh.,
30 μh. (10 turns), and over 100 μh. (30 turns). The effective or equivalent
inductance is easily computed by measuring the capacitance and the
wavelength of the radiation from the spark, using an absorption-type
radio wavemeter, for example. The added inductance reduces the background, i.e., the density on a plate between the spectrum lines; it also
reduces the intensity of the spectrum lines. Indeed, the use of increasing
inductance makes the spark discharge more arclike in character, acting
in the opposite way to the effect of capacitance. Considerably more inductance has been recommended for the analysis of aluminum and
magnesium alloys. A gentle air stream across the analytical gap is a
common practice in order to obtain more reproducible results.

The theory of the discharge in the Feussner circuit is recognizably
complicated, since it involves three gaps in series, two of which change
their lengths continuously during the discharge. The time of discharge,
as shown in the prints, is of the order of 5°—that is, about 250 μsec. If
the interrupter is set to break near the crest of the cosine wave, there
will not be much of a change of condenser voltage during a 5° or 10°
period. During that time, however, the stationary and fixed pins are
rapidly approaching each other; for a 6-inch radius of the interrupter
disk the speed is about 0.05-inch per electrical degree. Hence the voltage

gradient between the pins increases rapidly, and, in spite of the statistical spark time lag, the breakdown takes place at a reasonably constant voltage. It is quite possible to calculate L, C, and R values to obtain resonance and critical damping at various frequencies, but the final criterion is necessarily the stability of the spectra. A further complication is the specific effect of various metals on the sparking potential, either in the controls or in the analytical gap. Some typical values, from one laboratory using an oil-filled, water-cooled glass plate condenser, are given in tabular from.

Filter Resistance 26,900 Ohms

C (μf.)	R, primary (ohms)	L (μh.)	I, oscillatory, r.f. (amp.)	Frequency (kc.)
0.0095	6.1	10	13.8	519
0.014	8.0	33	15.8	234

The other method of control is to blow a nonturbulent air stream across the control gap at about 4 inches of mercury pressure. No air is used at the analytical gap. The discharge interruptions may be varied from 3 to 12 by changing values of R_1, C_2, and the applied voltage (primary). The secondary voltage is controlled by the distance between the electrodes in the control gap. These may be of either $\frac{3}{16}$-inch tungsten or $\frac{1}{4}$-inch magnesium rod. The capacity C_2 is usually less than in the Feussner circuit; the range is about 0.004 to 0.006 mf. A simple procedure to adjust this source is as follows: (1) open the control gap so that the breakdown is about one-half the undisturbed secondary voltage or, conversely, adjust the primary voltage to give the desired secondary breakdown voltage ratio; then (2) adjust R to give the desired number of interruptions per half-cycle. A slight primary-voltage adjustment may be necessary in order to keep the number of interruptions constant.

The character of the spark in the analytical gap is quite different in the two sources. The Feussner spark is a hard-driving spark with an intense central core and proceeds with a characteristic drumming sound. The air-interrupted spark appears to have a brushlike character, and apparently the single discharges wander all over the electrode surface. It operates with a rather shrill squeal.

Figures 2 and 3 and the accompanying table of values are representative of normal laboratory practice.

The Feussner spark source yields high precision in the analysis of ferrous metals. The air-interrupted (high-frequency) source is quite successful in the analysis of brass and bronzes. For that type of metal, the Feussner spark is too intense, zinc is rapidly boiled out, and the resultant analyses are unreliable.

Another type of spark source now on the market is provided with a large range of adjustment in L, C, and R. The voltage on the condenser is low, about 5000. The theory is to charge a stable condenser and then

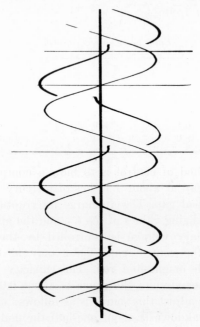

FIG. 2. Oscilloscope trace of Feussner circuit discharge.

rapidly discharge it, using electronic controls (thyratrons) through the analytical gap. The initial conditions at the moment of firing are critical. Considerable flexibility is claimed for this source with an accuracy approaching the Feussner-type circuit.

In conclusion it should be stated that the usual spark source is provided with a more or less elaborate system of controls, interlocks, and safety devices, depending on the ingenuity of the designer. The voltages and power ratings are not inconsiderable. With care they may be made entirely safe for operation by the usual laboratory technician, but attention must be given to all safety details.

The accompanying illustrations are enlarged reproductions of records made of a mechanical oscillograph directly connected to the primary leads of the high-voltage transformer. (A previous direct comparison of the primary and oscillating voltages by means of a cathode-ray oscilloscope had shown the two voltages to be exactly 180° out of phase.) The high-frequency discharge reflected into the primary of the transformer has produced a certain amount of distortion in the indicated trace of the discharge cycle that is ascribable to the galvanometer. For example, the peak of the voltage trace during the load cycle of the rotary inter-

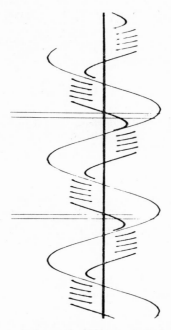

FIG. 3. Oscilloscope trace of air-interrupted circuit discharge.

rupted source is not exactly symmetrically located between the two zero voltages; i.e., the peaks are not at 90 and 270 electrical degrees, if the zero voltages are assumed to be at 0 to 180 electrical degrees. Nevertheless, the pictures illustrate the kind of information that could be accurately derivable from measurements of undistorted traces—for example, from high-speed moving-picture records of the screen of a cathode ray oscilloscope. Such information may prove to be indispensable to maintain ready interchangeability of excitation conditions between laboratories, as well as control within one laboratory.

The data in Table I are a summary of the measurements obtained from meters in the circuit and from the traces, neglecting trace distortion

TABLE I

	Fig. 2 Synchronously interrupted or rotary spark	Fig. 3 Air-interrupted spark
Gap and electrodes	Pins	Pins
Transformer ratio	150:1	150:1
Filter resistance	26,900 ohms	26,900 ohms
Primary resistance	5.1 ohms	11 ohms
Added secondary resistance	None	None
Capacity	0.0094 mf.	0.0035 mf.
Inductance	33.5 μh.	33.5 μh.
Oscillating current (r.f. meter)	13.8 amp.	8.0 amp.
Continuous trace, 60 cycle	151.6 volts, rms	151.6 volts, rms
Charging potential, primary	190 volts, rms	178 volts, rms
Discharge potential, primary	164.15 volts, rms	90.88 volts, rms
Residual potential, primary (end of discharge)	21.25 volts, rms	33.58 volts, rms
Phase of discharge (electrical degrees, referred to peak of primary potential)[a]	+36°	−20° to +20°
Duration of individual discharge, primary, in electrical degrees	5°	4°
Number of discharges per half-cycle, primary	1	5

[a] It is considered much better practice to adjust the interrupter so that the break occurs at about +5° beyond the peak of the voltage wave.

due to the galvanometer in the mechanical oscilloscope and to the optical or photographic process (enlargement).

To obtain peak secondary volts, multiply primary rms volts by 212.

5. Material and Electrode Preparation

The problem of material and electrode preparation is threefold: (1) as a sample or specimen under examination in an analytical procedure, it is necessary that the electrode should submit a representative portion of the material to be analyzed; (2) as an element of the gap or reaction zone, it is necessary that the electrode form employed will aid the stability and reproductibility of the arc; and (3) the electrode form should be easily obtained or prepared so that the speed of analysis is not retarded. The last is an important consideration for spectrographic analysis where time is measured in minutes per sample.

The sampling of metals presents a particular problem for spectrographic analysis. Spark excitation, with a solid specimen as one or both electrodes, is almost the universal practice for elements present in considerable amounts (ranging up from 0.5%). Spark excitation implies analysis of the surface, however. Consequently it becomes a metallurgical problem to prepare suitable specimens whose surface composition will be representative of the three-dimensional distribution of elements in the material sampled. This is not the place to discuss extensively the segregation of ferrous or nonferrous alloys due to different rates of cooling or location with respect to the ingot, or the peculiar difficulties encountered in some particular elements or alloys. For example, high lead-bearing metals or high silicon, aluminum, or magnesium alloys are unusually troublesome in this respect. Another surface effect may be attributed to grain size and its effect on the selective action of the spark, the so-called etching effect, or on the localization of the cathode spot. The difference between apparent or indicated composition when cast or wrought specimens of aluminum alloys are used has been reported several times. It may be seen that where it is the practice to cast specimens in a special mold these problems may be difficult to overcome.

Nonmetallic materials or metal powders present no sampling problems peculiar to spectrographic methods, other than would be expected in any procedure where small samples are used. These materials may be ground fine and well mixed, or they may be dissolved. The solution may be evaporated and the salts treated as a powder, or the evaporation may be effected directly on the electrode, usually graphite. Solution preparation may be employed for metals. Partial solution or precipitation procedures, when a proper part of an investigation, should be carefully considered, since the partition of some elements between soluble and insoluble portions, or between solution and precipitate, may be indeterminate. For example, the solution of antimonial lead as used for storage battery alloys for analysis of residual impurities is a delicate procedure. The solution is unstable, and the hydrolized or precipitated portions may adsorb the residual traces of impurities to a large and varying degree.

The preparation of metallic electrodes also presents some peculiar problems. The use of two rods, from $\frac{1}{8}$ to $\frac{1}{4}$ inch in diameter, in a symmetrical gap has been favorably reported by many ferrous laboratories.

The top of the rods may be kept flat or ground to a conical or hemispherical shape by special devices. A sharp cone, included angle about 90°, is conducive to a stable spark gap, but the tip is usually melted during the sparking, and some sampling difficulties are encountered. A commonly used cone is one with an included angle of about 150°.

The preparation of such rods, however, unless wire samples are submitted, by inspection laboratories not associated with foundries or rolling mills is too time-consuming to be practical even if suitable sample stock is obtainable. Probably the most popular and widely distributed solid metallic electrode is a flat surface, used with a graphite counterelectrode. A flat surface on a small specimen is easily produced by filing, emery belt, or machining. Such specimens are usually supported by a Petrey stand or modification. When chips are submitted or obtainable, it is a common practice to compress them into a pellet or briquet, with a hydraulic press, to a definite size, and hold them in specially constructed tubular holders. They may then be used as rods, but the reported precision is usually much less, since the pellet surface is rarely produced smooth enough, or free from sharp edges, not to disturb the uniform potential distribution over the electrode surface. In addition, a small edge may melt easily and localize the cathode spot.

A special form of metallic electrode, used with arc excitation, is the "globule" arc. A small piece of metal, about 0.2 g., is placed on an almost flat graphite rod, with a graphite (better carbon) counterelectrode. The metal is melted into a small bead, and the arc, when well adjusted, continues to play on the globule and will hardly ever wander off to strike the supporting graphite. This is a rather stable and reproducible form of an arc gap, and for some metals, such as copper, mild steel, nickel, or cobalt, it is capable of precise analysis. Partial distillation does take place, however, and besides it is impossible to form such a globule with some metals, such as high zinc-bearing brasses or stainless steel, either because of low boiling point or high rate of formation of a refractory oxide. It is usually necessary to reduce the current to a low value for stability. Sometimes, as in the analysis of ingot copper, it is better to use a pure copper rod as a counterelectrode.

Nonmetallic materials or solutions are usually employed with graphite or carbon electrodes. These have been prepared in a variety of forms (6). The electrode holding the material may be formed with a shallow or deep cup, a cup with thick or thin walls, and with or without a center post (to localize the cathode spot). The electrode below the cavity may be necked to concentrate the heat, or a sleevelike cap with a small hole in the top may be slipped over the material which is supported on the graphite rod.

The material may sometimes be mixed with carbon powder to promote smooth burning in the arc. In some instances, the admixing material, or "buffer," as it is called, promotes the volatilization of the material desired from a refractory base without much evolution of the base. Not merely does this expedite the analysis, but the base may have a complex spectrum, and simplification may be considerable. For example, Scribner and Mullin (23) used gallium oxide to good purpose as a buffer for the analysis of impurities in pure uranium oxide. Some laboratories use ammonium chloride as a buffer, which causes the material to burn almost explosively in the arc.

It may have been noticed that graphite and carbon rods and powder are used extensively in spectrographic procedure. The conductivity properties are different, and, as a rule, carbon rods will maintain a steadier arc, but graphite, or rather regraphitized carbon, is easier to form and is easier to obtain. The rods are available in almost all diameters, the most popular sizes being in the range from $3/16$ to $5/16$ inch. They are supplied in 12-inch lengths. The material is available in two grades—ordinary spectrographic quality, and purified or spectroscopically pure graphite. The difference in cost is considerable. Some laboratories use the ordinary grade with some sort of purification procedure, such as a hydrochloric and/or nitric acid wash for several days, followed by washing in ammonia and water, and heating in a muffle at a white heat. The ordinary variety of spectrographic graphite is usually adequate except where minute traces of commonly distributed elements such as calcium, copper, iron, etc., are sought.

A few words should be said about "spectrographically pure" materials. It can easily be seen that, at times, it may be difficult to decide whether a certain line is a strong line of a small amount of an element or a weak line of the base or matrix element, which perhaps may not be listed or definitely identified in spectrographic tables. Hence it is important to have access to highly purified "spectrographically pure" materials such as lead, tin, copper, and iron, or their compounds. These materials, in surprisingly good or adequate quality, are becoming commercially available through the chemical supply companies. The American Society for Testing Materials has long been interested in this problem, and a standing committee to develop sources and materials has been in existence for many years.

6. The Photographic Plate

Modern spectrographic observations are carried on almost entirely by means of photography. The efficiency of such work is, therefore, dependent to a large extent on the quality of the plates (or film) which are used and on their suitability for the work to which they are applied. Photographic plates can be of many kinds, and a choice of the correct plate for each purpose involves the consideration of many factors, including a careful evaluation of the plates available. The following discussion will be limited to photographic plates for industrial spectrographic purposes, where the exposure times are of the order of 10 to 100 seconds and the light levels are of the order of 0.1 meter-candle.

A logical discussion of the photographic plate would be to consider the problem in two parts, the chemistry of image production and the physics of the developed image. The latter is the more important phase.

6.1. CHEMISTRY OF DEVELOPMENT

When plates are exposed in a spectrograph to the light or radiation from the arc, the silver bromide in the gelatin emulsion is affected in such a way that a black image of silver can be developed when placed in a proper reducing solution called the "developer." The free silver is black and constitutes the image, which is made up of grains or minute coke-like masses of metal, which remains in the same position as the bromide crystals from which it was formed. After development, the emulsion, which still contains, in addition to the developed silver image, all the unexposed (not light-struck) and undeveloped grains of silver bromide must be treated to remove the latter, since they would darken, in time, if exposed to light and thus obliterate the image. Also, the emulsion containing the bromide is opaque, and a clear transparent background is required. To make the image permanent, and to supply the clear background, it is thus necessary to "fix" the image by dissolving the unused bromide salts without affecting the developed image. A solution of sodium thiosulfate, "fixer solution," is used for this purpose. The plate should then be thoroughly washed in cool running water and carefully dried in a dust-free atmosphere.

The chemical procedure is a delicate one but may be made surprisingly stable and reproducible if performed with the proper solutions and with time and temperature control. The theory of the preparation of developing and fixing solutions in order to prepare reproducible images and to prevent development of nonlight-struck silver bromide, or fog, is complicated. The details will not be discussed here, but the reader may consult refs. (10) and (18) for details. Unless there are strong indications to the contrary, it is advisable to use procedures and solutions recommended by the plate manufacturers.

The inhomogeneity of the image, with or without magnification, may give a "grainy" effect. This is an undesirable characteristic, since a grainy image is difficult to evaluate, but some graininess is unavoidable. A factor which may sometimes have to be considered is the "edge," or Eberhard effect. This evidences itself as a "hollow" line, i.e., a line which has darker edges and a lighter middle. It is probably due to local differences in the activity of the developer which may become exhausted where development is active and accumulate restraining products which hold back its action in that neighborhood. The effect diminishes as development is prolonged and undoubtedly can be minimized by adequate agitation, or brushing, during development.

Excessive graininess may also decrease the resolution of the plate, i.e., the ability to separate two close lines without blurring. In common with most chemical reactions, temperature exercises an important influence. Thus, not only is the temperature of the developer important, but also the temperature (and moisture content) of the emulsion at the time of exposure. These should be controlled for best results. Plates deteriorate in time, as is well known. They should be stored at about 35°F. but be at room temperature and humidity when exposed.

The most carefully made photographic material may show measurable differences in response from point to point even when the area used is relatively small. This is not of importance in ordinary work, but it is of great importance when these materials are used for precise quantitative measurements. The nonhomogeneity of response may be of sufficient magnitude to introduce serious errors. It is difficult to develop two samples of photographic plate exactly to the same extent, and it is also difficult to obtain uniform development over a large area. Hence it is important to establish strict control, including sufficient agitation during development, of the darkroom procedure.

6.2. Physics of the Developed Image

Certain commonly used functions in this phase of investigation will be defined. Concerning the exposure of the plate to radiation, if $I_\lambda \equiv$ the intensity of the incident light of wavelength λ, and $T \equiv$ the time of exposure, then $E_\lambda \equiv$ exposure $\equiv I_\lambda \times T$. The usual units of E are meter-candle-seconds. Some writers refer to log E as the exposure. With reference to the measuring beam in the densitometer, if $I_0 \equiv$ the intensity of the incident beam, and $I_t \equiv$ the intensity of the beam transmitted through the image on the plate, then $I_t/I_0 \equiv$ transparency, $I_0/I_t \equiv$ opacity; a commonly used measure of blackness is $\log_{10} I_0/I_t = D \equiv$ optical density, or simply density.

The significant properties of a spectrum line as it appears on a developed photographic plate are its width and density. Since the line images are diffraction images of the slit, and since the turbidity of the emulsion introduces some scattering, the width of a line is a somewhat uncertain parameter. At any rate, the customary practice is to use the density of the image as a measure of the plate response to the light stimulation.

The functional connection, or characteristic function of the plate (10, 18), is written

$$D = F(E_\lambda) \qquad \text{or} \qquad D = F(\log_{10} E_\lambda)$$

The dependance of D on λ is usually made implicit for other than spectrographic procedures. An important function, probably the most important for spectrography, is the derivative of the above relation: $\partial D/\partial(\log E) \equiv$ the contrast of the emulsion. $[\partial D/\partial(\log_{10} E_\lambda)]_{max}$ is of particular importance and is called the gamma (γ) of the emulsion. Sometimes γ is called the contrast, the contrast factor, or the slope. The characteristic function is nonlinear and has an S shape (10, 18). The curve as usually drawn, or discussed, has D as the ordinate, or vertical axis, and $\log E$ as the abscissa, horizontal, or x-axis (Fig. 4). Most emulsions used

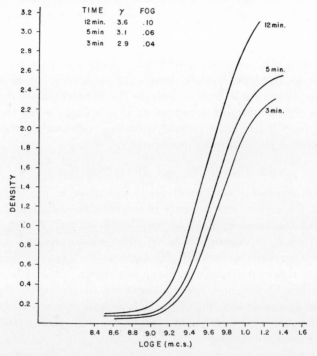

FIG. 4. Effect of time of development on plate characteristic curves (SA-1).

in spectrography have a characteristic, for $D < 0.5$, which is convex toward the $\log E$-axis, of positive slope increasing with D or $\log E$ and which is reasonably straight up to about $D = 1.5$. Hence γ is sometimes called the slope of the straight-line portion. The function, for higher values of D, curves concave to the $\log E$-axis, with decreasing slope for increasing D or $\log E$. For still larger values of $\log E$, the slope may become negative (solarization). Since most spectrographic work is in the range $D < 1.5$, the essential parts of the curve are a lower curved portion of increasing slope and an upper straight portion of constant maximum slope.

Different emulsions differ in the magnitude of D for a given value of log E_λ. This property is called the "speed" of the emulsion and is usually measured by the reciprocal of the exposure required to produce a given density above fog when the plate is developed under controlled

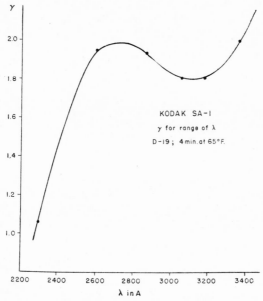

FIG. 5. Change of γ with λ on photographic plate.

standardized conditions. Speed is sometimes connoted by the term sensitivity. Gamma and speed are strongly dependent on λ, or the wavelength of the incident light (Fig. 5). Most emulsions have their maximum speeds in the range of about 2500 to 4500 A. In order to increase the speed for wavelengths down to about 1800 A. and up to about 12,000 A., it is necessary to introduce a suitable dye, fluorescent for the lower range, into the emulsion when it is prepared. These color-sensitized emulsions, as distinct from neutral, color-blind, or blue plates, are prepared in many different types in order to accentuate the speed for certain wavelength regions as much as possible, since no treatment will increase speed uniformly over a wide interval. The increase in speed of plates so tested may be considerable, so much so that regions that ordinarily would not record on a neutral plate at all may yield suitable densities in usual normal exposure times. Neutral emulsions are suitable for almost all metallurgical analyses. Sensitized plates are often necessary, however, for the analysis of minerals (higher wavelengths for alkali metals) or elements like phosphorus in small amounts (low wavelength). Relevant information concerning spectral sensitivity and development procedures may be obtained from the manufacturers (18).

Since spectrographic procedures are mainly concerned with estimation of the difference in the log I (Δ log I) between two lines from meas-

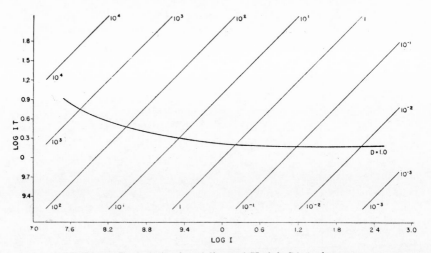

FIG. 6. Reciprocity law failure of Kodak SA-1 plates.

urement of their density or difference in density (ΔD) and density range, it can be seen that the determination of the slope of the characteristic function as a function of density is the important problem, called plate calibration. It is necessary only to determine the characteristic function as a function of log E up to an additive constant. The experimental effort is disturbed by the failure of the reciprocity law; i.e., if E is a general function of I and T, i.e., $E = \phi(I, T)$, it is found that ϕ is not a simple symmetrical function of $I \times T$ (Fig. 6). Thus there is a choice of procedure: (1) one may keep T constant and vary I in a known manner from exposure to exposure, i.e., an *intensity* or *normal* calibration; or (2) one may keep I constant and vary T in a known manner, i.e., a *time* calibration. Once the curve or the function has been determined, i.e., a smooth curve has been drawn between observed points, the average derivatives over a small interval of D may be measured by the usual differencing procedure. The experimental procedures and evaluation of their precision is quite similar to the analytical procedure and hence will be discussed later. Only a simple discussion of underlying theory will be given here.

A time calibration is easy to perform and was the original method. A step sector, with a known aperture ratio, may be rotated rapidly before a slit illuminated uniformly, say by an iron arc, and the densities of the various step along a line in a desired wavelength region are measured and plotted against the log aperture ratio (log T). Theoretically this is not sound, since photographic materials do not integrate an intermittent exposure (intermittency effect). The intermittency effect has been extensively studied (10), and it has been stated that, if the frequency of interruption is high enough, the error is small. As a rule, the integration of an interrupted exposure yields a lower density than a continuous exposure for the equivalent time. Since the difference in log I for a chosen pair of lines in one spectrum is necessarily determined for equal exposure times of the lines, however, the combination of reciprocity law failure and intermittency effect (which is assumed to be a consequence of it), and the difficulty of illuminating a long slit in a uniform manner by any usual spectrographic light source make the resultant curve badly lacking in requisite accuracy and precision for the required application. In addition, owing to the burstlike character of most sources there is the ever-present danger of a stroboscopic error, since a rapidly rotating sector disk must be used so that the entire line is exposed simultaneously to avoid error due to nonconstancy of the source if separate exposures (at various times) are used.

Intensity, or normal, calibrations may be affected with a constant source (such as a properly controlled helium or mercury lamp) by using the low of inverse square, or neutral filters of known transmission characteristics. This method requires a special experimental arrangement and usually does not furnish lines in the desired λ regions. The accepted procedure at present is to use a set of grouped lines in the spectrum of iron, for example, whose relative intensity values for the excitation employed are known or measured by a primary method such as the inverse square law. This method is particularly suitable because of its close similarity to spectrographic analytical procedures. Extensive tables of relative intensities of iron lines under different excitation means and wavelength regions have been reported (8). A cautionary remark about the published values should be made. Whereas a spectrograph receives the various wavelength intensities directly from the arc, the plate receives these intensities as transmitted through the spectrograph. There may be quite a decided change in apparent contrast of the plates due to the differences in the optics of the spectrograph, an effect which will be discussed in more detail under procedures.

It is not necessary to use primary lines of known relative intensity throughout the spectrum to determine the slope or contrast as a function of λ. On the basis of van Kreveld's work, Mees (18, p. 223) states the following relations: A generalized equation for the characteristic function may be derived, taking into account the factors of wavelength and exposure time based on certain fundamental relationships that have been found to hold. Although this equation contains several arbitrary functions of λ and t (time) which are still undetermined, it shows, nevertheless, how these functions must enter into any general equation of the characteristic function which includes these factors.

The log It values necessary to produce a constant density as a function of the exposure time can be expressed as

$$\log It = F_1(D, t) + F_2(D, \lambda)$$

Or, since the variations of log It occasioned by reciprocity law failure correspond to changes of only log I when the reciprocity functions are considered as functions of time, this equation may be rewritten as

$$\log I = F_1(D, t) + F_2(D, \lambda)$$

From experimental work carried out primarily to test the validity of an addition law for successive exposures to radiation of different λ, it has been found that the slopes of two intensity calibrations made to different wavelengths but having the same time of exposure bear a constant relationship to each other independent of density, i.e.:

$$\frac{\partial}{\partial D}\left[\frac{\partial(\log I_{\lambda_1}\partial D)}{\partial(\log I_{\lambda_2})\partial D}\right] = 0$$

Substituting into the above equations, we find that

$$\frac{F_1'(D, t) + F_2'(D, \lambda_1)}{F_1'(D, t) + F_2'(D, \lambda_2)}$$

is independent of D (primes indicate differentiation with respect to D). This requires that

$$F_1'(D, t) = \psi(D)f(t)$$
$$F_2'(D, \lambda) = \psi(D)\phi(\lambda)$$

These equations may be integrated, in general terms, to give

$$F_1(D, t) = \psi_1(D)f(t) + f_1(t)$$
$$F_2(D, \lambda) = \psi_1(D)\phi(\lambda) + \phi_1(\lambda)$$

and, by substitution,

$$\log I = \psi_1(D)f(t) + \psi_1(D)\phi(\lambda) + f_1(t) + \phi_1(\lambda)$$

or

$$\psi_1(D) = \frac{\log I - (f_1(t) + \phi_1(\lambda))}{f(t) + \phi(\lambda)}.$$

which, if certain general analytical conditions are satisfied, yields

$$D = F\left\{\frac{\log I - [f_1(t) + \phi_1(\lambda)]}{f(t) + \phi(\lambda)}\right\}$$

This expresses the remarkable fact that the shape of the characteristic curve obtained by variation of the intensity factor of exposure, with the time constant, depends on the time of exposure and the wavelength of the exposing radiation only to the extent of a bodily shift along the $\log It$ axis by the amount $[f_1(t) + \phi_1(\lambda)]$ and a stretching in the same direction by the factor $[f(t) + \phi(\lambda)]$.

Since a spectrum is exposed and photographed simultaneously, the time requirements of the above deduction are satisfied. Hence it is necessary to determine the shape of the charactristic function only for one wavelength region called the primary. The ratio of the slopes of the straight-line portion for the primary and any other regions are easily determined, and the shape of the curve for the second region is then a matter of simple computation with the determined ratio as a factor in a difference table.

6.3. Choice of Plates

The choice of a high- or low-γ plate is a matter to be decided for each application. Since most densitometers are useful only in the density range 0.1 to 1.3, it can be seen that, although a high-γ plate will give better discrimination between lines of small $\Delta \log I$ than a plate of lower γ, the $\log I$ range, or generalized latitude which is the projected interval of the density range on the $\log I$ range, is less for high-γ plates than for low-γ plates. This may seriously limit the range of concentration to which a method, including the line pair, may be applicable.

A brief characterization of some available Kodak emulsions is given below.

Blue-Sensitive Plates, 2400-4400 A.

Spectroscopic 103-0	A high-speed plate with fine granularity and medium contrast.
Spectroscopic 103-0 U. V.	Same as 103-0 with an ultraviolet sensitizing giving the plate higher sensitivity to the region of the spectrum below 2500 A.

Kodak Spectrum Analysis No. 1   A plate for use especially in the metallurgical industries, with contrast higher than the usual process plate, low background density, adequate sensitivity, and suitable for very rapid processing.

Kodak Spectrum Analysis No. 2   A plate with higher speed, lower contrast, and coarser granularity than Spectrum Analysis No. 1 but with more uniform contrast from 2400 to 4400 A.

Red-Sensitive Plates, 2400-6800 A.

Spectroscopic 103-F   A high-speed plate with fine granularity and medium contrast.

Spectroscopic III-F   A slow plate with high contrast and fine granularity.

Infrared-Sensitive Plates, 2400-8200 A.

Spectroscopic I-L   A high-speed plate with medium contrast and a reasonable amount of granularity.

Spectroscopic IV-L   A slow plate with high contrast and fine granularity.

The L sensitizing has found wide use, especially in preliminary surveys in spectrographic analysis. The plates are recommended for preliminary observations of broad spectral regions with a single exposure. They are suitable for use on instruments of small dispersion, especially on prism-type instruments, but offer no advantages for instruments of high dispersion.

7. Analysis

7.1. ANALYSIS I

It will be assumed that the laboratory has acquired the various instruments, sources, and other devices necessary for the producing, recording, and measuring of spectra and is now in a position to consider the manner in which these devices are to be used in order to obtain analytical estimates. This discussion may be divided into two parts: (1) the nature of spectra and general methods of analysis, and (2) a systematic presentation of the components of an analytical procedure.

7.1.1. Spectra and Spectrum Lines. A spectrum as it is displayed on the developed photographic plate consists of a number of diffraction slit images or lines, more or less closely spaced. The lines should be straight, at least for a short length, about 3 to 5 mm., parallel to each other, and at right angles to the spectrum length (i.e., the direction of dispersion). Spectrum lines from prism instruments are curved in a parabolic shape but symmetrically shaped with respect to the spectrum length; hence only the central portion should be used.

The spectra, considered as bands or strips of lines at right angles to the strip length, should be reasonably parallel to the edge of the plate. It is advisable to adjust the ways of the plate-racking mechanism of the spectograph if necessary, so that successive spectra are directly beneath each other with no systematic lateral shift from spectrum to spectrum.

The ideal line spectrum would consist of sharply imaged lines superimposed on a perfectly clear background. Most plates or spectra, however, exhibit a more or less foggy area between the lines. This background or fog may be inherent in the spectrum and be part of an emission band of the material or graphite electrode, or it may be due to external causes such as scattered white light in the spectrograph, air lines in a spark discharge, or chemical fog, i.e., blackening due to the action of the developer on unexposed or nonlight-struck emulsion. It is highly desirable to use lines in a fog- or background-free area. The presence of background will affect the apparent density of a line in an involved manner that is difficult to correct for. Fog or background correction involves added work and is hence undesirable, but a more serious objection is that a really good correction factor or function has not yet been established. Hence the presence of fog or variable fog may be a source of serious error. Fog due to chemical action of the developer may usually be diminished by better control of the development procedure or by the use of less sensitive or slower plates. Fog due to air lines in a spark discharge may be diminished by adding more inductance in the secondary circuit. Scattered white light in the spectrograph should be patiently eliminated as much as possible by means of baffles, dull black paint, by tilting the collimator lens, or by whatever means may be feasible. Some prism instruments cause a foggy background on the lower wavelength portion of the plate (or left side as customarily viewed) which may be corrected for by altering the wavelength adjustment of the instrument so that the desired lines are in the right-hand portion of the plate. Fog due to band emission is to be considered as part of the spectrum and may sometimes be diminished by change of electrode shape, material of the counterelectrode, change of current density, or use of buffers. If these measures are not effective, it may become necessary to select lines in a clearer portion of the spectrum, if possible.

The lines to be used should be in sharp focus and prismatic in section; that is, the density as recorded on slow-speed scanning should indicate the density $\times$ width curve to be a symmetrical plateau with the maximum density in the center. Emission lines are not absolutely sharp (8), however, but have a certain intensity distribution in the immediate vicinity, $v - v_0$, of the center of the line. This means that the (relative) amount of radiant energy in the frequency interval between v and $v + dv$ is proportional to $T(v)\,dv$, where $T(v)$ is the true distribution of energy and, considered as a function of v, represents the true shape of the line. The total intensity may thus be indicated as

$$ I = \int_0^\infty T(v)dv = \int_{-\infty}^\infty T(z)dz $$

where $z = v - v_0$. The nature of the distribution $T(z)$ is determined by the nature of the line in question as well as by the particular conditions in the light source. Lines due to the atom's dropping to the ground state many times exhibit self-reversal; i.e., the energy, or density, is less at $z = 0$ than at small distances away from the center. Such lines should be avoided as much as possible, even if the reversal may be small for the particular circumstances under consideration.

Another relevant characteristic of lines is their arc-spark sensitivity. It may be observed, as an empirical phenomenon regardless of theoretical investigation, that the relative intensities of two lines may change with the change from arc to spark excitation. Lines may thus be classified into three groups; (1) arc lines, i.e., those lines whose relative intensities are increased with the change from to spark to arc excitation, or with the increase of inductance and decrease of capacitance in the secondary circuit of a spark excitation; (2) "spark" lines, i.e., those lines whose relative intensities are increased with the change from arc to spark excitation, or with the decrease of inductance and increase of capacitance in the secondary circuit of a spark excitation; and (3) indifferent or stable lines, i.e., those whose relative intensities are unchanged by change in excitation conditions. It is clear that the exclusive use of stable lines would be an ideal condition. But it is impossible to realize it in a physical sense. All that can be hoped for is the selection of lines that appear stable over normally anticipated source variations. Indeed, if the stability is extensive over a sufficient range of source variation, the lines will be practically equivalent to stable lines.

7.1.2. *General Methods of Analysis.* In view of the lack of any theoretical correlation between the amount or concentration of an element and the intensity of an emitted line when the material is excited in a definite manner, spectrographic analyses must be based on empirical comparison with "standards." That is, the intensity of a line of a material is compared with, or interpolated between, the intensities of the corresponding lines in similar material whose composition with regard to the element sought is known or standard. The differences between the various spectrographic methods are due to the manners in which the comparisons are made.

The primitive procedure was to compare, visually, the density of a line in the spectrum of the material with the density of a line in a standard. The judgment was simply whether the sample had more or less, i.e., the line was darker or lighter than the standard. Later a refinement was introduced by the use of two standards, of high and low concentration, and the attempt was made to bracket the material between two known values. This procedure is still a useful one in some instances.

The present systems, as may have been observed, do not use density but a measure of the corresponding intensity as derived from the calibration curve of the emulsion. The proper measure is, of course, I or $\log I$. Hence, if a time calibration of the emulsion is used, one may obtain only E or $\log E$, and it is necessary to depend on the validity of the reciprocity law to use E as proportional to I. It will be assumed, hereafter, that plate readings are to be converted to $\log I$. And, to be sure, the values of $\log I$ are now obtained as a result of objective measurement rather than by visual estimate.

It was soon found, however, that it is practically impossible to prepare spectra of reproducible over-all density, because of fluctuations in the source and in plate response. It is therefore necessary to use, as a measure of the $\log I$ of a line, the difference in $\log I$ between the line of the element sought, A, and some comparison line, M, that is independent of the concentration of A, but whose $\log I$ will vary with the line A for any fluctuations due to the source or plate. There are essentially two ways in which the $\Delta \log I$ is obtained: (1) external comparison, or external standard, and (2) internal comparison, or internal standard.

1. Method of External Standard, or External Comparison. On each plate, or on each run, there are imposed spectra of material, M, which is similar to that being analyzed and which is of known composition with respect to the element A. In order to compensate for source fluctuation, it is usual to start with a definite amount of sample and then, with arc excitation, to burn it to completion. A scale may then be obtained either by using materials of graded composition or by using a series of graded initial amounts of the standard material. The samples are then exposed in similar fashion. A selected line is read in all spectra, and the interpolation is performed in the usual manner. (This is essentially the method in absorption spectra photometry using the rotating step sector as the means of obtaining the graded scale.) This method is evidently independent of plate calibration and hence is independent of the change of plate contrast as a function of wavelength. A variant of this method is to dispense with the exposures of similar standards but to use as reference the spectrum from an assumed reproducible source for an accurately measured time exposure. Some sources for this purpose

have been a high-intensity helium lamp or a globule arc of pure iron, nickel, cobalt, etc. The specimens are burned to completion as before.

The method, or methods, are clearly restricted to arc sources. They may be used with visual comparison, for rough go or no-go evaluations. Even with densitometric evaluation they have not been capable of the highest precision or accuracy. In certain instances, however, the accuracy and precision may be adequate, and this procedure is still in use in some laboratories.

2. Method of Internal Standard, or Internal Comparison. In this procedure, a comparison is made between a line of A and a line of the matrix material or element, M. Thus for ferrous materials M would be iron, for aluminum alloys M would be aluminum, for brass M would be copper, etc. The variation in the equivalent intensity of the line of M is assumed to compensate for local fluctuations of the source and plate. There are three main variants in this method.

(a) A series of lines of M_i, of graded intensity, are determined by the use of standards, so that the composition of the sample is obtained by bracketing the line A between two lines of M_i.

(b) If no suitable line of M is available, a known amount of extraneous material, say cobalt, chromium, gallium, or lithium, which is known not to occur in the sample is added to the sample as a tracer, and a line of the added material is used as the reference line M.

(c) A line of the base material, M, is used for comparison to obtain $\log I_A - \log I_M$. This is the method most commonly chosen for precise analysis, particularly of metals with spark excitation. It will be the only method to be discussed here and will be termed the method of internal standard, or internal comparison.

This method clearly requires the use of a calibration curve, and, although it is capable of highest precision, at present it involves certain difficulties. Thus, in order to minimize error, for a certain range of A it is necessary to find a line, M, whose density is close to that of line A at the center of its concentration range. The lines must be close together in wavelengths, since a wide separation of λ may involve, for a given emulsion, a significant difference in γ and sensitivity, a condition which is difficult to compensate or adjust. In addition, the two lines, if they are not arc-spark stable, should be equally variant or affected. In bases of complex spectra, such as iron, nickel, chromium or cobalt, there may be enough choice of lines, M_i, so that one may be selected that will yield reasonably precise results, but in bases such as aluminum or magnesium the scarcity of suitable lines for M_i presents a real and apparently insurmountable difficulty. For example, any error or unaccounted-for variation in γ will accentuate the error in the estimation of $\Delta \log I$, and hence in the final result.

The usual order of expressing $\Delta \log I$ is $\log I_A - \log I_M$; hence $\Delta \log I$ is an increasing function of the concentration or percentage of A. It has been almost universally observed that for limited percentage ranges $\Delta \log I$ is a linear function of log per cent, and this coordinate scheme and linear relation will be assumed as normal. It is apparent why there are changes in the selection of line pairs, i.e., correlated lines of A and reference M, for the same element A, but for different concentration or percentage ranges, since the density of line A should fall in the range of the densitometer, and $\Delta \log I$ should be small, less than ± 0.3, in order to minimize errors due to variations in γ. For plate calibration, it may be practical to use homologous lines, i.e., lines resulting from the same energy levels of the atom, since it is theoretically sound to anticipate that such lines would present a stable reproducible group with constant relative intensities independent of the source or source fluctuations. There are no truly homologous lines groups or pairs for different elements (8), however. The choice of line pairs thus becomes a matter of search and evaluation of all possible or expedient line pairs.

It has been frequently observed, for both external and internal comparison methods, that more reproducible comparisons (perhaps time-equilibrium values) are obtained if the samples are excited for a short time before exposing the plate. This period is usually called the preburn time.

7.2. ANALYSIS II

The following scheme may be taken as a typical systematic outline of an investigation for the analysis of low-alloy steel as a typical material. The elements sought are given in Table II, followed by the outline. Since an established spectrographic method should be an almost

TABLE II

Spectrographic Analysis of Steel

Method number	Elements to be determined and ranges in per cent	
13-S-	Aluminum	0.003-0.100
14-S-	Silicon	0.03-0.80
22-S-	Titanium	0.0015-0.10
23-S-	Vanadium	0.017-0.37
24-S-	Chromium	0.016-3.6
25-S-	Manganese	0.10-2.0
28-S-	Nickel	0.025-5.5
29-S-	Copper	0.065-0.65
42-S-	Molybdenum	0.020-0.90

completely mechanized procedure directed to produce the highest precision possible within the range of variation of parameters that are made possible by the flexibility of the equipment, it has been found that a statistical analysis of the investigative results is helpful, if not absolutely necessary. An elaboration of the statistical background, with illustrative examples, will be presented in the following sections.

7.2.1. Scope of Investigation. It is assumed that the development of methods for the analysis of steel will be primarily directed to those suitable for routine use in the field inspection laboratories. The essential difficulty will be in the effort to increase speed of performance and still retain requisite precision.

It is expected that difficulties will be encountered in the proper adjustment or control of most of the component individual operations or phases of a spectrographic method, the most important of which may be itemized as follows:

1. Excitation
   (a) Source: control, choice of parameters, adjustment
   (b) Arc geometry: electrode form and physical history of the sample
2. Photographic Plates
   (a) Processing
   (b) Calibration
   (c) Measurement of line density
3. Spectrography
   (a) Effect of spectrograph
   (b) Choice of line pair
4. Interpretation
   (a) Determination of analytical result
   (b) Evaluation of precision and accuracy
5. Uniformity between laboratories

It is not practicable to consider and investigate all difficulties simultaneously. A laboratory should realize the scope of the entire problem and then proceed on the basis of its own experience and suggestions submitted by other laboratories. The investigative results should be carefully evaluated, and the more serious sources of error or difficulty isolated as far as possible. Subsequent efforts should be directed to reduce or control these sources of error. Continued application of this step-by-step procedure, with objective self-criticism of the result, is bound to effect the most judicious choice of the details of an analytical method.

7.2.2. Coordination of Laboratories. Every laboratory in the spectrographic standardization group should partake in this cooperative effort, using whatever spectrographic equipment is available.

In general, a method should be considered in the "tentative" class until it has been submitted for comment to all cooperating laboratories using similar equipment and agreement has been reached on all essential details. It is highly important that uniformity of analytical results be obtained in all laboratories, and there is no better assurance of this condition than the use of uniform methods on similar equipment.

A. INDEX

1. *Spectromethod.* The code letter symbol for this series of methods is S. The element to be determined will be indicated by its full name in the upper left corner of each page, and the code number of the method in the upper right corner. The code number at the left is the atomic number of the element whose analysis is sought. The number at the right indicates the serial number of the method under discussion.

In order to facilitate the comparison and classification of tentative or proposed methods it is suggested that a symbol to indicate the particular combination of electrode form and spark source variety be placed in parentheses immediately after the method number. A suitable code is shown in the following table. For example: (a) A second method, for (b) analysis of molybdenum, using a (c) flat specimen, with (d) graphite counter electrode, and an (e) air-quenched spark, would be indicated as follows: No. 42-S-2 (A33)

Electrode form	Spark source	
	Rotary or synchronous	Air-quenched
Self-electrodes:		
Pins	R 11	A 11
Pellets	R 12	A 12
Flats	R 13	A 13
Iron counterlectrodes:		
Pins	R 21	A 21
Pellets	R 22	A 22
Flats	R 23	A 23
Graphite counterelectrodes:		
Pins	R 31	A 31
Pellets	R 32	A 32
Flats	R 33	A 33

2. *Superseded Methods.* A list of all previous used methods that are superseded by the proposed method.

3. *Simultaneous Determinations.* A list of all determinations that may be made on the spectrum produced in this procedure.

B. MATERIAL PREPARATION

This section in the usual method report is devoted to a discussion of the material to be analyzed, specification type, restriction on physical history, etc. In this outline this section will describe the preparation of the standards, which for present analytical purposes are to be considered as submitted specimens.

1. Material

(a) Type. The specimens were prepared from induction heats poured into heated cast-iron molds. The as-cast ingot was in the form of a rounded truncated right circular cone, the bases of which varied from about $4\frac{1}{2}$ to 2 inches in diameter with the height about 18 inches. Hot top had been provided for most of the ingots. The trimmed castings weighed about 200 pounds each. The castings were ground clean and forged into bars about 3 inches square and annealed. The long dimension of a bar is in the axial direction of the ingot. A section of each ingot was macroetched and examined for flaws, particularly those suggesting segregation.

(b) Form. Each ingot was prepared in three forms: pins, flats, and millings. Pins were prepared by forging part of the square bar into rods $\frac{5}{16}$ inch in diameter, annealed, and machined to $\frac{1}{4}$ inch in diameter by $2\frac{1}{2}$ inches long. The axis of a pin coincides with the axis of the original ingot. Flats were prepared by forging part of the square bar into a rectangular bar $2\frac{1}{2}$ inches by $\frac{1}{2}$ inch, annealed, and machined into pieces $2\frac{3}{8}$ inches by $1\frac{1}{4}$ inches by $\frac{3}{8}$ inch thick. The $1\frac{1}{4}$-inch dimension is in the axial direction of the original ingot. Millings or chips were prepared by machining a channel in part of the square bar, in the longitudinal direction. The pins, flats, and millings, as supplied, have been prepared in the completely annealed state. A few specimens of pins and flats have been hardened so that the effect of metallurgical treatment or physical history of a specimen on the spectrographic procedure may be evaluated.

Solution or spectrochemical methods will not be discussed in this outline. Such procedures are considered to be of a lower order of desirability compared to the direct use of specimens. If experimental conditions or results warrant the use of such procedures they should be adopted.

2. Electrodes

(a) Type. It is anticipated that self-electrodes will be used with pins and pellets and that an iron or graphite counterelectrode will be used with flats. The use of counterelectrodes with pins and pellets will be investigated.

(b) Form. Pins should be ground to a cone top, about 150° included angle, for use in the rotary or synchronous spark, and with a flat top for use in the air-interrupted spark. Flats should be ground clean and flat before using. The shape of the counterelectrodes, i.e., whether the iron or graphite counterelectrode should be flat or conical, is to be considered as one of the experimental factors to be determined. The shape of the pellets made from drillings should be carefully described.

(c) Preparation. Complete details of the manner of preparing the electrodes and the quality of the surface should be described.

3. Standards

(a) Type. A sufficiently detailed description of the relevant standards should be given to indicate their nature.

C. SPECTROGRAPHY

1. Spectrograph

(a) Type. The various laboratories will necessarily use the spectrographs that are available. Since grating spectrographs produce spectra with higher density differences on the photographic plate than are obtained with prism instruments under comparable conditions, it is expected that two sets of analytical conditions, or two methods, will be developed for the same analysis. Although the large Littrow prism spectrograph is probably the most commonly used instrument, it is anticipated that enough data on other instruments will soon be assembled to make possible valid estimates of the influence of the spectrograph on the analytical procedures and results.

(b) Wavelength Region. Because of the extensive use of prism spectrographs and nonsensitized photographic emulsions, it is suggested that the lines be restricted to the region 2200 to 3450 A. This is not intended to prevent laboratories with grating spectrographs from taking advantage of the normal dispersion and using longer wavelengths if warranted.

2. Optics

(a) Quartz. The delay in changing from quartz to glass prisms is sufficiently great to be discouraged unless proved to be highly advantageous.

(b) Focus of Arc. On the collimator lens. The concentrations of the residuals are considered to be sufficiently high so that there is no necessity for focusing on the slit.

(c) Field Lens. Plano-curvex, mounted immediately adjacent to the slit with the curved surface toward the arc.

(d) Distance Source to Slit. Every effort should be made to restrict the number of distances to the minimum, probably 2. The precise choice will be decided after the preliminary methods have been compared.

(e) External Condensing Lens. As far as possible no external lens is to be used.

(f) Filter. As far as possible no filter is to be used.

3. Slit

(a) Width. As far as possible one slit width is to be used on prism instrument on which a width of 25 μ (0.025 mm.) is suggested. A wider slit may be standardized for grating spectrographs.

(b) Length. The length of line is to be governed by the densitometer characteristics. The various lengths should be standardized, however; for example, 1.0, 1.5, 2.0, 2.5, 3.5, 5.5 mm.

4. Excitation

(a) Type. The following types of excitation should be considered: (I) High-voltage a.c. arc; (II) (a) high-voltage spark, synchronously interrupted, or (b) high-voltage spark, air-interrupted.

(b) Primary Circuit Input

(c) Secondary Circuit characteristics

(d) Control. A detailed account of the characteristics of excitation sources should be presented or referred to. The data given below are to be used as a guide for comparison of conditions.

(I) The high-voltage a.c. arc recommended is one operating at about 4000 volts and 2 to 2.5 amp. Control of the secondary current is to be effected by resistance in the secondary circuit. The 2000-ohm resistance will have a pronounced stabilizing effect, since the resultant current will not be unduly influenced by minor changes or fluctuations in the arc itself.

(II) The stability or control of the spark circuit, at present, is to be measured by the constancy and reproducibility of the oscillating current. The ammeter should be a carefully calibrated thermocouple activated r.f. instrument. Because the ammeter will give only an averaged value, it is necessary to indicate more constants or parameters of the electrical circuit. The usual data should include the following:

1. Secondary or oscillating voltage, to be measured on a calibrated cathode ray oscilloscope.

2. Capacitance, to be measured by a bridge or computed from the manufacturer's rating of the condensers used.
3. Inductance, to be calculated from the known capacitance and measured radiofrequency of the oscillating circuit.
4. Resistance in the primary, oscillating, and filter circuits.
5. Time elements, the location and duration of the discharge in the electrical cycle. This will include the frequency of the discharge in the air interrupted source.

It is to be understood that these factors are not of equal or even of critical importance; however, until the real connection between parameters of the electrical discharge and the quantitative stability of the radiated spectrum is determined, it is advisable to indicate the above quantities.

(e) Arc gap: $5/32$ inch. It is advisable to use a constant arc gap for all procedures, if possible.

5. Exposure

(a) Preburn
(b) Exposure

The methods should involve constant time conditions as far as possible. It is advisable to determine the effect of exposure time, of both the preburn and the exposure periods, within at least twice the range of the finally accepted values. The equilibrium conditions with respect to the preburn period should be carefully investigated with respect to the effect of surface conditions.

6. Photography

(a) Emulsion: Kodak spectrum analysis No. 1
(b) Processing: Develop 4 minutes in D-19 at 65°F. No difficulty is anticipated in arriving at the use of a common emulsion type and dark-room procedure.

D. ANALYSIS

1. Line Pairs

(a) Element
(b) Reference or Iron Line. The following line pairs are suggested for preliminary investigation, with no prejudice concerning their final acceptance (Table III).

2. Line Interference

(a) Interferences should be carefully evaluated with regard to the variety of compositions involved.

TABLE III

Analytical Line Paris

Element	Element line[a]	Reference iron line[a]	Range (%)	Equivalence point (%)	Excitation (arc a.c., or spark)
Mn	2933.06	2936.91	0.20 -0.45	—	S
	2933.06	2897.26	0.45 -0.65	—	S
	2558.59	2553.73	0.65 -2.0	—	S
	2886.69	2906.12	0.20 -0.80	—	S
	2886.69	2885.93	0.80 -1.50	—	S
	2886.69	2902.47	0.5 -1.2	0.92	S
Ni	3002.49	2980.54	0.03 -0.35		
	2316.04	2318.35	0.05 -0.25	0.11	A
	2316.04	2322.33	0.20 -0.50	—	S
	2303.00	2307.31	0.50 -1.0	—	S
	2303.00	2304.73	0.30 -1.0	—	S
	2300.09	2294.61	1.0 -1.8	—	S
	2300.09	2304.73	1.4 -4.0	—	S
	2302.47	2303.35	1.6 -2.5	—	S
	2302.47	2304.73	2.5 -3.5	—	S
	2302.47	2307.31	3.5 -5.5	—	S
Cu	3273.96	3277.35	0.05 -0.20	—	S
	3273.96	3286.76	0.20 -0.50	—	S
	3273.96	3265.62	0.04 -0.40	0.13	S
Mo	2816.15	2815.51	0.02 -0.15	—	A
	2775.40	2776.18	0.15 -0.70	0.29	S
	2775.40	2789.48	0.01 -0.05	—	S
	2775.40	2770.51	0.50 -1.0	—	S
Al	3082.16	3080.11	0.003-0.02	—	A
	3082.16	3078.43	0.02 -0.05	—	A
	3082.16	3053.44	0.05 -0.10	—	A
	3082.16	3075.72	0.7 -2.0	1.5	S
Si	2881.58	2886.32	0.03 -0.06	—	A
	2881.58	2875.30	0.06 -0.10	—	A
	2881.58	2874.17	0.10 -0.80	0.14	S
V	3110.71	3106.56	0.02 -0.10	—	S
	3110.71	3075.72	0.10 -0.40	—	S
	3185.40	3184.90	0.02 -0.15	—	A
	3102.30	3065.32	0.01 -0.15	—	S
	2924.02	2912.16	0.10 -0.40	—	S
	2906.46	2906.12	0.10 -0.50	—	S
Ti	3372.80	3355.23	0.002-0.100	—	S
	3234.50	2331.71	0.007-0.06	—	S
Cr	2843.25	2827.90	0.02 -0.35	—	A
	2677.16	2676.88	0.01 -0.12	—	S
	2677.16	2682.52	0.12 -0.25	—	S
	2677.16	2642.02	0.25 -0.45	—	S
	2862.57	2876.80	0.45 -1.2	—	S
	2818.36	2837.29	1.2 -2.0	—	S
	2818.36	3819.33	0.3 -1.5	0.80	S
	2822.37	2819.33	0.15 -1.0	0.25	S
	2862.57	2861.19	0.02 -0.45	—	S
	2921.24	2918.03	1.60 -3.00	—	S
	2812.01	2827.90	0.35 -1.10	—	S
	2834.26	2837.30	1.90 -4.0	—	S

[a] Line assignments are taken from (11), the best readily available compilation of wave-length assignments.

3. Densitometry

(a) Type. Each laboratory will necessarily adapt the methods to suit the range of its available densitometer. The discussion in this outline is based on the use of a Leeds & Northrup recording microphotometer.

(b) Scale: Density: Some laboratories may use transparency units. The conversion formulas and some examples are given below, where D = density and T = transparency.

$$D = \operatorname{colog}_{10} T = \log_{10} \frac{1}{T} \tag{1}$$

$$T = \operatorname{antilog}_{10}(-D) = \operatorname{antilog}_{10}(\text{complementary } D) \tag{2}$$

Examples:

(1)

T	0.132	0.428	0.526	0.927
$\log_{10} T$	9.121–10	9.632–10	9.721–10	9.967–10
$D = \operatorname{colog}_{10} T$	0.879	0.369	0.279	0.033

(2)

D			
Complementary $D = -D$	9.699–10	9.369–10	8.845–10
Antilog $(-D)$	0.500	0.234	0.070

For convenience, density measurements considered in the remainder of this outline will be multiplied by 1000 to do away with the decimal point.

4. Plate Calibration

(a) Normal or Intensity Scale
(b) Coordinates: density $\times$ log I

The following is a condensed treatment suitable for the practical calibration of plates or film for the analysis of steel using Kodak spectrum analysis No. 1 emulsion (SA-1).

It is known that the response of a photographic emulsion is not linearly connected with the *exposure*, where *exposure* is defined as dependent on the intensity of the light source and the time it is permitted to act on the plate. If a light source of constant intensity were permitted to act on a plate for various times, the response or blackness of the marks on the plate, measured in some consistent manner, would not be linearly proportional to the duration of exposure. In a similar manner, if a plate were exposed to various light sources of different intensities for the same duration or time, the response of the plate would not be linearly proportional to the various light intensities. Hence, one may seek to establish a procedure to take care of the variation of response of a plate to a constant source for different lengths of time (time scale calibration) or to the variation of response of a plate to sources of different intensities for equal duration or time (intensity scale calibration). The latter calibration will be termed *normal*.

For many reasons it is desirable to choose coordinate systems or units of measurement for the plate response and exposure in such a manner that the relation between them may be accurately represented by a straight line in the ranges of coordinates most frequently used in spectrographic analysis. As a result of many measurements, it has been concluded that the calibration or response curve for SA-1 emulsion is a straight line in density × log intensity ($D \times \log I$) or density × log exposure ($D \times \log E$) coordinates for densities between 500 and 1500. The line has a positive slope termed gamma (γ). In spectrographic applications it is necessary to consider only differences in log I; hence, the intercept of the straight line on the log I axis may be assigned any arbitrary value.

The fundamental relation may be written

$$\Delta D = \gamma \cdot \Delta \log I \qquad (D \geq 500) \tag{3}$$

where ΔD is defined as difference in density and $\Delta \log I$ as difference in log intensity.

The value of γ depends on the particular emulsion batch or lot and the particular plate or even portion of plate being used. It also depends on the wavelength of the radiation used to act on the plate. Thus at 2300 A. the value of γ may be about 1.1, whereas at 2600 A. it may be about 1.9.

So far nothing has been said about the curve for $D < 500$. The determination of this portion of the curve has been simplified since it was discovered "that the slopes of two intensity scale calibration curves made to different wavelengths but having the same exposure time bear a constant relationship (ratio) to each other" (see p. 299). It is thus necessary to determine the shape of the entire curve ($100 < D < 1500$) only for one wavelength portion of the spectrum. A determination of the γ's, or the slopes of the straight-line portions, for the various wavelength regions will be sufficient to determine the entire curve for all such portions. In addition, it has been found that the shapes of the curves as determined for different plates and for emulsion lots are essentially similar in their relationship of slopes for corresponding densities. Hence, a calibration curve prepared as an average calibration over a period of several years and computed to a γ of 1 may be used as a standard reference or rectification curve. The coordinates of such a curve are given in Table V. Many experimental procedures are available or may be devised to measure the γ on a given plate at a given wavelength. The method to be described here is based on the selected reference iron lines and will yield satisfactory results if the procedure is carefully followed. The procedure is divisible into two parts: (I) Determination of γ at 2650 A. or the fundamental region; (II) determination of γ at any other wavelength region.

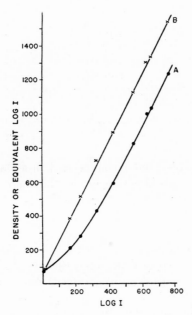

Fig. 7. Rectification of plate characteristic curve.

(I) *Determination of* γ *at 2650 A.* A synchronously interrupted spark is excited between two pins of mild steel, under the following conditions: capacitance, 0.009 to 0.012 μf.; inductance, 33.5 μh.; primary resistance, 5 to 6 ohms. added secondary resistance, none. The tops of the pins are ground to a conical top of about 150° included angle. The gap should be about $\frac{5}{32}$ inch. Exposure conditions, including the time, should be adjusted so that the density of line No. 1 is not much over 1200. The reference iron lines given in Table IV are used. Two procedures may now be followed.

(1) The densities of the nine lines are plotted against the log I indicated in Table IV (see curve A in Fig. 7). This is the simplest procedure. The results so obtained, however, yield no information concerning the accuracy or precision of

TABLE IV

Line no.	Wavelength (A.)	Log I
1	2633.194	760
5	2649.464	655
6	2658.251	630
3	2642.015	550
8	2682.518	425
9	2691.732	325
2	2635.393	230
7	2669.934	165
4	2646.217	0

the determination, and conclusions concerning the effect of the variation of the curve from plate to plate are not easily obtainable.

(2) The second and recommended procedure is based on the use of a rectification curve, the coordinates of which are given in Table V. The procedure is as follows:

(a) Five spectra are imposed on a plate, and the densities of the nine reference lines (Table IV) are measured.

(b) The equivalent intensities ($\gamma = 1$) corresponding to the densities are obtained from Table V.

(c) A straight line is passed through the mean values of the equivalent intensities of each of the nine lines (Y_i) and the corresponding log I values given in Table IV (X_i) by the method of least squares (curve B in Fig. 7).

The slope of this line is the γ of the emulsion. The precision of measurement, determined by statistical computation, furnishes estimates not only of the degree to which the points fit the straight line but also the degree to which the calibration curve determined for the specific emulsion is similar in shape to the standard curve. A calibration table, similar to Table V, is then prepared for the emulsion being measured by dividing the entries in Table V by γ as determined for the emulsion.

(II) *Determination of γ at any desired wavelength region*

(1) Ten spectra of mild steel are prepared, and the spectrograph adjustment is selected which will include the funda-

mental region and the wavelength region to be measured. The spectra should be divided into two exposure groups, five spectra within each group, with the exposures so controlled that the densities of the same lines within each group are as uniform as possible, but the difference in equivalent intensity ($\gamma = 1$) for the same lines between the two groups for the fundamental region should be from 500 to 600.

(2) The γ of the fundamental region as previously described is determined.

(3) The densities of about five lines are measured in each of the spectra in the fundamental region whose γ is to be determined. It is advisable to restrict the measurement to iron (spark lines), but this limitation is not too stringent. It is, however, necessary to measure the same line in each of the ten spectra.

(4) The measurements are tabulated, and the densities, in both regions and both groups, are converted to equivalent intensities by means of Table V.

(5) The mean or average equivalent intensity is computed for each line in each group for the two regions.

(6) The mean difference is computed between the two groups for the two regions.

(7) Let Δ_1 be the mean or average difference in equivalent intensity for the fundamental region.

Δ_2 be the mean or average difference in equivalent intensity for the other region being measured.

γ_1 be the γ of the fundamental region.

γ_2 be the γ of the other region to be determined.

Then

$$\gamma_2 = \frac{\Delta_2}{\Delta_1} \gamma_1$$

(8) A calibration table similar to Table V is then prepared for the region under consideration by dividing the entries in Table V by γ_2.

Notes: It is sufficient, for most analyses, to round off the value of γ to the nearest 0.05. A few tables for the most frequently occurring values of γ will then suffice for all practical use. The critical region at 2300 A. should be calibrated for every emulsion.

Example I: Calibration of the Fundamental Region

Emulsion 1-C-7

(Manufactured the 1st week of March, 1947)

Reference line	1	5	6	3	8	9	2	7	4
					Density				
Spectrum 1	1240	1060	1025	840	610	455	295	240	85
2	1200	990	960	815	570	400	265	195	70
3	1230	1030	1000	825	595	435	290	215	80
4	1220	1020	985	810	570	430	275	200	75
5	1260	1060	1020	840	590	420	285	210	70
Mean	1230	1032	998	826	587	428	282	212	76
				Equivalent intensity ($\gamma = 1$) (from Table V)					
	1540	1360	1325	1140	910	751	536	439	99
	1500	1290	1260	1115	870	686	485	352	60
	1530	1330	1300	1125	895	728	528	392	86
	1520	1320	1285	1110	870	722	502	362	73
	1560	1360	1320	1140	890	710	519	382	60
Mean	1530	1332	1298	1126	887	719.4	514	385.4	75.6 = Y
Intensity from Table IV	760	655	630	550	425	325	230	165	0 = X

Let n = number of terms; S = summation symbol; cf = correction factor

$$SY = 1530 + 1332 + \cdots + 385.4 + 75.6 \qquad = 7867.4$$
$$SY^2 = (1530)^2 + (1332)^2 + \cdots + (385.4)^2 + (75.6)^2 \qquad = 8790554$$
$$cf = (SY)^2/n = (7867.4)^2/9 \qquad = 6877331$$

$$Sy^2 = SY^2 - cf \qquad = 1913223$$
$$SX = 760 + 655 + \cdots + 165 + 0 \qquad = 3740$$
$$SX^2 = (760)^2 + (655)^2 + \cdots + (165)^2 \qquad = 2072400$$
$$cf = (SX)^2/n = (3740)^2/9 \qquad = 1554178$$

$$Sx^2 = SX^2 - cf \qquad = 518222$$
$$SXY = (1530 \times 760) + (1332 \times 655) + \cdots + (385.4 \times 165) = 4264891$$
$$cf = (SY)(SX)/n = (7867.4) \times (3740)/9 \qquad = 3269342$$

$$Sxy = SXY - cf \qquad = 995549$$
Gamma (γ) $= Sxy/Sx^2 = 995549/518222 \qquad = 1.921$

To estimate precision compute

$$rf = (Sxy)^2/Sx^2 = (995549)^2/518222 \qquad = 1912535$$
$$SS = Sy^2 - rf \qquad = 688$$
$$V = \text{mean square} = \frac{SS}{n-2} = \frac{688}{.7} \qquad = 95$$

Precision is estimated by the mean square, V. For a determination or procedure similar to that described the value of V should not be more than 450 (at most 500). If this value is exceeded, an investigation should be made into possible sources of error such as excitation condition (adjustment of interrupter), arc gap geometry, or development processing.

To obtain a calibration table for this emulsion, divide the entries in Table V by 1.921. For practical purposes, it does not make much difference if the γ is taken to be 1.90 or 1.95.

NOTES: A proper evaluation of the variation of γ from spectrum to spectrum (and similarly from plate to plate), with due account taken of the precision, may be arrived at by the methods of Statistical Analysis of Variance. Figure 8 illustrates the shapes of the characteristic curves for $\gamma = 1$ and $\gamma = 2$.

Example II. Calibration at 2300 A. (γ at 2650 A. = 1.921.). The data are based on the means of measurements on five spectra, within each group, after conversion of density to equivalent log I, from data in Table V.

Line	F1	F2	F3	F4	F5
			Fundamental region		
Line	F1	F2	F3	F4	F5
Dark group	1450	1245	985	850	1160
Light group	890	674	413	270	580
Δ_1	560	571	572	580	580
Mean Δ_1	—	572.6			
			2300-A. region		
Line	L1	L2	L3	L4	L5
Dark group	592	912	975	610	1065
Light group	260	576	633	260	713
Δ_2	332	336	342	350	352
Mean Δ_2	—	342.4			

$$\gamma_2 = \frac{\Delta_2}{\Delta_1}\,\gamma_1 = \frac{342.4}{572.6} + 1.921 = 1.149 = 1.15$$

5. Working Curve

(a) Comparison. This is usually a difference between the log intensity values of the reference and comparison lines. The use of intensity has been reported by some laboratories, however.

(b) Coordinates. Although log per cent of the element and Δ log I are the usual coordinates, other systems have been reported.

(c) Curve. A marked deviation from a straight line should be carefully investigated.

(d) Equivalence Point (per cent element at which log $I = 0$)

(e) Density at Equivalence Point. Every effort should be made

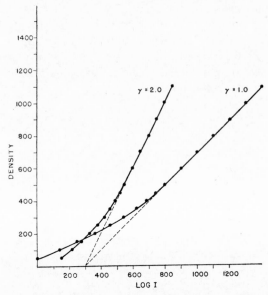

Fig. 8. Effect of γ on shape of characteristic curve (computed).

TABLE V

Spectrum Analysis No. 1 Calibration
$(\log I) \; \gamma = 1.0$

Density	0	10	20	30	40	50	60	70	80	90
0						6	33	60	86	112
100	137	162	186	210	233	256	278	300	321	342
200	362	382	401	420	439	458	476	494	511	528
300	544	560	576	591	606	620	634	647	660	673
400	686	698	710	722	734	746	757	768	779	790
500	800	810	820	830	840	850	860	870	880	890
600	900	910	920	930	940	950	960	970	980	990
700	1000	1010	1020	1030	1340	1050	1060	1070	1080	1090
800	1100	1110	1120	1130	1440	1150	1160	1170	1180	1190
900	1200	1210	1220	1230	1540	1250	1260	1270	1280	1290
1000	1300	1310	1320	1330	1340	1350	1360	1370	1380	1390
1100	1400	1410	1420	1430	1440	1450	1460	1470	1480	1490
1200	1500	1510	1520	1530	1540	1550	1560	1570	1580	1590
1300	1600	1610	1620	1630	1640	1650	1660	1670	1680	1690
1400	1700	1710	1720	1730	1740	1750	1760	1170	1780	1790
1500	1800	1810	1820	1830	1840	1850	1860	1870	1880	1890

to fix the equivalence point near the center of the range of analysis and in the most precise measurement range of the plate and densitometer.

A preliminary computation, similar to the example given, will in many instances indicate whether the assumed investigative conditions may be satisfactory. Hence, if the equivalence point is in the center of the concentration range, the range in per cent will be 4 to 1. If the

Gamma	1.85
Slope of working curve (average)	1.3
Desired density range	900-200
Equivalent intensity ($\gamma = 1$)	1200-365
Mid-point, intensity	782
Mid-point, density	500
Range of $\Delta \log I$ $(1200 - 365)/1.85$	450
Range in log per cent $= 450 \times 1.3$	0.585
Range in per cent (ratio)	4-1

equivalence point is off-center, either the percentage range will be decreased or the density range increased. In any event a decision may be made whether to proceed with the method or not.

E. REMARKS

1. *Standards.* A list of appropriate standards should be given for each method.

2. *Precision.* A precision table should be appended to each method.

8. Appendix

1. Before leaving the quantitative study of the methods of analysis it is advisable to consider a few topics concerning procedures with reference to conditions in which the general assumptions previously made are not satisfied. The problems may be considered as concerned with analysis for element A in matrix M, but (a) the standards or samples are not similar in general composition; (b) a high dispersion or resolution of the spectra is not necessary; (c) the dissimilarity of samples, always including standards, may be of two kinds: (1) the range of concentration of A is excessively great, and (2) specific effects of a third constituent or constituents, K, occur.

The concentration of an element is usually expressed as the per cent of that element, P, using the total sample as reference, i.e., $P = A/A + M + K$. Let A represent the concentration of the element A in this sense. In the method of true internal standard, however, not when a material is added, the spectrographic measure is $S = A/M$. Since, with the variables expressed in concentration measures, $A + M +$

$K = 1$, then $\partial P / \partial A = 1$; but $\partial P / \partial s = (\partial P / \partial A) \cdot (\partial A / \partial s) = M$ $(\partial P / \partial A)$, and $\partial P / \partial s = M$, or $\delta P = M \delta S$. Hence, for S to be a constant measure of P it is necessary for M to be constant. In any event, for extreme accuracy, it is necessary to multiply S into M to obtain a measure of P. If the variation in M is small, it may be neglected. If the variation is large, owing either to the large variation in A reflected in M, or to large variations in K (dissimilar general composition), the amount of adjustment is not trivial and should not be neglected. This type of adjustment is known as the correction for dilution. In general the dilution correction may be difficult to make, since, for example, the amount of iron (M) in steel is rarely determined in any analytic procedure, or, if it is, the precision is not high; a similar situation exists with reference to aluminum or magnesium in the light alloys, or lead in storage battery alloy. On the other hand, the amount of copper in a brass or bronze is usually determined with high precision.

2. A laboratory concerned with analyses using lines restricted to a few short-wave portions of the spectrum may shorten its plate calibration procedure in the following manner. Table V is used to rectify the plate characteristic curve, that is, to give values of *equivalent density, D,* defined as follows:

$D \equiv$ density $+$ arbitrary constant (to avoid negative numbers)
for density greater than 0.5.
$\equiv$ tabular entries in Table V if the density is less than 0.5.

Then

$$\Delta D = \gamma \cdot \Delta \log I$$

If the analytical curve is assumed to be a straight line,

$$P = g \cdot \Delta \log I + \kappa$$

where $P = \log$ per cent constituent, $g = $ slope of analytical curve, and $\kappa = $ constant. Then

$$P = \frac{g}{\gamma} \cdot \Delta D + \kappa = g' \cdot \Delta D + \kappa$$

Consequently, the laboratory need only determine the slope of a good (precise) analytical curve for the few wavelength regions used in order to be able to correct current analyses for variations of plate response. There is a possible objection to this procedure, namely, that any variation of the slope of the particular analytical curve that is used, g, will also affect g'. Hence the estimation of the variation in γ is not too sound, because, if $dg'/d\gamma$ for different analytical curves in the same wavelength band is not significantly constant, then the correction for variation of γ

may be meaningless as far as improvement of precision is concerned. In this case g' should be checked for each analytical curve.

This procedure reduces the method of plate calibration to the usual analytical procedure. It is clear that the entire characteristic curve of an emulsion, if the wavelength is kept sensibly constant, is made an implicit function of one parameter, γ.

3. A specific effect of one element on the emission of another has been frequently observed and reported (5). The effect is not confined to any peculiar element or variety of material but may occur in many instances. It has long been known that the presence of an easily ionizable material, i.e., of low ionization potential, may markedly reduce the total radiation of other elements. An excessive amount of sodium, in an arc excitation, is an example. High amounts of silicon in an aluminum alloy will decrease the over-all intensity of the aluminum spectrum in a spark excitation. More peculiar are the effects of bismuth and copper on the zinc-cadmium ratios in the arc of a synthetic mixture of their carbonates. High amounts of nickel and zinc (24) will affect the magnesium-aluminum ratios in the analysis of aluminum alloys. A rather involved version of this effect has been observed in the influence of zinc, lead, and tin on each other in the analysis of bearing bronzes containing these elements in appreciable amounts (28). In this case the estimates of each of these elements must be adjusted for the effects of the others. It appears as if the effect is in general not significant when the elements are present in low amounts with a large amount of the matrix element, hence the correction has apparently not been found necessary in the analysis of low-alloy steels. Even 2% nickel, however, will affect the analysis of 1% magnesium in aluminum alloys. The effect has been observed in analyses based on external standards (24) as well in the internal standard method.

4. Flame Photometry (3). Since sodium and potassium as well as the other alkali and alkaline earth metals emit intense radiation in the visible region even in the low excitation of a gas burner, with the emission concentrated in small spectrum regions that are generally widely separated, procedures have been devised that make possible rapid analysis with the simplest forms of apparatus. Appropriate optical filters may be procured, particularly of the recent diffraction type, that are sufficiently narrow in their transmission bands to effect the separation of the desired spectrum regions. The general method consists in atomizing an aqueous solution of the metal in a gas burner, whereupon the vapor is carried into the flame and ignited (similar to the Lundegårdh source). The light arising from the flame characteristic of the element being determined is filtered free of other radiation and is brought to fall upon a barrier-layer photo-

cell. By measuring the intensity of the light produced with solutions of known concentrations and preparing a calibration curve of intensity versus concentration, the metal content of other solutions may subsequently be determined from the curve. An internal standard method may be devised by adding an element known not to be present in the solution to be analyzed, for example lithium, in the analysis for sodium. By an appropriate optical arrangement the radiation may be brought upon two photocells, one filtered to transmit lithium radiation (standard of comparison) and the other to transmit sodium radiation (to be determined). By arranging the cells in a bridge circuit with a galvanometer and potentiometer, it is possible to compare the output of the sodium and lithium responding cells. Because of the electrical characteristics of the cells and damping of the galvanometer the resistances in the circuits must be carefully chosen. The precision of the method depends on the control of the atomization and burning conditions in the instrument as well as on the control of the other ions present in the solution. Sulfates, chlorides, nitrates, organic acids, ammonium salts, and excessive amounts of sodium or potassium have pronounced specific effects on the determination of either of the elements. A similar method may be used for the determination of fluorides when mixed with lime, using the green calcium fluoride band.

5. Semiquantitative Methods. The general procedures previously discussed depend on careful consideration and preparation of standards, exposure techniques, choice of line pairs, etc. Much valuable information may be derived, however, concerning the occasional sample by approximate methods. By appropriate preparation of synthetic mixtures, or immediate use of similar metals, a few known specimens may be exposed on the plate along with the samples under consideration. By a combination of external comparison or the use of line pairs selected on the spot, it is often possible to make quite satisfactory semiquantitative estimates of the desired elements. Nor hard and fast procedure may be laid down, of course, but an ingenious spectrographer with good judgment may quickly derive satisfactory results that otherwise may be quite troublesome or difficult to obtain.

6. Techniques. Spectrographic methods have been developed for applications that would have been considered impossible a few years ago. The detection of traces has been perfected and applied even to the analysis of inert gases. The determination of the relative abundance of isotopes, particularly of lithium, hydrogen, and uranium, is now an ordinary matter. In this connection, it is interesting to note that investigations are underway to procure the presentation of the spectrum on a Vidicon tube with the read-out by electronic scanning. This procedure

would be particularly valuable when only a narrow band of the spectrum is to be scanned, as in the estimation of the isotopic concentrations in uranium.

7. Methods and Standard Specimens. Considerable effort has been expended by the American Society for Testing Materials in collecting practical methods and preparing a report on the sources and availability of standard samples and related materials for spectrochemical analyses. The importance and usefulness of these references cannot be overestimated.

References

1. American Society for Testing Materials, Symposium on Excitation Sources, Buffalo, 1945.
1a. Andranow, A. A., and Chaikin, C. E., "Theory of Oscillations." Princeton Univ. Press, Princeton, New Jersey, 1949.
2. Baly, E. C., "Spectroscopy." Longmans, Green and Company, London, 1924.
3. Berry, J. W., Chappel, D. G., and Barnes, R. B., *Ind. Eng. Chem. Anal. Ed.* **18,** 19 (1946).
4. Boettner, E. A., and Brewington, G. P., *J. Opt. Soc. Am.* **35,** 681 (1945).
5. Brode, W. R., "Chemical Spectroscopy." Wiley, New York, 1939.
5a. Carslaw, H. S., and Jaeger, J. C., "Operational Methods of Applied Mathematics." Oxford Univ. Press, New York, 1949.
6. Churchill, J. R., *Ind. Eng. Chem. Anal. Ed.* **17,** 66 (1945).
7. Dieke, G. H., Reports W-193, W-193A, WPB Research Project 28, Office of Production Research and Development, Washington.
8. Dieke, G. H., Progress Report on a Study of Standard Methods for Spectroscopic Analysis (W-36, W-54, W-72, W-90, W-128), War Metallurgy Committee of the National Academy of Science. National Research Council, Washington, 1943-44.
9. Duffin, R. J., *Bull. Am. Math. Soc.* **55,** 963 (1947).
10. Eastman Kodak Co., "Photographic Plates for Use in Spectroscopy and Astronomy," rev. ed. Rochester, New York, 1948.
10a. Finkelnburg, W., *J. Appl. Phys.* **20,** 468 (1949).
11. Harrison, G. R., "M.I.T. Wave Length Tables." Wiley, New York, 1939.
12. Kaiser, H., and Wallraff, A., *Ann. Physik* **34,** 297 (1939).
13. Kaiser, H., *Spectrochim. Acta* **2,** 229 (1942).
14. Kryloff, N. M., and Bogolinboff, N., "Introduction to Non-linear Mechanics." Princeton Univ. Press, Princeton, New Jersey, 1943.
15. Loeb, L. B., Fundamental Processes of Electrical Discharges in Gases." Wiley, New York, 1939.
16. Loeb, L. B., and Meek, J. M., "The Mechanism of the Electrical Spark." Stanford Univ. Press, Stanford, California, 1941.
17. Lundegårdh, H., "Die quantitative Spektralanalyse der Elemente." G. Fischer, Jena, 1929.
18. Mees, C. E. K., "The Theory of the Photographic Process." Macmillan, New York, 1942.
19. Minorsky, N., "Non-Linear Mechanics." Edwards, Ann Arbor, 1944.

19a. Nachtrieb, N. H., "Principles and Practice of Spectrochemical Analysis." McGraw-Hill, New York, 1950.

20. Saunderson, J. L., and Caldecourt, V. J., *J. Opt. Soc. Am.* **34**, 117 (1944).

21. Saunderson, J. L., Caldecourt, V. J., and Peterson, E. W., *J. Opt. Soc. Am.* **36**, 654 (1946).

22. Sawyer, R. A., "Experimental Spectroscopy." Prentice-Hall, New York, 1944.

23. Scribner, B., and Mullin, H. R., *J. Research Natl. Bur. Standards* **37**, 379 (1946).

24. Smith, D. M., "Collected Papers on Metallurgical Analysis by the Spectrograph." British Non-Ferrous Metal Research Committee, London, 1945.

25. Stern, J., *J. Opt. Soc. Am.* **36**, 654 (1946).

26. Strock, L., "Spectrum Analysis with the Carbon Arc Cathode Layer." A. Hilger, London, 1936.

27. Twyman, F., "Spectrochemical Analysis of Metals and Alloys." Chemical Publishing Co., Brooklyn, 1944.

28. Wolfe, R. A., and Jemal, E. J., *ASTM Bull.* **129** (1944).

ADDITIONAL REFERENCES

The most complete bibliography to the literature on spectrochemical analysis, and one which is brought up to date from time to time, is:

Meggers, W. F. and Scribner, B. F., "Index to the Literature of Spectrochemical Analysis." American Society for Testing Materials, Philadelphia, Pennsylvania.

Infrared Spectroscopy

HARALD H. NIELSEN AND ROBERT A. OETJEN

Department of Physics and Astronomy, The Ohio State University, Columbus, Ohio

1. Introduction

The infrared region is that portion of the electromagnetic spectrum between visible light and radio waves. Physically, the different portions of the electromagnetic spectrum may be distinguished by the wavelength of the radiation involved. On this basis the infrared region may be said to extend from wavelengths of about 8000 A. (0.00008 cm.) to 0.1 cm. Or, since it is sometimes more convenient to refer to the recipro-

cal of the wavelength, the region extends from about 12,500 to 10 cm.$^{-1}$.
The region between about 7000 and 12,500 cm.$^{-1}$ is known as the photographic infrared region. This region may be investigated with instruments using glass optics and photographic or photoelectric detecting

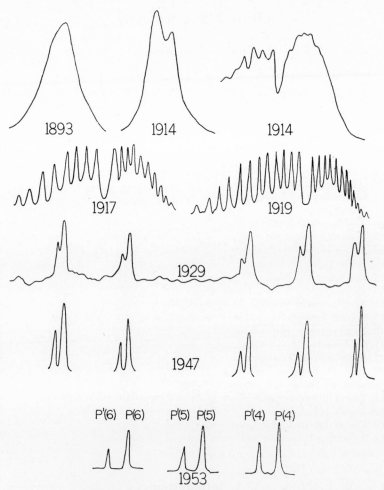

FIG. 1. Spectrograms of the 3.5-μ band of hydrogen chloride vapor showing
the best resolution available at the date indicated on each spectrogram.

devices. The causes of absorptions in this spectral region are somewhat
different from those in other regions. Because the instrumentation employed as well as the interpretation of spectra obtained are so dissimilar
to those characterizing other portions of the infrared spectrum, the

photographic portion of the infrared spectrum will not be considered in this discussion. The spectral region between about 400 and 8000 cm.$^{-1}$ has been developed considerably in the past few years and hence is now very useful both from academic and industrial points of view. This region will be most extensively discussed. In the region between 10 and 400 cm.$^{-1}$ experimental techniques have been recently developed sufficiently to provide some useful data and to give the promise of considerably more.

This chapter will deal with the spectral region principally between 400 and 8000 cm.$^{-1}$ from three points of view. First, the origin of the spectra will be considered. In discussing this, reference will be made to typical molecules and the spectra that are associated with these molecules. Attention will then be given to the translation of these spectroscopic data into useful information pertaining to the structural characteristics of the molecules, such as interatomic distances and force constants. The second point of view concerns instrumentation. There have been considerable strides in the development of infrared spectrographs. This is graphically shown in Fig. 1, in which a portion of the hydrogen chloride spectrum is reproduced at various stages of the instrumentation development, the numbers indicating the year in which that portion of the figure was recorded. At each of the stages the spectrogram was the best that could be obtained with the instrumentation available at this time. It will be observed that there has been a continuous increase in the amount of detail that can be seen and that this progress has not yet ceased. There is a third point of view represented in this discussion in that the industrial application of infrared spectroscopic techniques is also considered. Although it is similar to the point of view of the theoretical physicist who wants the data for obtaining information about molecules, the two points of view differ in that the uses to which the data are put are quite different.

2. The Origin of Band Spectra

The absorption band spectra originate when a molecule is raised from one molecular energy state to another of higher energy by the absorption of radiation. The frequency of an absorption line in cm.$^{-1}$ is given by the Bohr frequency relation:

$$\nu = \frac{10^4}{\lambda} = \frac{E' - E''}{hc} \tag{1}$$

where λ is the wavelength in microns; E' and E'' are the energies, in ergs, of the upper and lower states, respectively; h is the universal constant of Planck, 6.624×10^{-27} erg-sec.; and c is the velocity of light.

The energy of a molecular state may in a general way be written as the sum of four terms:

$$E = E_e + E_v + E_{rot} + \epsilon \qquad (2)$$

with E_e, E_v, and E_{rot} being, respectively, the electronic, vibrational, and rotational energies, and ϵ being a term of interaction between the types of motion. In general it is found to be true that $E_e \gg E_v \gg E_{rot}$. It is found experimentally that band spectra arising from transitions between levels where $E_e{}'$ and $E_e{}''$ are not the same lie in the visible or ultraviolet regions of the spectrum. We shall not be concerned with these spectra in this discussion.

2.1. The Vibrational Energies of Molecules

The vibrational energies of a molecule are the energies of the atomic nuclei oscillating about their positions of equilibrium in the electrostatic field of the electrons and the nuclei. The nature of this field is known accurately only when a solution to the quantum mechanical problem of the electronic energies is available. Since this can be realized only in the cases of the very simplest molecules, it is practice to replace the exact potential energy function by one which approximates it in the region of small displacements of the nuclei from their equilibrium positions, i.e., by a power expansion about the equilibrium values, s_{ij}^0, of the nuclear separations. An expansion which is completely general is the following:

$$V = V(s_{1,2}^0, s_{1,3}^0, \ldots, s_{ij}^0)$$
$$+ \sum_{ij} \left(\frac{\partial V}{\partial s_{ij}}\right)_0 \delta s_{ij} + \frac{1}{2} \sum_{ij} \sum_{kl} \left(\frac{\partial^2 V}{\partial s_{ij}\, \partial s_{kl}}\right)_0 \delta s_{ij}\, \delta s_{kl} + \ldots \qquad (3)$$

δs_{ij} being the difference $s_{ij} - s_{ij}^0$. In eq. (3) the first term is the value of V when the molecule is in equilibrium. Moreover, all the generalized force constants $(\partial V/\partial s_{ij})_0$ will vanish, since the slope of the potential energy surface along s_{ij} will be zero for the equilibrium value of s_{ij}. In studying the modes of oscillation of a molecule, we shall neglect all terms in expansion (3) beyond the quadratic. The quantities

$$(\partial^2 V/\partial s_{ij}\partial s_{kl})_0$$

may be regarded then as the generalized force constants which for convenience may be denoted by K_{ijkl}. These are then determined so as to give the correct positions of the fundamental bands in the spectrum. For eq. (3) we may more conveniently write

$$V_0 = V - V(s_{ij}^0) = \frac{1}{2} \sum_{ij} \sum_{kl} K_{ijkl}\, \delta s_{ij}\, \delta s_{kl} \qquad (3')$$

A completely general function like eq. (3′) has the disadvantage, frequently, that it contains more independent constants than can be determined from the experimental data. In such cases simplifying assumptions must be made that will supply additional relations between these constants. The actual form in which the potential energy function will appear depends on the nature of the assumptions adopted. One assumption, which has justified itself in many cases, is that of valence forces. This hypothesis supposes the valence forces between the atomic nuclei to be directed along the valence bonds and the deformation forces to be perpendicular to the valence arms. Another simplification which, in general, has been less successful is that of central forces. In this simplification it is assumed that in function (3′) all the coefficients $K_{ijkl} = 0$, where $i \neq j$, and $k \neq l$.

In studying the vibration of a molecule, it is important to be able to express the vibrational kinetic energy and potential energy in terms of the normal coordinates, q_s, of which there will be as many as there are degrees of vibrational freedom.* The number of degrees of oscillational freedom is determined in the following manner. If a molecule consists of N atomic nuclei, there will evidently be $3N$ degrees of freedom associated with motions of the nuclei. Three of these may be accounted for by the linear translational motion of the molecule, and three others are required to describe the rotations of the molecule in space about its center of gravity. There remain, therefore, $3N$-6 degrees of vibrational freedom.

The normal coordinates, q_s, are functions of the displacement coordinates, δs_{ij}, and are chosen in such a manner that the kinetic and potential energies will contain no cross product terms, i.e.,

$$T = \frac{1}{2} \sum_s \dot{q}_s{}^2 \quad \text{and} \quad V = \frac{1}{2} \lambda_s q_s{}^2 \tag{4}$$

where the classical frequencies of vibration, ω_s (sec.$^{-1}$), are given by

$$\omega_s = \frac{1}{2\pi} \sqrt{\lambda_s}$$

λ_s being the roots of the Lagrange secular determinant $|\lambda T - V| = 0$. In these coordinates the molecule may be regarded as an aggregate of $3N$-6 harmonic oscillators. In a given mode, s, the molecule as a whole oscillates with a given frequency, say ω_s. The actual methods for effecting the transformation to normal coordinates is beyond the scope of this

---

* In some cases the symmetry of the molecule is such that two or three modes of oscillation have the same frequencies. Such vibrations are said to be degenerate, and two or three coordinates are required to describe a single frequency ω_s. In such cases it is convenient to denote the normal coordinates by q_{s1}, q_{s2}, etc.

discussion, and for a complete discussion of this subject the reader is referred to a treatise on classical dynamics (80).

The normal vibrations of a great many molecules have been studied by several authors, but we shall here consider only a single case. We shall choose as our example the formaldehyde type of molecule (67) (ZXY_2) shown in Fig. 2. This molecule will evidently have $3 \times 4 - 6$,

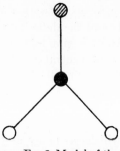

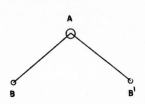

Fig. 2. Model of the formaldehyde molecule.

Fig. 3. Model of the CH_2 configuration in the CH_2O molecule.

or six degrees of vibrational motion. To analyze these we consider first the oscillation of the XY_2 group, which we shall imagine to be completely uncoupled from the Z particle. The oscillation of an XY_2 group is well known (66). Consider this configuration composed of two identical diatomic molecules, AB and AB′, as shown in Fig. 3. One may then regard two of the oscillations of the configuration as the vibrations of two diatomic molecules in phase with each other and 180° out of

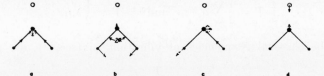

Fig. 4. Vibrations of the CH_2 group in the CH_2O molecule.

phase with each other. This is illustrated in Fig. 4a and c. The third mode of vibration may be illustrated approximately as a periodic variation of the angle 2α, the XY distances remaining unchanged as indicated in Fig. 4b. The nuclei XY_2 are, of course, not completely uncoupled from the Z nucleus as we originally assumed, and when its effect is included the motions are more nearly those shown in Fig. 5a, b, and c. A fourth type of motion is visualized if we assume the Z and X nuclei to be bound together strongly enough so that the two Y nuclei may be regarded as uncoupled from the molecule. The motion of the Z and X atoms relative to each other will then simulate the motions of the nuclei in a diatomic molecule. This is illustrated in Fig. 4d. When the motions of the two Y atoms, which, of course, are not uncoupled, are taken into account, the motion becomes more nearly like that indicated in Fig. 5d. The remaining two types of motion result from deformations of the molecule. One of these corresponds rather closely to a rocking of the XY_2 triangle in the plane of the molecule relative to the zx-axis, as

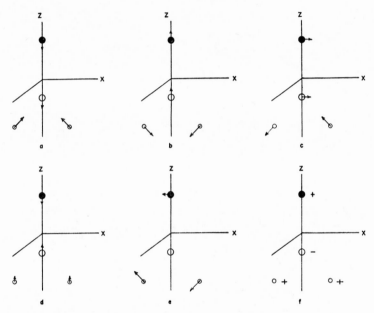

FIG. 5. Intermediate modes of vibration of the CH_2O type of molecule.

illustrated in Fig. 5e. The sixth type of motion arises from a displacement of the ZY_2 particles relative to the X particle normal to the plane of the molecule. This is shown in Fig. 5f.

Only one of the coordinates which would be needed to describe the motions suggested in Fig. 5, namely that associated with the motions 5f of the nuclei, will actually be a normal coordinate. The coordinates associated with the motions suggested in Fig. 5a, b, and d belong to the same symmetry class (i.e., they respond similarly to reflections in the xy-, yz-, and zx-planes and to a rotation through 180° of the configuration about the z-axis.) Similarly, the coordinates associated with the motions indicated in Figs. 5c and e belong to the same symmetry class. It may be shown that three of the actual normal coordinates will be three linear combinations of the coordinates associated with the motions 5a, b, and d, and that the remaining two are two linear combinations of the coordinates associated with 5c and e. The actual normal motions are more nearly like those shown in Fig. 6. The frequencies generally associated with these motions are shown below the figures.

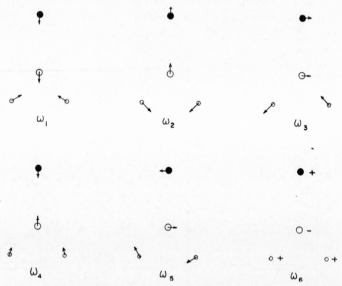

Fig. 6. Normal modes of vibration of the CH_2O type of molecule.

In the quantum theory the harmonic portion of the vibration energy takes the form

$$\frac{E_v}{hc} = \sum_s \left(v_s + \frac{g_s}{2} \right) \omega_s \tag{5}$$

where ω_s is the normal frequency, v_s is the vibrational quantum number, and g_s is a weight factor which takes the value of the degeneracy—i.e., one for a nondegenerate vibration, two for a twofold degenerate vibration, etc. In the example of the ZXY_2 configuration referred to, all the vibrations are nondegenerate so that all the factors g_s are equal to 1.

The motions of the nuclei in a molecule are, however, not such that the oscillations may be regarded as harmonic. When the contributions to the energy due to the anharmonicity of the oscillational motion are taken account of in the energy, a relation that takes the following form is obtained:

$$\frac{E_v}{hc} = \sum_s \left(v_s + \frac{g_s}{2}\right)\omega_s + \sum_s \sum_{s'} x_{ss'}\left(v_s + \frac{g_s}{2}\right)\left(v_{s'} + \frac{g_{s'}}{2}\right) + \sum_t \sum_{t'} x_{l_t l_{t'}} l_t l_{t'} \quad (5')$$

the x's being constants that depend essentially on the coefficients of the anharmonic terms in the potential energy relation. The numbers l_t are quantum numbers which have a value different from zero only for those frequencies that are degenerate; l_t is integral and takes the values v_t, $v_t - 2, \ldots, 1$ or 0, t being those values of s where a degeneracy exists.

2.2. The Rotational Energies of Molecules

The rotational energy of a molecule may to a reasonable approximation be regarded as that of a rigid rotator. The kinetic energy of the rotator may be written

$$T = \tfrac{1}{2}(I_{xx}\,\omega_x{}^2 + I_{yy}\,\omega_y{}^2 + I_{zz}\,\omega_z{}^2) \quad (6)$$

where the I_{aa} are the principal moments of inertia and the ω_a are the angular velocities. When rewritten in terms of the angular momenta (i.e., $P_a = \partial T/\partial\omega_a$), eq. (6) takes the form

$$T = \frac{1}{2}\left(\frac{P_x{}^2}{I_{xx}} + \frac{P_y{}^2}{I_{yy}} + \frac{P_z{}^2}{I_{zz}}\right). \quad (7)$$

When $P_x{}^2 + P_y{}^2$ is replaced by $P^2 - P_z{}^2$, P being the total angular momentum, eq. (7) becomes

$$T = E = \frac{1}{2}\left\{P^2 \frac{1}{2}\left(\frac{1}{I_{xx}} + \frac{1}{I_{yy}}\right) + P_z{}^2\left[\frac{1}{I_{zz}} - \frac{1}{2}\left(\frac{1}{I_{xx}} + \frac{1}{I_{yy}}\right)\right]\right.$$
$$\left. + (P_x{}^2 - P_y{}^2)\frac{1}{2}\left(\frac{1}{I_{xx}} - \frac{1}{I_{yy}}\right)\right\} \quad (8)$$

In the quantum mechanics, the quantum condition for P is fulfilled if P is replaced by $\hbar\sqrt{J(J+1)}$, J being an integer greater than or equal to zero, and $\hbar$ being the Planck constant divided by 2π. When the rotator is a symmetric rotator so that $I_{xx} = I_{yy}$, the last term of eq. (8) vanishes. In this case P_z is also quantized and is equal to $K\hbar$, where K is an integer such that $0 \leqslant |K| \leqslant J$. The energy is independent of the algebraic sign of K; i.e., all the levels where $K \neq 0$ are two-fold degenerate. The energy of the symmetric rotator may therefore be expressed as

$$\frac{E_{\text{rot}}}{hc} = J(J+1)\,B_e + K^2\,(C_e - B_e) \quad (9)$$

where
$$B_e = \frac{h}{8\pi^2\,I_{xx}c} = \frac{h}{8\pi^2\,I_{yy}c}$$

and
$$C_e = \frac{h}{8\pi^2\,I_{zz}c}$$

There are evidently $(J + 1)$ different energy levels for a given value of J.

In the case of the asymmetric rotator, the term $(1/I_{xx}) - (1/I_{yy}) \neq 0$, and in such cases the angular momentum P_z is no longer quantized so that the coefficient of the second term in eq. (8) ceases to be the square of an integer. The degeneracy of K is removed by the asymmetry so that there will be $2J + 1$ different energy values; i.e., there will be $2J + 1$ different coefficients, W, of the second term in eq. (8) for a given value of J. The evaluation of the coefficients W is, in general, a laborious task beyond the scope of this discussion. In such cases, however, where $(P_x^2 - P_y^2)[(1/I_{xx}) - (1/I_{yy})]$ is a quantity which may be regarded as small when compared to the first two terms in eq. (8), the K splitting is small, and it is possible to write the energy for the asymmetric rotator as that of a perturbed symmetric rotator. It may be shown to be the following:

$$
\begin{aligned}
\frac{E_{\text{rot}}}{hc} = {} & J(J+1)\,\frac{h}{16\pi^2 c}\left(\frac{1}{I_{xx}} + \frac{1}{I_{yy}}\right) + \frac{K^2 h}{8\pi^2 c}\left[\frac{1}{I_{zz}} - \frac{1}{2}\left(\frac{1}{I_{xx}} + \frac{1}{I_{yy}}\right)\right] \\
& - \left\{\frac{(J-K)(J-K-1)(J+K+1)(J+K+2)}{K+1}\right. \\
& \left. + \frac{(J+K)(J+K-1)(J-K+1)(J-K+2)}{K-1}\right\}\frac{h}{512\pi^2 c} \\
& \times \frac{\left(\dfrac{1}{I_{xx}} - \dfrac{1}{I_{yy}}\right)^2}{\left[\dfrac{1}{I_{zz}} - \dfrac{1}{2}\left(\dfrac{1}{I_{xx}} + \dfrac{1}{I_{yy}}\right)\right]}.
\end{aligned}
\tag{10}
$$

Expression (10) is, of course, invalid for the states where $K = \pm 1$. This state may be treated independently and gives the following corrections to the energy of the unperturbed rotator:

$$
\frac{\epsilon}{hc} = J(J+1)\,\frac{h}{32\pi^2 c}\left(\frac{1}{I_{xx}} - \frac{1}{I_{yy}}\right)
\tag{11}
$$

The splitting of the energy levels where $K \neq \pm 1$ occurs first in higher orders of approximation. This splitting, which is symmetric about the levels given in eq. (10), has been computed by Wang (78), who gives the following value:

$$
h\left\{\frac{\dfrac{1}{2}\left(\dfrac{1}{I_{xx}} - \dfrac{1}{I_{yy}}\right)}{\left[\dfrac{1}{I_{zz}} - \dfrac{1}{2}\left(\dfrac{1}{I_{xx}} + \dfrac{1}{I_{yy}}\right)\right]}\right\}^K \left\{\left[\frac{1}{I_{zz}} - \frac{1}{2}\left(\frac{1}{I_{xx}} + \frac{1}{I_{yy}}\right)\right](J+K)!\right\}
$$

$$
\times \{2^{3K}c(J-K)!(K-1)!^2\}^{-1}
\tag{12}
$$

There are, in general, two types of asymmetric rotators, the type approximated by the prolate type of symmetric rotator, and the type simulated by the oblate type of symmetric rotator. The former is frequently referred to as the carrot type or the cigar-shaped type; the

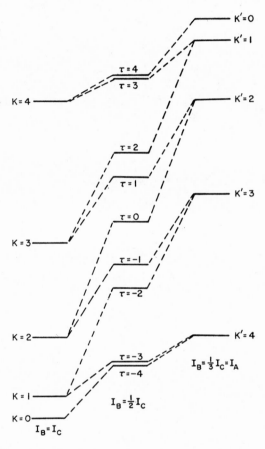

FIG. 7. Energy levels of the asymmetric rotator showing levels of the limiting symmetric rotators.

second is frequently referred to as the disk type or the tomato type. Let I_A, I_B, and I_C be the moments of inertia for a given molecule, where $I_A \leqslant I_B \leqslant I_C$. In the prolate rotator $I_B = I_C$, and the energies are given by the relation

$$E = J(J + 1)\frac{h^2}{8\pi^2 I_C} + \frac{K^2 h^2}{8\pi^2}\left(\frac{1}{I_A} - \frac{1}{I_C}\right) \tag{13}$$

For the oblate type of rotator $I_A = I_B$, and the energy is the following:

$$E = J(J + 1) \frac{h^2}{8\pi^2 I_A} + \frac{K^2 h^2}{8\pi^2} \left(\frac{1}{I_A} - \frac{1}{I_C} \right) \tag{13'}$$

The variation of the positions of the energy levels for an asymmetric rotator as it passes from the stage where its energies are simulated by a prolate symmetric rotator (i.e., where $I_B \approx I_C$) to the stage where its energies are approximately those of an oblate symmetric rotator (i.e., $I_B \approx I_A$) is illustrated in Fig. 7. At the extreme left the energies are those of the prolate rotator, and on the extreme right they are those of the oblate rotator. In the example shown $I_A = \frac{1}{3} I_C$ and the moment of inertia, I_B, is made to vary from $I_B = I_A$ in the one limiting case to $I_B = I_C$ in the other limiting case. The levels shown in Fig. 7 in the region intermediate between the two limiting symmetric rotator levels are those of an asymmetric rotator where $I_B = \frac{1}{2} I_C$. It may be seen that the highest energy levels (i.e., those where $\tau \approx J$) are best approximated by a prolate rotator spinning principally about its smallest axis of inertia, whereas those of lowest energy (i.e., those whose $\tau \approx -J$) are more nearly those of an oblate rotator spinning principally about its largest axis of inertia. This corresponds in a general way to the fact that rotation about the smallest and the largest axes of inertia are stable forms of motion for an asymmetric rotator. Rotation about the intermediate axis is an unstable form of motion, and the levels in Fig. 7, approximated badly by the levels of both of the limiting symmetric rotators, correspond in a rough way to the energies of rotation of the molecule about the intermediate axis of inertia. In the prolate example it will be seen that

$$K = (J + \tau)/2 \text{ or } (J + \tau + 1)/2,$$

and in the oblate example that

$$K = (J - \tau)/2 \text{ or } (J - \tau + 1)/2.$$

Explicit relations for the energies of asymmetric rotators cannot be achieved. Extensive calculations by Hainer *et al.* (33), by Turner *et al.* (75), and by Erlandsson (20) have, however, resulted in tables from which the energies of an asymmetric rotator of virtually any degree of asymmetry can be deduced. Moreover, certain approximation methods have been developed, notably those of Golden (26), Polo (58), and Gora (27), from which the energies of slightly asymmetric molecules may readily be computed. The latter is important, since many of the asymmetric molecules do not depart radically from the case of one of the limiting symmetric rotators.

The oscillational motion of the molecule causes the effective moments of inertia to vary from vibration state to vibration state. In most cases the moments of inertia increase in magnitude with vibrational quantum number, although abundant examples are known where the effective moments of inertia decrease. It may be shown that the reciprocals of inertia

$$X_e = \frac{h}{8\pi^2 \, I_{xx}^{(e)} c}, \qquad Y_e = \frac{h}{8\pi^2 \, I_{yy}^{(e)} c}, \text{ etc.}$$

must be replaced by

$$X_v = X_e - \sum_s \mathrm{x}_s \left(v_s + \frac{g_s}{2} \right) \text{ etc.}$$

where x_s are correction terms depending on the size and the shape of the molecule and the coefficients of the cubic anharmonic terms. Evidently then in the symmetric rotator B_e and C_e should be replaced by

$$B_v = B_e - \sum_s \alpha_s \left(v_s + \frac{g_s}{2} \right)$$

and

$$C_v = C_e - \sum_s \gamma_s \left(v_s + \frac{g_s}{2} \right)$$

The term ϵ in eq. (2) has a nonzero value only in symmetric molecules when the two- or threefold degenerate vibrations are excited and is zero for all asymmetric molecules. We shall confine ourselves here to the axially symmetric example. When a twofold degenerate oscillation, ω_t, is excited, the quantum number, l_t, may take the values $l_t = v_t$, $v_t - 2, \ldots$. The vibration possesses, therefore, an inherent internal angular momentum $l_t \zeta_t \hbar$, where ζ_t is a factor known as the Coriolis coupling factor, which depends on the nature of the normal coordinates in a rather involved manner. If more than one vibration is excited, the internal angular momentum will be equal to $\sum_t l_t \zeta_t \hbar$. The quantity P_z in eq. (7), which was the component of angular momentum of the rotator directed along the z-axis, will no longer be the total component of angular momentum of the molecule directed along this axis. The total angular momentum component, which we shall now designate as P_z', will be equal to $P_z' = P_z + \sum_t l_t \zeta_t \hbar$. The total angular momentum component directed along z is still quantized, so that $P_z' = K\hbar$ P_z, in the general case, will therefore be equal to $(K - \sum l_t \zeta_t) \hbar$. We have, therefore,

$$\frac{P_z'^2}{2I_{zz}^{(e)}} = \frac{K^2 - 2K \sum_t l_t \zeta_t + \left(\sum_t l_t \zeta_t \right)^2}{2I_{zz}^{(e)}} \tag{14}$$

The first term in eq. (14) is already included in eq. (8); the second term is the one that is designated by ϵ in eq. (2); and the third term, which depends entirely on the vibration of the molecule, is included in the coefficients $x_{l_t l_{t'}}$, which occur in eq. (5'). It is readily shown that for linear molecules the quantity $P_z \equiv 0$, or, what is the equivalent, $K = \sum_t l_t \zeta_t$. This condition requires that the terms containing $I_{zz}^{(e)}$ be absent in the energy relation for linear molecules.

2.3. The Intensities in Infrared Bands

The intensity with which a band occurs in the infrared spectrum depends on several factors, but is particularly related to the value of the electric moment of the molecule. We shall denote the x, y, and z components of the electric moment E by E_x, E_y, and E_z. Each component will, in general, to a first approximation consist of two parts, i.e.,

$$E_\alpha = E_\alpha^{(0)} + \sum_s \left(\frac{\partial E_\alpha}{\partial q_s}\right)_0 q_s \qquad (15)$$

with α taking the values x, y, and z. The quantities $E_\alpha^{(0)}$ in eq. (15) represent the x, y, and z components of the permanent electric moment, and the second term is the electric moment induced in the molecule when it oscillates in one of its normal modes.

Let us consider the nature of the electric moment of the XY_2Z molecular model referred to earlier. The permanent electric moment of the molecule is, because of the symmetry of the model, directed along the z-axis so that $E_x^{(0)} = E_y^{(0)} = 0$, but $E_z^{(0)} \neq 0$. We shall next inspect the electric moment induced in the molecule when it oscillates in each of its six modes. In the mode described by q_1 (Fig. 5a), the X and Z atoms move along the z-axis only, whereas the two Y atoms have component displacements along the z- and x-axes. The x components are, however, equal and opposite and therefore cancel each other. The same type of argument is valid for the modes described by q_2 (Fig. 5b) and q_4 (Fig. 5d), so that

$$\left(\frac{\partial E_x}{\partial q_1}\right)_0 = \left(\frac{\partial E_x}{\partial q_2}\right)_0 = \left(\frac{\partial E_x}{\partial q_4}\right)_0 = \left(\frac{\partial E_y}{\partial q_1}\right)_0 = \left(\frac{\partial E_y}{\partial q_2}\right)_0 = \left(\frac{\partial E_y}{\partial q_4}\right)_0 = 0$$

whereas

$$\left(\frac{\partial E_z}{\partial q_1}\right)_0, \left(\frac{\partial E_z}{\partial q_2}\right)_0, \quad \text{and} \quad \left(\frac{\partial E_z}{\partial q_4}\right)_0$$

will be different from zero.

When the molecule oscillates in one of the modes characterized by the coordinates q_3 (Fig. 5c) and q_5 (Fig. 5e) the X and Z atoms move parallel to the x-axis, and the two Y atoms have component motions parallel to the z- and x-axes. The components parallel to z are, however, equal and opposite and therefore cancel each other. The elecetric moment induced in these modes is therefore parallel to the x-axis, and consequently

$$\left(\frac{\partial E_y}{\partial q_3}\right)_0 = \left(\frac{\partial E_y}{\partial q_5}\right)_0 = \left(\frac{\partial E_z}{\partial q_3}\right)_0 = \left(\frac{\partial E_z}{\partial q_5}\right)_0 = 0$$

whereas

$$\left(\frac{\partial E_x}{\partial q_3}\right)_0 \quad \text{and} \quad \left(\frac{\partial E_x}{\partial q_5}\right)_0$$

are different from zero. The mode characterized by q_6 has all the atoms moving along the y-axis, and the induced electric moment is parallel to the y-axis. Therefore

$$\left(\frac{\partial E_x}{\partial q_6}\right)_0 = \left(\frac{\partial E_z}{\partial q_6}\right)_0 = 0$$

but

$$\left(\frac{\partial E_y}{\partial q_6}\right)_0 \neq 0$$

The theoretical intensity of absorption when a molecule makes a transition from a state τ'' to a state τ' has been studied by Tolman (74), who has derived the following relation:

$$(\tau''|I|\tau') = \frac{8\pi^3 \nu g_{\tau'} N_{\tau''}}{3hc g_{\tau''}} (\tau'|E|\tau'')^2 (1 - e^{-h\nu/kT}) \tag{16}$$

in which $g_{\tau''}$ and $g_{\tau'}$ are the statistical weights of the states τ'' and τ'; $N_{\tau''}$ is the number of molecules per cubic centimeter in the state τ''; and $(\tau'|E|\tau'')$ is the $(\tau'|\tau'')$ element of the electric moment determined quantum mechanically. When E is expressed in terms of its components, one has

$$(\tau'|E|\tau'')^2 = (\tau'|E_x|\tau'')^2 + (\tau'|E_y|\tau'')^2 + (\tau'|E_z|\tau'')^2$$

If we wish to make use of eq. (16) to study the intensities of near infrared bands of a molecule, only the second term in eq. (15) is of interest. It is then readily shown that, if the oscillational motion may be regarded as harmonic, the nonvanishing elements of E_a, where α takes the values x, y, and z, are the following:

$$(\tau'|E_\alpha|\tau'') = (v_1, v_2, \cdots, v_s, \cdots, v_n|E_\alpha|v_1, v_2, \cdots, v_{s-1}, \cdots, v_n)$$

$$= \left(\frac{v_s h}{8\pi^2 \nu_s}\right)^{\frac{1}{2}} \left(\frac{\partial E_\alpha}{\partial q_s}\right)_0 \tag{17}$$

Relation (17) is equivalent to saying that, if the force fields are harmonic, only the fundamental bands will occur in the spectrum (i.e., $\Delta v_s = 1$). In reality, of course, the force fields are such as to permit the motion to become anharmonic. We may therefore expect also overtone and combination bands to occur.

When the initial state of the molecule is the normal state, relation (16) becomes

$$(0, 0, \cdots, 1, 0, \cdots, 0|I|0, 0, \cdots, 0, \cdots, 0)$$

$$= \sum_{\alpha} \left(\frac{\partial E_\alpha}{\partial q_s} \right)_0^2 \frac{N_0 \pi g_1}{3 c g_0} (1 - e^{-h\nu/kT}) \quad (18)$$

Measurements have nearly always been made on absorption by gases at room temperatures, and under these conditions N_0 may be replaced by N, the total number of molecules per cubic centimeter. Moreover, the vibration frequencies, ν_s, are frequently larger than 1000 cm.$^{-1}$. When this is so, $e^{-h\nu/kT}$ will be small enough so that it may be neglected, and then eq. (18) becomes

$$(0, 0, \cdots, 1, \cdots, 0|I|0, 0, \cdots, 0, \cdots, 0) = \sum_{\alpha} \left(\frac{\partial E_\alpha}{\partial q_s} \right)_0^2 \frac{N \pi g_1}{3 c g_0} \quad (19)$$

In order to compare the actual intensities it is necessary to know the values of the quantities $(\partial E_\alpha / \partial q_s)_0$. Although various assumptions have been made concerning these quantities, no adequate method is known at the present time for calculating them theoretically.

Experimentally the intensity of a band is determined by evaluating the integral

$$I = \int k(\nu) \, d\nu \quad (20)$$

where $k(\nu)$ is the absorption coefficient that occurs in Lambert's law for the per cent transmission:

$$T = \frac{I_\nu}{I_\nu^0} = e^{-k(\nu)l} \quad (21)$$

The quantity l in the above relation is the length of the absorbing column.

The coefficient $(\partial E_\alpha / \partial q_s)_0$ may be evaluated if it is experimentally feasible to determine accurately the values of $k(\nu)$. The integral (20) may then be equated to relation (19). The term $(\partial E_\alpha / \partial q_s)_0$ is the slope of the curve of the dipole moment along the coordinate q_s when the molecule is in equilibrium, and, since the amplitude of the vibration may readily be determined, it is, in principle, possible to calculate the absolute change of dipole moment associated with the vibration.

It is frequently found to be true, however, particularly with gases, that the per cent transmission does not follow Lambert's law. The most common reason for a departure from Lambert's law is related to the difficulty of accurately determining the absorption coefficient. This difficulty may be understood in the following manner. An absorption band is composed of a group of rotation lines, whose natural width is of the order of 0.1 to 0.25 cm.$^{-1}$. In order to determine accurately the values of the absorption coefficient $k(\nu)$ it is necessary to explore the transmission with a spectrometer slit that subtends a frequency interval in the spectrum that is small compared to the line breadth. This would demand slit widths equivalent to frequency intervals of the order of 0.01 cm.$^{-1}$. At the present time it is impracticable to operate with slit widths of this size. It has been found experimentally and it may be justified from theoretical considerations (19, 45) that for small values of l the absorption by the molecules is proportional to the path length, i.e., l, and that for large values of l the absorption is proportional to the square root of the path length, i.e., $l^{1/2}$. For intermediate values of l the law is very complicated (F. Matossi, R. Mayer, and E. Rauscher, private communication).

Molecules in the liquid state are in much more intimate contact and collide with each other far more frequently. The molecules do not, therefore, rotate unhindered as they do in the gaseous state, and for this reason the rotational line structure virtually disappears, so that the absorption band becomes continuous and takes on, more or less, the appearance of an absorption line having a width of the order of 100 cm.$^{-1}$. It is possible to operate infrared grating spectrometers with slits so small as to be equivalent to about 0.05 cm.$^{-1}$ and infrared prism spectrometers with slits subtending frequency intervals of about 2 cm.$^{-1}$. One might therefore expect Lambert's law to be obeyed much more rigorously for liquids than for gases. This is, indeed, found to be the case experimentally. One might further expect in such cases that it would become feasible to determine the absorption coefficient $k(\nu)$ very accurately. It is, nevertheless, found that values for $k(\nu)$ determined by careful investigators vary considerably. This is apparently due to the fact that different spectrographs have different amounts of light of other frequencies than the one for which the instrument is set scattered by the optics. Moreover, different observers do not use the same slit width. To determine $k(\nu)$ accurately from a set of data the slit widths must be specified and all scattered light must be eliminated from the spectrometer, or at least the dependence of the scattered light on the frequency must be known so that an appropriate correction can be made. The difficulty in making exact measurements on the cell thicknesses is often also responsible for inaccuracies in the values given for the absorption coefficient, $k(\nu)$.

When several liquids are mixed together the transmission is given by the more general relation

$$T = \frac{I_\nu}{I_\nu^0} = e^{-[k_1(\nu)l_1 + k_2(\nu)l_2 + \cdots]} \tag{22}$$

Even though each liquid may individually give transmissions that conform to Lambert's law, apparent departures from the law stated in eq. (21) are known to occur when the liquids are mixed together. A discussion of such phenomena lies beyond the scope of this work, but the effect is related to the fact that the mixed molecules exert certain interactions on each other.

We have, in the preceding paragraphs, been considering the intensities of the vibration bands of a nonrotating molecule. For gas molecules, where it is possible to resolve the vibration bands into rotational fine structure, it is important to consider also the relative intensities of the individual rotation lines within a band. To accomplish this it is necessary to refer the electric moment of the rotating molecule to the axes fixed in space. The component along one of the space-fixed directions X, Y, or Z will be given by

$$E_{\alpha'} = E_x \cos(x, \alpha') + E_y \cos(y, \alpha') + E_z \cos(z, \alpha') \tag{23}$$

where α' takes the values X, Y, and Z. The direction cosines, $\cos(\alpha, \alpha')$, between the coordinate systems will be functions only of the rotational coordinates. Since the E_α depend only on the vibrational coordinates fixed in the molecule, we may write the matrix elements of the quantities $E_{\alpha'}$ symbolically as

$$(v'', R''|E_{\alpha'}|v'', R') = \sum_\alpha E_\alpha^{(0)} (R''|\cos(\alpha, \alpha')|R')$$

$$(v'', R''|E_{\alpha'}|v', R') = \sum_\alpha (v''|E_\alpha|v')(R''|\cos(\alpha, \alpha')|R') \tag{24}$$

where α is summed over the values x, y, and z, and α', as before, takes the values X, Y, and Z, and where v, and R are made to embrace all the vibration and rotation quantum numbers. It is, moreover, always convenient to identify the x-, y-, and z-axes with the principal axes of inertia of the molecule. The actual intensity of a transition will then be proportional to the sum of the squares of the matrix elements $E_{\alpha'}$, i.e., to

$$\sum_{\alpha'} (v'', R''|E_{\alpha'}|v'\, R')^2.$$

In a symmetric molecule, if a vibration induces an electric moment parallel to the z-axis fixed in the molecule, the z-axis being identified with the axis of symmetry, only the matrix elements $(v''|E_z|v')$ will have values different from zero. The intensity will then be proportional to

$$\sum_{\alpha'} (v'', R''|E_{\alpha'}|v', R')^2 = (v''|E_z|v')^2(R''|\sum_{\alpha'} [\cos (z,\alpha')]^2|R') \qquad (25)$$

When the effect on the spectrum due to rotational degeneracies is taken account of, it is found that the nonvanishing $(R''|R')$ elements of eq. (25) are the following: $(R''|A^2|R') = (J'', \quad K''|A^2|J'', \quad K'')$ and $(R''|A^2|R') = (J'', \quad K''|A^2|J'' \pm 1, \quad K'')$, where A^2 is used to denote

$$\sum_{\alpha'} [\cos(z, \alpha')].$$

These have been shown **(14, 45, 48, 61, 62)** to have the following values:

$$(J,K|A^2|J,K) = K^2/4J(J + 1)$$
$$(J,K|A^2|J - 1,K) = [(2J - 1)/(2J + 1)](J - 1,K|A^2|J,K)$$
$$= (J^2 - K^2)/4J(2J + 1) \qquad (26)$$

The type of transition here discussed is a parallel vibration (i.e., parallel to the axis of symmetry) and gives what is known as a parallel-type band.

When a vibration induces an electric moment normal to the axis of symmetry, a "perpendicular vibration" occurs and gives what is known as a perpendicular-type band. In such cases the matrix components $(v''|E_x|v')$ and $(v''|E_y|v')$ will be nonvanishing, and the intensity will be proportional to

$$\sum_{\alpha'} (v'',R''|E_{\alpha'}|v',R')^2 = (v''|E_x|v')^2(R''|\sum_{\alpha'} [\cos (x,\alpha')]^2|R') \qquad (27)$$

$$\sum_{\alpha'} (v'',R''|E_{\alpha'}|v',R')^2 = (v''|E_y|v')^2(R''|\sum_{\alpha'} [\cos (y,\alpha')]^2|R') \qquad (28)$$

When the effect on the spectrum due to the rotational degeneracies is taken into account and also the fact that the light is circularly polarized, the nonvanishing $(R''|R')$ matrix elements may be shown to be

$$(J,K|A^2|J,K \mp 1) = [(J \pm K)(J \mp K + 1)]/16J(J + 1)$$
$$(J,K|A^2|J - 1,K \mp 1) = [(J \pm K)(J \pm K + 1)]/16J(2J + 1) \qquad (29)$$
$$(J - 1,K|A^2|J,K \pm 1) = [(J \pm K)(J \pm K + 1)]/16J(2J - 1)$$

The expressions for $(\tau''|A^2|\tau')$ have here been derived on the basis that the interactions between the vibrational and rotational motions of the molecule can safely be neglected. Experience teaches that this is not actually the case. This problem has been studied experimentally by Benedict (private communication) and others, and theoretically, first by Oppenheimer (53), but more recently by Herman and Wallis, (36) Herman and Rubin (35), Hanson *et al.* (34), and Hanson and Nielsen (unpublished data). The interactions have the effect of multiplying the quantities $(\tau''|A^2|\tau')$ by a factor which is slightly J- and K-dependent.

When values (26) and (29) are used for E in eq. (18) and account is taken of the fact that the molecules are distributed in the rotational levels according to the law

$$N_{\tau''} = N_{J''K''} = \frac{N_0}{Z} g_{J''K''} e^{-E_{J''K''}/kT}$$

where

$$Z = \sum_{J''} g_{J''K''} e^{-E_{J''K''}/kT}$$

one obtains for the intensity

$(v'',J'',K''|I|v',J',K') =$

$$\frac{8\pi^3\nu_0 N_0}{3hcZ} (v'|E_\alpha|v'')^2(1 - e^{-h\nu_0/kT})(J',K'|A^2|J'',K'')g_{J'K'} e^{-E_{J''K''}/kT} \qquad (30)$$

The statistical weight $g_{J'K'}$ may be shown to have the values $(2J + 1)$ for levels where $K = 0$ and $2(2J + 1)$ for values of $K \neq 0$.

The foregoing discussion will be seen to be equivalent to establishing certain rules of transition for the symmetric rotator. Thus when a molecule executes a vibration inducing an electric moment parallel to the unique axis of the molecule, the transition or selection rules are evidently $\Delta J = \pm 1, 0; \Delta K = 0$. When, however, the molecular vibration is normal to the unique axis and the vibration is perpendicular, the selection rules will be seen to be $\Delta J = \pm 1, 0; \Delta K = \pm 1$. In the latter case the quantum numbers l_k will in general be different from zero in the excited state so that the term ϵ in eq. (2) will have a value different from zero. The selection rules are, therefore, incomplete unless the section rule for l_k is also stated. Teller and Tisza (73) have shown that the selection rule is $\Delta K = \Delta l_k = \pm 1$ so long as the vibrational motion is harmonic.

In the case of an asymmetric rotator it may be shown that the selection rule $\Delta J = \pm 1, 0$ persists. The selection rule for K will, however, no longer remain valid. The selection rules which take the place of that for K have been formulated by Wang (78), Kramers and Ittmann (42-44), and others. As long as the vibrations induce electric moments directed along the principal axes of the molecule, the section rules fall into three classifications, one classification for vibrations along each of the three principal axes of inertia. These give rise to bands described by Dennison

(15) and named by him as types A, B, and C. In certain asymmetric molecules vibrations may occur which induce electric moments having components along two, or even three, of the principal axes. In such instances the selection rules become hybrids, all classifications being permitted to a smaller or larger extent. An example of this type of molecule would be the HDO molecule.

2.4 THE SPECTROSCOPY OF LARGE MOLECULES

The infrared spectroscopy of large molecules is a subject which can here only be referred to in passing. It may be seen by reference to what has gone before that the spacing between rotation lines in a vibration band is an inverse relation of the moments of inertia. In large molecules the moments of inertia are large and therefore the spacing will be small. The smallest separations that can be resolved in the near infrared with certainty is of the order of 0.05 cm.$^{-1}$ with the best grating spectrographs now available. One may, therefore, in general conclude that the only rotational characteristics that can be of interest will be the examination of the contours of the bands themselves. Many of the problems of interest in smaller polyatomic molecules have no meaning here for this reason.

One may, nevertheless, from a knowledge of how lighter molecules behave, draw many helpful inferences concerning the spectra and the structure of large molecules. It is, for example, found to be true that in all molecules that have carbon-hydrogen bonds absorption bands will be found near 3.3 μ (i.e., 3000 cm.$^{-1}$). Similarly, molecules that have two carbon atoms joined by a triple, a double, or a single bond will exhibit absorption bands in their infrared spectra near 5.1, 6.0, or 10 μ, respectively. Molecules containing such other combinations between atoms as $C=O$, $C—N$, $C=N$, $O—H$, or $N—H$ will likewise exhibit bands in the infrared spectrum apparently characteristic of the respective atomic combination. This fact has been proved in certain cases by theoretical investigations (see for example the normal coordinate analysis of cyclopentane by Schuman and Shaffer (65)). For our purpose it may be visualized by reference to a particular example. Consider the instance of the molecule which may be written symbolically as

$$\begin{array}{cccc} & H & H & H \\ H— & C— & C= & C— & C—H \\ & H & H & & H \end{array}$$

This molecule will have $3N - 6$, or 30 degrees of vibrational freedom. In each of the normal modes in which the molecule may oscillate, every atom will participate in some more or less complicated manner. In certain of these modes, however, the contributions by the atoms of the molecule to the motion will be small except for a very few of them. Thus in our example one of these is approximately a vibration where the two central carbon atoms oscillate with respect to each other, the other atoms of the molecule remaining at rest. To this approximation the frequency associated with this motion will be.

$$\omega_{C=C} = \frac{1}{2\pi c} \sqrt{\frac{k_{C=C}}{\mu_{C=C}}} \tag{31}$$

where c is the velocity of light, $k_{C=C}$ is the force constant which exists between the carbon atoms joined with a double bond, and $\mu_{C=C}$ is the reduced mass (in this case $\mu^{-1} = m_C{}^{-1} + m_C{}^{-1}$) of the two carbon atoms oscillating with respect to each other. It is customary, because of the rather rough approximations resorted to in the foregoing, to set the harmonic frequency, ω, equal to the frequency observed in the spectrum. This, of course, is tantamount to considering the effect of the anharmonicity on the observed frequencies as negligible. If, then, the frequency $\omega_{C=C}$ is given the value which it is found to possess in the C_2H_4 molecule, namely 1623 cm.$^{-1}$, the force constant $k_{C=C}$ may be calculated from eq. (31). The reciprocal of the reduced mass is found to be

$$\mu^{-1} = 1.14 \times 10^{-24}(g)^{-1},$$

from which $k_{C=C}$ is found to be 9.77×10^{-5} dyne/cm.

The motions of the atoms of the molecule associated with two other modes of vibration may be approximated in the following ways. In one case the two extreme carbon atoms are periodically approaching and receding away from the two central carbon atoms, these two atoms remaining at rest with respect to each other. In the other case one of the outer C atoms approaches and recedes from the two central C atoms periodically, while the other outer C atom recedes from and approaches the two central C atoms periodically, these two atoms again remaining at rest with respect to each other. These motions are illustrated in Fig. 8a and b. It is easily demonstrated that, if the forces which the outer two atoms exert on each other are neglected, the two frequencies will be the following:

$$\omega_{C-C} = \frac{1}{2\pi c} \sqrt{\frac{k_{C-C}}{m_C}} \tag{32a}$$

and

$$\omega'_{C-C} = \frac{1}{2\pi c} \sqrt{\frac{2k_{C-C}}{m_C}} \tag{32b}$$

The latter has the same value as the frequency of two C atoms oscillating with respect to each other where the force constant is k_{C-C} and for this reason is often referred to as a C—C vibration. Frequency (32a) is, however, also a C—C vibration, since it too depends essentially on the force constant k_{C-C}. This illustrates the necessity of carefully defining what is meant when a particular valence vibration is referred to. It is probably safe to say, however, that if C—C bonds occur in a molecule at least one frequency will occur in the spectrum close to the value of (32b). We may then as in the preceding example make use of (32b) to evaluate the k_{C-C} force constant. When ω_{C-C} is taken to be 993 cm.$^{-1}$, the value it assumes in the C_2H_6 molecule, the constant k_{C-C} will be found to be 4.5×10^{-5} dyne/cm.

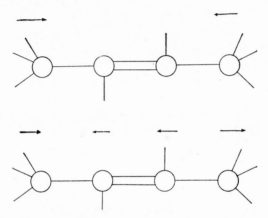

FIG. 8. Two vibrations of a C—C=C—C chain.

Still other modes of vibration will represent the types of motion characteristic of the CH_3 or methyl groups, and so forth.

A methyl group in a molecule will give rise to six bands, all of which might be different in a molecule like the one we are considering. In general, however, the bands will group themselves in two distinct parts of the spectrum, one group of three near 3000 cm.$^{-1}$ and the other three near 1450 cm.$^{-1}$. The former group has essentially the frequency of a hydrogen atom joined to a carbon atom with a single bond. The force constant k_{C-H} may be calculated as before by taking for ω_{C-H} the value it assumes in the CH_4 molecule and taking $\mu_{C-H}^{-1} = m_H^{-1} + m_C^{-1}$. One obtains $k_{C-H} = 5.07 \times 10^{-5}$ dyne/cm. With the aid of a LiF prism or with a grating spectrograph these may frequently be resolved. In symmetric molecules only two bands can result in this region, one of these being, however, twofold degenerate. The other set of bands has essentially the frequency resulting from a deformation of the CH_3 pyramid. In symmetric molecules there will again be only two bands, one of which will be twofold degenerate. The twofold degenerate oscillation remains very constant throughout many molecules and has a value of about 1450 cm.$^{-1}$. The nondegenerate frequency coincides almost exactly with the former in the spectrum of CH_3F, CH_3Cl, CH_3Br, and CH_3I. In general this frequency deviates considerably from the value 1450 cm.$^{-1}$, but it will be consistently found in this same region of the spectrum, always toward lesser frequencies. The reason for this is related in a rough way to the fact that in computing the reduced mass the presence of the rest of the molecule cannot be neglected. The reduced masses in these latter instances are all considerably more complicated than those associated with the valence vibrations. For this reason no force constant is readily evaluated. In general, it may be said that deformation frequencies of molecular configurations are apt to remain less constant from molecule to molecule than will the valence frequencies.

Many molecules have also CH_2 configurations; in fact, some even have all the combinations CH, CH_2, and CH_3 at the same time. Since the valence frequencies of a CH combination and a CH_2 group must lie in the same region as the valence frequencies of a methyl group, and particularly since the CH_2 deformation frequency lies in the same neighborhood (1500 cm.$^{-1}$) as the deformation frequencies of the methyl group, some difficulty may indeed be encountered in identifying which bands belong to which groups. It may be worth pointing out that quite generally the C—H valence frequency has a value slightly in excess of 3000 cm.$^{-1}$ if the hydrogen atom is attached to an unsaturated carbon atom, or if the hydrogen atom is attached to a saturated carbon atom the

TABLE I

Typical Interatomic Characteristics

Atom pair	Reduced mass	$k \times 10^{-5}$	Absorption frequency (cm.$^{-1}$)	Compound
C—C	$6m_H$	4.50	993	C_2H_6
C—O	$6.85m_H$	5.77	1034	CH_3OH
C—N	$6.46m_H$	—	1045	CH_3NH_2
C=C	$6m_H$	9.77	1623	C_2H_4
C=O	$6.85m_H$	12.06	1744	H_2CO
C=N	$6.46m_H$	—	1653	CH_3CHNOH
C≡C	$6m_H$	17.2	1975	C_2H_2
C≡O	$6.85m_H$	—	2169	CO
C≡N	$6.46m_H$	16.6	2089	HCN
C—H	$0.92m_H$	5.07	2915	CH_4
O—H	$0.94m_H$	—	3683	CH_3OH
N—H	$0.93m_H$	—	3370	CH_3NH_2
S—H	$0.97m_H$	—	2597	CH_3SH

CH valence frequency will be less than 3000 cm.$^{-1}$. In the spectrum of certain molecules, therefore, CH valence frequencies may be found at two slightly different frequencies.

The force constants for a considerable number of atomic linkages have been evaluated in the above manner by Barnes *et al.* (3). Their results for the force constants k are summarized in Table I together with the frequencies from which they were evaluated. Table II gives a more complete list of the frequencies characteristic of certain functional

TABLE II[a]

Positions of Absorptions Associated with the Presence of Functional Groups

	Range	
Group	Wavelength (μ)	Wave number (cm^{-1})
OH	2.66-2.98	3355-3760
NH	2.94-3.00	3335-3400
≡CH	2.95-3.04	3290-3390
=CH$_2$	3.06-3.60	2780-3270
CH$_3$	3.15-3.69	2710-3175
≡CD	3.71-4.13	2420-2695
=CD$_2$	4.26-4.86	2060-2350
CD$_3$	4.30-4.92	2030-2325
C≡N	4.31-5.25	1905-2320
N≡N	4.67	2141
C≡C	4.51-5.68	1760-2215
C=N	5.94	1684
C=O	5.47-6.25	1600-1830
C=C	5.48-6.60	1515-1825
N=N	6.35	1575
CH$_3$	6.72-7.66	1305-1488
CH$_2$	6.63-7.85	1274-1508
SH	7.76	1289
CH	7.22-22.3	450-1385
CF	8.3	1205
OF	9.01	1110
CCO	9.12-11.33	882-1096
C=S	6.57-15.22	657-1522
OF	12.05	830
N=N	16.68	600
CC≡N	19.7	508
CC≡C	29.8	335

[a] Part of Table IV in ref. 59.

groups. Additional information of this kind can be found in the literature (3, 4, 12, 59).

Certain inferences concerning the intensities of the infrared bands of large molecules may also be drawn from a knowledge of the spectra of smaller molecules. Thus, for example, in the instance of the 3-hexyne molecule it is found that the C≡C band occurs only very faintly in the infrared spectrum. In direct contrast to this the C≡C band occurs very strongly in the infrared spectrum of 2-hexyne. This may be understood if we once more visualize the C≡C vibration as one where the C atoms are the ones which participate principally in the motion. In the case of the 3-hexyne molecule which is nearly symmetrical about the center the dipole moments induced by the two atoms will be rather nearly equal and in opposing directions and will therefore approximately cancel each other. In the example of 2-hexyne, however, when the C atoms oscillate they may be expected to induce quite different dipole moments, since the parts of the molecule on opposite ends of the C≡C linkage are quite different. This principle may be tested further by investigating the C=C band in the spectrum of C_4H_8. Here as in the first example the molecule is essentially symmetrical about the center, and for this reason one might predict a weak C=C band. This is actually observed.

Methods of the kind here described are admittedly crude and can at best lead only to partially satisfactory results. They have nevertheless been sufficiently good to allow much progress to be made in cases where a complete analysis of the normal modes has proved impracticable even with the aids of group theory. It is to be hoped that more exact methods may be developed in the future.

3. Instrumentation for Obtaining Infrared Spectra

This section discusses infrared spectrographs and auxiliary apparatus for obtaining infrared spectrographic data. The arrangement of the optical components in all infrared spectrographs is basically the same. Discussion of spectrographic apparatus will be divided into three parts as follows: (1) sources of radiation; (2) the spectrometer in which the radiation is deviated, the amount of deviation depending on the frequency (or wavelength) of the radiation; and (3) a unit for detecting, quantitatively, the presence of radiation, together with an amplifier and recorder which are required in most instances. The components selected and the method of operation of the spectrograph vary considerably from one instrument to another. Typical components of infrared instruments and complete spectrographs which illustrate useful combinations of components will be discussed here.

3.1. Background

Fifteen years prior to the time that this is being written, it would have been necessary for a potential user of infrared spectroscopy to learn about the design of such apparatus and to have a spectrograph constructed according to specifications that he himself would devise. Seven years ago, when an earlier edition of this book was being prepared, the situation had changed to the extent that there were three infrared spectrographs being manufactured in the United States and sold by scientific apparatus makers. Hence, at that time it was appropriate to discuss some of the more important features of the three spectrographs so that the reader might be able to decide which, if any, would be most useful to him in solving a given problem. Perhaps, also, there was some feeling at that time that the development of infrared instrumentation was essentially at an end and that such a description would be useful for an extended period of time. Developments since then make clear the folly of such thinking.

Today, there are many manufacturers of infrared spectrographic equipment. These are located in several countries in America, Europe, and Asia. Some organizations have marketed many different models, each designed to be most useful in solving a particular type of problem. Furthermore, developments are now taking place so rapidly that a description of the best instruments that were available a year ago would already be out of date. This makes it clear that no attempt should be made to describe the specific details of infrared spectrographs that are being used at the present time. Rather, it appears to be better to discuss the basic instrumentation, and then to consider typical variations of this, and finally to look at the general trends in infrared instrumentation development as they appear today. The reader who wishes to consider the details of the design and functions of components of infrared instruments is referred to the book on this subject by Smith et al. (69).

3.2. Spectrographs in General

In the infrared, just as in other portions of the electromagnetic spectrum, the function of a spectrograph is to separate the radiation into components according to frequency. This is accomplished by using an optical train, one element of which bends the radiation different amounts, the amount being dependent in some manner on its frequency. Figure 9 shows the basic elements of a typical spectrograph in which the radiation has its origin in a source, an image of which is formed on the entrance slit. The collimator causes rays from each point on the entrance slit to be bent to be parallel to each other and almost parallel to rays from other points on the entrance slit. The dispersing device (a prism in Fig. 9) bends the rays different amounts according to the frequency of the radiation. A plane mirror is shown here as returning the radiation along essentially the same path to the collimator which forms a spectrum in the plane of the exit slit. This spectrum consists of a continuous series of overlapping monochromatic images of the entrance slit. That small spectral range that passes through the opening in the exit slit is condensed to a small image on the detector. At this place the optical signal is transformed into an electrical one which is appropriately amplified and registered.

In the diagram of Fig. 9 mirrors rather than lenses are used through-

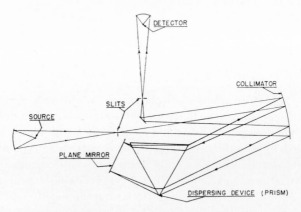

FIG. 9. Schematic diagram showing typical arrangement of components of an infrared spectrograph.

out. This is done because glass and most other materials that might be used as lenses are opaque to infrared radiation. It is true that lenses made of such materials as sodium chloride and potassium bromide are sometimes employed. Since atmospheric water vapor causes deterioration of surfaces of such lenses, however, it is only under special conditions that they are practical. Hence, it is common to use aluminized mirrors rather than lenses. Although this use of mirrors frequently increases the task of the instrument designer, it introduces folds in the radiation paths that usually result in a more compact piece of equipment. Another advantage of the use of mirrors is freedom from chromatic aberrations.

3.2.1. Dispersing Devices. The heart of the spectrograph is the dispersing device. A prism is suggested by Fig. 9 as serving that purpose. A diffraction grating is also used to advantage for certain investigations. A discussion of the relative merits of prisms and gratings is given in a subsequent section. Let it suffice at this point to suggest that whatever is used must be characterized by high optical quality or the usefulness of the data obtainable from the instrument will be curtailed.

3.2.2. Sources of Radiation. Almost any heated body can serve as a source of radiation. Since an increase in the radiance of the source results in improved data, it is worth while to consider briefly the factors that determine the radiance. The temperature of the source is one of these

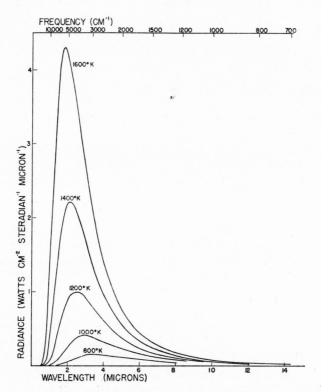

FIG. 10. Radiance of black bodies at various temperatures as function of wavelength and frequency.

factors. Figure 10 shows the power radiated by ideal black bodies at various temperatures. These curves are represented by the Planck law which gives, as the spectral radiance,

$$J_\lambda = \frac{C_1}{\lambda^5(e^{C_2/\lambda T} - 1)} \tag{33}$$

where T is the absolute temperature, λ is the wavelength of the radiation, e is the base of Naperian logarithms, and C_1 and C_2 are constants. Clearly, the radiant power will be increased at all wavelengths if the temperature is raised. But the increase is greater at the short-wave end than at the long-wave end of the spectrum. There are times when the gain that results from an increase in long-wave radiation may be more than offset by impurity that results from the considerably greater increase in short-wave radiation.

A second factor that is an important consideration in sources is that its emissivity is high. The curves of Fig. 10 are those for an ideal black body, which means that the emissivity is unity. Any departure from this ideal case decreases the radiant power available. Hence, for a good source, the emissivity in the spectral range to be investigated should be as large as possible.

If the size of the source is such that the entrance slit is filled, and if the dispersing device is properly filled with radiation, further increase in the size of the source is not fruitful. Although more radiant power is emitted by a larger source, it cannot be utilized for spectroscopic purposes.

Several types of sources are available. The rare-earth oxide Nernst glower and the silicon carbide Globar are widely used in the sodium chloride prism region. The carbon arc (63) operates at a higher temperature and therefore has certain advantages. Similarly, heated tungsten is a potentially useful source. For examining low frequencies, a coated platinum strip or a mercury lamp is commonly employed (52, 85).

3.2.3. Detectors. Since radiation detectors are components which are purchased and are almost never fabricated by the individual investigator, there is no need to provide more than a brief statement of the working principles of some of those most commonly used.

In widest application today is the thermocouple. In this, the radiation falls on a receiver attached to the junction of two wires of dissimilar materials. The radiation causes this junction to be warmer (or in some cases cooler) than a standard junction and hence gives a thermoelectric signal whose magnitude is related to the radiation falling on the receiver.

A second detecting device is a resistance thermometer (6, 8), known in this form as a bolometer. In this, radiation causes the resistance of the device to change. This change in resistance gives rise to an electrical signal which is a measure of the intensity of the radiation.

Another type of detector is a gas thermometer. Because this was brought to a state of usefulness by Golay (23, 79), it is frequently referred to as a Golay pneumatic cell. Radiation is admitted to a small chamber. A receiver in this chamber assists in transferring the energy from the radiant form into kinetic energy of the gas. One wall of the gas chamber is a flexible membrane which is a component in an auxiliary optical system. A change in the pressure in the cell, through this optical system, causes a change in the amount of visible light that reaches a photocell. Therefore, a change in the amount of radiant energy that reaches the detector produces a corresponding change in the output of the photocell.

A more recently developed detector is the photoconductive cell. In this, the conductivity of a small piece of material changes when radiation falls on it. The magnitude of the change is proportional to the intensity of the radiation. The mechanism involved in this detector may be thought of as a photon-triggering process. Therefore, the photons must be sufficiently energetic or nothing happens. This puts a lower limit to the frequencies of radiation that may be detected. As an example, lead sulfide at room temperature is a sensitive detector for frequencies greater than about 3000 cm.$^{-1}$. Cooling to liquid-air temperatures extends the range by a few hundred cm.$^{-1}$. Other semiconductors useful as detectors because their conductivity changes on irradiation with infrared photons are lead selenide, lead telluride, indium antimonide, and a specially treated germanium (41). When properly cooled, these materials can serve as detectors superior to the more conventional thermocouple for frequencies as low as 1000 cm.$^{-1}$. Research now in progress will undoubtedly extend this to even lower frequencies.

Except for the photoconductive cell, the detectors are classical devices—thermocouples, resistance thermometers, and gas thermometers. Even though the principles on which they operate have been understood for years, they could not be used successfully as infrared detectors until a large amount of painstaking engineering was carried out so that the weak signals, which are of the order of fractions of a microwatt, could be recognized and measured. One of the objectives of the engineering has been that of making the response of the detector fast so that the radiation can be interrupted many times each second. Doing this makes it possible to discriminate against other signals, to avoid complications resulting from changes in the ambient temperature of the detector, and to amplify the output of the detector more simply. As an example of the kind of engineering that has been done, it may be suggested that the volume of the gas chamber in a typical commercially available Golay detector is about 8 mm.^{3}.

3.2.4. Amplifying-Recording Systems. Although the amplifier and recorder may once have been accessories to the spectrograph, trends in instrument design are such that they are becoming more intimately a part of the basic apparatus. All modern spectrographs use a chopper to interrupt the radiation and an a.c. amplifier to increase the size of the pulsating electrical signal so that it may be recorded directly or put to other kinds of uses.

3.3. SPECTROPHOTOMETERS

One of the "other kinds of uses" of the output of the detector amplifier is the operation of a servomechanism which permits direct recording, as a function of frequency, of the fraction of the incident radiation transmitted by the sample. Presentation of data in this form rather than as a curve showing the amount of radiation received by the detector at each frequency makes utilization of the data much simpler in many cases.

In the ordinary use of the spectrograph, shown in Fig. 9, a sample is placed in the optical beam somewhere between the source and the detector. As the orientation of the dispersing device is changed, the spectral interval passing through the opening in the exit slit is continuously changed. As the spectrum is scanned, there is fluctuation in the amount of radiation reaching the detector. The curve showing this fluctuation as a function of frequency is the spectrum of the sample. Owing primarily to the fact, however, that the emission curve of the source is not at all flat, as suggested in Fig. 10, the resulting spectrum has a shape that is a combination of that due to absorption by the sample and that of the source and other parts of the instrument. It is the function of the spectrophotometer to eliminate the effect of the source and in fact effects of everything other than the sample.

The photometer unit may function by simultaneously comparing two samples, one of which is often a blank, and recording the ratio of the amounts of radiation transmitted by the two samples. Or, the same result may be accomplished by some other means. In different instruments, various devices are employed. The particular mechanism is unimportant. It is only essential to know that the device uses the output signal from the detector amplifier to operate some sort of servomechanism that is properly designed for giving a direct recording of the transmission of the sample when compared with the transmission of a standard sample.

3.4. MULTIPLE-PASS SPECTROGRAPHS

In Fig. 9, a plane mirror placed behind the prism makes it possible to pass the radiation through the prism a second time. This doubles the dispersion of the radiation and therefore increases the resolving power of the spectrograph, where resolving power, R, is defined by the equation

$$R = \frac{\nu}{\Delta\nu} = \frac{\lambda}{\Delta\lambda} \tag{34}$$

where ν (or λ) is the frequency (or wavelength) at which the investigation is being conducted, and $\Delta\nu$ (or $\Delta\lambda$) is the frequency (or wavelength) separation of the two closest absorption lines that can be recognized as being separate.

Increased resolving power increases the sensitivity of the spectrograph to absorption lines that may exist, and hence makes it a more valuable tool, both for investigating the structure of molecules and for making chemical analyses.

Because higher resolving power is advantageous, the proposal by Walsh (76, 77) that a prism can be used four or six or perhaps more times found ready acceptance. This is accomplished by replacing the exit slit by a combination of a slit and appropriate mirrors which return the radiation along essentially the same path to the collimator and the prism, and it then returns to the exit slit after having traversed the prism two more times. Thus, with the addition of only a small amount of additional apparatus, a significant gain in resolving power is obtained.

It has been suggested that a chopper is ordinarily used to interrupt the radiation, and an a.c. amplifier is then used to increase the signal to a value large enough for recording. With the double-pass arrangement, if the chopper is properly located, the ill effect of radiation of other wavelengths ordinarily scattered by the collimator in a single-pass instrument can be eliminated. This stray radiation originates in the undispersed radiation which falls on the collimator in Fig. 9 after coming through the entrance slit. A small amount is reflected in every direction; some of this goes directly through the exit slit and reaches the detector. Even though the radiation thus scattered is small, relative to the amount of monochromatic radiation that passes through the slit it may be large. In fact, when one uses the large slits required for investigating 600-cm.$^{-1}$ radiation with a sodium chloride prism, it is common to find that 15% of the radiation is of other wavelengths; in some instruments, half the radiation has been found to be impure. By placing the chopper at the intermediate slit in a double-pass spectrograph, the intense radiation scattered from the collimator is not interrupted and hence is not amplified. Thus, the effectiveness of this unwanted radiation is reduced to a negligible value. The same effect can be achieved by means of two spectrographs in series, with the chopper at the slit between the two spectrographs. This double monochromator is necessarily larger and more expensive than a double-pass single monochromator.

3.5. Grating versus Prism

Another way in which the resolving power may be increased is with a diffraction grating rather than a prism for dispersing the radiation into a spectrum. Although multiple use of a prism makes it possible to have resolution which is considerably higher than that of a prism used once, a grating can always be obtained which has larger dispersion than that of the best prism available and thus will provide higher resolution. Also, one may utilize gratings in a multiple-pass system in a manner similar to use of prisms multiple-passed. Thus, the chief advantage of gratings is for obtaining higher resolving power. Comparison of prism and grating spectrograms of water vapor, in the region around 1600 cm.$^{-1}$, suggests how the resolving powers differ. This is shown in Fig. 11.

In some spectral regions, viz., for frequencies less than about 200 cm.$^{-1}$, good prism materials are not known at present. A satisfactory prism material must be transparent, have the proper dispersing characteristics, and be available in sizes suitable for making prisms. Gratings, therefore, serve as dispersing devices in some spectral regions where prisms cannot be used.

To offset the advantages of a grating, there are some disadvantages when it is compared with a prism. One disadvantage is that the grating is less efficient in utilizing the radiant power. Whereas a prism bends monochromatic collimated radiation all in one direction so that it may ultimately reach the detector, a grating ordinarily diffracts the radiation into several orders, thus dividing whatever radiation there is into several parts, each part going in a different direction, only one of these parts ever getting to the detector. The echelette grating (82) does concentrate most of the radiation of a given wavelength in one order and in this way helps to eliminate this disadvantage. Furthermore the increased dispersion of a grating relative to that of a prism results in a substantial gain of resolving power if the proper grating is chosen.

A second disadvantage of the grating is also related to the existence of several orders. The well-established theory of the grating shows that the formula (35) holds,

$$n\lambda = \frac{n}{\nu} = d(\sin i + \sin r) \tag{35}$$

where n is the order, ν (or λ) is the frequency (or wavelength) of the radiation in cm.$^{-1}$ (or cm.), d is the separation of corresponding points on adjacent grating facets in cm., and i and r are, respectively, the angles of incidence and diffraction. For a given angle of incidence, i, and a given grating, if radiation leaving only in one direction is considered, so that a particular value of r is involved, the value of n/ν is a constant. Then, the first-order radiation of frequency ν_0, second-order radiation of frequency $2\nu_0$, third-order radiation of frequency $3\nu_0$, etc., will all be diffracted in the direction given by r. For the radiation to be pure, it is necessary to discriminate against the radiation of frequencies which are not being investigated. This is often troublesome in that it requires the use of filters or in some cases even a low-resolution prism spectrograph in series with

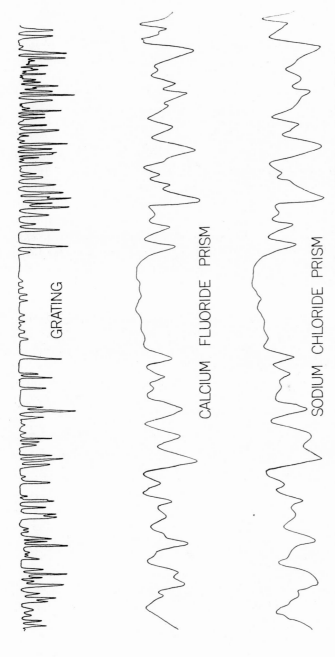

FIG. 11. Spectrograms of a portion of the 6-μ water vapor band obtained under different resolution. For the upper, center, and lower curves, the dispersing elements were respectively an echelette grating, a calcium fluoride prism, and a sodium chloride prism.

the grating spectrograph. This filtering problem is the same with an echelette grating as with an ordinary grating.

For an investigator to decide whether to use a prism or a grating for dispersing the radiation, he must consider the nature of the problem he wishes to solve and make the decision on the basis of the kinds of data that will be obtained, the importance of convenience in obtaining the data, and the application that will be made of the data. Decisions must be made in each case individually.

3.6. Extending to Higher Frequencies

Since about 1950, there has been considerable added interest in the spectral region of frequencies greater than about 3000 cm.$^{-1}$. In Section 4.3.6, some reasons for this are given. So far as instrumentation is concerned, it is merely required to choose the grating or prism that has relatively high dispersion in this spectral region, and an appropriate detector. The lead sulfide photoconductive cell is inexpensive, easy to operate, and very sensitive, so that it is quite satisfactory for this purpose.

Another recent development that has proved beneficial in this spectral region is the KBr pressed-pellet technique, first proposed by Stimson (70). In this, a solid sample is mixed with powdered KBr, and the mixture is formed into a wafer by means of a press. Because the KBr is transparent, it introduces relatively little change in the spectrum of the sample suspended in the KBr. Many cases have been noted, however, in which the closeness of the KBr molecules and those of the sample have introduced perturbations in the spectrum of the sample. It is necessary that the investigator be careful to avoid misinterpretation of the data.

3.7. Extending to Lower Frequencies

Because the spectral radiance of sources falls off in the low-frequency spectral region, relatively few investigations have been undertaken for radiation of frequencies below about 400 cm.$^{-1}$. In general, it is necessary to use gratings in this region. This requires that extensive filtering be employed in order to eliminate the large amount of high-order radiation that is necessarily present. Filtering techniques include use of selective transmitters, reflectors and scatterers, and devices which interrupt only low-frequency but not high-frequency radiation. The need for so much filtering makes it relatively more difficult to obtain these far infrared data. In addition, in much of this long-wave range, atmospheric water vapor is so strongly absorbing that data can be obtained only by evacuating the path traversed by the radiation. In spite of these discouraging factors, there is a growing interest in this spectral range.

3.8. Trend Toward Simpler Instrumentation

Before infrared instrumentation became commercially available the apparatus was always large and required highly skilled personnel in order to obtain useful data. Although the quality of the data that can now be obtained is much better and the data are presented in a more useful form, instrumentation has become more compact and in some sense simpler. There are now more electronic and complicated mechanical components, but much of the apparatus which can be purchased today may be operated efficiently by relatively unskilled personnel.

3.9. Special Features

Many pieces of apparatus are especially valuable for solving particular problems or represent new ways of obtaining spectroscopic data and therefore may serve as the basis for more common apparatus in the future. It would not be possible to describe all such apparatus here; however, to indicate the general nature of such developments, brief descriptions of three are given.

3.9.1. Integration of Area under Absorption Curve. Although it is sometimes sufficient to know the frequency and the magnitude of the absorption maximum, in other cases it is essential to know the area under the absorption curve. If the curve has been properly plotted, this information can be obtained with a planimeter. An alternative is that of making the detecting and recording components such that they will perform this function automatically. This may be accomplished by an electronic device that integrates the output developed by the detector when a portion of the spectral region is scanned according to a predetermined schedule.

3.9.2. Multislit Spectrograph. A second type of special feature is a multislit spectrograph developed by Golay (24, 25). In the ordinary spectrograph a monochromatic image of frequency v_0 of the entrance slit is formed on the exit slit. If three additional entrance slits were placed in line beside the first one—i.e., if the width of the slit were quadrupled—three additional monochromatic images of frequency v_0 would be formed in line beside the first one. If three additional exit slits were placed properly, the intensity of radiation of frequency v_0 would be quadrupled. Such a scheme by itself has the defect that the purity of the radiation passing through the fourfold exit slit is greatly reduced. Golay devised a scheme, however, for opening and closing the slits according to a rather complex pattern and then discriminating electrically against signals which, because they arose from radiation of frequency other than v_0, did not have the proper frequency pattern for amplification. In this way, with a four-slit arrangement, the useful power reaching the detector was doubled. Use of more slits has a correspondingly greater benefit.

3.9.3. Spectrum from an Interferometer. A third device is really not a spectrograph, but rather an interferometer (72) which makes it possible to derive spectroscopic information. If, in the Michelson interferometer shown in Fig. 12, the source is monochromatic and the mirror is moved as indicated by the arrow, as the two beams alternately give constructive and destructive interference, the output of the detector varies sinus-

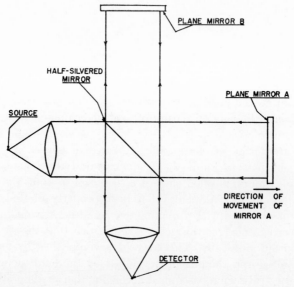

Fig. 12. Schematic diagram of interferometer used for obtaining the Fourier transform of the spectrum.

oidally. If the output of the source is changed to that of another monochromatic frequency, movement of the mirror produces a sinusoidal variation of the output of the detector that is different. If now a "white" source is used, the output of the detector is the combination of many such sine waves. A sample placed between the source and the half-silvered mirror attenuates radiation of some of the frequencies and accordingly modifies the pattern put out by the detector as plane mirror *A* is moved. Actually, this pattern is the Fourier transform of the spectrum. Hence, by subjecting the recording of the output of the detector to proper mathematical analysis the spectrum itself can be obtained. For such an interferometer to be useful for providing infrared data, a special kind of half-silvered mirror must be devised. For long-wave radiation, a fine wire grating has been employed. The chief advantage of this arrangement is that a large fraction of the radiant power reaching the instrument actually contributes to the output of the detector, whereas in a conventional spectrograph most of this is eliminated in the several filtering operations. On the other hand, in the interferometer, a complicated procedure is required in order to reduce the recorded data to the spectrogram which would be given directly by the spectrograph.

3.10. NONDISPERSION INSTRUMENTS

The apparatus described thus far provide data in the form of intensity as a function of frequency or wavelength. For certain purposes it is unnecessary to disperse the radiation. Nondispersion infrared apparatus may be used as a tool where knowledge of the composition of a mixture is required on a continuous basis.

A typical instrument for making such analyses has been described by Wright and Herscher (84). Subsequently the instrument has been made available commercially in a number of models suited to somewhat

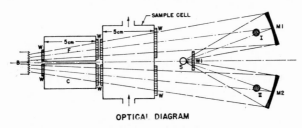

OPTICAL DIAGRAM

FIG. 13. Schematic diagram of a commercially available infrared gas analyzer. Courtesy Baird Associates. B—bolometer arms. S—infrared source. F—filter cell. C—compensator cell. I, II—light trimmers. M1, M2—front surface concave mirrors. W—windows silver chloride, lithium fluoride, calcium fluoride, quartz. W1—optional window.

different applications. Figure 13 is a diagram of the optical arrangement of one such commercially available model. It will be observed that there is no mechanism for dispersing the radiation into a spectrum. Rather, the entire gamut of frequencies emitted by the source, S, is reflected by the mirrors, $M1$ and $M2$, through the cells and onto two bolometers, B, which are arms of a Wheatstone bridge. There are several ways of operating this unit. One involves flowing the sample to be analyzed through the sample cell, having cell F filled with a sample of the compound, X, for which analysis is to be made, and cell C empty. If there is variation of the amount of X in the sample, it will reduce the radiation of certain frequencies that leaves the cell. That will vary the radiation that passes through the empty cell before falling on the bolometer. The radiation, whose intensity is varied, that falls on cell F is all absorbed by the material in F, however, and hence the radiation reaching that bolometer is constant. On the other hand, if there is variation of the amount of another component, Y, there will be no change in the balance of the Wheatstone bridge because presumably both cells C and F transmit the radiation whose intensity is varied by changes in the amount of component Y. Should the spectra of X and Y both absorb radiation of the same frequencies to the extent that it interferes with the analysis, it is possible, by means of additional cells, to eliminate this interference.

Many variations of this, including the use of quite different detecting systems, have been devised and made available commercially. A typical record showing the amount of butadiene present in a mixture of gases is shown in Fig. 14. The sensitivity and the accuracy of this type of analysis depends to a large extent on the compounds involved. In many analyses, accuracies of the order of 0.01% may be achieved.

3.11. CALIBRATION

In using infrared spectroscopy as an analytical tool, it is necessary to determine the amount of radiation of certain frequencies transmitted by various samples. This implies that both the amount and the frequency of the radiation reaching the detector must be measured with great enough accuracy to obtain a satisfactory solution to the particular analytical problem.

The frequency calibration may be made by any of three methods. To make an empirical calibration, substances are chosen whose spectra are known from the literature, or from measurements on a previously calibrated instrument. To be satisfactory these substances must possess characteristic lines or bands in one or more spectral regions. Spectrograms of these substances are obtained on the instrument being calibrated. From the observed positions of the lines or bands and the accurately known frequency values obtained previously, a calibration of the instrument is obtained. The choice of calibrating substances depends on the spectral region and the dispersing element. Compilations of calibration data particularly helpful for the calibration of prisms appear in the literature (17, 49).

A second method of calibrating is chosen where sufficient data are not otherwise available for making an empirical calibration or where such great accuracy is required that it is considered inadvisable to use the data in the literature. In this case the refracting angle of the prism and the dispersing characteristics of the substance must be known for calibration of a prism. It is then possible to calculate the angle through which the prism must be rotated in order to change the frequency of the radiation falling on the exit slit from one given value to another. To calibrate a grating, it is necessary to know only the spacing between ruled lines and certain constants which depend on the geometry of the instrument. Knowing these, one can calculate the rotation of the grating required to change the frequency of the radiation passing through the

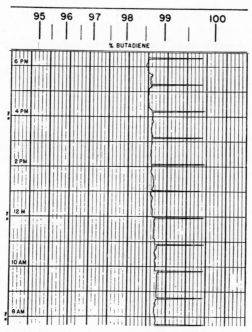

Fig. 14. Section of chart recorded by plant-installed infrared gas analyzer continuously determining the total butene impurity in a stream of butadiene. Standardized automatically at 45-minute intervals. (Disregard time scale at left.) Courtesy Dow Chemical Company. From *J. Opt. Soc. Am.* **36,** 199 (1946).

exit slit by a given amount. If a calculated calibration is employed it is necessary to be able to determine absolute angular rotations, whereas with an empirical calibration it is essential only that there be available some means for indicating relative angular positions of the prism or grating. The latter means that an accurately divided circle is not required. In most cases an empirical calibration is adequate.

With either of these procedures for making a frequency calibration it is necessary to take into account any change of temperature on the dispersing element. In a grating, a change in temperature causes a change in grating spacing, the magnitude of which depends on the material on which the grating is ruled. In a prism, for radiation of a given frequency, the index of refraction is a function of the temperature. The situation is further complicated by the fact that this temperature coefficient varies with frequency. Correction for changes in temperature may be made in any of several ways. Some spectrographs are equipped with appropriate bimetallic units which automatically compensate for changes in temperature. If no such device is included on the spectrograph, an empirically determined correction may be applied, or, if a calculated calibration is used, the correction may be calculated (64).

A method of calibration which may be regarded as a special application of what has just been discussed is the following. Two independent light beams are used, one of which may be identified with the sample to be studied and another which may be identified with a set of standard lines (either in emission or absorption). These beams are, in general, focused at slightly different places on the entrance slit of the spectrometer. They will, as a result, be focused after dispersion at two slightly different positions on the exit slit and, after passing through this, will be concentrated on two different detectors. The signals from the two detectors are then amplified independently and recorded simultaneously on a two-pen recording potentiometer. The frequency positions of the standard lines will be known to a high degree of precision, and frequency positions of peaks in the spectrum of the sample may be arrived at by interpolation methods between the standard lines.

Since the two beams do not enter the slit at the same place, they do not follow entirely identical paths in the spectrometer. For this reason the frequency scale of the two beams may be shifted very slightly with respect to each other. A correction to the standard scale may therefore have to be applied. This correction may be obtained by a trial run in which the standard source is made to replace the sample so that the light path of the standard beam is made identical with the light path of the sample.

A variation of the above method is to replace the beam from the standard source by a light beam passing through two parallel etalon plates separated by a thin spacer. This forms a Fabry-Perot interferometer system which produces a series of interference fringes which may be recorded on the paper along with the spectrum. The frequency interval between the fringes can be calculated and used for interpolation purposes if the spacing between the etalon plates is known. If at frequent intervals standard lines are observed on the same detector recording as the absorption spectrum, it is possible to determine the fringe spacing as well as the positions of the fringes.

In the determination of intensity, it is assumed that the response of the detector, amplifier, and recorder are linear—that is, that the output of the recorder or the galvanometer deflection is proportional to the rate at which the detector is receiving radiant energy. It is usually possible to verify the correctness of this assumption and to make the response linear if such is not already the case. To determine the per cent of the radiation transmitted by a substance, it is necessary to make correct measurements of the galvanometer deflection or recorder reading under three conditions. These conditions are: (1) a "sample" reading, i.e., one with the sample in the path; (2) a blank reading, i.e., one with no sample in the path; and (3) a zero reading, i.e., one with no radiation of that frequency falling on the detector. If these readings are designated R_s, R_b, and R_0, respectively, the fraction of incident radiation transmitted by the sample is then given by $(R_s - R_0)/(R_b - R_0)$. It is necessary that precautions be taken in determining R_b and R_0. If the sample is in a cell, the surfaces of the cell windows may reflect and absorb radiation, so that in order to obtain a correct value for R_b it is necessary that an equivalent cell but no sample be in the path.

If the sample is a liquid and the indices of refraction of the sample and the cell window are about equal, a single plate of the material from which the cell windows are made, and of thickness equal to the total thickness of all cell windows, will form a satisfactory equivalent empty cell. In this case it is not sufficient merely to use an empty cell for determining R_b. There are two reasons for this. First, because of two additional surfaces where there is a relatively large change of index of refraction, namely air to the window material, there is loss of energy by reflection. Second, if the space between the windows is small, as is usually the case, an interference pattern is superposed on the spectrogram. The resultant variation of intensity of radiation with frequency makes any individual intensity determination of dubious accuracy.

The contributions to R_0 that may make it incorrect are radiations of frequencies other than those being investigated. These contributions arise from the fact that surfaces of mirrors and prisms scatter radiation of all frequencies in all directions, and some of this reaches the detector. This is inherent in a spectrograph in which the same mirror is used for collimating the radiation and for focusing the spectrum on the exit slit, and it can be eliminated in such an instrument only by filters or by a double monochromator arrangement, or by locating the chopper before the second slit in a double-pass instrument. Because there is a greater amount of high- than low-frequency power available, such scattered radiation of higher frequencies than that being investigated gives rise to false values of R_0 if a shutter opaque to radiation of all frequencies is inserted in the light path to obtain this reading. A more correct reading may be obtained with a shutter of material opaque to the spectral region being investigated but transparent to higher frequency radiation. Or, if a metal shutter is used, and the magnitude of the deflection due to scattered radiation can be determined, this amount can be added to the observed value of R_0 to obtain a correct value.

3.12. MISCELLANEOUS TECHNIQUES

In using infrared apparatus, there are many minor techniques that must be mastered by the spectroscopist. These are optical, mechanical, electrical, and electronic. As an example, the need for absorption cells is cited. If the study is in the spectral region between 600 and 5000 cm.$^{-1}$, a region productive of much useful data, it is most convenient to utilize sodium chloride plates as cell windows. To obtain liquid layers of thickness of the order of 0.1 mm. requires that the windows be polished flat. Techniques that are not difficult to learn or to use, but nevertheless are rather special, must be employed. Summaries of such techniques have been prepared by Lord *et al.* (47) and by Williams (81). Although it is not appropriate to discuss such procedures here, it is necessary that the spectroscopist be aware of the need for them.

3.13. INFRARED EMISSION SPECTRA

The foregoing has dealt largely with absorption rather than emission spectra primarily because the former are most highly developed and because most utilization of infrared spectroscopic data are based on absorption spectroscopy. When one gas is burned in another gas, however, and the flame is used as a source of radiation, or when a heated gas is the source, the patterns obtained have some resemblance to the absorption spectrograms of the gas used as the source. Because this is the case, it is possible to obtain some information about molecular structure from emission spectrograms that supplements that obtained from absorption data. It is further possible that emission data may well serve as the basis for analytical methods.

Some studies have been made in this area (10, 16, 18, 68). It is to be expected that additional significant developments will take place in the next few years.

4. Utilization of Infrared Spectroscopic Data

4.1. USE OF INFRARED SPECTROSCOPY IN DETERMINING MOLECULAR STRUCTURE

The band spectrum of a gaseous molecule will frequently allow the investigator to infer a great deal concerning the size and shape of the

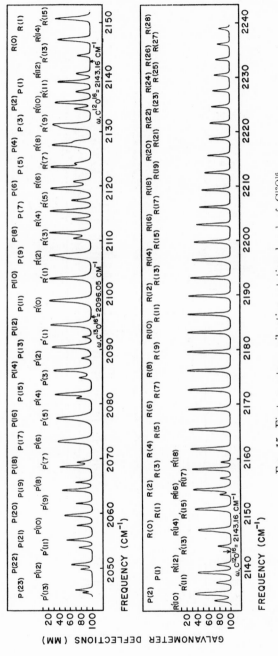

Fig. 15. First overtone vibration-rotation band of $C^{12}O^{16}$.
Unprimed lines refer to $C^{12}O^{16}$.
Primed lines refer to $C^{13}O^{16}$.

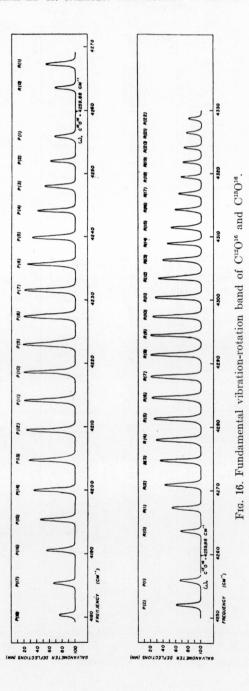

Fig. 16. Fundamental vibration-rotation band of $C^{12}O^{16}$ and $C^{13}O^{16}$.

molecule and the forces which hold the atoms together. The techniques for exploiting the information furnished by a band spectrum have been highly developed by spectroscopists working with diatomic molecules. We shall therefore consider here the spectrum of a diatomic molecule, namely carbon monoxide, which offers an excellent opportunity to note just what may be learned in an almost ideal situation.

The spectrum of CO has been extensively studied (46, 50, 55-57, 60), and very precise measurements were obtained for the lines in the fundamental and overtone bands of $C^{12}O^{16}$ and the lines in the fundamental band of the $C^{13}O^{16}$ molecule. A few lines in the overtone of the $C^{13}O^{16}$ band spectrum have also been observed. The bands of the two molecules are shown in Figs. 15 and 16. The observed frequency positions of the lines corrected to vacuum are set down in Table III. The lines in all three absorption bands have been identified, those on the low-frequency side of the band center forming the P(J) series and those on the high-frequency side the R(J) series, where J may be regarded as the value of the quantum number of total angular momentum in the initial state. The identifications of the lines are also given in Table III. In Fig. 16 the primes denote lines in the band spectrum of $C^{13}O^{16}$. The bands in the spectrum of molecules like CO, in which the electronic angular momentum directed along the internuclear axis is known to be zero, show no zero line or Q branch.

From the energy relations for a molecule stated in relation (9) one may, if the centrifugal stretching is neglected, obtain relations for the positions of the P and R lines by applying the selection rules

$$\Delta J = \pm 1.$$

These are verified to be

$$P(J) = [E'(J-1) - E''(J)]/hc = \nu_0 - J(B' + B'') + J^2(B' - B'')$$
$$R(J-1) = [E'(J) - E''(J-1)]/hc = \nu_0 + J(B' + B'') + J^2(B' - B'')$$
$$(36)$$

Equations (36) enable one to write certain relations known as the combination relations. These are

$$R(J-1) - P(J+1) = 4B''(J + \tfrac{1}{2})$$
$$R(J) - P(J) = 4B''(J + \tfrac{1}{2})$$
$$(37)$$

If eqs. (37) are plotted as ordinates against J as abscissas, straight lines result whose slopes are B'' and B', respectively.

Another helpful relation is the following:

$$R(J-1) + P(J) = 2\nu_0 + 2(B' - B'')J^2 \qquad (38)$$

TABLE III

Frequency Positions of the Rotation Lines in the CO Bands

Identification	Fundamental band of $C^{12}O^{16}$	Fundamental band of $C^{13}O^{16}$	Overtone band of $C^{12}O^{16}$
P(23)	2046.27		
P(22)	2050.85		
P(21)	2055.40		
P(20)	2059.91		
P(19)	2064.40		
P(18)	2068.85	—	4180.26
P(17)	2073.27	—	4185.28
P(16)	2077.65	—	4190.23
P(15)	2081.00	—	4195.10
P(14)	2086.32	—	4199.92
P(13)	2090.61	2045.79	4204.66
P(12)	2094.86	2049.85	4209.33
P(11)	2099.08	2053.88	4213.94
P(10)	2103.27	2057.85	4218.48
P(9)	2107.43	2061.78	4222.95
P(8)	2111.55	—	4227.35
P(7)	2115.63	2069.66	4231.68
P(6)	2119.68	—	4235.95
P(5)	2123.70	—	4240.14
P(4)	2127.69	2081.17	4244.26
P(3)	2131.64	2084.95	4248.32
P(2)	2135.55	2088.69	4252.30
P(1)	2139.43	2092.40	4256.22
R(0)	2147.09	—	4263.84
R(1)	2150.86	—	4267.54
R(2)	2154.60	—	4271.18
R(3)	2158.30	2110.45	4274.14
R(4)	2161.97	2113.96	4278.23
R(5)	2165.50	2117.44	4281.66
R(6)	2169.20	—	4285.01
R(7)	2172.76	2124.29	4288.29
R(8)	2176.28	—	4291.50
R(9)	2179.77	—	4294.63
R(10)	2183.22	2134.32	4297.70
R(11)	2186.64	2137.59	4300.69
R(12)	2189.01	2140.83	4303.62
R(13)	2193.36	2144.04	4306.47
R(14)	2196.66	—	4309.24
R(15)	2199.92	—	4311.95
R(16)	2202.15	—	4314.59
R(17)	2206.34	2156.52	4317.14
R(18)	2209.50	2159.55	4319.63
R(19)	2212.61	—	4322.05
R(20)	2215.69	—	4324.39
R(21)	2218.73	—	4326.66
R(22)	2221.73		4328.85
R(23)	2224.69		

where ν_0 is the frequency of the band center. If eq. (38) is plotted as ordinates against J^2 as abscissas, a straight line results that has the intercept $2\nu_0$ and the slope $(B' - B'')$.

The data observed in the CO spectrum have been used to obtain numerical values for relations (37) and (38). Since the initial state of the molecule is the normal vibration state, the value of B'' obtained from the data of both the fundamental and the overtone bands should be the

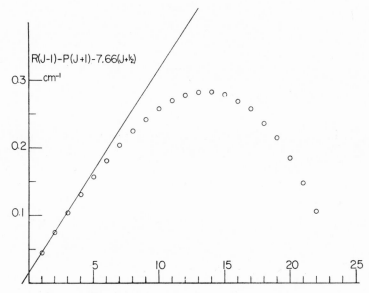

FIG. 17. Ground state combination plot for the 1-0 band of $C^{12}O^{16}$. The slope of the straight line gives a value of $4B''$. The deviation from this straight line is due to centrifugal distortion.

same. It is advantageous, therefore, to plot points defined by eq. (37) obtained from both the fundamental and the overtone bands on the same graph in order to obtain the best possible value of B''. This graph is shown in Fig. 17. The value of B'' obtained is 1.922523 cm.$^{-1}$

The graph of the points defined by relation (38) obtained from the data taken from the fundamental band plotted against J^2 is not shown. From it, however, a value of $2\nu_0 = 4286.54$ cm.$^{-1}$ is obtained, where ν_0 is the center of the fundamental band, and a value of $(B' - B'') = -0.017529$ cm.$^{-1}$ is found, B' being the reciprocal of inertia in the upper state. Similarly, when the corresponding relation obtained from the data on the overtone is plotted, a value of $2\nu_0 = 8520.12$ cm.$^{-1}$ and a value of $(B' - B'') = -0.035060$ cm.$^{-1}$ are obtained. The data stated before are summarized in Table IV.

TABLE IV

	$C^{12}O^{16}$	$C^{13}O^{16}$
ν_0 (fundamental)	2143.27 cm.$^{-1}$	2096.07 cm.$^{-1}$
ν_0 (overtone)	4260.06 cm.$^{-1}$	
ω_e	2169.83 cm.$^{-1}$	2121.41 cm.$^{-1}$
x	13.297 cm.$^{-1}$	12.67 cm.$^{-1}$
B''	1.922523 cm.$^{-1}$	1.8381 cm.$^{-1}$
$(B' - B'') = \alpha$ (fundamental)	-0.017529 cm.$^{-1}$	-0.0164 cm.$^{-1}$
$(B' - B'') = \alpha$ (overtone)	-0.035060 cm.$^{-1}$	
I_e	14.4924×10^{-40} gm.-cm.^{2}	15.159×10^{-40} gm.-cm.^{2}
r_e	1.1284 A.	1.1283 A.
k_3	-123.57 cm.$^{-1}$	-119.34 cm.$^{-1}$
k_4	26.46 cm.$^{-1}$	25.23 cm.$^{-1}$

It is now possible to determine the molecular constants. The band center is, in each case, just the difference in energy of the nonrotating molecule in the initial and final states. In the instance of the fundamental, $v'' = 0$ and $v' = 1$; for the overtone, $v'' = 0$ and $v' = 2$. Evidently, therefore, the band centers of the fundamental and overtone bands will be, respectively,

$$\nu_0 = \omega_e - 2x$$
$$\nu_0' = 2\omega_e - 6x \tag{39}*$$

From the data in Table IV and with the aid of relations (36), values for ω_e and x may be calculated. These will be seen to be $\omega_e = 2169.83$ cm.$^{-1}$ and $x = 13.297$ cm.$^{-1}$. The B_v values for the normal and first excited states may be written (see Section 2.2)

$$B_0 = B_e - \frac{\alpha}{2} = B''$$

$$B_1 = B_e - \frac{3\alpha}{2} = B' \qquad \text{(Fundamental)} \tag{40}$$

$$B_2 = B_e - \frac{5\alpha}{2} = B' \qquad \text{(Overtone)}$$

From the two values of $(B' - B'')$, i.e., $(B_1 - B_0)$ and $(B_2 - B_0)$, a value for α may be obtained. With α determined one may proceed to evaluate B_e. Evaluation gives $B_e = 1.93130$ cm.$^{-1}$. From the definition of $B_e = h/(8\pi^2 I_e c)$ the equilibrium value of the moment of inertia is found to be $I_e = 14.4924 \times 10^{-40}$ gm.-cm.^{2}. The quantity I_e is equal to μr_e^2, where $1/\mu = (1/m_1) + (1/m_2)$, m_1 and m_2, being the masses of the carbon

* The notation $x_e\omega_e$ is frequently used instead of the notation x in eqs. (39).

and oxygen atoms. A value of $r_e = 1.1284 \times 10^{-8}$ cm. may be calculated from the above value of I_e.

A similar analysis of the fundamental band of the isotopic molecule $C^{13}O^{16}$ may now be made. The analysis leads to values of $\nu_0 = 2096.07$ cm.$^{-1}$ and $(B' - B'') = 0.0164$ cm.$^{-1}$. Now it may be shown (F. Matossi, R. Mayer, and E. Rauscher, private communication) that for isotopic diatomic molecules like $C^{12}O^{16}$ and $C^{13}O^{16}$ the relation $(\omega_e/\omega_e')^2 = (x/x')$ exists; ω_e, the harmonic frequency for the isotopic molecule, cannot, of course, be evaluated without an analysis of the overtone band. The value may, however, be replaced by the ratio (ν_0/ν_0') with good accuracy. In this manner, one may calculate x' for the isotopic molecule. A value of $x' = 12.67$ cm.$^{-1}$ is derived. This leads to a value of $\omega_e' = 2121.41$ cm.$^{-1}$.

It is possible to test this value of ω_e' further, since one may expect the force fields that hold the two atoms together to be the same and therefore that the potential energy functions for the two isotopic molecules $C^{12}O^{16}$ and $C^{13}O^{16}$ will be the same also. The potential energy relation for a molecule like CO as obtained from relation (3) will be

$$V = hc\left[\left(\frac{K_2}{2}\right) Q^2 + K_3 Q^3 + K_4 Q^4 + \cdots\right] \tag{41}$$

where Q is the displacement coordinate $Q = r - r_e$, r_e being the equilibrium value of the interatomic distance. The harmonic frequencies ω_e and ω_e' for the two isotopic molecules will be given by the relations $\omega_e = (1/2\pi c)(K_2/\mu)^{1/2}$ and $\omega_e' = (1/2\pi c)(K_2/\mu')^{1/2}$, μ and μ' being the reduced masses of the two molecules. This leads at once to the relation $(\omega_e/\omega_e') = (\mu'/\mu)^{1/2}$. If the value of ω_e for $C^{12}O^{16}$ is assumed to be correct, the value of ω_e' may be calculated to be 2121.55 cm.$^{-1}$, which is in good agreement with the value stated before.

It is moreover possible to determine the coefficients of the cubic and quartic terms in the potential energy expression from the above data on the band spectrum of CO. To accomplish this it becomes convenient to replace Q by the dimensionless coordinates so defined that

$$Q = (h/4\pi^2 c\mu\omega_e)\,q.$$

Then V becomes

$$V = hc\left(\frac{\omega}{2} q^2 + k_3 q^3 + k_4 q^4 + \cdots\right) \tag{42}$$

where

$$k_3 = K_3\left(\frac{h^2}{16\pi^4 c^2 \mu^2 \omega_e^2}\right)^{3/4} \quad \text{and} \quad k_4 = K_4\left(\frac{h^2}{16\pi^4 c^2 \mu^2 \omega_e^2}\right)$$

It is possible to show (51) that α_v and x have the following values when expressed in terms of the k_j:

$$\alpha_v = -6(B_e^3/\omega_e)^{1/2}[(B_e/\omega_e)^{1/2} + \sqrt{2}k_3/\omega] \tag{43}$$

$$x = \tfrac{1}{4}(6k_4 - 15k_3^2/\omega_e) \tag{44}$$

The values of α and x given in Table IV, when used with relations (43) and (44), suffice to evaluate k_3 and k_4. The values obtained are the following for the $C^{12}O^{16}$ molecule:

$$\begin{aligned} k_3 &= -123.57 \quad \text{cm.}^{-1} \\ k_4 &= 26.458 \text{ cm.}^{-1} \end{aligned} \tag{45}$$

The constants α and x for the potential energy function for $C^{13}O^{16}$ may then also be computed with the aid of relation (45). The value for k_3 may be tested by using it to compute α for the isotopic molecule $C^{13}O^{16}$. The value of α' obtained for the isotopic molecule is 0.0168 cm.$^{-1}$, which is in good agreement with the value determined from the data taken on the fundamental band in the spectrum of $C^{13}O^{16}$.

The example discussed here represents an almost ideal illustration of the information which may be obtained concerning a molecule if its infrared band spectrum is known. The techniques are also applicable to the spectra of polyatomic molecules, although the difficulties in applying them satisfactorily are much greater in many cases. This is due to the fact that the spectra of such molecules cannot be resolved completely. Nevertheless, it has been possible to interpret exactly the spectra of carbon dioxide and water vapor and in much the same way as in the foregoing example to determine the constants of the molecule.

4.2. USE OF INFRARED SPECTROSCOPY IN MAKING CHEMICAL ANALYSES

4.2.1. Principles Involved. Because the infrared spectrum is a characteristic that depends on the structure of the molecule, its use has been likened to a fingerprint, in that the spectrogram can reveal the presence, sometimes quantitatively, of the molecule. Analytical methods based on infrared spectroscopic data all involve comparison of the spectrogram of the sample whose analysis is wanted with spectrograms of pure compounds known or thought to be components of the sample.

The simplest analysis would require the identification of a sample known to be one of a given group of compounds. This analysis can be made readily if there are available spectrograms of the sample being investigated and of each of the compounds of which the sample is known to be one. This brings out one very important aspect of the method. It is necessary to have available spectrograms of pure compounds with which the spectrograms of unknown composition may be compared. This is emphasized because the method breaks down without the spectrograms of the pure compounds and because it is frequently difficult to obtain satisfactory spectrograms for comparison.

One can refer to the literature and find spectrograms that are satisfactory for identification of the sample in analyses as simple as the one proposed above. Or, reference may be made to one of the collections of infrared spectrograms that are available commercially.*

Such spectrograms as have been obtained by other investigators are useful for orienting the investigator by providing information as to the spectral regions in which there are absorption bands or lines characteristic of a certain compound and the relative amounts of absorption that can be expected in the various spectral regions. Because the characteristics of the instrument used for obtaining such reference spectrograms are likely to be different, however, from those of the instrument used in the analytical laboratory, the value of the reference spectrogram is limited, and usually it will be necessary for the analyst to obtain a spectrogram of the pure compound from his own apparatus. This is especially true when quantitative analyses are being made.

As an example of a simple quantitative analysis, suppose that it is desired to determine the amount of one compound in a mixture. As a further simplification, assume that that compound absorbs radiation of a certain frequency strongly and that none of the other compounds absorb radiation of that frequency. Admittedly this is an ideal situation that rarely, if ever, exists. In this ideal case, with synthetic mixtures, a calibration curve is made in which the amount of the compound in question is plotted as a function of the fraction of the radiation transmitted at that frequency. This curve is applicable only for the radiation of that particular frequency. If the assumption that the other compounds do not absorb radiation in that spectral region is modified to permit only slight absorption relative to that of the compound for which analysis is being made, such a calibration curve provides a basis for good analyses if the thickness of the cell is always maintained the same. In that case,

---

* Information about the scope, form, and availability of collections of spectrograms may be obtained from: (1) American Petroleum Institute Research Project 44, Frederick D. Rossini, Director, Carnegie Institute of Technology, Pittsburgh, Pennsylvania; (2) Samuel P. Sadtler and Sons, Inc. Research Laboratories, 1517 Vine Street, Philadelphia 2, Pennsylvania. (3) National Research Council—National Bureau of Standards, E. Carroll Creitz, Secretary, National Bureau of Standards, Washington 25, D.C.; (4) Documentation of Molecular Spectroscopy, Butterworths Scientific Publications, 88 Kingsway, London, W.C. 2, England; (5) American Society for Testing Materials, M. D. Huber, 1916 Race Street, Philadelphia 3, Pennsylvania.

rather than plotting the amount of the compound against radiation transmitted, the per cent of that compound present, by weight or by volume, can be plotted against radiation transmitted.

In the general case it may be assumed that all compounds absorb radiation of all frequencies, and that the absorption coefficients vary with spectral position. If it is known that there may be N compounds present in a mixture, the spectrograms of the pure compounds are examined and an attempt made to find a spectral region for each compound in which that compound absorbs strongly and all the others absorb only weakly.

There are other criteria involved in selection of the group of N "key frequencies" at which the analysis may best be made, which need not be mentioned here, but which experience will verify to produce results of increased accuracy. For example, it is better to select a spectral region at which all compounds have spectrograms that show little or no change in the amount of transmission with frequency, rather than to choose a place that is on the side of an absorption band for one of the components. It is then necessary to determine the absorption coefficient, $k(\nu)$ in Lambert's law (eq. 21) for each of the N components at each of the N spectral positions. This means that a total of N^2 absorption coefficients are determined. These absorption coefficients are determined by observing the transmission that results when different amounts of the substance are put into the optical path. Having determined the absorption coefficients one may then observe the transmission at each of the N frequencies of the sample to be analyzed. The general relation that applies when several absorbing compounds are present has been given as

$$T = \frac{I\nu}{I_\nu^\circ} = e^{-[k_1(\nu)l_1 + k_2(\nu)l_2 + \cdots]} \tag{22}$$

For a mixture of liquids or gases the l_i can be replaced by concentration, c_i, of the ith component. This modifies eq. (22) by the introduction of a new absorption coefficient, $k_i(\nu)$. In this form, it is commonly known as Beer's law. From logarithms, a set of N simultaneous linear equations is obtained. Since the $k_i(\nu)$ are known for each of the N components at each of the N spectral positions, and the T can be determined experimentally for each of the N frequencies, these simultaneous equations can be solved for the N values of c_i. The assumption is made that the laws of Lambert and Beer are applicable to each of the constituents at all the frequencies examined, and that each of the absorption coefficients is uninfluenced by the presence of the other components. In principle, it is always possible to solve this set of simultaneous equations. It has been found, however, that certain arrangements of the equations give results which are superior to those obtained from other arrangements. This is equivalent to making the determinant, involved in the solution of such equations, of large magnitude. If the number, N, of simultaneous equations is large, the process for solving for the N unknown quantities is extremely laborious. Hence, mathematical shortcuts have been devised (7, 13). Through such methods, in which successive approximations are involved, it is ordinarily possible to arrive at a satisfactory solution in a relatively short time. Alternatively, if the analysis is one that is to be made repeatedly and frequently, modern electrical computers may be utilized to greatly simplify the procedure.

The above considerations assume that the conditions under which the samples are being analyzed are such that the absorption laws of Lambert and Beer are applicable. There are discussed in Section 2.3 several factors that make these laws inapplicable under certain conditions. These considerations are pertinent here, inasmuch as the conditions under which quantitative analyses are made are those which render the Lambert-Beer laws inapplicable. Therefore, the careful investigator will wish to take adequate precautions to ensure that he is not overlooking a cause of error in the analysis. Analysis of synthetic mixtures of known composition will ordinarily be adequate for this purpose.

4.2.2. Example of Analysis of Mixture of Gases. If a given analysis is to be repeated a number of times, it is necessary to establish a procedure that can be reproduced faithfully each time the analysis is made. For example, the cell thickness should always be the same. A fixed-thickness cell may be sufficient to assure this. Analysis must always be made at the same position in the spectrum. If a continuous spectrogram is recorded, it is ordinarily possible to determine frequencies accurately by means of calibration marks recorded simultaneously. It is clear that all other experimental conditions must be reproduced if the analysis is to be correct.

Because it has been found that the above conditions can be satisfactorily reproduced, and because the infrared spectra of compounds are different when other physical and chemical properties are very similar, a large number of methods suitable for making particular analyses have been developed. Among the first of the numerous published articles is one by Wright (83) in which he describes several methods for making infrared analyses and gives examples showing the usefulness of this tool. It is not in order to attempt to catalog the analytical methods of this type that have been developed. It will be noted that several of these problems are those found in the petroleum industry. Its significance is that the petroleum laboratories have found in infrared spectroscopy a means of solving problems that could not otherwise be solved and hence have devoted much effort to development of the methods. A similar statement could be made about the chemical and other industries.

An excellent example of a case where infrared spectroscopic techniques have been developed for routine gas analysis is discussed by Brattain *et al.* (7). The method was developed and used for analyzing mixtures of isobutane, *n*-butane, 1-butene, trans-2-butene, cis-2-butene, and isobutene. Spectrograms were obtained for each of the pure compounds. These were studied, and key frequencies, at which the analysis was to be made, were chosen. It should be pointed out that it is necessary to select as key frequencies those most appropriate to a certain analysis. It would be advantageous if one or two could be chosen as the proper frequencies for any analysis involving a given compound. In choosing these, however, one must take into account the frequencies at which other compounds may also absorb and accordingly select an optimum combination of frequencies. Instrumental conditions were determined that would lead to the greatest accuracy. These included sample pressure and slit settings. The thirty-six absorption coefficients required were all determined. Finally, appropriate iterative methods of simplifying the calculations involved in solving the six linear simultaneous equations were developed. After the method was thus set up, synthetic samples were prepared, and analysis of these was made. The accuracy with which each component could be determined was within 1% of the total sample in practically all tests. The average absolute deviation was 0.23% in 81 checks. The time required for such an analysis is about 30 to 45 minutes.

4.2.3. Example of Analysis of Mixture of Liquids. Using essentially the same techniques, Fry *et al.* (22) have extended the method to the analysis of liquid samples. A typical liquid mixture tested consisted of 2,3-dimethylbutene-1, 2,3-dimethylbutene-2, 2,2,3-trimethylbutene, and several methylpentenes. The methylpentenes were treated as one component, and synthetic mixtures were tested. In this case the maximum error in determining any component was 1.9% of the total sample, and the average error was about 0.5%. This analysis, like the one above, can be made in 30 to 45 minutes, once the procedure has been established.

4.2.4. Use of Punched Cards in Qualitative Analysis. Some of the collections of spectrograms, discussed earlier as being available commercially, are presented on punched cards. Part are of the IBM type; others are of the type having holes punched around the edges of the cards. If the analysis is qualitative, comparison of spectrograms in the form of punched cards is rapid. This coupled with other physical characteristics of the sample can often lead to a positive identification of a compound quickly.

4.3. Use of Infrared Spectroscopy in Special Problems

Almost all uses of infrared spectroscopic data involve comparison of spectrograms. We have already discussed the one major exception, in which the spectrum is analyzed to provide information about the size and shape of the molecule, the strengths of force constants, and such. This section will briefly cite examples in which comparisons of the spectrogram of a sample with one or many spectrograms of known substances can greatly assist in solving complex problems of a chemical nature. It is hoped that these brief discussions will stimulate the reader to imagine some of the hundreds of similar applications which are made but not mentioned here—and then to extend the use of infrared spectroscopy to the solution of problems not yet attempted.

4.3.1. Mechanism of Polymerization. In the polymerization of N-carboxyanhydrides of α-amino acids to produce high-molecular-weight polypeptides, investigation by Idelson and Blout (39) of the spectra showed that the monomer has characteristic absorption lines at 1790 and 1860 cm.$^{-1}$, and that the monomer is free from absorption in the 1500- to 1700-cm.$^{-1}$ region. On the other hand, the polymer has absorptions at 1550 and 1655 cm.$^{-1}$ and is free from absorption in the 1700- to 1900-cm.$^{-1}$ region. As polymerization progresses, the intensities of the 1790- and 1860-cm.$^{-1}$ lines decrease and the intensities of the 1550- and 1655-cm.$^{-1}$ lines increase. Therefore, determination of the 1500- to 1900-cm.$^{-1}$ spectrum of a sample readily shows the degree of polymerization. Such data, obtained at various stages of the polymerization process and under different conditions of processing, can lead to determination of the most effective conditions of promoting or retarding polymerization. It will also help in bringing about an understanding of the mechanism by which polymerization takes place.

4.3.2. Degradation of Polyvinyl Chloride. The effects on polyvinyl chloride of temperatures as high as 400°C., exposure to oxygen, and irradiation with ultraviolet light were studied by Stromberg *et al.* (71) by observing changes in infrared spectra. Only small changes were observed except when the polymer was heated strongly in a vacuum. Under these conditions the spectrum changed from one indicating the presence of only aliphatic groups to one which shows also the presence of aromatic groups.

4.3.3. Baking of Wire Enamels. In an investigation of Arndt (1), information about the best baking conditions for Formvar and polyurethane enamels used for coating wire, and for predicting performance of the enamels under special conditions, was determined with the assistance of infrared data. The enamel was baked on the wire. Toluol extractions of the enamels were made after the baking. The extracts were analyzed by infrared techniques. The presence or absence of resinous compounds in the extract was a measure of the effectiveness of the baking conditions.

4.3.4. Catalyst Studies. The question of how catalysts function is of considerable interest to chemists. This is especially true in the petroleum industry, where large amounts of catalysts are utilized in refining processes.

The catalyst studied in an investigation of Pliskin and Eischens (54) was Ni on silica gel. Infrared spectroscopic techniques were developed for determining what products were adsorbed on the catalyst. Ethylene, $H_2C{=}CH_2$, was passed through the catalyst. Examination of the catalyst showed

$$\begin{array}{cc} * & * \\ HC{-}CH \\ H & H \end{array}$$

as being present, with the * representing attachment of the hydrocarbon to the Ni. No double bonds and no CH_3 groups were shown to be present. Subsequent passage of hydrogen through the catalyst brought it to the place where

$$\begin{array}{cc} * & H \\ HC{-}CH \\ H & H \end{array}$$

was indicated. That is, there were then CH_3 groups.

Starting with a new catalyst, acetylene, $HC{\equiv}CH$, was passed through it. Analysis proved the adsorbed material to be

$$\begin{array}{cc} * & * \\ HC{-}CH \\ H & H \end{array}$$

the same as that in the experiment using ethylene. The absence of triple and double bonds indicates that two acetylene atoms must contribute hydrogen and there must be a surface carbide present. This kind of information will assist in advancing the understanding of catalytic action.

4.3.5. The Structure of Penicillin. An extensive investigation in which a large number of personnel at several laboratories successfully undertook to determine the structural arrangement of the penicillin molecule has been reported (59). Inasmuch as this is a complicated organic compound, there are many bands in the absorption spectrum. In order to find with what functional groups this particular arrangement of bands could be identified it was necessary to examine several hundred compounds whose purity was above question and whose structural formulas had previously been definitely established. By forming a catalog of data, it was shown that certain bands could be identified with known structural groups, and that modification of this relationship in a predictable way would result when certain other groups were present. Through this type of procedure it was possible to determine the formula of penicillin.

4.3.6. Use of Radiation of Frequencies Greater than about 3000 cm.$^{-1}$. Most absorptions caused by transitions from one vibrational energy level to the one next higher are in the spectral region of frequencies between about 400 and 3000 cm.$^{-1}$. If the vibration involved, however, is that between a hydrogen atom and the remainder of the molecule, absorption of radiation of frequencies greater than 3000 cm.$^{-1}$ results. Or, if the transition is between energy levels that are not adjacent but rather are separated by two or more energy intervals, absorption of radiation of frequencies between 3000 and 15,000 cm.$^{-1}$ takes place. Thus, the type of information that can be obtained by examining spectroscopic data in this spectral range is to a certain extent unique.

The availability of highly sensitive lead sulfide photoconductive detectors simplifies the taking of high-frequency data.

In a paper reviewing the usefulness of this spectral region, Kaye (40) has summarized, among other things, some of the analytical applications. Under conditions that may be readily achieved, the following amounts may be detected: acids in anhydrides, 0.5 to 1.0%; water in alcohols, 0.035 to 0.08%; acids in hydrocarbons, 0.005 to 0.03%; water in hydrocarbons, 0.004 to 0.02%. It is further suggested that these are not presented as the lowest possible limits, but that use of differential techniques may lower these limits by as much as a factor of 10 in favorable cases.

4.4. LITERATURE PERTAINING TO USES OF INFRARED SPECTROSCOPY

Because the literature dealing with applications of infrared spectroscopy is growing so rapidly, it is not feasible to include an exhaustive bibliography here. A two-volume collection of abstracts of infrared literature has been prepared, however (5). There are also several papers or groups of papers that summarize researches in fields or in periods of time and which contain extensive bibliographies (2, 9, 11, 21, 28-32, 37, 38, 69a).

Periodicals that are constantly carrying reports of newer developments include, among others, *Journal of Molecular Spectroscopy, Journal of Chemical Physics, Journal of the American Chemical Society, Analytical Chemistry, Spectrochimica Acta,* and *Journal of the Optical Society of America.* Some advanced information may be obtained from programs and abstracts of the papers presented at two annual meetings, the Pittsburgh Conference of Analytical Chemistry and Applied Spectroscopy held at Pittsburgh, Pennsylvania, each March, and the Symposium on Molecular Structure and Spectroscopy held at Columbus, Ohio, each June.

References

1. Arndt, R. P., *in* "Pittsburgh Conference of Analytical Chemistry and Applied Spectroscopy." Pittsburgh, Pennsylvania, March, 1957.
2. Barnes, R. B., and Gore, R. C., *Anal. Chem.* **21**, 181 (1949).
3. Barnes, R. B., Gore, R. C., Liddel, U., and Williams, V. Z., "Infrared Spectroscopy, Industrial Applications and Bibliography." Reinhold, New York, 1944.
4. Bellamy, L. J., "The Infrared Spectra of Complex Molecules." Methuen, London, 1954.
5. "Bibliography of Published Information on Infrared Spectroscopy," Vols. I and II. Her Majesty's Stationery Office, London, 1955.
6. Brattain, W. H., and Becker, J. A., *J. Opt. Soc. Am.* **36**, 354 (1946).
7. Brattain, R. R., Rasmussen, R. S., and Cravath, A. M., *J. Appl. Phys.* **14**, 418 (1943).
8. Brockman, F. G., *J. Opt. Soc. Am.* **36**, 32 (1946).
9. Brown, C. R., Ayton, M. W., Goodwin, T. C., and Derby, T. J. (eds.), "Infrared—A Bibliography." The Library of Congress, Technical Information Division, Washington, 1954. Part 2 issued by same source in 1957 under editorship of Ayton, M. W., Derby, T. J., Boteler, V. H. and Brown, C. R.
10. Bullock, B. W., and Silverman, S., *J. Opt. Soc. Am.* **39**, 200 (1949).
11. Coblentz, W. W., "Investigations of Infrared Spectra." Carnegie Institution, Washington, 1905.
12. Colthup, N. B., *J. Opt. Soc. Am.* **40**, 397 (1950).
13. Crout, P. D., *Trans. Am. Inst. Elec. Engrs.* **60**, 1235 (1941).
14. Dennison, D. M., *Phys. Rev.* **28**, 318 (1926).
15. Dennison, D. M., *Revs. Modern Phys.* **3**, 280 (1931).
16. Donovan, R. E., and Agnew, W. G., *J. Chem. Phys.* **23**, 1592 (1955).
17. Downie, A. R., Magoon, M. C., Purcell, T., and Crawford, Bryce, Jr., *J. Opt. Soc. Am.* **43**, 941 (1953).
18. Dows, D. A., Whittle, E., and Pimentel, G. C., *J. Chem. Phys.* **23**, 499 (1955).
19. Elsasser, W. M., *Phys. Rev.* **54**, 126 (1938).
20. Erlandsson, G., *Arkiv för Fysik* **10**, 65 (1956).
21. Faraday Society Symposium, "The Application of Infra-Red Spectra to Chemical Problems." *Trans. Faraday Soc.* **41**, 171 (1945).
22. Fry, D. L., Nusbaum, R. E., and Randall, H. M., *J. Appl. Phys.* **17**, 150 (1946).
23. Golay, M. J. E., *Rev. Sci. Instr.* **18**, 357 (1947).
24. Golay, M. J. E., *J. Opt. Soc. Am.* **39**, 437 (1949).
25. Golay, M. J. E., *J. Opt. Soc. Am.* **41**, 468 (1951).
26. Golden, S., Jr., *J. Chem. Phys.* **16**, 78 (1948).
27. Gora, E. K., *J. Mol. Spectroscopy* **3**, 78 (1959).
28. Gore, R. C., *Anal. Chem.* **22**, 7 (1950).
29. Gore, R. C., *Anal. Chem.* **23**, 7 (1951).
30. Gore, R. C., *Anal. Chem.* **24**, 8 (1952).
31. Gore, R. C., *Anal. Chem.* **26**, 11 (1954).
32. Gore, R. C., *Anal. Chem.* **28**, 577 (1956).
33. Hainer, R. M., Cross, P. C., and King, G. W., *J. Chem. Phys.* **17**, 826 (1949).

34. Hanson, H., Nielsen, H. H., Shaffer, W. H., and Waggoner, J., *J. Chem. Phys.* **27,** 40 (1957).

35. Herman, R. C., and Rubin, R. J., *Astrophys. J.* **121,** 533 (1955).

36. Herman, R. C., and Wallis, R. F., *J. Chem. Phys.* **23,** 637 (1955).

37. Herzberg, G., "Infrared and Raman Spectra of Polyatomic Molecules." Van Nostrand, New York, 1945.

38. Herzberg, G., "Molecular Spectra and Molecular Structure, I. Spectra of Diatomic Molecules," Van Nostrand, New York, 1950.

39. Idelson, M., and Blout, E. R., *in* "Symposium on Molecular Structure and Spectroscopy." Columbus, Ohio, June, 1956.

40. Kaye, W., *Spectrochim. Acta* **6,** 257 (1954).

41. Klass, P., *Aviation Week* p. 50 (March 4, 1957); p. 78 (March 11, 1957); p. 89 (March 18, 1957).

42. Kramers, H. A., and Ittmann, G. P., *Z. Physik* **53,** 553 (1929).

43. Kramers, H. A., and Ittmann, G. P., *Z. Physik* **58,** 217 (1929).

44. Kramers, H. A., and Ittman, G. P., *Z. Physik* **60,** 663 (1930).

45. Ladenburg, R., and Reiche, F., *Ann. Physik* **42,** 181 (1913).

46. Lagemann, R., Nielsen, H. H., and Dickey, F. P., *Phys. Rev.* **72,** 284 (1947).

47. Lord, R. C., McDonald, R. S., and Miller, Foil A., *J. Opt. Soc. Am.* **42,** 149 (1952).

48. Mannebach, C., *Physik. Zeits* **28,** 72 (1927).

49. Mills, I. M., Scherer, J. R., Crawford, Bryce, Jr., and Youngquist, M., *J. Opt. Soc. Am.* **45,** 785 (1955).

50. Mills, I. M., and Thompson, H. W., *Trans. Faraday Soc.* **49,** 224 (1953).

51. Nielsen, H. H., *Phys. Rev.* **60,** 794 (1941).

52. Oetjen, R. A., Haynie, W. H., Ward, W. M., Hansler, R. L., Schauwecker, H. E., and Bell, E. E., *J. Opt. Soc. Am.* **42,** 559 (1952).

53. Oppenheimer, J. R., *Proc. Cambridge Phil. Soc.* **23,** 327 (1926).

54. Pliskin, W. A., and Eischens, R. P., *J. Chem. Phys.* **24,** 482 (1956).

55. Plyler, E. K., Benedict, W. S., and Silverman, S., *J. Chem. Phys.* **20,** 175 (1952).

56. Plyler, E. K., Blaine, L. R., and Connor, W. S., *J. Opt. Soc. Am.* **45,** 102 (1955).

57. Plyler, E. K., Blaine, L. R., and Tidwell, E. D., *J. Research Natl. Bur. Standards* **55,** 183 (1955).

58. Polo, S. R., *Can. J. Phys.* **35,** 880 (1951).

59. Randall, H. M., Fowler, R. G., Dangl, J. R., and Fuson, N., "Infrared Determination of Organic Structure." Van Nostrand, New York, 1949.

60. Rao, K. Narahari, *J. Chem. Phys.* **18,** 213 (1950).

61. Reiche, F., and Rademacher, H., *Z. Physik* **39,** 444 (1926).

62. Reiche, F., and Rademacher, H., *Z. Physik* **41,** 453 (1927).

63. Rupert, C. S., and Strong, J., *J. Opt. Soc. Am.* **40,** 455 (1950).

64. Schaefer, C., and Matossi, F., "Das Ultrarote Spektrum." Springer, Berlin, 1930.

65. Schuman, R., and Shaffer, W. H., *in* "Symposium on Molecular Structure and Spectroscopy." Columbus, Ohio, 1946.

66. Shaffer, W. H., and Newton, R. R., *J. Chem. Phys.* **10,** 405 (1942).

67. Silver, S., *J. Chem. Phys.* **10,** 565 (1942).

68. Silverman, S., *J. Opt. Soc. Am.* **39,** 275 (1949).

69. Smith, R. A., Jones, F. E., and Chasmar, R. P., "The Detection and Measurement of Infrared Radiation." Oxford Univ. Press, New York, 1957.

69a. *Spectrochim. Acta* **14,** 1-318 (1959).

70. Stimson, M. M., *in* "Symposium on Molecular Structure and Spectroscopy," Columbus, Ohio, June, 1951.

71. Stromberg, R., Bersch, C., Harvey, M., Straus, S., and Achhammer, B., *in* "Pittsburgh Conference of Analytical Chemistry and Applied Spectroscopy," Pittsburgh, Pennsylvania, March, 1957.
72. Strong, J., *J. Opt. Soc. Am.* **47**, 354 (1957).
73. Teller, E., and Tisza, L., *Z. Physik* **73**, 791 (1932).
74. Tolman, R. C., "Statistical Mechanics with Applications to Physics and Chemistry." Chemical Catalog Co., New York, 1927.
75. Turner, T. E., Hicks, B. L., and Reitwausner, G., Report No. 878, Dept. of the Army, Project No. 503-02-001. Ord. Res. & Development, Project No. TB3-0110V, Ballistic Research Lab., Aberdeen Proving Ground, Maryland, 1953.
76. Walsh, A., *Nature* **167**, 810 (1951).
77. Walsh, A., *J. Opt. Soc. Am.* **42**, 94, 96 (1952).
78. Wang, S. C., *Phys. Rev.* **34**, 243 (1929).
79. Weiss, R. A., *J. Opt. Soc. Am.* **36**, 356 (1946).
80. Whittaker, E. T., "Analytical Dynamics," 4th ed., p. 178. Cambridge Univ. Press, London, 1937.
81. Williams, Van Zandt, *Rev. Sci. Instr.* **19**, 135 (1948).
82. Wood, R. N., *Phil. Mag.* **20**, 770 (1910).
83. Wright, N., *Ind. Eng. Chem. Anal. Ed.* **13**, 1 (1941).
84. Wright N., and Herscher, L. W., *J. Opt. Soc. Am.* **36**, 195 (1946).
85. Yoshinaga, H., Fujita, S., Minami, S., Mitsuishi, A., Oetjen, R. A., and Yamada, Y., *J. Opt. Soc. Am.* **48**, 315 (1958).

Raman Spectra

James H. Hibben [*]

United States Tariff Commission, Washington, D.C.

1. Introduction

The application of the Raman effect to the quantitative analysis of chemical compounds has expanded more slowly than other spectroscopic methods such as emission spectra, absorption spectra in the infrared, visible, or ultraviolet regions, and perhaps fluorescence spectra. Physical equipment necessary to produce Raman spectra is fairly costly, and, until recently, the method was time-consuming. Furthermore, its correlation with other known physical phenomena required nearly a decade (1928-1938).

The Raman effect can be employed as a method of qualitative identification of chemical compounds and for quantitative analyses within certain limits, since it is indirectly dependent on the different types of vibration and rotation in a molecule. These types of vibration and rotation are as uniquely characteristic of the molecule as electronic emission spectra are characteristic of atoms. However, as analysis by means of Raman spectra consists essentially in comparing the spectrum obtained from the unknown sample with the spectrum of known sub-

[*] Died June 15, 1959.

stances, it has been first necessary to determine accurately the spectrum of literally hundreds of compounds before the method could be generally applied in routine analytical work. Before 1940 most of the work on Raman spectra was exploratory.

During the war the use of the Raman method for analytical purposes was considerably expanded, particularly for mixtures of petroleum hydrocarbons. But, before any review of these new developments, the origin and nature of the Raman spectra and the general type and limitations of equipment used will be discussed in some detail, since the interpretation of the information obtained by this method requires complete familiarity with the principles involved.

2. Origin and Nature of Raman Spectra

The Raman effect is related to Rayleigh scattering, fluorescence, and absorption—particularly infrared absorption. In Rayleigh scattering, the oscillating electric and magnetic forces comprising the incident light induce a dipole moment in the molecules which, in turn, radiate light of the same frequency as the incident or exciting radiation but in a different direction. Rayleigh scattering is therefore always present along with Raman scattering. Fluorescence is the re-emission of absorbed light with high efficiency in measurable time; in infrared absorption the appearance of an absorption frequency is a result of change in dipole moment of a molecule during intramolecular motion.

When a molecule is irradiated by light of a given wavelength and there is a change in the polarizability of the molecule during intramolecular motions, discrete quanta (hv) may be obtained from the irradiated material not present in the original light, where h is Planck's constant and v is the frequency of the light. This phenomenon, known as the Raman effect, is of low intensity, instantaneous, and independent of absorption. It is measured by separating the newly created light by means of prisms or diffraction gratings and then recording them either as spectral lines on a photographic plate or directly by means of photoelectric cells, in much the same manner as the usual electronic emission spectra are measured.

Unless the molecule is in an activated state, the Raman frequencies will be lower than the exciting frequency (or incident radiation). The difference between this exciting frequency and the frequency of the scattered Raman light is primarily a function of the masses of vibrating or rotating atoms and the valence forces between them, and their arrangement in space. In Raman spectra it is the magnitude of this frequency difference that is important.* As the number of Raman lines obtained and their frequency difference from the incident light are independent of the absolute frequency of that light, it follows that for each exciting frequency there is a separate and complete series of Raman lines which may, and frequently do, overlap.

Although the Raman effect thus owes its origin to the existence of molecular vibrational and rotational energy levels, transitions from one level to another in a molecule do not necessarily result in the appearance of a specific Raman shift. Some types of vibration are neither Raman-active nor infrared-active, and some are double or triple vibrations of the same frequency (degenerate vibrations), with the result that the total Raman and infrared frequencies may be less than the maximum permitted. The number of vibrational degrees of freedom (or normal vibrations) is $3N - 6$ for a nonlinear and $3N - 5$ for a linear molecule, where N is the number of atoms in each molecule. This limits the number of normal vibrational frequencies. On the other hand, combinations of frequencies and harmonics of frequencies do occur in the infrared but more rarely in the Raman spectra, resulting in a greater number of Raman lines than expected.† In brief, therefore, the number of Raman frequencies which may be obtained from a molecule depends on the number of atoms contained therein and the symmetry of the molecule. If the symmetry of the molecule is preserved during vibration, this type of vibration, i.e., symmetrical valence type of oscillation, usually yields the most intense Raman effect and is forbidden in infrared absorption. No vibration can appear in the Raman effect which is antisymmetrical to the center of symmetry of the molecule. Vibrations which are antisymmetrical or degenerate may be active or forbidden, depending on the symmetry elements present. Consequently certain types of vibration or rotation can be determined by absorption, and others by Raman spectra. The two methods are, therefore, complementary rather than competitive.

Besides the magnitude of the Raman shifts, two other sources of information are of value in connection with Raman spectra: these are the intensity of the lines and their degree of polarization. Like the Rayleigh

---

* The frequency difference ($\nu_{\text{exciting}} - \nu_{\text{Raman}}$) is usually expressed in reciprocal centimeters (cm.$^{-1}$) and is referred to as the Raman shifts, displacements, spectra, etc. It is derived as follows: Wavelength (λ) $\times$ frequency (ν) $=$ velocity of light (c), where λ is expressed in angstrom units (A.), ν is the number of vibrations per second, and $c = 3 \times 10^{18}$. In the number of waves per centimeter or wave numbers per centimeter: $\lambda\nu_1 = 10^8$ for the exciting light and $\lambda\nu_2 = 10^8$ for the Raman line; $\nu_1 - \nu_2 = \Delta\nu$ per cm.$^{-1}$

† A consequence of vibrational anharmonicity.

scattering, the Raman scattering increases in absolute intensity roughly according to the fourth power of the frequency of the incident radiation. These Raman intensities, though very low, are proportional to the concentration of each individual species unless intermolecular coupling is present. Intensity measurements are therefore used in quantitative analysis by Raman spectra. However, the relative intensity of each individual line in a given spectrum depends in part on the type of interatomic linkage and the type of vibration and other factors. The other source of information is the degree of depolarization of the Raman lines, that is, the ratio of the intensity of the horizontal light vibration, i, to the vertical vibration, I. The depolarization factor ($\rho = i/I$) approaches 0 for symmetrical vibrations and 6/7 for the asymmetrical types. These parameters are generally of less value than the magnitude of the Raman shifts for analytical purposes but are of great value in the determination of molecular constitution, which after all is a form of analysis. Furthermore, in routine identification of certain very similar compounds any additional information is of great value.

3. Experimental Procedure

3.1. Spectrographic Equipment

The standard equipment for studying the Raman effect of organic and inorganic compounds in all states of aggregation is a wide-aperture spectrograph and a strong source of radiation that is as nearly monochromatic as possible, since Raman scattering is very weak. The light is concentrated by means of reflectors or lenses on the material to be investigated. If the material is a liquid it is usually contained in a tube with a flat window on the bottom facing the front of the spectrograph. A volume inside the tube is then focused on the spectrographic slit by means of an auxiliary lens. The incident light passes through the liquid at right angles to the axis of the collimating tube, care being taken that as little as possible is reflected from the walls of the container which are kept out of focus of the collecting lens.

The spectrograph may be of simple design without wavelength scale and fixed prisms but it must have high speed, good resolution, and reasonable dispersion. An effective aperture of F:4 having a dispersion of 20 A. or less per millimeter would be advisable for routine qualitative analysis when time is not too great a factor. The amount of time required to make a suitable photograph ranges from a few minutes (without filter) to several hours, depending on the material irradiated and the apparatus.

It is a decided advantage to use a high-frequency light source in

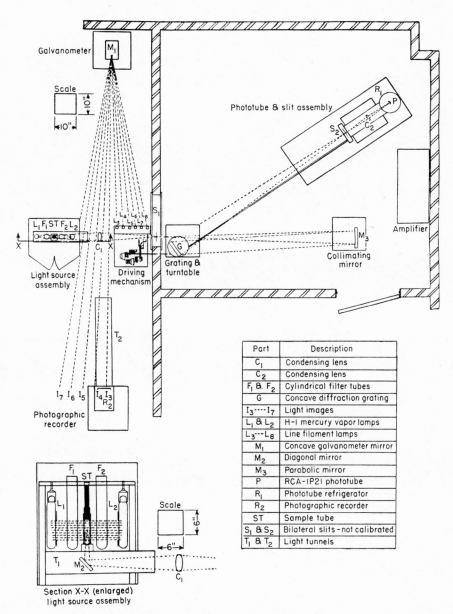

Fig. 1. Schematic diagram of grating spectrograph with direct photo-electric recording. From Rank and Wiegand (47).

conjunction with a quartz spectrograph when practicable because the intensity of the Raman effect increases exponentially as the exciting frequency increases.

A grating spectrography ruled to 15,000 lines per inch and having a resolution of 6 wave numbers per centimeter has been used successfully. It has a high speed, requiring about 2 minutes to give adequate densities

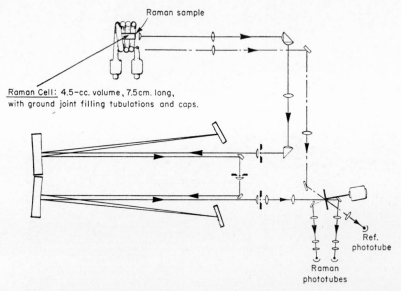

FIG. 2. Schematic diagram of Applied Physics Corporation (Carey) model spectrophotometer.

for $\Delta\nu$ 801 cm.$^{-1}$ from cyclohexane and $\Delta\nu$ 992 cm.$^{-1}$ from benzene (54). Recently direct recording of Raman spectra has been made possible by a photoelectric technique in which an electron multiplier phototube (style IP21 or 930A) is used in conjunction with a diffraction grating (2,3,6,7,14,21,28,32,33,35,37,41,44,45,47,53-56). Schematic diagrams of this type of spectrographic system are shown in Figs. 1, 2, and 3.

3.2. LIGHT SOURCES

Since a complete series of Raman lines appears for each exciting frequency, it is highly desirable that the radiation reaching the specimen be monochromatic, a condition that can be achieved to a degree only by the use of selected sources, combined with filters. The mercury arc is the most practical. The low-pressure arc is an intense source of the 2537 mercury line. However, the frequency of the exciting line must not

contain sufficient energy to raise the irradiated molecules into an observable excited electronic state, which would result in fluorescence or
photochemical decomposition of the irradiated material. Furthermore, if
the irradiated material absorbs strongly in the ultraviolet, the use
of lower frequency (longer wavelengths) is unavoidable. Sometimes the
3888 helium line is used, but the 4358 mercury line is generally preferred

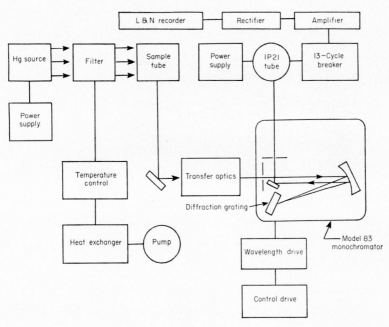

Fig. 3. Schematic diagram of Perkins-Elmer Corporation Raman spectrophotometer.

in both high- and medium-low-pressure arcs. Cadmium arcs (29) and
lamps of zinc, thallium, and other metals have been described (27) for
special investigations.

3.3. Optical Systems and Recording Systems

Many arrangements of optical systems are possible, each being
especially adaptable to the source of incident radiation and the material
to be irradiated. Figure 4a shows a dismantled apparatus, using a hot
cathode water-cooled helium tube, glass filters, and parabolic mirrors;
and Fig. 4b is a photograph of the Raman spectrum of nitrobenzene,
using a mercury lamp with similar equipment. Multiple mercury arcs
spaced at intervals around the specimen tube have been used by many.

One of the most elaborate of these units (54) is illustrated in Fig. 5, which also shows how circulating liquid filters can be employed. A Toronto type of mercury arc in the form of a helix with a filter assembly between arc and cell is used in some instruments (2-4). Some instru-

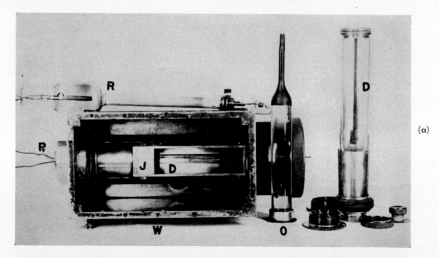

(a)

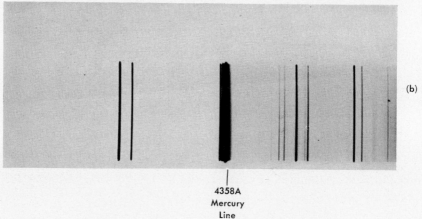

(b)

4358A
Mercury
Line

FIG. 4. (a) Raman apparatus using water-cooled helium tube: *R*—helium tube; *O*—Raman tube; *J*—mounting for filters; *D*—parabolic reflectors; *W*—watertight box. (b) Raman spectrum of nitrobenzene.

ments may be used either with photographic recording or with the direct photoelectric method.

For photographic recording there is a wide variety of spectrographic plates on the market especially designed for speed where speed is nec-

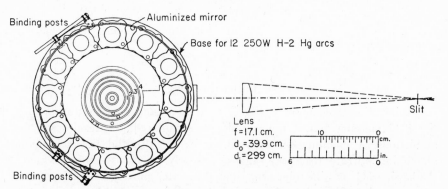

Fig. 5. Typical arrangement of mercury arcs, filters, and receiving cells. From Stamm (54).

essary, or fineness of grain where resolution is necessary, and especially sensitive to various regions of the spectrum. In general, however, if one quality is especially desirable, it can be obtained only at the sacrifice of some other desirable characteristic. For quantitative analysis such plates are used with a microphotometer that scans the exposed plate by a point of light and plots the intensity of the lines recorded thereon. To represent accurately the comparative intensity of the Raman lines, the characteristics of the plate, the time of exposure, and the development must be such that the degree of blackness of the plate increases in uniform increments with uniform increases in exposure. These difficulties are largely avoided when direct-recording photoelectric systems

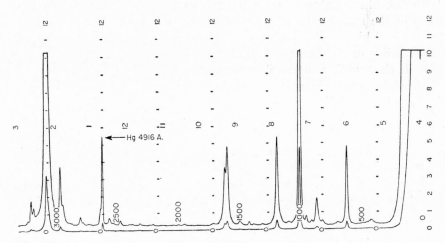

Fig. 6. The Raman spectra of benzene as recorded on a strip at two sensitivities. (Courtesy of Applied Physics Corporation.)

are employed. Figure 6 shows the Raman spectra of benzene as recorded on a strip at two degrees of sensitivity. The line at $\Delta\nu$ 984 corresponding to the C^{13} isotope is clearly visible.

3.4. LIGHT FILTERS

When the 4358 mercury line is used as a source of excitation and the 4047 mercury line is not completely eliminated, the results will be ambiguous. A combination of sodium nitrite (19) and praseodymium ammonium nitrate (57) was suggested nearly twenty-seven years ago; rhodamine 5G, m-dinitrobenzene, nickel nitrate, cobaltithiocyanate, and numerous glass filters have been tried. A combination of filters is usually fairly satisfactory but almost always at the sacrifice of considerable intensity. No perfect filter has yet been found.

3.5. SAMPLE PROCESSING

Proper preparation of samples is an essential feature of Raman spectra techniques. Samples containing dust, even in small quantities, will scatter the exciting frequency by Rayleigh scattering to such an extent that the background is partly fogged. Fluorescence may also be severe, particularly when hydrocarbons or photochemical decomposition products of high molecular weight are present. Both conditions usually can be improved by filtering through activated gel and sintered glass combined with distillation (sometimes with continuous distillation), although filtering through activated gel can cause a change in composition of the sample. Quenching of fluorescing molecules by collisions of the second kind is sometimes possible by using acceptors such as potassium iodide or nitrobenzene (22).

If the sample material is permanently colored, the only alternative is to choose an exciting frequency that is in a region where its absorption and that of the resultant Raman frequencies do not occur.

As the intensity of Raman spectra is proportional to the concentration of the individual components, traces of soluble impurities (1% or less) are without appreciable effect. The Raman spectra or substances dissolved in water or other solvents can readily be determined provided the solvents do not fluoresce or absorb, and provided the material to be analyzed possesses covalent chemical bonds. Electrovalent bonds give rise to no Raman spectra. For dissolved substances this method has a distinct advantage compared with infrared absorption, which is very sensitive to traces of water.

4. Raman Spectra Technique Applied to Analytical Problems

4.1. QUALITATIVE ANALYSIS

The next step is to interpret the results and apply them to specific problems. It is common practice for qualitative purposes to plot the lines shown in Fig. 7 in terms of $\Delta\nu$ ranging from zero to about 3200

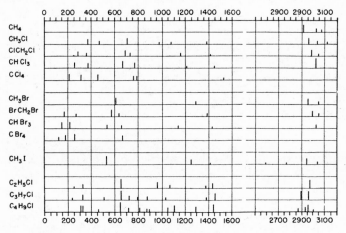

FIG. 7. The Raman spectra of some halogenated hydrocarbons.

cm.$^{-1}$; visual estimates of the relative intensities are indicated by the relative heights of the vertical lines. Fig. 7 shows the Raman spectra of some halogenated hydrocarbons (24). It may be readily seen that, although the spectra of these compounds have many similarities, they are nevertheless quite different.

The symmetrical valence vibration in methane corresponding to the expansion of the molecule as a whole (tetrahedral symmetry, T_δ) is $\Delta\nu$ 2914 which, in general, is ascribed to the $H_3C \leftrightarrow H$ type of motion. The corresponding valence oscillation for methyl chloride, methyl bromide, and methyl iodide is $\Delta\nu$ 710, 600, and 530, respectively, and for ethyl chloride it is somewhat lower, owing to a weaker valence force constant. Generally speaking, for each type of symmetrical oscillation there is a characteristic Raman shift which may vary according to the nature of the substituents attached to the adjacent atom (Fig. 7). Some typical linkages and their characteristic frequencies are given in Table I.

These Raman shifts can be exceedingly useful in indicating the presence or absence of certain groups and consequently assist in the identification of chemical compounds and mixtures of such compounds.

TABLE I

Typical Linkages and Characteristic Raman Shifts

Type of Linkage	Wave numbers per cm.	Type of Linkage	Wave numbers per cm.
H—H	4158	C=C	1620
O—H	3650	C=O	1700
N—H	3370	O=O	1600
Cl—H	2880	C=N	1650
Br—H	2558		
S—H	2572		
C—C	993	C≡C	2120
C—O	1030	C≡N	2150
C—N	1033	C≡O	2146
C—S	650	N≡O	2224

For qualitative analytical purposes, if the components of a mixture are known, it suffices to compare the relative intensities of any Raman line characteristic of each component. From a qualitative point of view, if the components are not known, the variations from the characteristic Raman shift for a particular type of valence linkage are about as important as the shift itself. In ethylene, for example, the C=C shift is $\Delta\nu$ 1620, but in propylene and other derivatives of the type $CH_2=CHR$ (where R is an aliphatic radical) it is about 1647. If the compound is $CH_2=CHCl$, the shift is 1608; if $CH_2=CHCHO$, $\Delta\nu$ 1618. It is interesting to note that, if a CH_2 group is introduced between the R and C=C group such as $CH_2=CHCH_2Cl$, the shift is nearly normal, i.e., $\Delta\nu$ 1640. At the same time, if the compound is of the type $CH_2CH=CHR$ (thus permitting *cis-trans* isomerism), the *cis* form is always about 20 cm.$^{-1}$ lower than the *trans* but higher than in compounds of the type $CH_2=CHR$. In substituted hydrocarbons of this type the shifts are $\Delta\nu$ 1658 (*cis*) and 1674 (*trans*) and are still lower if the substituent group is chlorine, a CHO group, or other radical.

The same approach applies to compounds containing carbonyl groups. In esters of the type XCOOR, in which R is a hydrocarbon radical and X is hydrogen, the C=O frequency is $\Delta\nu$ 1718; and if X is CH_3, the frequency becomes $\Delta\nu$ 1739. Under the same conditions, if X is, successively, CH_2Cl, $CHCl_2$, and CCl_3, the carbonyl frequency is about $\Delta\nu$ 1747, 1752, and 1765. In general, the carbonyl frequencies as determined by Raman spectra in the common acids, ketones, aldehydes, esters, and acyl halides and anhydrides are about $\Delta\nu$ 1648, 1710, 1720, 1739, and 1790, respectively; the doublet frequency for anhydrides is

1775, 1856. Up to the present, the interest in these results has been primarily directed toward determining chemical constitution. The examples given are only illustrative; they could be multiplied many times and applied, within limits, to analytical processes.

From the point of view of inorganic chemistry the same general precepts also apply; the tetrahedral structure of the $SO_4^=$ ion, for example, yields about 450, 620, 980, and 1100, and nitrates with a plane triangular structure (symmetry D_{3h}) about 720, 1050, and 1350 cm.$^{-1}$. In inorganic chemistry the scope of application remaining is, however, perhaps larger, since the greater proportion of work thus far completed is on organic compounds. Furthermore, in inorganic chemistry the molecular species present in complicated mixtures is often less understood, and ordinary analytical methods may throw little light on the existence of equilibrium combinations. The molecular species in mixtures containing high concentrations of sulfuric acid and nitric acid, for example, have been identified (8), and the constitution of boric acid and the repression of ionization in solution have been investigated (33).

The purport of the foregoing discussion is to demonstrate that certain empirical and other characteristics of a molecule may be used in certain types of qualitative analysis. Without the latter, of course, any quantitative analysis would be less significant. In the following section some of the quantitative applications of Raman spectra will be considered in detail.

4.2. QUANTITATIVE ANALYSIS

If specific Raman lines can be ascribed to different molecular species in a mixture, then the relative proportion of the components can be determined to an accuracy of about 1 to 5% from the measurable intensities of the spectral lines. These lines may be photometrically measured with a microphotometer once they are recorded on a plate, or they may be measured directly by photoelectric means (see Figs. 1, 2, and 3).

The method of analysis by means of Raman spectra is especially useful when other methods are unsatisfactory; however, all spectroscopic methods are not without their complications. The optical density (D), or opaqueness, for example, of a Raman line on a photographic plate is a measure of the light-stopping substance deposited on the plate after development. The density is a function not only of the intensity of the light producing it but also of the time of exposure, the frequency of the light, the type and age of the plate, the conditions under which it is developed, the presence of fluorescence, and the background caused by Rayleigh scattering of the continuous spectrum in the arc. These variables must be controlled for optimum results. The lines used for comparative purposes, moreover, must be sharp, not too greatly modified by intermolecular effects, free from overlapping lines, and strong enough to be readily measured but not so strong that they are practically opaque to the scanning beam. They must also possess a density in the linear range of the D versus log E^* curve of the photographic emulsion. Direct measurement of intensities by photoelectric means eliminates some of these difficulties.

Various mixtures have been quantitatively investigated with considerable success. There are four general methods of procedure.

4.2.1. Standard Method A. A graduated series of exposures of known intensity is made on each plate. When these are microphotometered, D, the optical density, is determined from the relation $D = \gamma$ log $(I_{incident}/I_{transmitted})$ for each exposure, where γ is a proportionality factor. A graph is then made of D as a function of the time of exposure, with constant light intensity assumed, or as a function of intensity, with constant exposure time assumed. The density of a selected Raman line on the same plate is then determined from its microphotometer tracing in the same manner and its intensity read off from the density versus intensity calibration curve already obtained. Since the intensity of a Raman line is directly proportional to the number of molecules present, the concentration of a given molecular species can be determined by comparing the Raman intensities observed with those of the pure substances obtained under the same experimental conditions. This method takes considerable time, is susceptible to variations in the light intensity, and does not take into account any intermolecular interaction.

4.2.2. Standard Method B. The intensity of a suitable Raman line of substance A in a pure state is measured and that of substance B likewise determined under similar conditions. The observed intensity ratio of i_A/i_B is then calculated for a solution containing equimolecular parts of A and B by incorporating the ratios of the molecular weights and densities $(i_A/i_B)_{1:1}$. As $i_A \sim$ moles of A, and $i_B \sim$ moles of B, then in a mixture of A + B of unknown composition $i_{A'}/i_{B'} = c$ (moles A′/moles B′). In the 1:1 mixture $(i_A/i_B)_{1:1} = c$. Therefore $i_{A'}/i_{B'} = (i_A/i_B)_{1:1}$ (moles A′/moles B′). Hence moles of A/B = $(i_{A'}/i_{B'})/(i_A/i_B)_{1:1}$. Since the intensity ratio of $i_{A'}/i_{B'}$ in the unknown mixture can be directly measured and $(i_A/i_B)_{1:1}$ calculated, the ratio of A′/B′ can be determined without making up a number of standard solutions.

4.2.3. Synthetic Standard Methods. This procedure is based on the calibration of each system from a few mixtures of known composition. It takes into account some of the mutual interference of overlapping

---

* E is the measured time of exposure.

lines and some intermolecular effects. In principle, a series of solutions of A and B of known concentration are made up, and the ratios of i_A/i_B of two suitable lines in the spectra are obtained for each known ratio of grams A/grams B. The observed intensities of ratios are then plotted against the weight ratios and unknown compositions are read from the graph.

A typical example of this method is the determination of the composition of mixtures of 2-methyl-1-butene and 1-pentene (15) by the use of $\Delta\nu$ 772 cm.$^{-1}$ of the former and 1298 cm.$^{-1}$ of the latter in constructing a standard reference curve from the ratio of the intensities

$$\frac{I_{772}}{I_{1298} + I_{772}}$$

as a function of the composition in terms of per cent by weight. The results are shown in Fig. 8. By plotting $I_{772}/(I_{1298} + I_{772})$ rather than

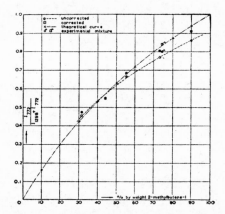

FIG. 8. Composition curve plotted from the Raman spectra of mixtures of 1-pentene and 2-methyl-1-butene. From Gerding et al. (15).

I_{772} versus I_{1298} it is possible to extrapolate from zero to the boundaries of the system. In the figure the theoretical curve assume that the scattering power of both kinds of molecules is constant, and the "corrected" curve includes a correction for the intensity of parasitic lines which may influence the total intensity measurements.

Another example, applicable to multicomponent systems, is of considerable interest (51). In this case the density of each Raman line together with the background density near each line is obtained from the microphotometer tracing as previously described. The antilog of the background density, is, however, subtracted from the line density to give an effective intensity of the Raman line (I_c). Along the linear portion of the exposure-density curve plotted from $D = \gamma \log E$, γ depends on the emulsion and the development conditions.* These conditions may be regulated so that the value of γ is nearly equal to 1, and therefore $E =$ antilog D. The effective intensity would therefore be a linear function of the concentration under these conditions. As this is not always realized in practice, empirical averaging processes are used, and intensity ratios, as described, are employed rather than absolute intensities.

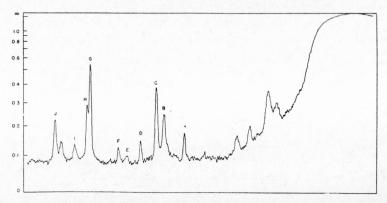

FIG. 9. Raman spectra of a mixture of 9.5% each of o-xylene, p-xylene, and ethylbenzene, and 71.5% of m-xylene. From Rosenbaum *et al.* (*51*). The designated lines are identified as follows: *A*, 459 cm.⁻¹, p-xylene; *B*, 514 cm.⁻¹, m-xylene; *C*, 538 cm.⁻¹, m-xylene; *D*, 582 cm.⁻¹, o-xylene; *E*, 620 cm.⁻¹, ethylbenzene; *F*, 644 cm.⁻¹, p-xylene; *G*, 724 cm.⁻¹, m-xylene; *H*, 733 cm.⁻¹, o-xylene; *I*, 768 cm.⁻¹, ethylbenzene; *J*, 827 cm.⁻¹, p-xylene.

In calibrating each known mixture of effective intensity, I_e of each suitable Raman line or lines is divided by the intensity of the same line or lines in the pure compound, resulting in an average ratio (ρ_{av}), which, in turn, is corrected to add up to 100% (P_c). The ratio, R, of each of the corrected percentages is obtained, and the corresponding known percentages are averaged over the mixture (R_{av}).

The intensity of each Raman line of the pure compound used for analysis is multiplied by its average ratio, which yields an intensity factor corrected for deviation from average conditions. In setting up calibration curves for a series of compounds it is desirable to divide them into groups of three, using two or three known mixtures. To extend this calibration to other mixtures, including the group already calibrated, it is necessary to use at least one compound of that group to ensure proper correlation. If the analysis does not include all the compounds in

---

* This is the classical density versus exposure relation; i.e., exposure increase is in geometrical progression, the density increase is in arithmetical progression.

the mixture, it is necessary to determine the total percentage by independent means. An example of the application of this method is shown in Table II and Fig. 9.

TABLE II

Analysis of Four-Component Mixture (22)

Component	Raman line frequency (cm.$^{-1}$)	I_e	P	P_{av}	P_c	P_{known}	Dev.
p-Ethyltoluene	818	0.348	61.6				
p-Ethyltoluene	806	0.352	65.2	61.8	25.5	25	+0.5
p-Ethyltoluene	644	0.251	58.5				
Pseudocumene	744	0.578	57.2	59.0	24.5	25	−0.5
Pseudocumene	557	0.502	60.9				
m-Ethyltoluene	520	0.290	62.1	62.1	26	25	+1
Mesitylene	576	1.244	57.4	57.4	24	25	−1

4.2.4. Internal Standards. Another method is the use of internal standards consisting of known amounts of such materials as carbon tetrachloride or carbon disulfide (46, 54). These have strong but few Raman lines generally removed from those of the material to be analyzed. Standard solutions of the mixture to be studied are made up of a known percentage of substance A and a known percentage of substance B, to which has been added fixed amounts in weight per cent of standard S (approximately 10% of carbon tetrachloride).

The ratios of the intensities i_A/i_S and i_B/i_S are then determined for each standard solution of known composition. The ratio of i_A/i_S is plotted against A_{grams}/S_{grams}, and the ratio i_B/i_S is plotted against B_{grams}/S_{grams}. If approximately the same quantity of S is added to the standard, the quantities may be read from the calibration curve. This method, though convenient, will contaminate the sample through the addition of the standard.

In this connection the intensity of the reference material (carbon tetrachloride, carbon disulfide, etc.) may be obtained, however, not admixed with the unknown to be analyzed, but introduced in a separate tube identical in shape, location, and scattering potential with the unknown mixture, thus obviating contamination but introducing optical difficulties. In one case electronic rather than photographic methods were used for intensity determinations (47). Here the intensities of the Raman lines in an unknown, for analytical purposes, were measured simply by determining their height, since the intensity scale is linear. The ratio of the peak height of the lines in question to the peak height of the lines of the reference material may be termed the scattering coefficient. This ratio was obtained for the same lines in the spectra of the pure components of the mixture and for the mixture. The percentage of the component for which the analysis is being made and which is present in the unknown mixture is simply the ratio of the scattering coefficients, i.e., unknown/pure substance × 100%. An example of the Raman spectra of a synthetic mixture and its components as obtained by means of photoelectric recording is shown in Fig. 10, and the analytical results of a sample of aromatic concentrate are shown in Table III.

TABLE III

Analysis of a Sample of an Aromatic Concentrate
from a Special Gasoline (26)

Component	Per cent of volume from analysis of	
	Fractions	Original sample
o-Xylene	2.5	1.4
Isopropylbenzene	0.7 ⎱	2.5
n-Propylbenzene	2.6 ⎰	
m-Ethyltoluene	18.5	21.7
p-Ethyltoluene	8.7	10.5
1,3,5-Trimethylbenzene	13.2	14.2
o-Ethyltoluene	4.5	7.2
1,2,4-Trimethylbenzene	41.5	40.5
1,2,3-Trimethylbenzene	. . .	3.0
Not analyzed [a]	7.7	
Total	99.9	101.0

[a] The last fractions of the fractionation and the residue and holdup were not submitted for Raman analysis. Distillation data showed it to be essentially 1,2,3-trimethylbenzene.

5. Summary

The object of this discussion of the uses of the Raman effect in qualitative and quantitative analyses is to describe briefly its theoretical background and the experimental methods employed, and to demonstrate its multitudinous applications. This procedure is not a substitute for direct, quick, and inexpensive methods of procedure. (Like any other method of analysis, it has its limitations.) The tendency, however, has been to be more critical of newer than of older methods of analytical

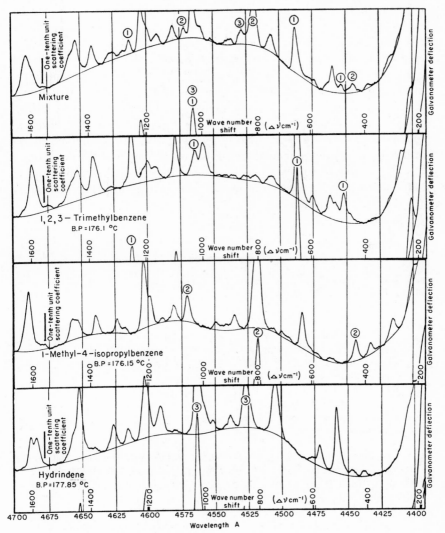

Fig. 10. Raman spectra of a synthetic mixture and its components. From Rank and Wiegand (47).

Synthetic sample "Q"	Composition, known	Volume % determined
1,2,3-Trimethylbenzene	28.2	28.7
1-Methyl-4-isopropylbenzene	43.8	43.5
Hydrindene	28.0	28.3
Total	100.0	100.0

approach. There would be no quantitative chemical analysis today if its development depended on the acquisition of a completely lucid theory of atomic and molecular structure before empirical applications were accepted. The Raman effect has proved beyond a doubt to be invaluable in the field of structural and qualitative analyses. As far as quantitative analysis is concerned, it has proved eminently practicable, particularly in dealing with multicomponent systems of similar substances, at high concentrations. This phase of Raman spectra has not as yet been exploited to its fullest extent. The development of new technique in recording Raman spectra, increased speed of operations, and the availability of commercial instruments has greatly stimulated the utilization of Raman spectra in research and commercial application. The constantly increasing interest in its special applications augurs well for its continued development.

References

1. Andant, A., *Publs. sci. et tech. ministère air* **21**, 1 (1933).
2. Applied Physics Corporation, Pasadena, California.
3. Applied Research Laboratories, Glendale, California.
4. Banerje, S. B., *Indian J. Phys.* **28**, 205 (1954).
5. Birchenback, L., and Goubeau, J., *Ber.* **65**, 1140 (1932).
6. Brehm, R. K., and Fassel, V. A., *J. Opt. Soc. Am.* **43**, 886 (1953).
7. Busing, W. R., *J. Opt. Soc. Am.* **42**, 774 (1952).
8. Chedin, J., *Ann. chim. (Paris)* **8**, 20 (1937).
9. Crigler, E. A., *J. Am. Chem. Soc.* **54**, 4199 (1932).
10. Delwaulle, F. F., and Wiemann, J., *Chim. & ind. (Paris)* **56**, 292 (1946).
11. Duyckaerts, G., *Ind. chim. belge* **16**, 445 (1951).
12. Duyckaerts, G., and Michel, G., *Anal. Chim. Acta* **2**, 750 (1948).
13. Feneant, S., *Chim. anal.* **32**, 299 (1951).
14. Fenske, M. R., Braun, W. G., Wiegand, R. V., Quiggle, Dorothy, McCormick, R. H., and Rank, D. H., *Ind. Eng. Chem. Anal. Ed.* **19**, 700 (1947).
15. Gerding, H., and van der Vet, A. P., *Rec. trav. chim.* **64**, 257 (1945).
16. Goubeau, J., *Z. angew. Phys.* **1**, 146 (1948).
17. Goubeau, J., *Oel u. Kohle* **37**, 840 (1941).
18. Goubeau, J., and Schneider, V., *Z. angew. Chem.* **53**, 531 (1940).
19. Goubeau, J., and Thaler, Z., *Ver. deut. Chemiker Beih.* **No. 41** (1941).
20. Grosse, A. V., Rosenbaum, E. J., and Jacobson, H. F., *Ind. Eng. Chem. Anal. Ed.*, **12**, 191 (1940).
21. Heigel, J. J., Black, J. F., Dudenbostel, B. F., and Wilson, J. A., *Anal. Chem.* **21**, 554 (1949).
22. Hibben, J. H., *Ind. Eng. Chem.* **26**, 646 (1934).
23. Hibben, J. H., *J. Chem. Phys.* **5**, 710 (1937).
24. Hibben, J. H., "The Raman Effect and Its Chemical Applications." Reinhold, New York, 1939.
25. Hilger and Watts, Ltd., *J. Sci. Instr.* **30**, 29 (1953).
26. Hirschler, E., and Faulcover, W. B. M., *J. Am. Chem. Soc.* **68**, 210 (1946).

27. Hoffman, I., and Daniels, F., *J. Am. Chem. Soc.* **54,** 4226 (1932).
28. Jarrell-Ash Co., Newtonville, Massachusetts (Hilger and Watts, Ltd.).
29. Krishnamurti, P., *Indian J. Phys.* **5,** 587 (1930).
30. Landsberg, G. S., Bazhulin, D. A., Rozenberg, Y. V., and Eliner, A. S., *Bull. acad. sci. U.R.S.S. Sér. phys.* **4,** 158 (1940).
31. Lespieau, R., Bourguel, M., and Wakeman, R. L., *Compt. rend.* **193,** 238 (1931).
32. Luther, H., Bergmann, G., and Muhlfeld, A., *Naturwissenschaften* **39,** 255 (1952).
33. Marrinan, H. D., *J. Opt. Soc. Am.* **43,** 121 (1953).
34. Matutano, J. R. B., *Zaragoza* **10,** 15 (1950).
35. Menzies, A. C., and Skinner, J., *J. Sci. Instr.* **26,** 299 (1949).
36. Michel, G., *Spectrochim. Acta* **5,** 218 (1952).
37. Michel, G., and Duyckaerts, G., *Comp. rend 27ᵉ congr. intern. chim. ind., Brussels, 1954, I; Ind. chim. belge* **20,** 193 (1955).
38. Mizushima, S., *J. Soc. Chem. Ind. Japan* **45,** 209 (1942).
39. Nakamara, H., and Obata, I., *Busseiron Kenkyu* **No. 85,** 36 (1955).
40. Okazaki, H., *J. Chem. Soc. Japan* **63,** 368 (1942).
41. Perkins-Elmer Corporation, Norwalk, Connecticut.
42. Pfund, A. H., *Phys. Rev.* **42,** 581 (1932).
43. Pierce, W. C., and Nachtrieb, N. H., *Ind. Eng. Chem. Anal. Ed.* **13,** 774 (1941).
44. Rank, D. H., Pfister, R. J., and Coleman, P. D., *J. Opt. Soc. Am.* **32,** 390 (1942).
45. Rank, D. H., Pfister, R. J., and Grimm, H. H., *J. Opt. Soc. Am.* **33,** 31 (1943).
46. Rank, D. H., Scott, R. W., and Fenske, M. R., *Ind. Eng. Chem. Anal. Ed.* **14,** 816 (1942).
47. Rank, D. H., and Wiegand, R. V., *J. Opt. Soc. Am.* **36,** 325 (1946).
48. Robert, L., *Rev. inst. franç. pétrole et Ann. combustibles liquides* **3,** 245 (1948).
49. Robert, L., *Spectrochim. Acta* **6,** 115 (1953).
50. Rosenbaum, E. J., Grosse, E. J., and Jacobson, H. F., *J. Am. Chem. Soc.* **61,** 689 (1939).
51. Rosenbaum, E. J., Martin, C. C., and Lauer, J. L., *Ind. Eng. Chem. Anal. Ed.* **18,** 731 (1946).
52. Simon, A., Kriegsmann, H., and Steger, E., *Z. physik. Chem. (Leipzig)* **205,** 190 (1956).
53. Skinner, L. S., *Spectrochim. Acta* **6,** 110 (1953).
54. Stamm, R. F., *Ind. Eng. Chem. Anal. Ed.* **17,** 318 (1945).
55. Stamm, R. F., Salzman, C. F., Jr., and Mariner, T., *J. Opt. Soc. Amer.* **43,** 119 (1953).
56. White, J. U., Alpert, N. L., and de Bell, A. G., *J. Opt. Soc. Am.* **45,** 154 (1955).
57. Wood, R. W., and Collins, G., *Phys. Rev.* **42,** 386 (1932).

Books and Review Articles

Biffin, Frank, and Seaman, William, "Modern Instruments in Chemical Analysis." McGraw-Hill, New York, 1956.

Bhagavantam, S., "Scattering of Light and the Raman Effect." Chemical Publishing Co., 1945.

Braun, W. G., and Fenske, M. R., "Raman spectra." *Anal. Chem.* **21,** 12 (1949).

Braun, W. G., and Fenske, M. R., "Fundamental analysis: Raman spectra." *Anal. Chem.* **22,** 11 (1950).

Glockler, G., "The Raman effect." *Revs. Mod. Phys.* **15,** 111 (1943).

Goubeau, J., *in* "Physikalische Methoden der Analytischen Chemie" (W. Boettger, ed.). Akademische Verlagsgesellschaft, Leipzig, 1939.

Herzberg, G., "Infrared and Raman Spectra of Polyatomic Molecules." Van Nostrand, New York, 1945.

Hibben, J. H., "The Raman Effect and Its Chemical Applications." Reinhold, New York, 1939.

Goubeau, J., *in* "Houben-Weyl Methoden der Organischen Chemie," Vol. 3/2 (E. Müller, ed.) G. Thieme Verlag, Stuttgart, 1955.

Pajenkamp, Forst, "Advances in the scientific and practical application of the Raman effect." *Fortschr. chem. Forsch.* **1**, 417 (1950).

Sheppard, H., "The infrared and Raman frequencies of hydrocarbon groupings." *J. Inst. Petrol.* **37**, 95 (1951).

American Petroleum Institute Project No. 44 issues a catalog of Raman spectra.

Refractive Index Measurement

LEROY W. TILTON AND JOHN K. TAYLOR

National Bureau of Standards, Washington, D.C.

1. Basic Conditions

1.1. Definitions

The refractive indices of a substance are numbers (quotients) evaluating the ratios of the standard velocities of light in air (or in vacuum) to the corresponding velocities in the substance. Using these indices we can express the extent by which various substances cause a decrease in the speed of light as compared with its speed in air or vacuum. The retardations are different for different colors (wavelengths), and they depend also on the temperature, pressure, chemical composition, physicochemical constitution, homogeneity, purity, state, etc., of the substance. Thus it is easy to understand that refractive indices are important tools for many practical purposes in the testing and control of products and in established methods of analysis, particularly in the case of chemically homogeneous media where they afford a sure means of distinguishing between analogous substances. For purity of materials which are subject to limited variations in chemical composition, because of the known methods of their preparation, it is easy to set tolerance limits for the refractive index. In true and in colloidal solutions there are very useful relationships between concentration and refraction. The successful measurement by refraction of the amount of water in milk and of albumin in the blood shows that the solution may even be of complicated composition. Fortunately, the actual measurement of indices has been important in the optical industry for over a century, and many devices have contributed to the ease and reliability with which indices may be measured.

The fundamental basis of refractive index measurement is the phenomenon of refraction. When (see Fig. 1a) light of given wavelength in medium G is incident, at any angle, i, with the normal, on a plane interface between G and a second and optically denser medium, L, then, in general, part of the light enters L and proceeds therein at a corresponding angle, r, with the normal, and $v \sin r = v' \sin i$, where v and v' are the velocities of light in G and in L, respectively. For various values of the angle i, *the ratio of the sines of the angles of incidence and refraction is a constant*, $n = (v/v')$, for this phenomenon between these media, and n is the *relative* refractive index of medium L with respect to medium G, for light of a given wavelength.

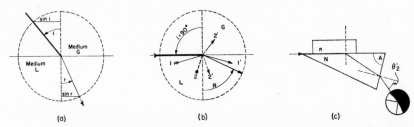

(a) (b) (c)

FIG. 1. Fundamental bases of prism refractometry. If G is a standard medium (say air, $n = 1$), then the refractive index of medium L is $n = \sin i/\sin r$. For the important special case (b) of $i = 90°$, the light in G travels along the interface at *grazing incidence* and is *critically* refracted at the limiting or *critical* angle, R, for which $\sin R = 1/n$. No light from G can traverse medium L at angles greater than R. Light in L directed toward G at angles greater than R cannot enter G but is totally reflected in L (see arrow 1, 1' of diagram b); at angles less than R it is partially reflected in L and partially refracted into G (see dotted arrow 2, 2' of b). The general equation for prism refractometry is $n = \sin A \sqrt{N^2 - \sin^2 \vartheta_2'} + \cos A \sin \vartheta'_2$, where A is the refracting angle, N is the index of the secondary reference prism or block of the refractometer, n is the index of the unknown sample, and ϑ_2' is the angle of emergence (positive if toward the refracting edge, see diagram c).

In most cases it is convenient to use air as medium G for making refractive index measurements, and it became customary to do so. Therefore air is generally accepted as the standard with respect to which the refractive indices of liquids and solids are expressed. From the definition of refractive index it is evident that any index of L relative to G may be converted to refer to another standard, say vacuum, by simple multiplication $n_{(L/G)} \cdot n_{(G/V)} = n_{(L/V)}$ provided the index, $n_{(G/V)}$, of medium G with respect to vacuum is known. For gases and vapors it is customary to refer all indices to vacuum. Whenever refractive indices are referred to vacuum as standard they are called *absolute* indices, $\bar{n}$, and the relation between absolute and relative indices is, as above, $\bar{n} = \mu n$, where μ is the index of air (with respect to vacuum).

1.2. AIR AS STANDARD

The "standard" with respect to which refractive indices are measured is usually air as it is found from day to day in the laboratory, at various temperatures and pressures, with varying content of moisture and carbon dioxide. Much care in controlling conditions is necessary in work on primary standards of index, and even for some precise secondary work it may be necessary to pay attention to the temperature of the air. At high altitudes or during extremes of weather conditions the pressure can be of importance.

It is sometimes desirable to distinguish clearly between the effects of temperature, pressure, etc., on the reference medium and on the refracting media themselves. In this section only the reference medium (72) is considered.

If a solid of high index, say 1.8 (which for the moment we shall assume to be invariant with temperature), is measured on a warm day in summer, say at 37°C., and again in a cold laboratory in winter, say at 15°C., the index at low temperature would be judged lower by 4×10^{-5} merely because the reference air is denser. For a sample of index 1.4 the corresponding apparent change of an invariant medium would be -3×10^{-5}.

Similarly, if the barometer stands higher by 30 to 45 mm. when an index determination is repeated, the second result will appear lower by 2×10^{-5}. The presence or absence of moisture in air is of much less importance than is a precise knowledge of the temperature or pressure of the air. As for the CO_2 content of air, its effects are altogether negligible in fifth-decimal-place refractometry. Tolerances for the control or measurement of air conditions are included in Table VII of this paper.

1.3. TEMPERATURE COEFFICIENTS

Media selected for precise refractive index measurement should be homogeneous and more or less transparent. Solids should be free from stress effects and from striations and visible defects. Liquids should be free from impurities, and if mixtures they should preferably contain no components having materially different boiling points.

The absolute refractive indices, $\bar{n}$, of media are affected by temperature in two ways. First, and best known, the heat changes the density, d, of the sample and consequently its refractive index, $\bar{n}$, according to the equation

$$\frac{\partial \bar{n}}{\partial t} = f(\bar{n}) \frac{dd}{dt} \tag{1}$$

where $f(\bar{n})$ is a positive function, variously approximated, for example as

$\bar{n} - 1$, $\bar{n}^2 - 1$, $(\bar{n}^2 - 1)/(\bar{n}^2 + 2)$, etc. This change in index is usually negative because most media expand when heated, and it is not a function of wavelength. The second way in which temperature effects the indices of media is through changes in the resonance frequencies of certain vibrators in the media. Usually, there is a capacity for absorbing radiation of longer wavelength, and ultraviolet absorption bands, for example, are "shifted" toward the visible region of wavelengths. For media whose principal effective absorptions lie in the ultraviolet, this absorption-band component of refractive index increases as temperature increases, whereas the reverse is true for media with predominant infrared absorption. For most glasses, as an example, the index change in and near the visible spectral region is chiefly ascribable to ultraviolet bands, and the corresponding increased index, as temperature rises, predominates over the decrease in index that is directly caused by the decreasing density. For some crown glasses, however, the opposing tendencies are about equal in absolute value, and the index sensitivity to temperature is quite negligible for visible radiation. Then, for a few unusual glasses of very low index, the pure density effect and the infrared effects predominate, and negative temperature coefficients of absolute index are found, especially for the longer wavelengths of the visible spectrum.

In general the index of glass is relatively insensitive to temperature, only fused-quartz glass and the high-index flint glasses having positive temperature coefficients that reach 1.0 to 1.5×10^{-5}. For crystals the range in refractive index sensitivity to temperature is greater than for glasses. For sylvite the value is -3.4×10^{-5}; for KRS-5, a mixed crystal of thallium iodide and thallium bromide, the value is $+2.5 \times 10^{-4}$; and for calcite (extraordinary ray), $+1.1 \times 10^{-5}$.

Numerous published data concerning the temperature coefficients of refractive index of liquids show that such values are all negative (direct density effect predominating over that of the absorption shift in the ultraviolet) and very much larger in numerical value than those for most solids.* For a large number of transparent and semitransparent liquids (including numerous oils) the value of $\Delta\bar{n}/\Delta t$ is approximately expressed as -4×10^{-4}, although a number of organic liquids have values ranging from -4 to -6×10^{-4}. Water, with a value of -1×10^{-4}, is a most important exception; on the other hand, there are some optically dense liquids that have unusually large negative temperature coefficients of

---

* The absolute value of the ratio between temperature coefficients of liquids, on the one hand, and of glasses and common optical crystals, on the other, may be very roughly expressed as 100. For liquids, coefficients of relative and of absolute refractive index are practically identical, whereas for glasses and crystals they frequently are numerically quite different and may be of opposite sign.

index, such, for example, as -7 and -8×10^{-4} for methylene iodide and carbon disulfide, respectively.

It is evident that temperature tolerances (72) for fifth-decimal-place refractometry of solids are not severe. Probably $\pm 0.5°C$. will be satisfactory. For liquids, however, the requirements are $\pm 0.1°C$. for water and aqueous solutions and about $\pm 0.02°C$. for liquids of average thermo-optical sensitivity.

TABLE I

Spectral Lines for Refractometry

Source	Designation	Relative visual intensity				λ in air (A.)	λ^2 (μ^2)
Potassium arc	A′		II			7678.58*	0.5896059
Helium tube	—				IV	7281.349	0.5301804
Helium tube	—			III		7065.188	0.4991688
Mercury arc	—			III		6907.496	0.4771350
Helium tube	He red	I				6678.149	0.4459767
Hydrogen tube	H_α, C	I				6562.793	0.4307025
Krypton tube	—		II			6456.324	0.4168412
Cadmium	Cd red	I				6438.470	0.4145390
Mercury arc	—			III		6234.310	0.3886662
Sodium	D_1	I				5895.930	0.3476199
	D_m	I				5892.62*	0.3472297
	D_2	I				5889.963	0.3469166
Helium tube	d	I				5875.618	0.3452289
Krypton tube	—	I				5870.946	0.3446801
Mercury arc	—	I				5790.66	0.3353174
Mercury arc	—	I				5769.60	0.3328828
Mercury arc	e	I				5460.740	0.2981968
Cadmium	Cd green	I				5085.824	0.2586561
Helium tube	—			III		5047.736	0.2547964
Helium tube	He green	I				5015.675	0.2515700
Helium tube	—		II			4921.929	0.2422539
Mercury arc	—			III		4916.036	0.2416741
Hydrogen tube	H_β, F	I				4861.327	0.2363250
Helium tube	He blue		II			4713.143	0.2221372
Krypton tube	—		II			4502.379	0.2027142
Helium tube	He violet	I				4471.477	0.1999411
Mercury arc	g	I				4358.342	0.1899514
Hydrogen	H_γ, G′			III		4340.466	0.1883964
Mercury arc	h_1		II			4077.828	0.1662868
Mercury arc	h_2		II			4046.563	0.1637467
Helium tube	—				IV	4026.189	0.1621020
Helium	—				IV	3888.646	0.1512157

* Intensity-weighted means.

1.4. Sources

Although much refractometry is accomplished with white light, the use of monochromatic-light refractometers is rapidly increasing, even in semi-industrial applications. The ease with which excellent sodium arcs are operated has done much to further the use of the D lines instead of white light. The demand for accurate measurements of dispersion has rapidly increased the use of the mercury arc, the hydrogen (Geissler) tube, and the helium tube as sources for industrial refractometry.

For use with interferometers in which appreciable path difference is involved, krypton tubes and certain lamps and arcs of cadmium are useful. Spectral lines for precise refractometry should be simple in structure, well spaced in the spectrum, isolated from each other, easy to identify, outstanding in intensity, and easy to produce. No one source seems able to provide all that is desired in these respects, but Table I gives data concerning the sources of lines that are much used.

1.5. Absolute, Comparison, and Substitution Methods

Absolute methods of (relative) refractive index measurement involve the primary standard (air) and one or more refractions, such as are illustrated in Fig. 1. The angles are directly measured, usually with a special goniometer called a spectrometer. Several prismatic methods are well known, and it is possible to measure index in this way with reproducibility, for a given laboratory, within about ± 1 to 3×10^{-6}, especially on samples of isotropic crystals, homogeneous glass, and distilled water. Time-consuming effort, painstaking care, and considerable experience are necessary to achieve success in the many details that must be mastered.

Fortunately for the growth of refractometry as a tool, it was early discovered that a homogeneous block of transparent medium L will, after it has itself been carefully measured with respect to air, serve as a *comparison standard* with respect to which other *similar* media can be more easily measured than with respect to air directly. When a sample S is compared with L there are always some difficult-to-control sources of error that can be assigned more liberal tolerances than is the case in absolute measurements because, to the extent that S resembles L, they may be affected alike during the comparison measurement. Thus the result for S is automatically free from the effect of certain conditions that prevailed during the comparison, and the result holds good, to a large extent, for the conditions that were more carefully controlled when L was compared with the primary standard.

Most refractometers in use are *comparison instruments*. In general, they are more reliable, the shorter their total range in the scale of refractive index. Their relatively high precision and the recognized value of such comparison, has led to some, perhaps numerous, unwarranted assumptions regarding the accuracy that is being reached. One of the writers has been testing refractometers for over thirty years and is unable to say that he has attained an accuracy better than ± 2 or 3×10^{-5} in refractometry of solid samples with commercial instruments. The errors made on liquids are, on the average, larger. In fact, it sometimes seems impossible to *repeat* better than $\pm 2 \times 10^{-5}$ with the same solid sample on a given instrument after independently resetting the sample for elimination of wedge effect in the contact liquid. These statements refer to work done with care to eliminate systematic errors, and they relate to averages of four or more "single observations." Probably there are many different residual small errors that now and then add up unfavorably to prevent a higher precision.

Consequently, whenever in refractive index measurement an accuracy better than $\pm 10 \times 10^{-5}$ or a precision better than $\pm 5 \times 10^{-5}$ is seriously desired, the writers recommend that *substitution* processes be used in so far as possible. That is, the unknown and a standard sample very like the unknown should be compared, either simultaneously or in rapid succession, at as near the same test conditions as possible. If the principle of substitution can be strictly followed, the accuracy attained will necessarily closely approximate the precision with which the whole comparison operation can be done.

1.6. Reference Standards

If a laboratory is to do excellent work by comparison methods over a wide range in index it should be provided with a number of refractometers, each covering a short interval in the index scale. In order to work by substitution methods it must, in addition, be supplied with a series of standard refractive index samples for which the indices are known over an appropriate range of temperatures.

Since some refractometers do not always give the same results for liquids and for solids of identical index, it is necessary to have some liquid as well as solid standards. This, of course, is particularly unfortunate because the questions of original purity, contamination, sensitivity to temperature, and expendability make the use of liquid standards much less convenient. However, for all serious problems concerning liquids that can be handled by immersion refractometers, it will be satisfactory to use solids, if obtainable, as the substitution standards.

Solid standards in the form of 60° prisms (with polished triangular ends for use on refractometers) (75) can be certified to the fifth decimal place by the National Bureau of Standards (test fee schedule 202.205). Glass can be commercially obtained for the purpose only from 1.46 to 1.9, but lithium fluoride, 1.39 and fluorite 1.43 are satisfactory also. Equivalent solid standards for any index can be made, as suggested by Richter (68), and such prisms are furnished in some instances by Zeiss for adjusting refractometers.

Among standard liquids, distilled water takes first place. Its indices for sodium light are given for every 0.1 degree from 0 to 60°C. on p. 449 of RP 1085, *Journal of Research of the National Bureau of Standards,* and at every 0.5 degree for thirteen different wavelengths on pp. 446 and

TABLE II

Sodium-Lines Index of Refraction of Distilled Water

t (°C.)	n_D	t (°C.)	n_D	t (°C.)	n_D
0	1.333 949	20	1.332 988	40	610
1	947	21	897	41	463
2	940	22	803	42	314
3	927	23	706	43	162
4	908	24	606	44	008
5	884	25	503	45	1.329 852
6	855	26	396	46	693
7	821	27	287	47	533
8	782	28	174	48	370
9	738	29	059	49	204
10	691	30	1.331 940	50	037
11	638	31	819	51	1.328 867
12	582	32	695	52	696
13	521	33	569	53	522
14	456	34	440	54	346
15	387	35	308	55	168
16	315	36	173	56	1.327 989
17	238	37	036	57	807
18	158	38	1.330 897	58	623
19	075	39	754	59	437
				60	249

447 of the same paper. Excerpts are given here as Tables II and III. Other standards are toluene 1.49693, 2,2,4-trimethylpentane 1.39145, and methylcyclohexane 1.42312 (for D lines at 20°C.), which are available

from the National Bureau of Standards as certified samples 211a, 217a, and 218a, respectively, with fifth-decimal indices at 20°, 25°, and 30°C. for each of seven wavelengths, as listed in Table IV.

TABLE III

Index of Refraction of Distilled Water for Various Spectral Lines
(These values were computed by means of a general interpolation formula.)

t (°C.)	Wavelengths (A.)												
	7065.2 Helium	6678.1 Helium	6562.8 Hydrogen	5892.6 Sodium	5875.6 Helium	5769.6 Mercury	5460.7 Mercury	5015.7 Helium	4861.3 Hydrogen	4713.1 Helium	4471.5 Helium	4358.5 Mercury	4046.6 Mercury
0	1.330 948	1.331 816	1.332 094	1.333 949	1.334 003	1.334 345	1.335 440	1.337 339	1.338 113	1.338 925	1.340 425	1.341 214	1.343 756
5	889	755	032	884	1.333 937	279	372	269	042	854	352	141	681
10	704	567	1.331 843	691	744	085	176	070	1.337 842	653	149	1.340 938	476
15	410	269	545	387	440	1.333 781	1.334 869	1.336 760	531	341	1.339 835	623	158
20	020	1.330 876	151	1.332 988	041	380	466	353	123	1.337 931	423	210	1.342 742
25	1.329 545	398	1.330 672	503	1.332 556	1.332 894	1.333 977	1.335 860	1.336 628	435	1.338 925	1.339 710	239
30	1.328 993	1.329 843	116	1.331 940	1.331 993	331	411	289	055	1.336 860	347	131	1.341 656
35	371	218	1.329 489	308	360	1.331 697	1.332 774	1.334 647	1.335 411	215	1.337 699	1.338 481	001
40	1.327 685	1.328 528	1.328 798	1.330 610	1.330 662	1.330 998	071	1.333 940	1.334 702	1.335 504	1.336 984	1.337 765	1.340 280
45	1.326 939	1.327 778	047	1.329 852	1.329 904	238	1.331 308	171	1.333 932	1.334 731	208	1.336 987	1.339 497
50	136	1.326 971	1.327 239	037	089	1.329 422	1.330 489	1.332 346	104	1.333 902	1.335 375	152	1.338 655
55	1.325 280	111	1.326 378	1.328 168	1.328 220	1.328 552	1.329 615	1.331 467	1.332 223	018	1.334 487	1.335 261	1.337 758
60	1.324 373	1.325 200	1.325 466	1.327 249	1.327 301	1.327 631	1.328 690	1.330 536	1.331 290	1.332 082	1.333 547	1.334 319	1.336 809

2. Evaluation of Optical Constants

2.1. SPECIFIC REFRACTION

The relation between refractive index and density has been the subject of investigation since the time of Newton, who considered $(n^2 - 1)/d$ as worthy of attention because it was approximately constant for several different substances.

TABLE IV

Indices of Refraction of 2,2,4-Trimethylpentane, Methylcyclohexane, and Toluene

Wavelength (A.)	Designation of line	Index of 2,2,4-trimethylpentane			Index of methylcyclohexane			Index of toluene		
		20°C.	25°C.	30°C.	20°C.	25°C.	30°C.	20°C.	25°C.	30°C.
6678.1	Helium	1.38917	1.38671	1.38425	1.42064	1.41812	1.41561	1.49180	1.48903	1.48619
6562.8	Hydrogen, C	1.38945	1.38698	1.38452	1.42095	1.41843	1.41592	1.49243	1.48966	1.48682
5892.6	Sodium, D₁, D₂	1.39146	1.38899	1.38651	1.42313	1.42059	1.41807	1.49693	1.49413	1.49126
5460.7	Mercury, e	1.39317	1.39068	1.38821	1.42499	1.42244	1.41991	1.50086	1.49803	1.49514
5015.7	Helium	1.39545	1.39295	1.39046	1.42744	1.42491	1.42234	1.50620	1.50334	1.50041
4861.3	Hydrogen, F	1.39641	1.39390	1.39139	1.42847	1.42591	1.42335	1.50847	1.50559	1.50265
4358.3	Mercury, g	1.40030	1.39778	1.39524	1.43271	1.43011	1.42754	1.51800	1.51506	1.51206

Gladstone and Dale investigated the changes in n and d as the temperatures of liquids were varied, and, instead of the Newton constant, they found better constancy for $(n-1)/d$, and this ratio became known as specific refractivity.

Lorenz of Copenhagen and Lorentz of Leyden independently derived the expression $(n^2-1)/d(n^2+2) = C$ for a certain class of liquids of which water was said to be typical. This ratio, called specific refraction, has enjoyed wide popularity and been applied, probably in many cases, under circumstances for which it was never intended. The constant term 2 in the denominator is only an approximation in special cases for a more generally applicable variable, X. It is not surprising to find that Eykman, after much work on organic liquids, advocated $(n^2-1)/d$ $(n+0.4) = C$ as more suitable for the particular kinds of media and the particular variability in which he was interested. This Eykman relation has been favored by Kurtz and Ward (46) in certain work on petroleum products, and also by Gibson (26) in his work on benzene at high pressures.

When Zehnder (91) and Röntgen and Zehnder (69) applied pressure to liquids, they concluded that the $(n-1)/d$ relation was the more closely followed. When Pockels (65) analyzed his data on unidirectional pressure applied to glass, he favored the Newton constant, $(n^2-1)/d$. Tool and Tilton (76) at the National Bureau of Standards, when investigating the effect of annealing temperatures on the refractive indices and densities of glasses, found that Newton's relation was approximated. Finn (90) and some of his co-workers at the National Bureau of Standards have favored the use of $(n-1)/d$ when dealing with variations caused by small changes in the chemical composition of similar glasses.

In the field of gases much testing of the various relations has been attempted, especially with variations in pressure, but some of these relationships become so nearly alike when the density of oscillators is low and n approaches unity, as in gases, that it is difficult to find experimental data that are sufficiently accurate for discriminatory use in such tests.

It should be remembered that index and density are influenced by many variables, such as temperature, pressure, chemical composition, isomeric rearrangements, physicochemical rearrangements (heat treatment), change of state, etc. Thus, when specific refractions are being used for various purposes, and atomic factors derived, and when, subsequently, the additivity of molecular refractions is in question, it is suggested that the arbitrary nature of the cases be considered before relying altogether on the various explanations that are sometimes offered for lack of expected perfection of these relationships. They are of value only as they are proved useful in investigation and analysis and not as a basis for negative arguments. Present theories indicate that no single simple and widely applicable relation exists between refractive index and density.

2.2. Indices of Mixtures

If two fluids mix without significant volume change, as usually happens with gases but not very generally with liquids except possibly for dilute solutions, the index of a mixture of them may be estimated from their volumes, v_1, v_2, as $n = (n_1 v_1 + n_2 v_2)/(v_1 + v_2)$ or, similarly, with $(n - 1)$ in place of n, $(n_1 - 1)$ in place of n_1, etc.

If there is reason to suppose that Gladstone and Dale's constant is applicable, one writes

$$\frac{100(n - 1)}{d} = \frac{p_1(n_1 - 1)}{d_1} + \frac{(100 - p_1)(n_2 - 1)}{d_2} \tag{2}$$

where p is per cent by weight. A similar equation can be written for Newton's constant, $(n^2 - 1)/d$, or for the Lorenz-Lorentz constant, etc., depending on the individual investigator's experience or preference.

In cases where one knows the contraction or expansion of volume

$$c = \frac{v_1 + v_2 - V}{v_1 + v_2} \tag{3}$$

one may write (7)

$$\frac{100(n - 1)}{d} \cdot \frac{1 - ac}{1 - c} = \frac{p_1(n_1 - 1)}{d_1} + \frac{(100 - p_1)(n_2 - 1)}{d_2} \tag{4}$$

where a varies with temperature and wavelength.

In general, however, one should whenever possible rely only on interpolations from known data rather than resort to computation by any rule for mixtures.

2.3. Dispersion

Two general formulas for index as a function of wavelength have been derived from electron theory. The oldest, called the Sellmeier or Drude form, is

$$n^2 - 1 = \sum_j \frac{K_j \lambda^2}{\lambda^2 - \lambda_j^2} \tag{5}$$

Later the form

$$\frac{n^2 - 1}{n^2 + 2} = \sum_j \frac{K_j \lambda^2}{\lambda^2 - \lambda_j^2} \tag{5'}$$

was derived by Lorenz of Copenhagen and independently by Lorentz of Leyden. In both forms n is the refractive index, λ_j represents the wavelengths of the absorption bands of the material, and the constants K_j arise from electromagnetic theory. Each K_j term has implicit in it the density factor and the strength of the oscillators, i.e., transition probabilities. That the two forms are equivalent was demonstrated by Herzfeld, and some work by Krishnan and Roy has helped to clarify the meanings of the λ_j and K_j terms. The term 2 in the denominator of the second form is an approximation resulting from certain assumptions concerning the effect of the local field on the atomic oscillators.

Because of the complexity of these equations graphical methods are frequently used to show the quantitative variation of index with wavelength. For certain materials, over limited wavelength ranges, various approximations have been found to ve valid. For example, in Cauchy's, $n = A + B/\lambda^2 + C/\lambda^4 \ldots$, the number of terms to be taken depends on the range of wavelengths concerned. Another useful form, given by Nutting (62), is $1/(n-1) = c + D/\lambda^2$. Both forms are easy to use but are valid only for short ranges of wavelengths and in regions not close to any absorption band. Either graphic or numerical interpolation is frequently advisable when working with various wavelengths, in order to compare the results with each other and with those of other observers, perhaps at still other wavelengths. A plot of n against $1/\lambda^2$ is frequently a close approximation to a straight line, as must be true if the two-term Cauchy formula is applicable. Whenever the index data are good only to a few units of the fourth decimal, and the range of wavelength is short, it will probably be satisfactory to try graphical methods and very simple dispersion formulas.

If, however, the data are of any value in the fifth decimal, and if most of the visible spectrum is involved, some more elaborate dispersion formula is advisable. The Conrady (12) formula, $n = n_0 + a/\lambda + b/\lambda^{3.5}$, has proved very successful for optical glass, and it is suggested as worthy of trial in other fields, perhaps with a modification of the exponent of λ in the last term. Incidentally, the formula that Wright (88) found useful for optical glass, namely,

$$n_y - n_x = a(n_F - n_C) - b \tag{6}$$

where y and x denote any two spectral lines, is very similar to that of Waldmann (79),

$$(n_D - n_C) = K(n_F - n_C) \tag{7}$$

in which K is said to be constant within 10% for a wide range of organic compounds excepting those of high dispersion. Equations of this type are very useful in computing specific dispersions, $(n_F - n_C)/d$.

Numerous tests made with the Hartmann equation

$$n = n_0 + C/(\lambda - \lambda_0)^a \tag{8}$$

indicate that it is remarkably reliable to the fifth decimal of index for glass, plastics, and other media. Special coordinate paper exists for use with this form of dispersion equation; also, Weidert's tables facilitate its use [see Ewald (18)].

3. White-Light Refractometers

3.1. Compensators

All commercially used refractometers depend for their functioning on critical-angle phenomena, and the sample is in contact with a medium of known higher index in the form of a glass block or refracting prism that constitutes the most essential part of the instrument. The grazing-incidence method of introducing the light is preferable whenever the sample is sufficiently transparent, because in that case there is a sharp contrast in the field of the viewing telescope between the region where refraction takes place and the region where only total reflection permits illumination. For dark and opaque media, however, the light must be introduced by reflection at and near the critical angle on one side of the normal, and one sets the cross hairs in the telescope on the line of demarcation corresponding to the critical angle on the other side of the normal. In other words one must, for opaque media, distinguish between the regions where total and partial reflections occur, and such contrast is never as sharp as is desirable.

The refractometers used most extensively are of the Abbe type. These instruments are, or were, characterized by the addition of one or more direct-vision prisms to form an achromatizing device, often called the compensator, that permits one to use a white-light source and yet measure indices for the D lines of sodium. The achromatizing device is usually a pair of Amici prisms that may be turned so that their dispersions either add to or neutralize each other. Thus they may be set to give just the dispersion necessary to neutralize that caused in the double-prism and sample system. If these Amici prisms are nondeviating for sodium light one actually measures n_D.

To equalize small dispersions, such as occur within the narrow range of low-index liquids on the dipping refractometer, a single Amici prism will serve. The uncompensated component of dispersion falling laterally along the border line in those cases causes no trouble.

In a sugar refractometer a simple, fixed dispersing prism can be used because the dispersion to be compensated is not only small but constant. Or, as in some other special-purpose simplifications of the Abbe refractometer, a color-free line can be obtained, for the particular sample to be used, by suitably selecting a refracting prism of the proper dispersion.

A matter that can be easily tested is the possible deviation of sodium light by the compensator (74). This is so important and some of its effects are so well concealed that it should receive explicit attention from every careful user of white-light instruments with rotatable compensators. First, the observed index almost always differs for the two possible achromatizing positions. This is caused by lateral deviation of sodium light by the Amici prisms and is very difficult to avoid in the construction of the prisms but is easily eliminated by using only the averages of readings taken for opposite achromatizations.

Deviation of sodium light in the principal plane of the Amici prisms can be present and may be serious. The effects cannot be eliminated experimentally, and a double-entry table of corrections would be necessary to correct for such a defect. One should observe with sodium light the index readings for some one sample while the compensator is rotated. The "high" and "low" readings for a given sample should not differ by more than, say, 2 or 3×10^{-4}.

3.2. TEMPERATURE CONTROL

Temperature control in refractometry is required not only because of the effect of temperature on the medium (Section 1.3) but also because refractometers function somewhat differently as temperature varies. Some instruments are designed to work correctly at 17.5°C., some at 20°C., and probably others at or near 25°C. In many cases the normal working temperature is unknown to the user and perhaps cannot be specified very precisely by the manufacturer. In all cases it is much more important to know the temperature of test or calibration than it is to know the temperature for which the instrument was designed. For some reasons it is desirable to have the entire instrument at the temperature of measurement, as will be seen later (Section 3.4) in the case of the dipping or immersion refractometer. If, on the other hand, high temperatures are being used and the instrument has a 2-Amici compensator for which one does not have reliably established corrections, then it probably is better to insulate the compensator as completely as possible from the jacketed-prism system.

The error, Δn, in determining, on the usual Abbe-type refractometer, the relative index of any sample at temperature t (not far from t_0) with respect to air at the same temperature is fairly well represented as

$$\Delta n = 0.87 (t - t_0) \Delta N$$

where t_0 is the temperature for which the instrument was designed or calibrated, and ΔN is the temperature coefficient of relative index of the refractometer block (see Table V).

TABLE V

Temperature Coefficients[a] of Relative (ΔN) and Absolute ($\Delta \bar{N}$) Index of Refraction (Units of Fifth Decimal) for Refractometer Blocks and Similar Glasses at Room Temperatures

Highest index measurable	Block N_D	ν^b	$\dfrac{t + t_0}{2}$	$\lambda =$ 6563 A. ΔN	$\Delta \bar{N}$	$\lambda =$ 5893 A. ΔN	$\Delta \bar{N}$	$\lambda =$ 4861 A. ΔN	$\Delta \bar{N}$	$\lambda =$ 4340 A. ΔN	$\Delta \bar{N}$	$\lambda =$ 4047 A. ΔN	$\Delta \bar{N}$
	1.5045	64.7	30°	0.29	0.16	0.32	0.19	0.38	0.25	0.44	0.31		
	1.5175	64.2	35°	0.16	0.03	0.17	0.04	0.22	0.09	0.25	0.12	0.28	0.15
1.50	1.5220	58.5	28°	0.17	0.04	0.19	0.06	0.24	0.11	0.27	0.14	0.30	0.17
	1.5202	59.6	30°	0.34	0.21	0.35	0.22	0.40	0.27	0.44	0.31	0.48	0.35
(I$_b$) 1.613	1.6220 R, Z^c	35.9	55°	—	0.24	—	0.28	—	0.39	—	0.50		
	1.6227	55.6	33°	0.33	0.19	0.34	0.20	0.38	0.24	0.44	0.30	0.48	0.34
	1.6561	33.2	35°	0.44	0.30	0.46	0.32	0.60	0.46	0.75	0.61	0.92	0.78
1.70	1.7167	29.4	28°	0.66	0.51	0.74	0.59	0.94	0.79	1.14	0.99	1.33	1.17
(II$_b$) 1.713	1.7474 R, Z	27.8	57°	—	0.70	—	0.78	—	1.05	—	1.31		
(II$_c$) 1.746	1.7548	27.6	30°	0.77	0.62	0.85	0.70	1.12	0.96	1.36	1.20		
	1.7537	27.6	30°	0.70	0.55	0.81	0.66	1.09	0.93	1.34	1.18		
1.75	1.7619	27.1	26°	0.77	0.62	0.86	0.71	1.17	1.01	1.43	1.27		
(III$_b$) 1.899	1.9068 R, Z	21.7	?	—	1.03	—	1.21	—	1.71	—	2.26		
(III$_c$) 1.910	1.9180	21.0	30°	1.12	0.95	1.30	1.13	1.83	1.66	2.44	2.27		

[a] With the exceptions noted, the coefficients were determined with the apparatus described in *J. Research Natl. Bur. Standards* **17**, 389 (1936) RP919.

[b] Abbe's value, $\nu = (N_D - 1)/(N_F - N_C)$, is the reciprocal of the relative mean dispersion.

[c] R, Z: These coefficients of $\Delta \bar{N}$, as listed on p. 37 of "Refraktometrisches Hilfsbuch," by W. A. Roth and F. Eisenlohr (Leipzig, 1911), are almost identical with those recommended by Carl Zeiss for their Pulfrich refractometer. For block I these values are those found by C. Pulfrich [*Ann. Physik* **45**, 606-665 (1892), for Jena glass O. 544 over the range 11° to 99°C.; similarly for block II, they list Pulfrich's values for glass O. 165 over the range 14° to 100°C. Their values for block III agree with interpolations between those found by J. O. Reed [*Ann. Physik* **65**, 707-741 (1898)] for glasses O. 163 and S. 57.

3.3. ABBE TYPE

This comparison instrument (see Section 1.5) has, in its traditional standardized form, a glass block or refracting prism of refractive index $N = 1.74$, say, and refractive angle $A = 60°$, approximately. The block has one polished face, about 1.5×3.5 cm., which is set slightly above and parallel to the larger surface of a metal water jacket, prismatic in shape. A second face of the glass block, about 1.5×2 cm., is polished so that light, after two refractions, emerges through an opening in the metal housing to the observing telescope. A second or illuminating prism, also jacketed, is hinged to the first to form a "double prism" or "prism pair" between whose members a small sample of liquid can be placed in a thin layer for measurement. The double prisms are rotatably mounted on a horizontal axis, and a sector carrying a telescope and scale is concentrically mounted about the same axis. An alidade, rigidly affixed to the refracting prism, carries a fiducial mark that moves over the scale as the prisms are turned until the critically refracted rays fall on the cross hairs at the focal plane in the telescope, the light from a convenient source having entered the illuminating prism by way of an adjustable mirror below the prisms.

The index, n, of a sample relative to air is computed from the equation

$$n = \sin A \sqrt{N^2 - \sin^2 \vartheta_2'} + \cos A \sin \vartheta_2' \qquad (9)$$

where ϑ_2' is the emergent angle with respect to the normal to the second surface of the block (positive for emergence toward the refracting edge; see Fig. 1c). From this equation the maker computes the direct-reading scale of index that is mounted on the sector.

These instruments permit readings directly in refractive index over a wide range, usually from 1.3 to 1.7. They are especially designed for work on liquids, but serve equally well for solids if the illuminating prism is opened. They are manufactured in this country by the Bausch & Lomb Optical Co., Rochester, New York, the Valentine Technical Instrument Corporation of Richmondville, New York, and in England by Hilger & Watts Ltd. Similar instruments are available from other European countries.

Currently, variants of the traditional Abbe instrument are being manufactured with built-in illumination and other features enclosed within elaborate housings that completely transform the instruments in appearance and facilitate their use in routine measurements.

The performance of every refractometer should be frequently checked by means of the test slab furnished with the instrument or with other samples of known index. The zero error should be determined by each individual user because of the "personal equation" that may exist. The actual lateral adjustment of the telescope objective, by means of a small screw in the telescope tube, need not be made by each user unless the error exceeds a few units of the fourth decimal place in index. In correcting for small errors, however, it should be remembered that the refractometer scale is not equicrescent and that to an error of three units at index 1.5 there corresponds an error of approximately one unit at 1.7 and an error of approximately four units at 1.3 on the index scale of the instruments that are most extensively used.

The use of white light, suitable tables, and a compensator permits the Abbe refractometer to determine approximate values of $(n_F - n_C)$, the difference in index for the blue and the red lines of hydrogen. The theory of dispersion measurements by these instruments was published by Abbe. The errors in $(n_F - n_C)$ he found to lie between 1.5 and 2%. Presumably, then, Abbe must have worked with but one source of white light, probably daylight, because the writers (73) have found that errors in $(n_F - n_C)$ can often be as large as 6% when working with a given source, A, and may be twice (or one-half) as large for a second source, B, with a different spectral distribution of energy. Certain observed errors of 30% in $(n_F - n_C)$, at low index and low dispersion, may have been caused by incorrect mounting of the achromatizing prisms.

3.4. DIPPING TYPE

The dipping or immersion refractometer is essentially an Abbe type of short index range without an illuminating prism and without water jackets for temperature control. The refracting prism is dipped or immersed to a depth of 3 or 4 cm. in the sample to be measured, and the grazing light must be introduced from below, often by means of a mirror. The index and angle of the block or refracting prism are so chosen by the designer, with respect to the small index range to be measured, that the instrument shall have maximum openness of scale compatible with approximately normal emergence of the rays from the second face of the prism. The total range in emergent angle is small, and a small linear scale enclosed in the instrument at the focal plane of the objective is substituted for the sector and scale as used on the Abbe. A table of the refractive index equivalents of the scale readings is provided.

Originally, the Zeiss firm made only one dipping refractometer with range 1.325 to 1.367 (known later as the range for the A prism), and they standardized the model so well that much work during two or three decades was done and published in terms of scale divisions of the dipping refractometer without reference to refractive index. When other makers began marketing the dipping refractometer, they did not always adhere exactly to the same table of index equivalents, and thus some care is necessary in order to avoid appreciable error when making intercomparisons of some of the published work.

The index range of dipping refractometers has been greatly extended by interchangeable refracting prisms so that they can be used for measurements anywhere in the range 1.325 to 1.544. For each prism at least one standard is provided for adjusting the zero, and after every change of prism on one of these instruments it is necessary to recheck the zero. Otherwise some fine lint or other material may be enclosed between the surfaces that must be precisely seated for correct performance.

For checking these instruments precisely with solid standards it is advisable to mount the tube on a stand so that the polished surface of the dipping prism is nearly horizontal, and interference fringes should be used in the elimination of wedge-effect errors causable by the contact liquid. Care must be taken not to bend the tube. Possibly one should not allow gravity to flex it, if highest repeatability is desired.

The control of temperature for dipping refractometry is ordinarily obtained by the partial immersion of the unknowns in small beakers in a water bath, and the instrument depends from a wire above to which it is hooked. As an alternate procedure, one can sometimes employ the metal cups that are provided with the instrument for especial use with solutions or mixtures that may evaporate rapidly or differentially. These cups are provided with ground joints and a window through which light may enter at the proper angle. They give good temperature control when immersed in a well-stirred bath, but one cannot be sure about leaks, and there is a cleaning nuisance, if not a problem.

At the National Bureau of Standards (35) a huge "test tube" of glass, with an inch or two of water therein, is sometimes immersed in a large stirred water bath, and the sample in a small beaker is lowered by means of a stiff wire to a platform so placed in the tube that the beaker is partially immersed. The dipping refractometer is suspended as usual, but inside the test tube, together with a thermometer which can be read from above by means of a lens-mirror system. The air space between refractometer eye piece and glass tube is filled loosely with previously washed cheese cloth.

Under such circumstances, and for temperatures near those of the room, the repeatability of readings with a dipping refractometer approximates $\pm 1 \times 10^{-5}$. There is no question about getting true critical angle if reasonable care is taken in adjusting the mirror, and the conditions regarding cleaning and preservation of purity are excellent. Although several cubic centimeters of sample are required, very little is lost. The source problem is difficult except for white light and, possibly, for very bright lines.

It cannot be assumed, however, that results obtained with a dipping refractometer are accurate because they are precise. The makers apparently endeavor to standardize their processes only within such tolerances that the finished instruments may be accurate within ± 0.1 division, or $\pm 4 \times 10^{-5}$. Perhaps the accuracy of scale rulings is not commensurate with the repeatability. Certainly the writers have found errors of $\pm 4 \times 10^{-5}$ in the performance of very good dipping refractometers.

The dipping instrument is the only commonly used refractometer that handles liquids in such manner that both illumination and purity of sample are above criticism. It is also the best for solutions of acids. It is suggested that they should be made without compensators, with tubes that are somewhat more rigid, and with better scales in the focal plane, so that with proper tables they would be suitable for a few lines other than sodium.

Dipping refractometers were manufactured by Zeiss in Germany and are made by the Bausch & Lomb Optical Co., Rochester, New York. A few special dipping refractometers have been made by Zeiss with special water jackets and hinged illuminating prisms. The weight of these jackets would seem to be objectionable because of possible differential flexure of the long tubes under different conditions of support and mounting during their testing and subsequent use. The same questions arise in connection with the "Goldbach flow-through cells," which can be made for any dipping instrument and slipped on over the glass prism and fastened to the metal of the instrument by a screw collar.

A most extensive use of the dipping refractometer was made by B. Wagner who published in detail the indices for the total range in concentration of seventy-nine acids, hydroxides, salts, acetates, alcohols, etc., in his *Tabellen zum Eintauchrefraktometer* printed at Sonderhausen, Germany in 1907 and again in 1928.

3.5. Other Instruments (White Light)

Of special refractometers, probably those for the sugar industry are of most importance. They usually read in "per cent total solids" rather than index, but sometimes in both ways. Sugar refractometers made in this country, and some of the older Zeiss models, were essentially standard Abbe instruments except that the compensators were usually much simplified.

The Zeiss firm has sold one model particularly different in form and appearance, an industrial type for sugar and oils, index 1.33 to 1.54. It is very compact and almost entirely enclosed for protection of the optical surfaces and moving parts. The compensator is a revolving triple prism like that used in the dipping refractometer. The scales are engraved in per cent solids for sugar and in refractive index for oils. The prisms are hinged at their sides rather than at the ends, and their interfaces are always horizontal. The illumination for total reflection is particularly well arranged, and the enclosure of telescope, etc., results in but little scattered and nonuseful light. Thus the low contrast conditions characteristic of this method, so necessary on dark oils and sirups, are usable with relatively higher precision than is ordinarily obtained by total reflection on a standard Abbe instrument.

The Zeiss "Works Refractometer" is an instrument designed for installation in the side of a vacuum pan or other vessel, or in the wall of a large pipe or tube in a system through which a liquid is being treated or conducted. A small portion of one polished surface of a large rhombic prism is exposed to the liquid while light critically reflected inside the glass is observed by a telescope. A suitable wiper on the far side of the wall, but actuated by a lever arm just below the refractometer, serves to protect the glass prism except momentarily during readings. The instrument reads 70 to 95% dry substance (sugar scale) and can be used at temperatures between 60° and 100°C. It could probably be adapted for measurements on liquids under moderate pressures.

A small pocket model of a sugar refractometer, with fixed refracting prism and hinged illuminator, is available for field use on drops of juice crushed from beets or cane. It is about 8 inches long and fits in a leather case of about 1.5 inch in diameter. The focal-plane scale is divided to 1% from 0 to 10% and to 0.5% from 10 to 30% sugar.

Zeiss also made several special refractometers for particular processes involving oils, butter, and certain fats. Some of these seem to possess no advantages over the standard form of Abbe refractometer except that the instruments are simplified and thus cheaper for their special purposes.

Warren P. Valentine, Haddonfield, New Jersey, was the pioneer in this country in departing from European models of refractometers (77). Many of his instruments are still in use, and the manufacture of Valentine models is continued by the Valentine Technical Instrument Corporation, Richmondville, New York.

The American Optical Company, Buffalo, New York, currently manufacture, for use with white light, a Goldberg process refractometer, a hand refractometer, and a combination hand and dipping refractometer.

4. Monochromatic Refractometers

The present trend in the development of highly precise refractometers is to use the Abbe double prism but to eliminate the compensator for white light. By using an arbitrary scale on the instrument (either degrees of arc or equispaced lines) and tables of the corresponding index equivalents for various wavelengths, all measurements of index are equally easy if the line sources are available and the tables have been computed. Of course, the intensity of the source is important, and suitable filters must in some cases be available to prevent overlapping of the refracted light of various wavelengths. Details, different for solids and liquids, must be considered if a gain in precision is to be a gain in accuracy also.

4.1. Solid Samples

It is imperative that the source be placed so that, optically, it is in an extension of the plane of contact between sample and refractometer block without intervention of any object that can shield the grazingly incident rays. False edges can be readily detected by their variable behavior during relative movements of the instrument and the source. This is one of the most useful and most frequently necessary tests in accurate refractometry.

The glass refracting block must be so cemented in its metal housing that no portion of the metal or cement rises above the plane of the polished glass surface. Otherwise an unfavorable condition exists for the use of solids. Even though the solid sample is small and parallelism with the block is obtained through the layer of contact liquid, the metal or cement may shield the sample in such manner that truly grazing incidence does not exist in the sample. Whenever two polished surfaces of a sample intersect at an angle less than 90°, and the surfaces of the glass block and its metal housing are approximately coplanar, then it is impossible to obtain truly grazing incidence unless the sample can extend approximately as far toward the source as does the housing. The breadth of source is usually sufficient to take care of sample-face intersection angles somewhat greater than 90°, but a beveled edge of the intersecting polished faces of the sample is almost necessarily fatal. Also, if there is a slight excess of contact liquid, it may emerge toward the source and by refraction or reflection prevent the introduction of light at truly grazing incidence.

The use of a finely ground edge toward the source is safer than a polished surface in these and in related cases, but there is sometimes a serious loss of light which may impair precision of index settings if the light is of low intensity. In all cases false edges ascribable to geometrical shielding give rise to lower than normal index readings.

For fifth-decimal refractometry it is certainly imperative to test and adjust the liquid contact layer to parallelism by means of interference fringes. The safe procedure is to view the fringes in the exit pupil of the telescope with the aid of an auxiliary eyepiece or a simple hand magnifier while one adjusts and readjusts the sample with gentle pressure and thus obtains the parallelism precisely where it is required. A fringe parallel to the refracting edge of the block may appreciably affect refraction in the plane of measurement, but a few fringes normal to the refracting edge produce negligible effect on measurements. If fringes are viewed through the sample, their permissible number increases as the difference in index between sample and contact liquid decreases, but the number seldom exceeds one or two per centimeter of contact for an error of 1×10^{-5} in measured index of sample. For viewing in the exit pupil the tolerance is always $\frac{1}{3}$ fringe per centimeter for yellow light. However, by choosing a suitable contact liquid for given samples the required tolerance condition is more easily attained.

On the other hand, the index difference between sample and contact liquid must not be too small lest internal reflections be seriously changed at some interfaces, and contrast decreased either for the fringes or for the critical border line, or lest partial overlapping occur for the critically refracted rays corresponding to sample and to contact liquid.

It is suggested that one should use a light oil of index of, say, 1.45, when measuring lithium fluoride, $n = 1.39$; that ethylene bromide, 1.54, or anise seed oil, 1.55, be used for low-index crown glass; and the usual monobromonaphthalene, 1.66, and methylene iodide, 1.74, be used for higher-index glasses as may be necessary.

Some samples such as plastics and rubber can be used on an Abbe refractometer without contact liquid. In some cases they can be put in optical contact by pressure against the refracting prism, or they may be allowed to dry from solution on the prism, or cooled thereon after melting. Or, approximately flat and parallel pieces of glass (microscope slide glass) can be used to receive the films, and then the slide glass can itself be placed in optical contact with a refracting prism by means of contact liquids. If the glass plate is higher in index than the film, it will simply act as an additional contact layer and the index of the film will be measured. If reflected light is used for illumination through the refracting prism, the contrast can sometimes be much improved, according to West (82), if a polarizing screen is placed between source and prism with a crossed cap analyzer over the eyepiece.

4.2. LIQUID SAMPLES

With an illuminating prism it is difficult to ensure that light at sufficiently near grazing incidence enters the liquid sample. Careful consideration is important because Abbe refractometers are usually adjusted for correct performance on solids, and it is often assumed that they are then ready for correct performance on liquids also. Since the ground face of the illuminating prism is limited in extent and does not actually touch the polished face of the refractometer block, the light indirectly introduced in this manner cannot be truly grazing within the liquid sample. The glass of the Abbe double prisms should be at least $2\frac{1}{2}$ inches long and filled with the liquid sample for about two-thirds of that length (toward the light source), if a systematic shielding error is to be held to 1×10^{-5} in its index effect.

In making this statement it is assumed that the axis of the observing telescope is so directed that the effective area of the large surface of the refracting prism is near the center of that surface, and that the prism separation is 0.10 mm. In other words the use of *minute samples* cannot yield results of highest accuracy on a double-prism refractometer unless the prism separation is appreciably reduced, say to 0.05 mm. In studying this question it is important to know that halving the shielding angle reduces the index error to one-fourth its former size. The errors are such that readings are too low in index and the more so for higher-index samples. This shielding error has been discussed by Forrest (20), who points out that it may be minimized with an illuminating prism of index near to that of the sample.

A troublesome phenomenon in precise refractometry of liquids is the production of Herschel interference fringes in the thin layer of liquid between the Abbe prisms. They are observable as narrow dark bands in the light half of the field, and there is danger that some of them may be so close to the critical border as to appear continuous therewith and thus mask the true critical border. The consequent errors again are readings that are too low, but this time the more so for lower-index liquids.

Originally, both prisms of the Abbe refractometer had polished surfaces, and Abbe relied entirely on adequate prism separation for avoidance of these fringes. Later Pulfrich introduced the modification of fine grinding of the surface of the illuminating prism in order to avoid these fringes and also certain disturbing and well-defined images of the source. In most refractometers, however, the makers use such fine abrasive in grinding the surface of the illuminating prism that the Herschel fringes are not avoided. They are formed by interference between directly transmitted light and light that is multiply reflected between the prism surfaces. The finer the grinding, the sharper will be the fringes; and the closer the prism surfaces, and the lower the index of the liquid sample, the greater is the distance between successive fringes. Also, the widths, separations, and visibilities of the fringes vary with the degree of inclination of the prism surfaces.

In so far as thinness of sample is concerned, there seems no reason to fear that the index so measured is systematically different from an index that might be measured on a thicker sample. Suppose there are changes in properties in the immediate vicinity of an interface. They probably would not penetrate far in units of molecular dimensions, and one would not expect the change to be a decrease in index on contact with the higher index of the glass block. If a molecular layer should increase in index that layer would simply act as a plane-parallel contact layer, and the lowest index layer inside the liquid sample would determine the critical border of total reflection. Abbe placed the lower limit of layer thickness at 0.03 to 0.05 mm., not because of any impairment of the critical-angle method but on account of the disturbing effects of the interference fringes.

The obvious results of contact between liquid samples and the cement used in mounting the block are probably of far greater importance than possible changes in properties of thin films. Portions of liquid samples that penetrate the interstices, or are absorbed by the cement, are afterwards leachable by the succeeding samples, and, because of the very small quantities involved, the possible percentage of contamination is very serious. Extreme care should be taken in repeatedly cleansing both prisms, and the sampling must be repeated until available leaching is over and no progressive changes are noticed in successive readings that are properly comparable in all respects, including equal durations of contact between cement and sample.

Another important source of contamination is water from the air that may condense on the prism surfaces when working at water-jacket temperatures lower than the dew point of air in the room.

4.3. PULFRICH TYPE

Instead of 60° for the refracting angle, A, Pulfrich used $A = 90°$, and eq. (9) becomes

$$n = \sqrt{N^2 - \sin^2 \vartheta_2'} \tag{10}$$

He used three different blocks: $n = 1.62$ primarily for liquids, 1.75 primarily for solids, and 1.90, each of which could be mounted in turn on a given base which was provided with a graduated circle to measure the rotation of an observing telescope that could be set (1) normal to the emergent face of the block (for zero adjustment) and (2) with cross hairs on a critical edge or border for a given color of light.

A tangent screw is provided so that small rotations of the telescope, from a setting on one color to that for a second, third, etc., can be measured with somewhat greater precision than is obtainable by reading the vernier. Ordinarily a Geissler tube and a sodium arc are the sources, at the observer's left, and tables are provided for reading indices of the lines C, D, F, and G′ as functions of the observed angles.

The upper polished face of the block is limited to a circular area about 15 mm. in diameter, the peripheral portions being ground off so that a hollow cylinder with axis vertical can be cemented on the block to contain liquid samples in such manner that truly grazing-incidence light can enter the liquid through the walls of the cylinder. The bottom and three sides of the block are surrounded by a metal water jacket. A silver plunger with thermometer and flowing water is lowered into the liquid in the vertical glass cylinder.

The Pulfrich type of instrument, as marketed by Zeiss, was probably superior to the standard Abbe (Section 3.3) even for the D lines of sodium, but not so much so as was generally assumed. (The standard Abbe is a more rugged instrument, and some have been known to perform correctly within $\pm 1 \times 10^{-4}$ for years.) Aside from the tangent screw error pointed out by Guild (28), the Pulfrich is vulnerable because the alignment of its telescope tube is not rigidly maintained and because the readings are influenced by the amount of pressure that one uses when clamping the telescope in a given position.

If two opposite vertical sides of the 90° block are polished and parallel, and if the grazing light can be introduced also at 180° from its usual direction, then there are interesting possibilities of measuring the angle from deviation on the right to deviation on the left with elimination of error due to contact wedge and to variations from the 90° refracting angle. Old models of the Pulfrich refractometer, as made by Zeiss, permitted this symmetrical usage.

Improved models of the Pulfrich refractometer have been made in England by Hilger and Watts and by Bellingham and Stanley. In France a refractometer of the Pulfrich type was designed and constructed by the Societé des Lunetiers (71).

4.4. VALENTINE INSTRUMENTS

A number of Valentine refractometers were made without compensators for use with sodium light. In some cases only an angular scale was ruled, and charts were provided for the use of the C and F lines of hydrogen and the D lines of sodium. In some of these instruments the glass faces of the prisms are especially long to reduce shielding angle, and no hinge or other metal intervenes between the source and the tips of the glass prisms. This procedure would seem meritorious in view of the slight falsity of edge that is very frequently found when illuminating prisms of the usual types are used.

4.5. BAUSCH & LOMB PRECISION REFRACTOMETER

This instrument is essentially a large Abbe double prism, rotating around a vertical axis in front of a fixed telescope to which is attached an arbitrary linear scale. More or less integral with the prism mount is an alidade with fiducial mark that moves over the scale. Tables are provided for the prominent lines of sodium, hydrogen, helium, and mercury.

Two models are available, differing in index range, 1.33 to 1.50 for sugar, and 1.40 to 1.70 for oils and other purposes. For solids, these instruments are, in the writers' opinion, almost as easy to use as the standard Abbe; for a single index they are more accurate than the Pulfrich, and for dispersions about as good as the Pulfrich. For liquids, however, the conditions are not so satisfactory. In order to get more light for measuring with some of the lines of lower intensity, the face of the illuminating prism was polished on many of these instruments, and the Herschel fringes are prominent and may very slightly mask the true critical edges.

In the writers' opinion, if an illuminating prism is to be used as such, a fairly coarse grinding of the surface is safest for ensuring critical illumination for liquids. It is suggested, however, that light can be introduced directly, or by reflection, into the liquid sample itself instead of through an illuminating prism. Greater prism separation would then be advantageous for light admittance and for preventing Herschel fringes; it would, however, be limited by rapidity of leakage and volatilization.

4.6. Gaertner Turbid-Liquid Refractometer

This instrument resembles the conventional Abbe in its refractive principles, but in front of one-half of the objective is a reversing prism so that there are two critical border lines in the telescope field that travel in opposite directions as the prism pair is rotated. A "setting" is made when the two hazy and indistinct edges have approached to such an extent that the field is uniformly illuminated. There is provision for temperature control, the index range is 1.33 to 1.435, and the stated accuracy is 1×10^{-4} in index. Early models have been used in the canning industry. A sodium laboratory arc is recommended.

4.7. Other Instruments

In accord with trends, and the demand for monochromatic refractometers, the American Optical Company have at times offered three instruments for use with sodium, hydrogen, and mercury sources. One is the usual Abbe, the second is their sugar refractometer, and the third is their high-index instrument, 1.450 to 1.840. In each case the scale is graduated for sodium light, and correction tables are given for other lines. Some of these instruments are still available from dealers.

For years the Bausch & Lomb Optical Company has been supplying a standard Abbe refractometer, without compensator and with the necessary correction charts for various wavelengths, for the special purpose of index measurements on small fragments by the Emmons double-variation method (see Section 5.2).

The names of Wollaston, Terquem and Trannin, and Wiedeman are associated with a direct method of measuring the critical angle of a liquid by immersing therein a layer of air between two plane-parallel plates measurably rotatable around a mechanical axis perpendicular to the axis of an observing telescope. The liquid may be in a box with glass windows and placed in collimated light, as on the table of a spectrometer. Collimated monochromatic light should be used in order that the whole beam will be totally reflected almost simultaneously. By turning the plates from extinction on the right to extinction left, one measures twice the critical angle, C, for liquid to air, and the index is computed as $n = 1/\sin C$.

Similarly, with a liquid of known index this method can be applied to measure the index of an unknown in the form of a plane-parallel plate of lower index. These total reflection methods seem worth consideration especially if accurate index measurements are required at temperatures appreciably higher than those of the room.

An old instrument still worthy of mention on account of its simplicity, and because of certain inconveniences in other methods for refractometry of very high index liquids, is the Pulfrich refractometer with variable refractive angle, according to Newton's procedures. The liquid is placed in a box or a vertical cylinder with a plane-parallel glass base plate. Monochromatic light enters the base plate at grazing incidence along the liquid-to-base-plate boundary and is refracted at the critical angle with the normal to the base plate. A telescope, with a 180° glass terminal prism in front of the objective, dips into the liquid to permit accurate settings on the critical boundary and thus to measure this angle in the liquid with respect to the normal. Pulfrich claimed an accuracy of 4 to 10×10^{-4}.

Lafay (47) has proposed a somewhat similar instrument in which the corresponding fluid container rotates and throws the critically refracted rays into a 90° deviating prism and thence into a vertical telescope. The rotation of the vessel about the telescope axis can be measured in both symmetrical positions, and thus certain errors are eliminated.

Other recently designed instruments include a refractometer for glass control (21) and a linear-scale critical-angle refractometer (20).

4.8. Infrared Refractometer

The difficulties in infrared refractometry as compared to the visual range are formidable. Aside from the necessarily indirect procedures in detection and interpretation of the results, the block of the instrument is more difficult to construct and more easily damaged than glass. Light absorption in samples means troublesome corrections even in the visible range, and it becomes indeed formidable when present also in the block. Consequently, infrared refractometry is not readily applicable to industrial applications. For help in research applications the reader should consult papers by Joffe (38-40) of the Weizmann Institute of Science, Rehovoth, Israel. He has also experimented with an Abbe-type critical-angle instrument using prisms of arsenic trisulfide, which is of high index (2.45 to 2.37 in the range 1 to 6 μ) so that most liquids may be compared with it. The block is resistant to water and organic liquids. With this refractometer Joffe and Oppenheim (40) have measured six (transparent) solvents.

5. Immersion Techniques

5.1. Powder Method

If very small grains of an isotropic solid or powders of average cross-sectional extent greater than, say, 0.01 mm. are immersed and stirred in a liquid of nearly the same but slightly lower refractive index in a small vessel on the block of a monochromatic critical-angle refractometer, a diffuse bright line may be seen. If the match is exact the critical border for powder and for liquid coincide and precise setting can be made. If the liquid has a higher refractive index two borders may be seen, one for the liquid and one for the solid. Of course, liquids must be selected that will not appreciably dissolve the solid while a match is being obtained.

5.2. Small Fragments

Immersion methods for small fragments are widely known through their use by the petrographer in the identification of small crystals. The minimum requirements for apparatus are a microscope and a series of liquids of known refractive index, the intervening index steps being small and approximately regular. The unknown is examined for visibility in the different liquids in turn until one finds that the unknown lies between standards K and L in index. An interpolation between K and L can be roughly made by knowing the proportions in which they are mixed for a "match" with the fragments. For more precise work the index of the liquid must be measured after the match is obtained.

A match can be determined while using a narrow central cone from a bright source of monochromatic illumination and observing the Becke line effect, or by the method of oblique illumination. Saylor (70) has discussed the errors of these methods and described a greatly improved procedure that uses a system of oblique illumination and involves double diaphragms.

The match can be obtained (a) by changing the concentration of the liquid, (b) by varying the temperature, or (c) by varying the wavelength used for the source. Emmons (17) used both (b) and (c) for his double-variation method and then used a calibrated Abbe refractometer for index measurements (see Section 4.7).

A variant of these methods has been employed by Kofler (43) and his associates in determining the percentage composition of binary mixtures of organic substances.

5.3. Large (Transparent) Pieces

In Martin's (57) method the specimen is immersed in a suitable liquid, such as carbon disulfide, in a prismatic cell on the prism table of a spectrometer. By suitable dilution, as with alcohol, the liquid concentration is adjusted to match that of the specimen, and when the collimator slit image is in sharp focus the index of the stirred liquid mixture is measured by minimium deviation.

In Cheshire's (8) method a double diaphragm is used to improve the sensitivity of the "match," and a rectangular cell is "cemented" to the block of a Pulfrich refractometer so that when a match is effected the index can be read immediately.

Anderson (1) described a similar procedure involving not only index-measuring apparatus but also a Hilger constant-deviation spectrometer in order that a match between glass and liquid can be made by varying wavelength instead of varying concentration. Useful details concerning methods of these types are given on pp. 130-136 of Vol. IV of "Dictionary of Applied Physics," Macmillan and Co., London, 1923.

A method was developed by Faick and Fonoroff (19) at the National Bureau of Standards for either rough fragments or finished optical components. It requires inserting a diaphragm that shades out almost one-half of the beam of light at the focus of a condensing lens. The emerging beam is then passed through the immersion liquid and again brought to a focus by a second converging lens. At this focus a second diaphragm shades out most of the remaining portion of the beam. By means of a telescope the field is seen dimly but uniformly lighted, and the immersed specimen is almost invisible if the match is perfect. A monochromator is used for isolating particular spectrum lines, and a precision refractometer in thermal parallel connection with the immersion tank serves to compare the immersion mixes with known standards of index.

6. Differential Refractometers

The importance of differential refractometers lies in having both known and unknown in the same environment during their simultaneous comparison. Satisfactory temperature control is thus easily reached. Also, small differences are more accurately measurable than large ones. The principle of elimination of various errors by the exchange of containers for the known and the unknown is usually applicable. The handicap is that the maximum permissible range of comparison is small for any given instrument.

A simple type of differential refractometer is used when two similar unknowns are placed side by side on a refractometer block and the two critical borders are observed simultaneously, or in rapid succession by alternate shielding. The Pulfrich refractometer is supplied with a special large prism on top of which is a divided cylinder to accommodate two liquids, side by side.

6.1. OSTWALD (ZEISS)

A differential refractometer sold by Zeiss consists of four water-jacketed hollow prisms of approximately 45°, two in the upper and two in the lower half of a beam of parallel light between an objective and a mirror, an upper transparent diagnoal at 45° being approximately normal to a lower diagonal. One liquid fills both upper and lower prisms adjacent to a plane-parallel glass near the objective, and a second liquid fills the prisms near the mirror. An illuminated scale (80 divisions) just above the axis and in the focal plane of the objective is imaged twice by autocollimation just below the axis. These images coincide if the liquids are of equal refractive index and the instrument is in adjustment. For a difference in indices the images are displaced in opposite directions and a separation of 1 scale division corresponds to from 2 to 4×10^{-5} in index. It is advisable to calibrate the scale with liquids of known index difference.

6.2. HALLWACHS

A somewhat more accurate device is the double rectangular cell of Hallwachs for use on a spectrometer table. Light falls at grazing incidence on the plane-parallel plate separating the two liquids. If the entrance and the exit plates are also plane parallels and the construction is otherwise error-free,

$$n_1{}^2 - n_2{}^2 = \sin^2 E$$

where E is the observed angular deviation. For practical purposes one would use it in one direction only with simply a collimator and a telescope provided with an eyepiece micrometer. For research one would turn the cell through 180° between observations and perhaps repeat such a double observation after switching the liquids in the two compartments. In this way differences of 1.5×10^{-6} can be determined and errors of the cell eliminated. The Hallwachs cell is among those described by Anderson (2) in connection with his own somewhat similar differential refractometer for liquids, namely, a prism immersed in a rectangular cell.

6.3. Rau and Roseveare

Rau and Roseveare (66) have described a differential refractometer (for transference number determinations on dilute aqueous solutions) that uses white light and has a sensitivity of 5×10^{-7} over an index range of 0.002. The apparatus resembles the Rayleigh interferometer in that light from a vertical slit passes through two vertical slits near a lens that converges the two wedge-shaped pencils to a distant intersection where interference fringes are formed. Also, the objective is divided horizontally so that the lower pencils traverse a cell (9-cm. long) containing distilled water while the upper pencils traverse an inner obtuse immersed hollow prism (137°) containing 5 ml. of solution. The deviation of the pencils by means of the excess refractivity of the solution in the immersed prism is in part compensated by that of a prismatic wedge (3°) of water, and the residual lateral translation at the image plane is compensated by measurably translating the water wedge along a horizontal scale between the cell and the image plane.

The device makes use of interference fringes, in lieu of images of the original slit, as fiducial markers of the plane of reference. Because of similarities in dispersion, the water in the translatable prism compensates better than glass for the excess dispersion of the solution and thus permits the use of white-light fringes for a long range. Temperature troubles with the water wedge and elsewhere are minimized by frequent zero readings.

7. Interference Refractometers

Interference refractometers are essentially differential instruments (see Section 6). They are the most accurate and the most convenient instruments for measurements on gases and vapors, which have very small indices. In fact for these media their comparison with air or with vacuum is not only a differential but an absolute measurement. For all small differences in index, as between a pure solvent and its solutes in very dilute solutions, interference methods are applicable.

For measurements of larger differences in index, there are serious handicaps because of the limitations in total index range that can be covered with an interferometer at one operation.

7.1. INTERFERENCE PHENOMENA

Only those light pencils that proceed in somewhat the same direction from the same luminous particle of a source are capable of affecting each other to produce observable interference fringes on bands. Such pencils are called coherent. For other pencils, the patterns change so rapidly that only uniform intensity is perceived by the eye.

An interferometer is an arrangement for separating a coherent pencil or beam into distinct parts along different paths and then reuniting them to form measurably observable interference fringes. In all cases the fringes are actually formed and located in the region common to the two pencils where they intersect, and they can be seen on a screen except in the special case for which the beams are parallel and the fringes are formed at infinity.

A bright fringe will be formed at the plane of optical symmetry with respect to the two interfering pencils because both were in phase when they were separated and at this plane both have traveled their separate paths in the same time. To the right and left of this central bright fringe are regions where the paths for the two pencils of light differ by one-half wavelength, $\lambda/2$, and where in consequence the pencils differ in phase and dark fringes are formed. Further on each side bright and dark fringes are formed in succession. The distance between like fringes is directly proportional to the wavelength of the light.

With interferometers used for index measurements the optical path lengths for the two separated coherent pencils are usually nearly identical, and white light can be used. The central bright fringe in the plane of symmetry will be colorless, but, since red light has longer wavelengths than blue light, the lateral bright fringes will be tinged with red on their edges away from the central fringe.

Arago seems to have been first to recognize that when an optical medium of higher index, n, is substituted in place of a lower one, n_0, such as air or vacuum, throughout a definite length, L, of the geometrical path of one of the coherent pencils or beams, the central fringe of the system will be displaced toward the side of the higher-index medium. The number, N, of the fringes that pass the station previously occupied by the central fringe permits one to compute the difference in index according to the equation

$$(n - n_0) = (N\lambda)/L$$

7.2 Arago-Rayleigh-Haber-Löwe Type

Arago is thought to have used a slit, a lens, and two holes in a screen near the lens.

Lord Rayleigh (67) used a vertical slit source and two lenses between which the two tubes of gas were placed, side by side, in one half of the parallel beam. Two vertical slits were placed near one of the objectives, and he used a cylindrical lens, with axis vertical, for observation of the two sets of interference fringes that were formed in the focal plane of the second lens through the upper and lower portions of the lenses.

The one set of fringes, formed by light that travels through air and lenses only, serves as a fiducial mark or zero with respect to which the displacements of the second set are referred by merely counting fringes. Thus there is a valuable automatic element of zero adjustment in response to short-time changes in the instrument.

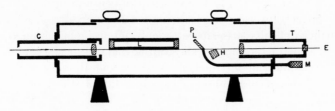

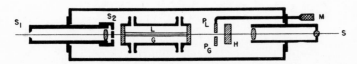

Fig. 2. Sectional elevation and plan diagrammatically showing the essential parts of a laboratory interferometer for gases and liquids, as manufactured by Zeiss. The collimator, C, is provided with a slit, S, and a double slit, S_2, so that an interference pattern is produced in the focal plane of the telescope, T, and is magnified by the ocular, E. The lower half of the beam passes below the gas or water chambers, G and L, and through an auxiliary plate, H, by means of which the height of the fiducial pattern can be adjusted in the field of the telescope. The upper half of the beam passes in part through G, which contains the sample, and in part through L, which contains the standard. The difference in refractivity of the media in G and L causes the interference pattern to shift right or left in the field of view, and this can be restored by tilting the compensator plates, P_G and P_L, through required amounts that are measurable with the micrometer, M.

Rayleigh and his co-workers allowed gas pressures to vary slowly as the fringes were counted and could not work on liquids, for which sudden gross shifts of the fringes are involved.

Haber and Löwe (30) fitted the instrument (Fig. 2) with an optical compensator of the Jamin type so that by merely turning a micrometer drum any sudden displacement of the fringes, within range, can be restored gradually and thus counted. They also provided a suitable prismatic "lifter" to raise or lower the movable fringe system with respect to the fiducial fringes as formed by the other half of the lens system. So far as possible white light is used for determining the total number of fringes, and then one changes to monochromatic light for the precision setting to a fraction of a wavelength. A difficulty arises because there is a difference in the dispersion of the optical glass compensator and that of the media to be measured. Consequently for some very accurate measurements it is necessary to calibrate (3, 4, 16) the compensator in terms of fringe breadth for certain wavelengths.

Further difficulty arises because only intense monochromatic sources can be used with the narrow slit widths that are necessary in the conventional commercial instruments. Watson and Ramaswamy (80) used a 4-amp arc between a cadmium-mercury alloy and a tungsten anode in an evacuated tube of Pyrex glass.

The conventional instruments are (or were) made by Zeiss in Germany and by Hilger in London, and detailed instructions for their use are issued. Suitable cells of various lengths from 10 to 100 cm. are sold for use with gases, and other cells from 1 to 80 mm. long for liquids. This apparatus is widely used for comparisons of dilute solutions, for tests of

TABLE VI

Accuracy and Index Range (White Light)
(Zeiss Laboratory Interferometer)

Cell length (cm.)		Error (Δn units of 7th decimal)	Range (n units of 5th decimal)
100		0.2	5
50		0.4	10
25	Gases	0.8	20
10		2.	50
8		2.5	63
4		5.	125
2		10.	250
1	Liquids	20.	500
0.5		40.	1000
0.1		200.	5000

purity, and for rates of progress of certain reactions. The accuracy (Table VI) exceeds that of any other commercially available devices, and the apparatus is simple and stable.

A smaller model, called a portable gas and water interferometer, was made by Zeiss. In it Löwe applied the principle of autocollimation and substituted a mirror for one objective.

The conventional design of the large interferometer has been importantly modified by Hilger, as specified by Williams (83), so that wider slits may be used at the source and the brightness of fringes increased manyfold.

Geffcken (24) has shown that one may dispense with compensator and instead measurably rotate both cells as a unit through a small angle, the cell unit being immersed in a larger fixed cell filled with the comparison fluid. The beam through the comparison medium is not changed, but through the unknown there is refraction and increased path length. Such a cell has been described in detail (44) and was obtainable from the firm of Ertel in München. A modified Rayleigh interferometer of this type, in combination with a spectrograph, has been used (25) for accurately measuring the dispersion of water from 0.668 to 0.212 μ by photography.

O'Bryan (63), of Baird Associates, Cambridge, Massachusetts, has announced a four-compartment gas interferometer having twice the sensitivity of the conventional Rayleigh type.

Many details regarding the calibration and use of an interferometer for the analysis of a mixture of gases, and for other problems involving gases, are given by Berl and Andress (3).

In general, the potential accuracy claimed for interferometry of liquids refers to work on aqueous solutions. Cohen and Bruins (10) have discussed the additional precautions that are necessary for getting comparable accuracy in work on organic solutions.

7.3. JAMIN

Jamin (36) made an interferometer with two thick glass plates which he cut from one large plane-parallel plate to ensure approximate equality of index and thickness. The first plate serves as an amplitude or beam splitter; the second plate is a beam united. Separation of the two paths of the coherent rays is accomplished by the oblique (near 41°) incidence and the thickness of the plates. For perfectly parallel adjustment of perfect plates, the path difference would be zero and no localized fringes would be observed, the field being uniformly illuminated as part of one very broad fringe. Slight rotation of one of the plates produces localized fringes which then may be used for refractive-index measurement when a path difference is inserted. If L is the effective length of a cell containing a medium of index n and a like cell contains a medium of index n_0, then one can write

$$N\lambda = (n - n_0)L \tag{11}$$

where N is the number of fringes that traverse the field.

In the usual method, a parallel beam of monochromatic light is directed by a collimator through the mirrors and is received by a microscope or a telescope in which the localized interference fringes are observed with respect to cross hairs. Several observers have noted more or less "drift" of the fringes, and the Cuthbertsons (14) and Huxley and Lowery (32) have attempted its elimination. A proper remedy, it would seem, is division of the objectives so that automatically fiducial fringes may be available, just as is done for the Rayleigh instrument.

The cost of the really fine quality of glass that is required in a Jamin-type interferometer probably discourages its commercial use or manufacture for sale. The advantage of this instrument over the Rayleigh conventional types is that, because of the principle of superposition, wider sources or slits are usable and thus monochromatic sources of lower intensity are available.

7.4. ZEHNDER-MACH

If an interferometer is to be used to study differential effects on a given medium, especially heat effects, the proximity of the cells may be disadvantageous, or very inconvenient, or both. Michelson (58) indicated by one of his many diagrams and Zehnder (92) showed in detail how Jamin's interferometer could be modified so that the separate paths of the coherent beams would be much farther apart. Mach (54) built such an instrument. Here, by means of the additional freedom in independent adjustment of plates and mirrors, it is possible to gain additional control of fringe widths and locations.

8. Phase-Contrast Refractometers

A phase-contrast refractometer of high accuracy for measurements on gases and liquids has been developed by Ingelstam (33). It is useful for the determination of refractive index relatively and, by inserting end gauges in the cell to establish precise cell thickness, for absolute determinations as well.

A cell consisting of three vertical layers is used. The gas or liquid to be measured occupies the central layer, and the reference material fills the upper and lower portions. Two plano-convex lenses form the end windows of the cell.

An image of an entrance slit, illuminated with monochromatic light, is formed by the cell on the central part of a phase mirror, from which it is passed by means of a mirror and lens to form a phase-contrast image of the cell. This image may be viewed with an eyepiece or a microscope. For comparison of the intensity of a defined part of the image of the central cell with that of the outer cell, photomultiplier tubes are used. A visual comparison can be made also if results of slightly lower precision are acceptable.

The phase mirror is based on the principle described by Françon and Nomarski (23). To render the instrument uniformly sensitive over the entire range of measurement, it consists of several portions giving different phase-turning angles. Two Polaroid sheets serve to determine and vary the vector origin.

The difference in refractive index between the two media, $n_2 - n_1$, is determined by the intensity ratio between the two fields. This is a function of the path difference or, more exactly, of the phase difference angle, $(n_2 - n_1) \cdot t \cdot 2\pi/\lambda$, where t is the geometric path in the liquids (cell thickness) and λ is the wavelength of the incident light.

One advantage of the method is the small size of sample that is required to give precise results. Thus, only about 0.1 cm.^{3} (lower limit of about 0.03 cm.^{3}) of the liquid or gas under examination and about 10 cm.^{3} of the reference media are needed.

When working with the highest precision possible with the instrument, the accuracy obtainable using the photoelectric detector is about 1/1000 of a wavelength, which for a cell of 10 mm. in thickness corresponds to about 0.04×1^{-6} in refractive index. If visual measurements are made, the accuracy is about one-fifth of that given above.

As an example of the utility of the method, it has been shown that it can be used for the analysis and control of the D_2O content of aqueous solutions within about 0.002 mole % at all concentrations (34).

9. Microrefractometers

Aside from the use of a microscope in immersion refractometry (Section 5.2) there is a demand for refractive index determinations on very small samples of liquid in qualitative chemical analysis, and on crystals with very small surfaces.

9.1. JELLEY-FISHER

On the basis of a design by Jelley (37), the Fisher Scientific Company of Pittsburg, Pennsylvania, makes a refractometer for measuring very minute quantities of liquid to ±0.001 for any wavelength for which the scale is calibrated. Jelley suggests three separate direct-reading scales for C, D, and F lines. Light from a slit traverses a 45° prism of liquid and then an opposed tiny 45° prism of glass. The eye is applied to a small opening and sees a virtual image of the slit superimposed on an index scale. A small water jacket can be used, and determinations can be made at high temperatures on fused materials. If one observes repeatedly on the same sample it is possible to detect mixtures of differential volatility by a systematic change in index.

9.2. NICHOLS

The A. H. Thomas Company, of Philadelphia, Pennsylvania, sells a microrefractometer mounted on a microscope slide, as designed by Nichols (61). Two small opposed glass prisms of the same angle and index are cemented side by side in a metal ring about 5 mm. in diameter to be filled with a very small amount of liquid. When light is incident normally from below, a fine line just below the prisms appears doubled, and the separation can be measured in the image plane of the microscope. After plotting a curve with liquids of known index, a graphic determination of an unknown is easily made. A water jacket surrounds the ring.

9.3. CRYSTAL REFRACTOMETERS

Crystal refractometers, especially adapted for crystallographical and mineralogical investigations, were designed by Bertrand and by Abbe and built by Zeiss and by Fuess in Germany. A similar instrument has been developed by Haacke and Hartmann (29). The optical block of the instrument is usually a hemisphere of high-index glass, well polished on both plane and spherical surfaces. Either grazing-incidence or critically directed (monochromatic) light can be radially thrown on or into the hemisphere by means of a mirror, but the reflected-light method is used almost exclusively on crystals because only one crystal surface is necessary in that case.

As with the Pulfrich refractometer, the angle through which the observing telescope revolves is measured on a vertical circle, and tables are provided for the corresponding index of refraction. The telescope objective can be removed and a microscope objective substituted in order to observe a crystal directly, or match it with an immersion liquid, as it lies on the plane surface of the hemispherical block. The hemisphere is measurably rotatable around a vertical axis.

By using a reducing telescope, and with suitable diaphragms, indices can be measured by reflection from surfaces less than 1 mm.^{2} in area. This refractometer can be used on larger polished solids and for liquids in a special temperature-stabilizing cell with plane-parallel base and a thermometer.

A critical-angle instrument similar to the crystal refractometer in that it utilizes a hemispherical block has been described by Pfund (64). This instrument makes use of a rutile hemisphere and permits measurements up to $n = 2.61$.

10. Spectrometers and Hollow Prisms

If in any research program it is necessary to measure refractive indices and dispersion absolutely and accurately to better than ±2 or 3×10^{-5}, time may perhaps be saved by resorting at once to a good spectrometer.

In this method a source capable of producing a discrete line spectrum (see Table I) is used to illuminate a slit or fine line located in a slit situated at the focal point of a collimator lens. The essentially parallel light from this source is passed through the sample in the form of a prism (axis vertical) placed on a rotatable table. The light is received in a telescope mounted on a vertical axis. The telescope is provided with a suitable horizontal scale to measure the angle of deviation of the light caused by the prism. The prism is rotated until the minimum angle of deviation of the light is observed and measured. A different orientation of the prism and a correspondingly different angle of deviation will be observed for each spectral line used.

The refractive index is calculated by the equation

$$n = \frac{\sin\left[(A + D)/2\right]}{\sin\left(A/2\right)}$$

where A is the prism angle and D is the angle of minimum deviation.

Solid samples must be transparent, reasonably free from occlusions, bubbles, or opacities, and formed into prisms with optically plane and polished faces. Liquid samples are contained in hollow prisms with polished plane-parallel windows.

A modification of the instrument described above incorporates the collimator and observing telescope into a single unit. The opposite face of the prism is silvered, and at minimum deviation the light beam returns to the collimator-telescope from whence it came. Such instruments are called autocollimating, and the equation given above is applied for the calculation of the results.

Spectrometers of both types are made by the various optical instrument producers. An autocollimating spectrometer of special design has been described by Forrest (21).

TABLE VII

Summary of Sources of Refractive-Index Error that Have Been Quantitatively Discussed

Vol-ume	Page	For-mula	Name	Sym-bol	Unit	$n = 1.3$	$n = 1.5$	$n = 1.7$	$n = 1.9$	Provisory remarks[a]
1929										
2	921	8	Prism angle	ΔA	Second of arc	0.57	0.33	0.22	0.16	(Index error always +)
2	921	9	Double deviation	$\Delta 2D$	Second of arc	0.56	0.62	0.80	1.5	
1931										
6	72	14	Prism orientation	*P. E. A*	Minute of arc	3.9	3.1	2.7	2.4	1-cm. diameter of surface area
1933										
11	41	23	Prism surface sagitta	s'	Wavelength	0.27	0.14	0.08	0.04	$s' = 0.02\lambda$
11	42	24	Prism translation	*P. E.* e_0	Millimeter	1.3	0.7	0.4	0.2	$s' =$ tabulated values
11	47	33	Eccentricity of prism-table axis	e	Millimeter	0.3	(Very large)	0.2	0.1	
11	52	45	Collimator focusing	ΔFc	Millimeter	2.9	2.0	1.8	2.7	$f_c = 400$ mm.; $e = 0.2$ mm.
1934										
13	117	—	Air composition	—	Proportion by volume	(Relatively large tolerances—see reference cited)				CO2-free dry air
1935										
14	400	10	Air temperature	Δt_a	Degree C.	0.77°	0.67°	0.59°	0.53°	$t = 0$°C.
14	400	12	Air pressure	Δp_a	Millimeter of Hg	2.2	1.9	1.6	1.5	
14	401	16	Air humidity	Δv	Millimeter of Hg	15.	13.	12.	11.	
14	403	21	Abnormal CO2 in air	Δc	Proportion by volume	0.005	0.004	0.004	0.003	
14	408	—	Temperature of certain glasses	—	Degree C.	—	{ Soda lime 0.3° / Fused quartz 0.1°	} Dense flint 0.2°	Densest flint 0.7°	$\lambda = 5893$ A.
14	408	—	Temperature of certain liquids	ΔP	Degree C.	Water 0.01°	Many oils 0.002°	CS2 0.001°		$\lambda = 5893$ A.
14	411	32	Hydrostatic pressure on glass	ΔP	Atmosphere	—	0.5	0.5	0.5	
14	411	33	Hydrostatic pressure on certain liquids	ΔP	Millimeter of Hg	{ Water 47. / Ether 12.	Glycerin 72. / Benzene 17.	CS2 12.		
14	412	36	Stress-birefringence in glass	Δn_b	mμ/cm.	12.	9.	3.	2.	(? at $n = 1.8$ +)
14	415	37	Striae in glass	s	Proportion	0.003	0.003	0.003	0.003	$n_2 - n_1 = 0.0003$
14	416	40	Wavelength of light source	$\Delta \lambda$	Angstrom	Water 0.10	Fluorite 0.13	CS2 0.014	Densest flint 0.010	$\lambda = 4000$ A.

Column header group: **References to J. Research Natl. Bur. Standards** (Vol-ume, Page, For-mula); **Quantity evaluated or controlled** (Name, Sym-bol, Unit); **± Tolerances for various refractivities of sample** ($\Delta n = \pm 1 \times 10^{-6}$, $A = 60$°).

[a] For explanations and for other pertinent limitations and conditions, see discussions given in references cited in columns 1 to 3.

Although spectrometers capable of moderate precision are generally available and are to be found, for example, in most university laboratories, instruments of high precision are relatively scarce. The latter must be equipped not only with accurately calibrated scales and optical components of high quality but also with provision for precise adjustments and for centering and leveling of the prism; also, they must have temperature-regulated prism table housings and similar features. In addition, for precise results, attention must be given to optical quality, particularly the flatness of the prism surfaces.

An extensive investigation of the sources of error in prism refractometry has been made by Tilton; this is summarized in Table VII, which includes references to the original papers. A discussion by Guild will be found on pp. 754-778 of Vol. IV, "Dictionary of Applied Physics."

11. Continuously Recording Refractometers

Several refractometers have been described for the continuous recording of refractive index of liquids. The refractometric cell may be incorporated in a feed line and the apparatus used to monitor and/or control an industrial process.

An apparatus described by Jones et al. (42) depends on the measurement of the intensity of internal reflection near the critical angle. Two trapezoidal prisms are used, one of which is in contact with the sample while the other is bathed by a reference material. The light source consists of a tungsten-filament projection lamp and a collimator provided with a holder for filters. The beam is split into two components, one passing through the sample prism and the other through the reference prism. The reflected light from the prism-liquid boundaries is finally converted into an electrical signal by either vacuum phototubes or barrier layer cells. In the latter case, the difference in output is recorded by a standard recording potentiometer. Calibration is made with liquids of known refractive index.

The method is independent of coloration of the liquid but is not applicable to those liquids which deposit a colored film on the prism, since only a very thin layer will seriously interfere with its operation. Little maintenance is required except for periodic cleaning of the prisms and restandardization, and the apparatus will operate for long periods of time with an accuracy of about ±0.0001 refractive index unit.

A recording refractometer of the spectrometer type with hollow prism was developed by Johnson and Schnelle (41). The light source is a mercury arc and includes interference filters to isolate a particular wavelength to give monochromatic radiation. A photocell mounted on a carriage automatically tracks the position of the slit image. A wiping contact attached to the carriage traverses a slide wire across which a fixed voltage is maintained so that the carriage position is indicated by a voltage change at the wiper arm. A thermistor is mounted in the hollow prism to compensate for changes in cell temperature, and the algebraic sum of this voltage and the carriage-position voltage is fed into a conventional self-balancing potentiometric recorder.

The instrument was designed for a refractive-index spread of $\Delta n =$ 0.0161, about a mid-point value of $n = 1.5250$. An optical lever of 120 inches is required to give a displacement of the carriage of about 3 inches. A series of first-surfaced mirrors is used to make the instrument more compact.

The apparatus is calibrated with liquids of known refractive index, and its precision is about ± 0.00007 to ± 0.00008 refractive-index unit for temperature variations of no more than $\pm 10°C$. It was designed to measure the styrene content of ethyl benzene solutions in the range 40 to 70% styrene so that changes in composition of 0.15% are detected reliably and accurately.

A line of recording differential refractometers is produced by the Phoenix Precision Instrument Company of Philadelphia, Pennsylvania. A narrow-band beam is transmitted through a differential prism and is focused on the apex of a hexagonal prism where it is split into two beams. Each beam is alternately interrupted by a synchronous chopper and monitored by a photomultiplier tube.

Any change in refractive index of the flowing solution causes a displacement of the beam and a corresponding change in the intensities of the beams emerging from the prisms, resulting in an unbalanced signal. This is transmitted to a servo system which drives the beam-splitting prism table laterally to restore balance. The motion of the table actuates a potentiometer for recorder operation.

The sensitivity of the apparatus is 3 units in the sixth decimal place of refractive index. A calibrated optical-range extender is provided which gives the instrument a span of 7000 units of the sixth decimal place.

Recording differential refractometers for use in the process industries are also produced by the Barnes Engineering Company of Stamford, Connecticut, and by the Consolidated Electrodynamics Corporation of Pasadena, California.

12. Applications

A comprehensive or detailed discussion of the applications of refractive index measurements to chemical analysis, or even a reasonably complete bibliography of such applications, is beyond the scope of this chapter. The emphasis has been rather on the general physical principles and the special precautions that must be observed to ensure precise index measurements. However, some typical applications will be described which illustrate the scope of usage and versatility of the tool.

Precise values for refractive index and dispersion are important physical constants in the identification of liquids and in the specification of their purity. Although not usually specific enough to offer a positive means of identification when used alone, they are most valuable in connection with precise values for other physical properties such as boiling point and melting point. Refractive-index determinations have one important advantage over the determination of most of the other physical constants in that a fairly accurate measurement can be made with only a few drops of material, and when a few milliliters are available very accurate values of both index and dispersion can be made.

One of the most serious limitations in the use of refractive indices for purposes of identification frequently arises from the unavailability of precise values for comparison. Many of the values in the literature were obtained for impure materials and/or with faulty technique. As a result, much of the older data, especially, must be scrutinized critically before they may be used with confidence.

When the qualitative nature of a solution is known and the dependence of the index on the composition has been determined from the study of known systems, refractive index measurements often offer a simple, fast, and reliable means of solving many analytical problems. For many aqueous solutions containing a single solute the index is found to be a linear function of the concentration. It has been shown that

$$\frac{n - n_0}{C} = k \tag{12}$$

is practically independent of temperature when the concentration, C, is expressed in grams of solute per 100 ml. of solution. In this equation, $n - n_0$ represents the difference in refractive index between the solution and the pure solvent. Clemens (9) has discussed the use of the immersion refractometer in the analysis of aqueous solutions and gives examples in which two solutes may be determined from a knowledge of both the density and refractive index of a solution.

Refractive-index measurements have been used for many years for determining the concentration of sugar solutions (60). It has been shown that solutions of a number of sugars and related substances have approximately the same refractive index for equal percentage compositions by weight. As a result, refractive-index determination may be used to calculate the amount of soluble carbohydrates in a solution or the amount of a given species if the solution is known to be pure. Moreover, impurities in the form of mineral salts, although introducing error, are not so serious when using refractive index as when using density to determine the percentage of dry substance in a sirup.

The determination of the oil content of oil-bearing seeds (11, 81) is an interesting application of refractometry. A known weight of flaxseed, for example, is ground in a mortar with a known amount of hallowax oil, which has a high index of refraction. The oil from the seeds lowers the index of the hallowax oil, and determination of this lowering permits, after suitable calibration, the per cent of oil in the seeds to be computed. The method is also applicable to pressed cake or meal, and the average difference between the optical and the more laborious extraction method is about 0.2% regardless of the oil content of the material.

Refractometry is a convenient and precise tool for determining the sulfur content of rubber. McPherson and Cummings (55) have shown that, for unvulcanized rubber, the refractive index is a linear function of the weight per cent of dissolved sulfur in the sample. Owing to the high viscosity, supersaturated solutions containing up to 4% of sulfur can be measured, and they show the linear relationship. When equilibrium was established, the saturated solution was found to contain 1.2 weight % of sulfur. Vulcanized rubber was also found to show a linear relationship between the refractive index and the sulfur content for material containing up to 19% of this constituent.

This work led to the development of the method currently in use for determining the bound styrene content of GR-S synthetic rubber (a copolymer of butadiene and styrene) (86). The method involves a measurement of the index of a sample from which impurities have been removed by extraction, and the reproducibility is such that successive determinations rarely differ by more than 0.2% in the normal GR-S which contains about 24% of bound styrene.

Another interesting application is in the determination of the efficiency of distillation columns. Values for the refractive index versus composition of several binary test mixtures have been published (5, 84), and measurement of the index of samples from the "head" and the "pot" of the column gives the compositions which are substituted in the appropriate equations to give the number of equivalent theoretical plates of the still.

The product of the specific refraction and the molecular weight of a substance is designated as the molecular refractivity. Considerable experimental work has shown that the refractivity depends not only on composition but also on the constitution of the compound, and values have been assigned for the contributions of the elements and linkages usually found in organic substances. These have proved useful not only for predicting the refractive index of known compounds but also in deciding questions of the structure of molecules.

The additivity of refractivity has been applied with considerable success by petroleum chemists. Kurtz and Ward (45) have modified the Gladstone and Dale relationship by replacing the constant, 1, by an empirical constant, b, to obtain

$$\frac{n - b}{d} = 0.5 \tag{13}$$

and when this is written in the slope-intercept form

$$n = \frac{d}{2} + b \tag{14}$$

the constant b is called the refractivity intercept. These investigators then showed that b is a constant for certain homologous series with the following values:

Series	Refractivity intercept
Paraffins	1.0461
Saturated monocyclic	1.0400
Saturated polycyclic	1.0285
Aromatics	1.0627
Monoöelfins	1.0521
Nonconjugated diolefins	1.0592
Conjugated diolefins	1.0877
Cyclic unsaturates	
One double bond	1.0461
Two conjugate double bonds	1.0643

One application of the refractivity intercept is in the critical review and evaluation of data, because wide deviations in the experimental intercept from the expected value normally indicate errors of some kind. Thus errors in transcription of data, lack of correction for temperature, the presence of impurities in compounds, and other causes of unsound data have been detected.

Qualitative identification of organic liquids is also facilitated by means of the refractivity intercept. Values for nonhydrocarbons are in general less than 1.000, whereas hydrocarbons, except some high-molecular-weight polynuclear naphthenes, are above 1.010. The method of identifying the homologous series for pure materials is self-evident from what has been said.

In recent years, a considerable number of papers has appeared in which refractive index and dispersion are used in connection with other physical properties for the qualitative identification and quantitative estimation of the constituents of hydrocarbon mixtures (22, 31, 49, 50, 51, 59). Also, the specific dispersion, defined as $(n_F - n_C)/d$, has been used, especially in the determination of the aromatic content of hydrocarbons boiling in the gasoline and naphtha range (27). These subjects are too extensive to be treated here.

Periodic determinations of refractive index are very helpful in identifying the output of distilling columns. This method in petroleum technology is well known. Applications have also been made in the qualitative and quantitative analysis of fatty acids (52, 89) and drying oils (13).

A rather interesting application occurs in the analytical determination of aromatic hydrocarbons by adsorption (56). For example, a gasoline fraction is passed through a column containing a solid absorbent, and the effluent which first appears is aromatic-free. The volume of aromatic-free filtrate is determined from observations of the refractive index of the filtrate as a function of its volume. The concentration of the aromatic hydrocarbons is determined by means of a calibration chart established from experiments on known solutions. The method is applicable to straight-run gasolines and to those containing olefins.

Numerous examples could be cited in which refractive-index measurements are used for the control of manufacturing processes, as in the fermentation industries, in dyestuffs, and in the canning and preservation of foods. Special refractometers are available for installation in or near processing vessels and pipe lines. A recording instrument (15) has recently been described that should be especially valuable in industrial processing. Such special instruments are being used for controlling fractionating-tower separations, controlling the concentration of aqueous solutions, blending gasoline additives, and identifying products from industrial feed lines.

Refractive index measurements often offer a positive means of identification of crystalline substances (87). Immersion methods are usually employed, and techniques have been developed whereby either perfectly formed or crushed specimens may be measured. Identification is made by comparing the optical properties with tabulated values or with measurements obtained on known substances.

Both organic and inorganic crystalline materials may be studied in this way. In case of the former either the original substance or some derivative of it may be investigated. Indices of refraction are often as easy to measure as the more familiar melting points (85), and in some instances their interpretation is more positive. The greatest difficulty on organic compounds is to find suitable immersion liquids in which they are sufficiently insoluble.

The identification of constituents of minerals and rocks is greatly facilitated by optical examination, and extensive tables of optical properties are available (48). Such identifications are made in the study of heterogeneous equilibriums. Melts of known composition are prepared and held at a given temperature until equilibrium is established. The system is then quenched, and the liquidus phase may be obtained by comparison of its index with that of glasses in the proper range of composition; the crystals are identified by their optical properties.

A new simple and rapid interferometric method for studying diffusion and other phenomena giving rise to refractive-index gradients in a solution has been described by Bryngdahl (6). The method utilizes birefringence interferences and possesses a high degree of precision which cannot be obtained by other methods where the optical resolving power sets a limit to the degree of accuracy obtained. The method is sensitive to very low concentration differences, thus providing a convenient means of studying the concentration dependence of the diffusion coefficient.

In all these examples the refractive index measurement is used more or less directly in identifying or assaying some solid, liquid, or constituent of a solution. Indirect applications of refractometry are also possible. For example, the refractive index of water varies with the applied pressure, and an interferometer may be used as a very satisfactory pressure gauge (78). This method has been adopted in the study of the osmotic pressure of solutions (53).

References

1. Anderson, J. S., *Trans. Opt. Soc. London* **21**, 195 (1919-20).
2. Anderson, J. S., *Collected Researches Natl. Phys. Labs.* **17**, 57 (1922).
3. Berl, E., and Andress, K., *Z. angew. Chem.* **34**, 370 (1921).
4. Brodskii, A. I., *Chem. Abstr.* 1257 (1942).
5. Bromley, E. C., and Quiggle, D., *Ind. Eng. Chem.* **25**, 1136 (1933).
6. Bryngdahl, O., *Acta Chim. Scand.* **11**, 1017 (1957).
7. Chéneveau, M. C., "Les Propriétés optique des Solutions," p. 58. Gauthiers Villars, Paris, 1907.
8. Chesire, R. W., *Phil. Mag.* **32**, 409 (1916).
9. Clemens, C. A., *Ind. Eng. Chem.* **13**, 813 (1921).
10. Cohen, E., and Bruins, H. R., *Proc. Koninkl. Akad. Wetenschap. Amsterdam* **24**, 114 (1921).
11. Coleman, D., A., and Fellows, H. C., *U.S. Dept. Agri. Bull.* **1471** (1927).
12. Conrady, A. E., *Monthly Notices Roy. Astron. Soc.* **64**, 458 (1903-4).
13. Cowan, J. C., Falkenburg, L. B., and Teeter, H. M., *Ind. Eng. Chem. Anal. Ed.* **16**, 90 (1944).

14. Cuthbertson, C., and Cuthbertson, M., *Proc. Roy. Soc.* **A135**, 40 (1932).
15. Donzelot, P., and Camus, G., *Compt. rend.* **224**, 336 (1947).
16. Edwards, J. D., *Bull. Natl. Bur. Standards* **14**, 474 (1917); *J. Am. Chem. Soc.* **39**, 2382 (1917).
17. Emmons, R. C., *Am. Mineralogist* **13**, 504 (1928); **14**, 414 (1929).
18. Ewald, W., "Die optische Werkstatt," p. 215. Borntraeger, Berlin, 1930.
19. Faick, C. A., and Fonoroff, B., *J. Research Natl. Bur. Standards* **32**, 67 (1944).
20. Forrest, J. W., *J. Opt. Soc. Am.* **46**, 657 (1956); **45**, 132 (1955).
21. Forrest, J. W., Straat, H. W., and Dakin, R. K., *J. Opt. Soc. Am.* **46**, 143 (1956); **46**, 488 (1956).
22. Francis, A. W., *Ind. Eng. Chem. Ind. Ed.* **33**, 554 (1941); **36**, 256 (1944).
23. Françon, M., and Nomarski, G., *Compt. rend.* **230**, 1392 (1950).
24. Geffcken, W., *Z. Elektrochem.* **37**, 233 (1931).
25. Geffcken, W., and Kruis, A., *Z. physik. Chem. (Leipzig)* **B45**, 411 (1939).
26. Gibson, R. E., *J. Am. Chem. Soc.* **60**, 517 (1938).
27. Grosse, A. V., and Wackher, R. C., *Ind. Eng. Chem. Anal. Ed.* **11**, 614 (1939).
28. Guild, J., *Proc. Phys. Soc. (London)* **30**, 157 (1918).
29. Haake, H., and Hartmann, J., *Optik* **11**, 380 (1954).
30. Haber, F., and Löwe, F., *Z. angew. Chem.* **23**, 1393 (1910).
31. Huggins, M. L., *J. Am. Chem. Soc.* **63**, 916 (1941).
32. Huxley, H., and Lowery, H., *Proc. Roy. Soc.* **A182**, 207 (1943).
33. Ingelstam, E., *Arkiv Fysik* **6**, 287 (1952).
34. Ingelstam, E., Djurle, E., and Johansson, L., *J. Opt. Soc. Am.* **44**, 472 (1954).
35. Jackson, R. F., and Mathews, J. A., *J. Research Natl. Bur. Standards* **8**, 412 (1932).
36. Jamin, J., *Pogg. Ann.* **98**, 345 (1856).
37. Jelley, E. E., *J. Roy. Microscop. Soc.* **54**, 234 (1934).
38. Joffe, J. H., *J. Opt. Soc. Am.* **41**, 166 (1951).
39. Joffe, J. H., and Kimel, S., *J. Chem. Phys.* **25**, 374 (1956).
40. Joffe, J. H., and Oppenheim, U., *Bull. Research Council Israel* **2**, 297 (1952); *J. Opt. Soc. Am.* **47**, 782 (1957).
41. Johnson, S. E. J., and Schnelle, P. D., *Rev. Sci. Instr.* **24**, 26 (1953).
42. Jones, H. E., Ashmann, K. E., and Stahley, E. E., *Anal. Chem.* **21**, 1470 (1949).
43. Kofler, L., and Baumeister, M., *Z. anal. Chem.* **124**, 385 (1942).
44. Kruis, A., and Geffcken, W., *Z. physik. Chem. (Leipzig)* **A166**, 16 (1933).
45. Kurtz, S. S., Jr., and Ward, A. L., *J. Franklin Inst.* **222**, 563 (1936).
46. Kurtz, S. S., Jr., and Ward, A. L., *J. Franklin Inst.* **224**, 583 (1937).
47. Lafay, A., *Rev. opt.* **4**, 24 (1925).
48. Larsen, E. S., and Berman, H., *U.S. Geol. Survey Bull.* **No. 848** (1934).
49. Lipkin, M. R., and Martin, C. C., *Ind. Eng. Chem. Anal. Ed.* **18**, 380 (1946).
50. Lipkin, M. R., and Martin, C. C., *Ind. Eng. Chem. Anal. Ed.* **18**, 433 (1946).
51. Lipkin, M. S., Martin, C. C., and Kurtz, S. S., Jr., *Ind. Eng. Chem. Anal. Ed.* **18**, 376 (1946).
52. Longenecker, H. E., *Oil & Soap* **21**, 16 (1944).
53. Lotz, P., and Frazer, J. C. W., *J. Am. Chem. Soc.* **43**, 2501 (1921).
54. Mach, L., *Z. Instrumentenk.* **12**, 89 (1892).
55. McPherson, A. T., and Cummings, A. D., *J. Research Natl. Bur. Standards* **14**, 553 (1935).
56. Mair, B. J., and Forziati, A. F., *J. Research Natl. Bur. Standards* **32**, 151 (1944).
57. Martin, L. C., *Trans. Opt. Soc. (London)* **17**, 76 (1916).

58. Michelson, A. A., *Am. J. Sci.* **39,** 118 (1890).
59. Mills, I. W., Hirschfelder, A. E., and Kurtz, S. S., Jr., *Ind. Eng. Chem. Ind. Ed.* **38,** 442 (1946).
60. *Natl. Bur. Standards (U.S.) Circ.* **No. C440,** 254 (1942).
61. Nichols, L., *Natl. Paint Bull.* **1,** 12 (1937).
62. Nutting, P. G., *J. Opt. Soc. Am.* **2,** 61 (1919).
63. O'Bryan, H. M., *J. Opt. Soc. Am.* **34,** 774 (1944).
64. Pfund, A. H., *J. Opt. Soc. Am.* **39,** 966 (1949).
65. Pockels, F., *Ann. Physik* [4] **7,** 745 (1902).
66. Rau, D., and Roseveare, W. E., *Ind. Eng. Chem. Anal. Ed.* **8,** 72 (1936).
67. Rayleigh, Lord, *Proc. Roy. Soc.* **A59,** 203 (1896).
68. Richter, R., *Z. Instrumentenk.* **50,** 254 (1930).
69. Röntgen, W. C., and Zehnder, L., *Ann. Physik* [3] **44,** 49 (1891).
70. Saylor, C. P., *J. Research Natl. Bur. Standards* **15,** 277 (1935).
71. Swain, G. C., *Optician* **92,** 437 (1937).
72. Tilton, L. W., *J. Research Natl. Bur. Standards* **14,** 393 (1935).
73. Tilton, L. W., *J. Opt. Soc. Am.* **32,** 378 (1942).
74. Tilton, L. W., *J. Research Natl. Bur. Standards* **30,** 314 (1943).
75. Tilton, L. W., and Tool, A. Q., *J. Research Natl. Bur. Standards* **3,** 622 (1929).
76. Tool, A. Q., and Tilton, L. W., *J. Opt. Soc. Am.* **12,** 490 (1926).
77. Valentine, W. P., *J. Franklin Inst.* **207,** 116 (1929).
78. van Doren, L., Parker, H. K., and Lotz, P., *J. Am. Chem. Soc.* **43,** 2497 (1921).
79. Waldmann, H., *Helv. Chim. Acta* **21,** 1053 (1938).
80. Watson, H. E., and Ramaswamy, K. L., *Proc. Roy. Soc.* **A156,** 144 (1938).
81. Wesson, D., *Cotton Oil Press* **4** (3), 70 (1920).
82. West, C. D., *Ind. Eng. Chem. Anal. Ed.* **10,** 628 (1938).
83. Williams, W. E., *Proc. Phys. Soc. (London)* **44,** 451 (1932).
84. Willingham, C. B., and Rossini, F. D., *J. Research Natl. Bur. Standards* **37,** 15 (1946).
85. Winchell, A. N., "The Optical Properties of Organic Compounds." Univ. Wisconsin Press, Madison, Wisconsin, 1943.
86. Wood, L. A., *Natl. Bur. Standards (U.S.) Misc. Publ.* **M185** (1947).
87. Wright, F. E., *J. Am. Chem. Soc.* **38,** 1647 (1916).
88. Wright, F. E., *J. Opt. Soc. Am.* **5,** 389 (1921).
89. Wyman, F. W., and Barkenbus, C., *Ind. Eng. Chem. Anal. Ed.* **12,** 658 (1940).
90. Young, J. C., and Finn, A. N., *J. Research Natl. Bur. Standards* **25,** 759 (1940).
91. Zehnder, L., *Ann. Physik* [3] **34,** 91 (1888).
92. Zehnder, L., *Z. Instrumentenk.* **11,** 275 (1891).

Bibliography

Beńkovskiĭ, V. G., Refractometric determination of losses of petroleum due to evaporation. *Neftyanoe Khoz.* **26** (No. 7), 46 (1948).

Fischer, R., and Kocher, G., Identification of very small quantities of liquids by the measurement of the index of refraction; also the index of refraction of minerals. *Mikrochemie ver. Mikrochim. Acta* **32,** 173 (1944).

Kahma, A., and Mikkola, T., Statistical method for the quantitative refractive index analysis of minerals in rock. *Bull. comm. géol. Finlande* **138,** 27 (1946).

Klevens, H. B., Effect of temperature on micelle formation as determined by refraction. *J. Colloid Sci.* **2,** 301 (1947).

Klevens, H. B., Critical micelle concentrations as determined by refraction. *J. Phys. Colloid Chem.* **52,** 130 (1948).

Marek, K., Detection of the composition of rubber mixtures. *Chem. obzor* **22,** 209 (1947).

Melville, H. W., and Watson, W. F., Refractometric method for following reactions in closed systems. *Trans. Faraday Soc.* **44,** 68 (1948).

Murgulescu, I. G., and Latiu, E., Refractometric methods for the analysis of solutions. *Z. anal. Chem.* **128,** 193 (1948).

Öholm, L. W., Refractometric determination of the concentration of a substance during diffusion studies. *Finska Kemistamfundets Festskrift 1891-1941,* **1944,** 177.

Raw, R., The control of fractional distillation by means of refractive index measurements, *J. Soc. Chem. Ind.* **66,** 451 (1947).

Treloar, L. R. G., Stress-optical properties of rubber. *Nature* **159,** 231 (1947).

Wood, L. A., and Tilton, L. W., Refractive index of natural rubber for different wave lengths. *Proc. 2nd Rubber Technol. Conf. London, June, 1948* p. 142. W. Heffer & Sons, Ltd., Cambridge, England.

Mass Spectrometry

Charles F. Robinson

*Research Division, Consolidated Electrodynamics Corporation,
Pasadena, California*

1. Introduction

1.1. Definition

A mass spectrometer is an apparatus which ionizes a sample, then separates the resulting mixture of ions into groups in which all the ions in any one group have the same mass,* and finally measures the number of ions formed in a given time in each group. We choose a functional definition because mass spectrometers have been built in such extraordinary variety that a descriptive definition would be either too nebulous or too complex to be useful; almost the only feature that is common to all mass spectrometers is a vacuum system.

1.1.1. Elements of a Mass Spectrometer. The three distinguishing elements of a mass spectrometer are the ion source in which ions are produced from the material to be studied, the mass resolving system in which some characteristic—kinetic energy or position in space—is imparted differently to ions of different masses emerging from the ion source, and the ion collector, where ions of one mass can be selected from the remainder on the basis of their kinetic energy or their location in space. These three elements constitute the mass spectrometer proper. They constitute only a small part, however, of an operating mass spectrometer installation (260). Most of the cost, in both money and effort, and including not only the initial investment but the day-to-day operation, lies not in the mass spectrometer proper but in the auxiliary equipment— the sample-handling system, the vacuum system, the electronic circuitry, the recording system, etc. We shall discuss each of these elements in some detail because much time and effort can be wasted in attempts to employ instrumentation or techniques that are inappropriate to the task to be done; in Barnard's words, "to entertain the idea that it is a comparatively simple job is to invite confusion and disaster in any major application of the mass spectrometer" (12).

1.2. THE IONIZATION PROCESS

When an electron passes through a vapor, interactions between the electrons and the vapor molecules occur because of the mutual electrostatic forces involved. With electron energies of less than several kilovolts, any energy transfer that occurs takes place mainly between the impacting electron and the valence electrons of the bombarded molecule, since, under these circumstances, it is impossible for the impacting electron to transfer substantial kinetic energy to the atomic nuclei. Thus ionization as it occurs in mass spectrometry is a process in which one or more of the valence electrons in the bombarded molecule is simply stripped off. A definite amount of energy, variable from one molecule to another, is required to effect this process; the amount of energy required

---

* We follow conventional practice by using the term mass to imply mass-to-charge ratio, which is the quantity that mass spectrometers actually measure. A doubly charged ion of mass 40 (A^{++}, for example) exhibits an apparent mass of 20 atomic mass units (a.m.u.); triply charged, 13.3 a.m.u., etc. (See Fig. 7.)

varies from about 4.5 volts for cesium to about 25 volts for helium, all the other elements and most chemical compounds lying between these limits. When the impacting electron has just enough energy to effect ionization, the ionization process is energetically possible but statistically very improbable, the probability increasing with increasing energy of the impacting electron until the energy available becomes equal to a few times the minimum required.

Curves of ionization probability as a function of bombarding electron energy for several gases are shown in Fig. 1. Two facts are plain

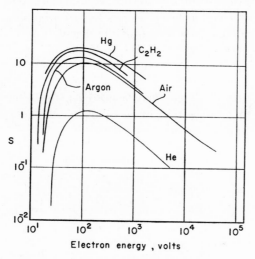

Fig. 1. Probability of ionization by electron impact, S, as a function of electron energy, for various molecules. The ionization probability, S, is expressed as the total number of ions formed, per centimeter of electron path length, at 1 mm. Hg vapor pressure of the molecular species in question.

from the figure. First, the bombarding energy for which the ionization cross section is a maximum is not critically defined and does not vary markedly from one gas to another, so that it is possible to select a single value for the kinetic energy of a bombarding electron stream which will work, with efficiency reasonably near the optimum, and with efficiency which does not change much if the electron beam energy should change slightly, for all gases and vapors. Second, if an ion source is designed to work with the ionizing electron beam energy near the threshold—the "appearance potential"—then anything that changes the kinetic energy of the electron beam even slightly will alter the ionization efficiency, and thus the ion beam intensity, very markedly, and lead to severe instabilities in the operation of the ion source.

It is possible in principle to operate an ion source with electron beams of such low energies that one molecular species can be distinguished from another on the basis of the appearance potential alone, or free radicals can be distinguished from stable molecules (since their ionization potentials are generally lower), or a molecule can be ionized without fragmentation, since a little more energy is required for ionization with fragmentation than for ionization alone. Experimentally, difficulties arise from two main sources. First is the fact that the energy of an electron beam, whether it arises from a thermal emitter, a photoelectric emitter, a cold-emission process, or what not, is never completely well-defined; any electron beam always has associated with it a certain distribution in energies, the width of the distribution depending on the temperature of the emitter. Thus the electrons emitted from a tungsten filament will show kinetic energies distributed through the better part of a volt. Second is that fact that contact potentials, thermal electromotive force, or surface charges may cause even the mean energy of the electron beam to be uncertain by a volt or more. For these and other reasons, the operation of a mass spectrometer at very low ionizing voltages is a quite specialized field, the discussion of which will be deferred to a later section (section 3.3.1).

1.3. The Nature of the Mass Spectrum

A mass spectrum is a pictorial representation of ion abundance as a function of the mass of the ions. In the first mass spectra, ion abundance was represented by the intensity of fluorescence of a Willemite screen or the image density on a photographic plate, ions of different mass occurring at different positions on the recording medium. In the great majority of instances, however, the mass spectrum is a line graph in which ion abundance is the ordinate and mass the abscissa, ions of different mass appearing as peaks on a curve. (See Fig. 7)

When a mass spectrum is examined, it is found that in all but the simplest cases the spectrum consists of a number of peaks, sometimes a very considerable number indeed. In conventional practice, the ionizing mechanism operates at energies substantially higher than the minimum energy necessary for ionization to occur. Thus there is sufficient energy available not only to ionize any material that may be introduced to the ion source but to produce multiply charged ions and to fragment any molecular bonds as well. Consequently, even in the case of a monatomic element, ions will appear not only at masses corresponding to each isotope but at positions corresponding to half these masses (doubly charged ions) and to even higher degrees of ionization to the extent that the necessary energy is available. In the case of chemical compounds, ions will usually be produced from every possible molecular fragment so that the mass spectrum of a pure substance having a molecular weight in the neighborhood of 100 a.m.u. may contain dozens of peaks.

The array of peaks produced when a pure substance is examined in a mass spectrometer is called a "pattern." The pattern is characteristic not only of the molecular weight but of the structure of the molecule being examined. For example, consider the case of *n*-butane and *i*-butane, differentiation of which was one of the first industrial problems to which

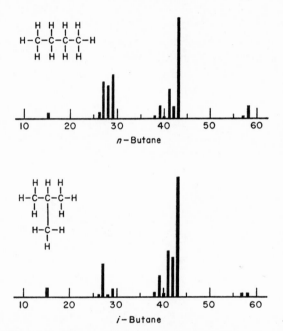

FIG. 2. Structural diagrams and the principal peaks in the mass spectra of *n*-butane and *i*-butane, illustrating the structure-dependent differences in mass spectra between two molecules of the same empirical chemical formula.

mass spectrometric analysis was applied. Both molecules have a molecular weight of 58 and so are indistinguishable on that basis. From examination of Fig. 2 it can be anticipated that both molecules will also show strong peaks at mass 43 (the whole molecule minus a CH_3 group). Arguing qualitatively, it can be seen that there are two ways of splitting off a CH_3 group in *n*-butane by breaking a single bond, and three possible ways to do this in *i*-butane, so that it seems plausible that the resulting mass 43 peaks would be stronger in the latter spectrum than in the former, by a factor of about 3:2. This is just what is observed. Thus it is possible to determine the relative abundances of *n*-butane and *i*-butane, in a mixture of the two, by measurement of the 43 and 58 peaks alone, and to complete the analysis in a few minutes, whereas the same analysis might require hours or days to complete by fractional distillation or other older methods. The patterns produced in a mass spectrometer are sufficiently characteristic of the substances being examined that an experienced analyst can often deduce, on the basis of a brief examination of the pattern, not only the molecular weight of the substance being examined but a great deal of detailed information regarding the molecular structure as well (305).

1.4. HISTORICAL BACKGROUND

The first mass spectrometer, as we have defined the term, was built shortly after the turn of the century by Thomson (353) for use in study-

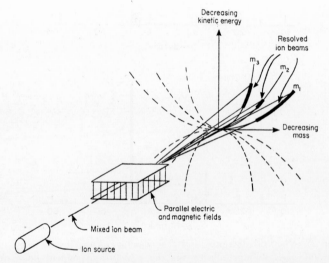

FIG. 3. The parabola mass spectrograph. In the figure, the ions have masses increasing in the order $m_3 > m_2 > m_1$: m_3 has the lowest mean kinetic energy; m_2 and m_1 have about the same mean kinetic energy, but m_1 exhibits much higher spread in energy than does either m_2 or m_3. Under any given set of operating conditions, only one quadrant of the image plane is utilized, the particular quadrant in use being determined by the four possible combinations of $\pm B$, $\pm E$, and by the sign of the ion charge.

ing the positive rays which had been discovered by Goldstein in 1886 (126) and investigated during the intervening years by Wien (390) and others. With this instrument Thomson investigated the positive rays from hydrogen and helium and showed for the first time that positive rays from these elements were deflected by different amounts in a magnetic field. The first mass spectrometer to be used as a more or less routine investigative tool was Thomson's so-called positive-ray apparatus. In it, a narrow pencil of positive ions was directed through electric and magnetic fields, the two fields being in parallel directions. The ion beam was dispersed into a series of cones of parabolic section, ions of different mass lying on different cones. Thus on a plane situated normal to the common axis of the cones, ions of different mass produced parabolic traces having common vertices and focal lengths proportional to the mass of the ions. This so-called "parabola spectrograph" is still in limited use today, being the preferred form in certain restricted classes of problems (62, 144) (Fig. 3).

The ions were detected initially by the fluorescence that they excited when they impinged on a Willemite screen placed normal to the beam, and permanent records were obtained by photographing the screen with a conventional camera through the glass envelope of the apparatus (69). Detection of positive ions by their direct action on a photographic plate was accomplished first by Königsberger and Kuchewski in 1910 (199), and, a year later, the same technique was applied by Thomson independently to the so-called positive-ray apparatus (354).

With the original positive-ray apparatus it was shown that, within the limits imposed by the resolving power of the apparatus, all atoms of each element have one or another of a limited number of well-defined masses; atomic weights, previously determined by chemical methods, are not statistical means of a large range of weights distributed about some average value. This finding, the discovery of the isotopic constitution of the elements, reconciled Dalton's hundred-year-old hypothesis that all atoms of each chemical element have precisely the same mass as all the others with the conflicting suspicions of Crookes, Soddy, and others, based on the chemistry of the naturally radioactive elements, that the chemical elements are mixtures of atoms of identical chemical properties but unequal masses.

The first instrument designed to be used as a mass spectrometer was built by Aston in 1920.* With this instrument, the masses of the elements could be determined with an accuracy of about 1:1000, although the intrinsic mass resolving power by modern criteria was only about 1:130. With this instrument Aston began the systematic study of the isotopic constitution of the elements, beginning with neon and continuing to in-

---

*For a long time the term mass spectrograph has been used to denote an instrument in which ions are detected by their impingement on a photographic plate, the term mass spectrometer denoting an apparatus in which the ions are detected electrically. The distinction seems to us to be of mainly historical interest, and we abandon it in favor of the simpler definition already given.

clude most of the periodic table. This study marked the beginning of mass spectrometry as we now use the term.

For twenty years, mass spectrometry was exclusively a research tool. In Great Britain and continental Europe, mainly in Germany, work was concentrated on the measurement of atomic masses; by 1927 Aston had established the main features of the packing fraction curve of the atomic nuclei (5), and through work in Germany, notably by J. Mattauch and his collaborators, atomic masses have been measured with steadily increasing precision until today atomic masses are determined to an accuracy approaching 10^{-5} atomic weight unit. In the United States, on the other hand, attention has been directed more to the measurement of isotope *abundances,* using electrical means rather than photographic plates to measure the intensities of the ion beams and working at comparatively modest mass resolving power. Work in this field was done originally by Dempster (70), followed first by Bainbridge (9) and a little later by Bleakney (33), by Nier (259, 263), and more recently by many others. Perhaps the ultimate in this work so far is the work of Urey and his colleagues, who have (for example) measured oxygen isotope ratios in fossil $CaCO_3$ with such precision that they can establish the temperature of the water in which the fossil deposits were laid down to an accuracy better than 1°C. (see Section 3.3.4).

1.5. POTENTIALITIES AND SCOPE OF MASS SPECTROMETRY

We have already mentioned the use of mass spectrometers to make precise measurements of nuclear masses. Such measurements serve as an invaluable check on the energy balance in nuclear reactions, since a discrepancy between the observed yields and those predicted on the basis of the masses of the reacting particles suggests the presence of additional particles whose existence might otherwise be unsuspected (Section 3.3.6). In principle, a sufficiently precise mass measurement should be enough to determine uniquely the empirical chemical formula of any chemical compound, since (for example) CH_2 and N, and S^{32} and O_2, do not have precisely the same molecular weights.* In practice, chemical analysis by precise mass determination is a field of great promise that is just beginning to be explored (Section 3.2.2.).

We have also mentioned the use of mass spectrometers to make precise measurements of isotope abundances. Such measurements may establish the age and the origin of mineral deposits; they permit tracing the career of an isotopically tagged element through a biochemical process *in vivo,* through chemical processes to establish yield data, or through

* The precise weights are $CH_2 = 14.0201051$, $N = 14.0075263$; $S^{32} = 31.9822401$; $O_2 = 32.000000$.

the processes of abrasive wear or weathering. Study of the mass spectra of isotopically enriched compounds has been used to investigate the strengths of the various chemical bonds within a molecule. Yet the largest field of application of mass spectrometry, on the basis of the number of instruments involved, is in problems which involve neither very high mass resolution nor the measurement of isotope ratios. These fields include the routine chemical analysis of solids, liquids, and gases (136, 167, 225), as well as studies of ionization potentials of both whole molecules and radicals and appearance potentials of molecular fragments (which yields information on chemical bond strengths). In some analytical problems the mass spectrometer is uniquely powerful; extreme examples are the analysis of transient phenomena in chemical reactions, where the mass spectrometer may be able to perform an analysis in less than a tenth of a second (including the time required to admit the sample); leak detection, where a mass spectrometer may be able to detect a tracer gas such as helium in abundances of a fraction of a part per million and in a few tenths of a second; and problems such as air pollution (244, 271, 285, 324), in which the amount of sample available is very limited (10^{-12} to 10^{-15} g.) or occurs at very low vapor pressure (10^{-11} mm. Hg). It will be obvious from the above that mass spectrometry is not restricted to any field of application. On the contrary, it is difficult to name any fields having to do with the intrinsic properties of materials in which mass spectrometry does not contribute to an important degree.

2. Mass Spectrometer Instrumentation

Mass spectrometer instrumentation occurs in great variety as regards both the instrumentation itself and the field of application. We regard it as important to discuss the instrumentation itself in enough detail to permit its selection for, and use on, a particular problem with a minimum of lost motion on the part of the reader whose main interests will presumably lie elsewhere. We shall discuss here, however, only the instruments which have proved their usefulness in the field, mentioning the more exotic instruments in less detail, in a later section, and only to the extent that they possess features which make them peculiarly suited to certain special problems.

2.1. MASS RESOLVING SYSTEMS

In studying the behavior of mass resolving systems, it is convenient to define as an optic axis the trajectory of a particle of a stipulated mass m_0, which moves away from an object point in a given direction and with a given velocity v_0. One then examines the behavior of a neighboring particle of mass m_0 $(1 + \gamma)$, moving with a velocity v_0 $(1 + \beta)$, which intersects the optic axis, at the object point, at an angle α (radian), where α, β, and γ are dimensionless variables assumed to be small compared to unity. The departure of the neighboring particle from the optic axis, x, may then be expressed as a power series:

$$x = \sum A_{ijk} \, \alpha^i \, \beta^j \, \gamma^k \tag{1}$$

where the A_{ijk} are functions of the space coordinates of the neighboring particle (measured along the optic axis) and the various parameters of the mass resolving system under study. In this approach, the point at which $A_{100} = 0$ is defined as the focal point, and A_{010} and A_{001}, both evaluated at the focal point, are defined as the velocity dispersion and the mass dispersion, respectively.

Since α, β, and γ are small compared to unity, the power series, eq. (1), converges rapidly, and the main features of the mass resolving system can be understood by studying only the first-order terms. Excellent discussions of first-order theory have been given by Barnard (12) and by Ewald and Hintenberger (91). In the actual design of a mass resolving system, however, failure to consider the high-order aberrations may lead to a mass resolving system whose performance falls disastrously short of what is desired. This fact, fully appreciated only recently, has led to extensive treatments of second-order aberrations and their effects during the last few years by König, Hintenberger, Wende, Voorhies, Johnson and Nier, and Robinson (151, 154, 181, 264, 299, 300, 369).

2.1.1. Single-Focusing Magnetic Analyzers. An ion of mass m (atomic weight units), of kinetic energy V (volts), and moving in a plane normal to a magnetic field of strength B (gauss) exhibits a trajectory whose radius of curvature r (centimeters) is given by

$$r = \frac{144}{B} \sqrt{mV}. \tag{2}$$

It can be shown further that a group of ions which are homogeneous in energy, emanating from a point and moving in a plane normal to a magnetic field, will converge again to an approximate focus ($A_{100} = 0$, in the notation of Section 2.1) after moving through a rather simple orbit in which the size of the orbit—that is, the scale of the figure—varies with the radii of curvature, and hence with the masses, of the ions involved. Thus the foci of ions having different masses will occur at different points in space, and ions of one mass can be distinguished from those of another mass by the location of their focal points. The locus of the various focal points defines a line, and ions may be detected either by placing a photographic emulsion on the focal line or by placing a slit on the focal line such that ions of only one mass at a time can pass through the slit and be detected by appropriate means located behind it. Under the assumption of uniform magnetic field and rectilinear magnetic field boundaries, the theory enunciated almost simultaneously by Barber (11), by Stephens (337), and by Herzog (146) describes the focusing action of the fields; the principle involved is shown in Fig. 4. The first

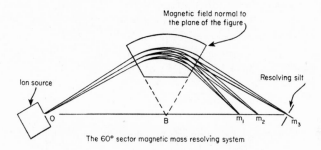

The 60° sector magnetic mass resolving system

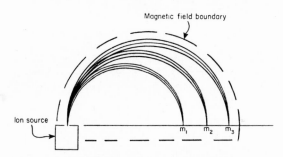

The 180° sector magnetic mass resolving system

FIG. 4. Typical magnetic mass resolving systems. In the 60° sector, the foci lie on the line OB extended. In the 180° sector, the focal line passes through the object slit and normal to the direction in which the ions pass through it. In both systems, $m_3 > m_2 > m_1$.

mass spectrometer of this type, built by Dempster (70) after an earlier instrument by Classen (56), employed a sector angle of a full 180° so that the entire resolving system was immersed in the magnetic field. Nearly all the instruments that have been intended for routine mixture analysis in the United States have been of this totally immersed 180° sector type until very recently. However, since the simplest theory calls for the mass resolving power in a sector-type mass spectrometer to be independent of the sector angle, there are sometimes points in favor of using small sector angles because the size, weight, and cost of the magnet are thereby reduced.

Equation (1) illustrates that the resolving power of a mass spectrometer will be improved by making as many as possible of the aberration coefficients, A_{ij0}, vanish while maintaining the mass dispersion coefficient A_{001}, at a constant value. It will be clear from eq. (2) that it is impossible to make the velocity dispersion term, A_{010}, vanish, in a simple magnetic sector instrument, without permitting the mass dispersion term, A_{001}, to vanish too, since mass and kinetic energy enter similarly into the expression for the radius of curvature. It is possible, however, to cause the second-order angular aberration coefficient, A_{200}, to vanish either by employing a nonuniform magnetic field or by using curved boundaries for the magnetic field (12, 151, 198). An interesting variant of this scheme has been devised by Alekseevskii *et al.* (2), who use a nonuniform sector-shaped magnetic field in which the gradient is chosen so that A_{001} (the mass dispersion), and, from eq. (2), A_{010} (the velocity dispersion), becomes very large without a corresponding increase in A_{020} (the angular aberration). These arrangements are useful only in cases where the energy spread in the ion beam is so low that the velocity dispersion term, A_{010}, makes essentially no contribution to the image width. Such cases are not very frequent; for this reason, the use of shaped or nonuniform magnetic fields in simple magnetic sector instruments is helpful only in special problems.

2.1.2. Double-Focusing Mass Spectrometers. The simple magnetic sector mass spectrometers (including Dempster's 180° form) are useful only in cases where the ion beam is very nearly homogeneous in energy, as we have seen. Often it is possible, by exercising care, to produce an ion beam whose energy is sufficiently homogeneous that no serious irresolution results from energy inhomogeneities. Unfortunately there are also many situations in which it is impossible to produce an ion beam sufficiently homogeneous in energy to satisfy the requirements of a particular problem in a simple magnetic sector instrument, and in these cases the so-called double-focusing mass resolving systems must be used. These are resolving systems in which, in the notation of Section 2.1, the velocity dispersion term, A_{010}, vanishes. Aston's "second mass spectrograph" (7) was arranged so as to compensate for velocity dispersion in the ion beam, even to second order ($A_{010} = A_{020} = 0$), although it was unique in that it made no provision for angular focusing (A_{100} did not vanish at the point at which the detector was located). Bainbridge devised an instrument which circumvented the velocity spread in the ion beam not by a true double-focusing system but by an energy monochromator placed, at substantial cost in sensitivity, ahead of a simple 180° magnetic sector arrangement (346); the complete first-order theory of double-focusing instruments was worked out by Herzog (146) and by Mattauch and Herzog (234) in 1934. Meanwhile Dempster had built one double-focusing mass spectrometer (71), and Bainbridge and Jordan another (10), to be followed shortly by Mattauch and Herzog (235). The Mattauch instrument is unique in that it is double-focusing for all masses simultaneously and in that, with it, a theoretically unlimited range of masses

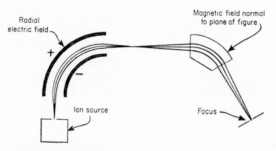

The Nier Tandem double-focusing mass spectrometer

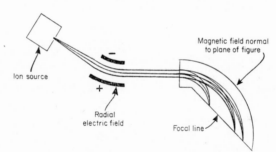

The Mattauch-Herzog double-focusing mass spectrometer

Fig. 5. Two tandem double-focusing mass spectrometers in current use. Nier's form is double-focusing for only one mass at a time and is usually used with a resolving slit and electrometer at the focus; the Mattauch-Herzog form is double-focusing to first order for all masses simultaneously and can be used with either a single resolving slit or with plates to cover an extended mass range (see Fig. 17).

can be recorded at one time; experimentally, instruments have been built to cover a range of masses as great as 40:1 (Fig. 5).

The first-order theory of double-focusing instruments has been extended by Hintenberger et al. (154) to cover a special form in which the second-order angular aberration coefficient, A_{200}, vanishes, and an embodiment of one form of this instrument has been built by Nier (261). Nier's instrument is distinguished from Mattauch's in that it is double-focusing for only one mass at a time. Studies of second-order aberrations applicable to the case of rectilinearly bounded uniform fields have been published by Johnson and Nier (181, 264), by Voorhies (369), and by Hintenberger *et al.* (154); the last treatment, in particular, is very general. The effect of curved field boundaries in a double-focusing resolving system has been discussed by Robinson (299) and by König and Hintenberger (198). The treatment illustrates the importance of controlling the effective radius of curvature of any stray magnetic field that may be present, a conclusion that had already been enunciated from quite different points of view by Paul (273), by König and Hintenberger (197), and by Herzog (147). Detailed discussions of some of the effects of second-order aberrations have been published by Robinson (300).

We have mentioned the necessity of using a double-focusing resolving system in cases where the energy spread in the ion beam is objectionable. Satisfaction of the requirements for double focusing does not, however, fix all the parameters that are available; the designer may then choose the free parameters so as to minimize the second-order geometrical (A_{200}), second-order velocity (A_{020}), or cross-product (A_{110}) aberration coefficients as well. Thus it is always possible to obtain higher performance in a double-focusing instrument than in a simple magnetic sector instrument, simply because the designer has more parameters at his disposal.

In all single- and double-focusing mass spectrometers in which the ion beam passes through regions of varying magnetic field strength, excepting only the Mattauch type, the image of a line source is not a line but a curve, as has been shown by Berry (27). Since the imaging in practically all mass spectrometers is astigmatic, the result of this curvature is that the image is not only curved but somewhat blurred. In some instruments this effect may dominate some or all of the other aberrations.

There is one mass resolving system, and thus far only one, in which the focal properties are rigorously invariant to changes in either the initial direction of motion or the initial energy of the ion beam. That is the cycloidal-focusing mass spectrometer (Fig. 6), treated first by Bleakney and Hipple (34), and later by Mariner and Bleakney (228), by Monk *et al.* (251), and by Robinson and Hall (301). This resolving system is not only free of geometrical and velocity aberrations to all orders of approximation—that is, all the A_{ijk} of eq. (1) except A_{001} vanish simultaneously—but it is also free of the image curvature treated by Berry. In cases where the relative inaccessibility of the ion source and the ion collector is not a factor, this resolving system shows exceptional promise, since, as Robinson and Hall have shown, it is possible to build a mass spectrometer of mass resolving power that is adequate for many purposes and shows quite acceptable analytical accuracy, in a very modest size. Mass spectrometers based on cycloidal-focusing resolving systems have come into wide use within the pass year or two in a great variety of problems in the analysis of gas and vapor mixtures, and they are beginning to be used in isotope ratio measurement and even in the analysis of some metals and alloys (Section 3.3.3.).

2.1.3. Miscellaneous Limitations on Resolving Power. The effects of angular and velocity deviations of the ion beam on resolving power have been studied in detail. Additional factors which are not by any means always negligible are gas scattering, space charge, and nonuniform elec-

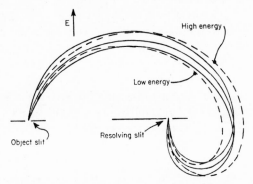

FIG. 6. Cycloidal ion trajectories in crossed electric and magnetic fields, illustrating the angular and velocity focusing in this system. The solid lines represent ions of median energy injected at different angles; the dotted lines represent the trajectories of ions injected with more and with less kinetic energy than the median. The entire trajectory is immersed in a magnetic field normal to the plane of the figure, and an electric field is superposed in the direction shown.

tric and magnetic fields. Gas scattering is especially noticeable in cases where it is desired to measure a weak ion beam adjacent to a very strong one, as in the search for rare isotopes of the elements to abundance limits several orders of magnitude smaller than that of the nearest neighboring isotope (61).

When examined in detail, the intensity of resolved ion beams is seen not to diminish sharply to zero at a well-defined point but to be surrounded out to a considerable distance by a weak halo which consists both of ions scattered out of the resolved beam by collisions with the residual gas in the vacuum system and of ions formed in the residual gas itself by such collisions. The intensities of these halos (which give rise to long "tails" on the peaks as they are recorded) can be reduced by several measures. Obviously they are reduced by operation under the best possible vacuum conditions. They are reduced by operating with high accelerating voltages on the ion beam; although the nature of the scattering process undoubtedly depends on the nature of the residual gases in the vacuum system, high accelerating voltages help to some degree, regardless of the details of the mechanism. Probably the most successful means for combating gas scattering is the dual mass spectrometer concept due to White and Collins (389). Resolving systems of this type consist essentially of two simple magnetic sector resolving systems in series, arranged so that ions scattered out of the beam in the first resolving system cannot enter the second system and reach the ion collector without being scattered again in the second resolving system. Thus the scattered ion intensity is proportional not to the scattering probability (as it is in a single sector) but to the *square* of the scattering probability, which may be smaller by a factor of as much as 10^4.

In any mass spectrometer, the positive charge carried by the ion beam gives rise to electric fields which can disturb the focal properties. It can be shown that the first-order effect of space charge, in both magnetic sector (296) and the cycloidal-focusing (298) instruments, is simply to shift the focal point so that it no longer coincides with the plane of the resolving slit, leaving the quality of the focus approximately undisturbed, so that in instruments which are to be used continuously under reasonably constant conditions the effects of space charge can be compensated by appropriate relocation of the resolving slit. This is sometimes done in mass spectrometers intended for large-scale electromagnetic separation of isotopes. A second measure which is helpful is to take advantage of the fact that the ion beam travels in a potential maximum of its own making and thus tends to trap any free electrons which may be present. Free electrons formed in the resolving system by collision of the ion beam with residual gas may be trapped so effectively as to mitigate the effects of ion space charge to an important degree. A third measure useful in combating space charge is to introduce electric fields or field gradients of the appropriate nature to produce a compensating displacement of the focal point, thus pulling the focal point back into coincidence with the resolving slit. This method of space-charge compensation is available in principle on any mass spectrometer but has been used successfully only on the cycloidal-focusing type (298), perhaps because the cycloidal-focusing type is the only one in which this method of space-charge compensation can be used without introducing special electrodes for the purpose.

In designing any ion-optical system, the designer assumes a particular combination of electric and/or magnetic fields. Anything which causes the fields to depart from their assumed nature may disturb the focal properties either by causing the focal point to move without substantial deterioration of the image quality, or by causing the image quality to deteriorate, or both. Svartholm and Siegbahn (345) have discussed the focal point shift due to a radial gradient in the magnetic field of a magnetic sector instrument, and Robinson (297) has shown that the first-order effect of field nonuniformities in a cycloidal-focusing instrument can be a simple shift in the focal point under a considerable range of conditions. It seems quite probable that gradients which are uniform through any normal section of the ion beam will do no more than shift the focal point, whereas gradients which are not constant through a normal section can impair the image quality, although this has not been demonstrated analytically to be a generally valid principle.

The usual cause of unexpected electric field gradients is isolated surface charges on the parts of the mass spectrometer to which the ion beam is exposed, due to insulating surface deposits which are often too thin to be visible. As regards the initial cleanliness of the surfaces, Barnard (12) states that chemical cleaning seems largely to avoid such surface deposits; Aston (6) found that gold plating made the deposits negligible in his instruments. After a period of use, however, the metal surfaces in a mass spectrometer will become coated with material which is usually an insulator, regardless of how carefully the surface may have been cleaned initially. The origin and detailed nature of this material are obscure, although it is generally felt that it originates in the action of the ion beam on the residual gases in the resolving system or adsorbed on its walls and that it is probably a hydrocarbon polymer of some sort (90). Fortunately this material is usually a poor enough insulator that it causes no trouble at temperatures well above 200°C., so that trouble from this source can often be avoided simply by heating the surfaces exposed to the ion beam. There is some evidence, indeed, that operation at elevated temperatures can sometimes prevent the formation of such deposits altogether (89).

2.1.4. Metastable Ions. When a molecular ion is formed by electron bombardment, the molecule nearly always acquires some energy in excess of the minimum required for ionization, this excess energy being distributed among the various possible modes and levels of excitation. Many molecular ions are metastable with respect to such excess energies and so may undergo fragmentation during their course through the mass resolving system (156, 157, 311). Such metastable fragmentations may be triggered by high electric field gradients or by collisions with residual gases in the resolving system (240, 242, 309) as well as by purely statistical considerations, so that the nature of the metastable processes, and the positions at which metastable ions appear in the mass spectrum, will vary somewhat from one instrument to another even of the same basic design. The process most frequently observed, however, is one in which the disintegration occurs soon after the ion has acquired its full kinetic energy and before substantial mass dispersion has occurred. In that case each fragment, carrying that portion of the original kinetic energy corresponding to its mass, appears as a more or less well-resolved ion but in an anomalous position in the spectrum. The metastable transition of n-butane, for example, may be written

$$n—C_4H_{10}^+ \rightarrow CH_3 + C_3H_7^+ \tag{3}$$

where the C_3H_7 fragment carries 43/58 of the original kinetic energy. In a simple magnetic sector resolving system (including the 180° form) in which the mass dispersion depends not on the mass alone but on the *product* of the mass and the kinetic energy of the ion, the C_3H_7 fragment thus appears not at mass 43, but at mass $43 \times 43/58$, or mass 31.9.

In cycloidal-focusing instruments, the behavior of metastable ions is somewhat more complex. No adequate treatment has been published, although the results of an unpublished study have been summarized by Robinson and Hall; the main conclusions are that the fragments from metastable transitions within the ion source appear at positions corresponding to their true masses, whereas the products of metastable transitions in the resolving system may appear on the mass scale either at, above, or below the mass of the original ion, depending on the part of the trajectory in which the transition occurs. It appears that this peculiar property of the cycloidal-focusing system should make it a particularly convenient one for the study of metastable processes, although no such studies have been reported as yet.

Metastable ions can be troublesome in some situations, since they appear in the spectrum as poorly resolved peaks which may interfere with the peaks it is desired to measure. Since they possess less kinetic energy than an unfragmented peak they can be rejected, usually fairly easily, by interposing appropriate potential barriers between the resolving slit and the ion collector (107) or by arranging the relative potentials of the ion source and the ion collector so that only ions having essentially the full design value of kinetic energy can reach the collector (157) (Fig. 7).

2.1.5. Mass Discrimination. With exceptions that are too few to be important here, the imaging in all mass spectrometer resolving systems is essentially astigmatic; the electric and/or magnetic fields act as cylindrical lenses; an ion which possesses an initial velocity component normal to the plane of its principal motion will retain that velocity component throughout its trajectory. Thus ions which originate at a given point on the object slit converge not to a corresponding point image but to a line image at the resolving slit, the intensity distribution along the line image being broader, the higher the initial velocity and the longer the transit time of the particle. Since the resolving slit is of limited length, it will very often be the case that the line image is longer than the resolving slit, so that the ions which possess high-velocity components directed normal to the plane of their principal motion will be lost. This phenomenon is called discrimination, the term originating in the fact that the resolving system discriminates against ions in which the product

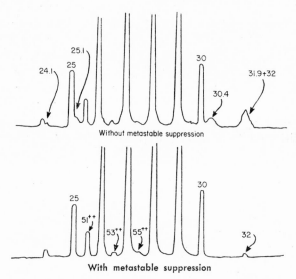

Fig. 7. Metastable ions and their suppression. The figure shows portions of the *n*-butane spectrum without metastable suppression and with metastable suppression. The small peak at mass 32 is due to a slight oxygen contamination. The peaks with apparent masses 25.5, 26.5, and 27.5 are not metastables but are due to doubly charged ions of masses 51, 53, and 55, respectively.

(initial velocity) × (transit time) is large. The magnitude of the loss tends to be proportional simply to the mean normal velocity multiplied by the transit time of the ion in the resolving system. Since the transit time of an ion is inverse to the magnetic field strength, discrimination is noticeably greater at low magnetic field strengths than at higher fields. For given slit lengths it tends to be independent of the size of a magnetic sector instrument, depending only on the magnetic field strength and the sector angle, since the ion transit time can be expressed as a function of only these two quantities. Discrimination effects tend to be larger in a cycloidal-focusing instrument than in the 180° magnetic sector type, as Robinson and Hall have pointed out, because the ion transit time in the former instrument is just twice as long as in the latter when the magnetic field strengths are equal.

For a given initial kinetic energy, the mean velocity of an ion is inverse to the square root of its mass, whereas the transit time in a magnetic instrument varies directly with the mass (for constant magnetic field strength), so that the discrimination effects are larger for heavy ions than for lighter ones of the same initial energy. The initial disordered kinetic energy of an ionized whole molecule is essentially just that due to its thermal motion; in conventional ion sources, which operate at temperatures of 400° to 500°K., this is at most a few tens of millivolts (23). But the random initial energies imparted to fragment ions by the Franck-Condon process (108) may be a volt or more (248), so that fragment ions are much more strongly discriminated against than are ionized whole molecules. Thus the ratio of the intensities of fragment ions to whole molecule (parent) ions will vary with magnetic field strength, sector angles, operating temperature, and other factors. A detailed discussion of discrimination has been given by Berry (24) and by Washburn and Berry (379).

2.1.6. Vacuum Problems. Vacuum systems in mass spectrometry have different requirements from those used in, for example, high-energy particle accelerators or even some ultrahigh vacuum apparatus. Under the best possible vacuum conditions there will be residual background gases and vapors which give rise to a background mass spectrum when no sample is admitted. Differences in gross background pressure between one system and another are often accounted for by large differences in the height of only a few of the background peaks; for example, differences between a metal vacuum system employing an oil diffusion pump plus activated charcoal trap without bakeout, an all-glass system with mercury diffusion pump plus a liquid nitrogen trap but without bakeout, and an all-glass or metal-gasketed metal vacuum system with mercury diffusion pump, liquid nitrogen trap, and prolonged bakeout are likely to consist largely in differences in the size of the water vapor background, there being disappointingly little difference in the magnitudes of the other background peaks although the differences in gross background pressure may be two or three orders of magnitude. Gasketing materials such as Teflon or polyethylene, though perfectly acceptable in ordinary vacuum practice, may be very slightly permeable to certain gases (84, 266, 267, 293) and may be intolerable in mass spectrometers intended for measurement of small amounts of such gases (oxygen, for example). It appears that much of the hydrocarbon background in a mass spectrometer can originate in the forepump even if an oil diffusion pump is used, and that most of the vapors which give rise to hydrocarbon backgrounds are often introduced during pumpdown; certainly it is well established that the magnitude of the hydrocarbon background depends on the nature and the condition of the forepump fluid (159) and that the hydrocarbon backgrounds are reduced by inserting a high-impedance trap between the forepump and the diffusion pump (282). It is also well established that, in mass spectrometers using oil diffusion pumps, the magnitude of the hydrocarbon background depends much less on the gross vapor pressure of the diffusion pump fluid than it does on its thermal stability and on details of the pump construction (282). Silicone diffusion pump fluids appear to give somewhat greater difficulty from insulating deposits than do straight organic fluids and are seldom used.

High-temperature bakeout of the vacuum envelope during pumpdown is often used as an aid to obtaining very low gross background pressures. Baking of critical surfaces at temperatures much above 250°C. in the presence of as much as 10^{-6} mm. Hg of water vapor or other oxidants can cause formation of insulating deposits on the electrodes (288, 377) and must be done with caution, particularly in instruments operating at low voltages, since they are generally very sensitive to any insulating surface deposits.

Steps that have been shown to be useful in reducing mass spectrometer backgrounds are: (1) inserting of a high-impedance trap between the forepump and the diffusion pump and exercising care that, during pumpdown, the system is left on the forepump alone for the shortest possible time; (2) using a liquid nitrogen trap, preferably of the type described by Meissner (238), which has the best possible communication with the part of the vacuum system in which backgrounds are to be minimized (a cold trap at dry ice temperature can cause "hangup" of water vapor, and there are many situations in which such a trap will do more harm than good); (3) minimizing the number, the size, and the chemical reactivity of any heated metallic surfaces. Carbon monoxide backgrounds have been shown to be generated, at least in part, by reaction of oxidants such as water vapor with carburized tungsten emitters (129), and it has been shown that CO backgrounds are often reduced sharply by the use of rhenium emitters instead, since rhenium does not form carbides that are stable at high temperatures in vacuum (303). Carbon monoxide backgrounds can also be generated at the hot filament of an ionization gauge. Hydrogen backgrounds can be generated by thermal decomposition of hydrocarbon background molecules on a hot filament; particularly when a gas discharge vacuum gauge of the Penning type is used, in which the voltages are high enough that extensive stripping of the hydrocarbon background molecules can occur, the hydrogen backgrounds may be reduced markedly by turning the vacuum gauges off during routine operation (193).

2.2. THE ION SOURCE

Ion sources used in mass spectrometry have been built in tremendous variety, nearly every independent investigator having his own favorite variant of some basic design. Almost all of them fall into one or another of four basic classes, however: the gas ion source, the crucible source, the surface ionization source, and the spark source. In the first two, ionization is effected by an electron beam moving through a cloud of vapor which is (in the first case) admitted to the ion source as such or (in the second) evaporated from an internal crucible provided for the purpose. Thus the external inlet system may be thought of as an accessory to the gas ion source, and we shall discuss it in that context.

2.2.1. The Gas Ion Source. The first ion sources used with gases and volatile materials were simple arcs, and such ion sources are still used, though not widely and only in double-focusing mass spectrometers which can accommodate the very wide energy spread of the ion beam produced by them.* In simple magnetic sector instruments, however, the enormous energy spread of the ion beam formed in a high-voltage arc is intolerable; the ion source must be of the type in which the energy spread of the ion beam is inherently small. The first gas ion source which produced a beam having low energy spread and which was satisfactory in other respects was due to Bleakney and has served as the basic pattern for almost every succeeding one (Fig. 8). In instruments such as the 180° sector and cycloidal-focusing forms, where the ion source is immersed in a strong magnetic field, this kind of ion source is outstandingly successful. In the sector-type instruments, however, where the ion source is removed from the main magnetic field, magnetic collimation of the ionizing electron beam requires a supplementary magnet at the ion source; this introduces a multiplicity of problems, some of which may involve compromises between two mutually incompatible requirements, and all of which tend to be rather subtle. There have been a few attempts (13, 55, 130, 131) to avoid these problems by doing away with the magnetic field at the ion source altogether, using electrostatic collimating means for the electron beam, and still achieving a nearly monoenergetic ion beam, but such attempts have thus far met with limited success.

In any ion source, attention must be given to the materials used.

---

* Ion sources used in mass spectrometers intended for the bulk separation of isotopes constitute a special and separate class which we shall not attempt to discuss.

First of all, the materials must be nonmagnetic if the ion source is one which requires a magnetic field for collimating the ionizing electron beam. They must not catalyze chemical reactions in a mixed sample; they must not react chemically with a constituent of a mixed sample and thus cause its depletion in a mixture; and they must not absorb a component of a sample and so cause its disappearance from one mixture and

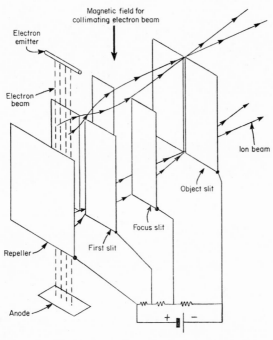

FIG. 8. The Bleakney ion source. In preferred practice the volume defined by the repeller and first slit is often enclosed except for the openings required for the entrance and exit of the electron beam, the admission of sample, and the withdrawal of the ion beam. Additional electrodes are frequently provided for controlling the angular divergence of the ion beam and for other purposes.

its reappearance in one subsequently introduced. Since the voltages used in an ion source may be low, insulating deposits must be avoided, which requires the utmost attention to every detail of choice of material, cleaning procedures, and operating techniques. The material most widely used in ion sources is Nichrome V, a proprietary alloy whose main constituents are nickel and chromium in the ratio 4:1 plus small amounts of Si, Mn, and Al together with the minor contaminants usual in most metals.

In an ion source which is to be used conveniently in chemical analysis of gas or vapor mixtures, it is important that the ion currents due to a given substance be linear with the partial pressure of the substance in question and invariant to the nature or the partial pressure of the other components of any chemical mixture in which the substance in question occurs, and that the fragmentation pattern of ions from a given substance be stable in time. These requirements place stringent limits on both the design and the operation of ion sources which are to be used for chemical mixture analysis. First, they must be operated at pressures at which the behavior of a given gas molecule is determined largely by its intrinsic properties (mass, temperature) and those of the ion source; the pressure must be low enough that collisions of a given gas molecule with other molecules are negligibly infrequent. Second, the ion source must be operated under conditions in which the electric fields due to ionic space charge exert only negligible effects on its behavior; otherwise the ion currents produced by a given component of a gas mixture will depend on whether the remaining components have a large ionization cross section and so influence the fields strongly (for example, n-butane) or have a very small ionization cross section and exert smaller effects (for example, helium). A detailed study of the effects of space charge in an ion source of the Bleakney type has been given by Brubaker (42).

The most delicate test for difficulty due to space charge in an ion source is the gas interference test due to Washburn. In this test, a gas sample is introduced at a given pressure, and the ion current, I_0, on a given peak is noted. An additional amount of some other gas is then introduced, and the change, ΔI, in the intensity of the original peak is noted. The amount of gas interference, in per cent, is $100 \, \Delta I/I_0$. A well-designed ion source, properly operated, will show gas interferences of a few tenths of a per cent to perhaps 3%; larger interferences are an indication that trouble may be encountered if it is attempted to use the ion source for chemical mixture analyses.

Gas interferences in the ion source proper are due directly to ion space charge (assuming no chemical reactions) and so are exaggerated by high pressures, by high electron beam currents, and by low applied electric fields in the ionizing region of the ion source (which may be due to the charging of insulating surface films as well as to low applied voltages). Occasionally gas interferences will be found which are relatively independent of electrode voltages or electron beam currents; such interferences are usually in the gas inlet system and not in the ion source.

In an ion source employing a magnetic field for collimating the electron beam, the ions undergo some magnetic deflections before emerging, the deflections being higher for lighter ions than for heavier ones and higher for low-energy ions than for those with more energy. These deflections result in what has been called mass discrimination (more usually, simply "discrimination"), which is a phenomenon in which the ion source does not produce ions of all masses or all energies with equal efficiency, even in cases where the ionization cross sections may be identical. Discrimination is minimized by making the radii of curvature of the ions within the ion source as large as possible compared to the dimensions of the ion source itself; compact design, the weakest magnetic field consistent with satisfactory collimation of the electron beam, and the use of the highest possible electric field strengths in the ion source all help to reduce discrimination. Holding the magnetic field in the ion source proportional to the magnetic field in the main resolving system (in cases where the two fields are separate) also helps to reduce discrimination, since it can then be arranged that the ions for which the resolving system is focused are also those which the ion source is producing with optimum efficiency. But after everything has been done that can be done, the measurement of *absolute* ionization cross sections, or *absolute* isotope ratios, with high precision, is probably the most difficult task in mass spectrometry and the one most strongly dependent on intangible skills of the experimenter.

In cases where the gas sample is admitted directly to the ionizing region, the sample pressure in the ionizing region, p_1, is given by

$$p_1 = Q \, (S_1^{-1} + S_2^{-1} + S_3^{-1}) \tag{4}$$

where Q is the sample admission rate, and S_1, S_2, and S_3 are the combined pumping speeds of the apertures connecting the ionizing region with the exterior of the ion source, the effective pump speed between the exterior of the ionizing region and the pumps, and the speed of the pumps themselves, respectively. Obviously, it is desirable for S_1 to be small compared to S_3, since, in that event, the term $1/S_1$ will be large compared to $1/S_3$, and the sample pressure in the ion source, and hence the sensitivity, will be relatively unaffected by changes in S_3 due to changes in power input, ambient temperatures, etc. Since the hot electron emitter also acts as a pump for reactive materials such as oxygen, it follows that S_1 should also be as small as possible compared to S_2. Making the communication between the ionizing region and the pumps (including the filament) as poor as possible is called *differential pumping*. With differential pumping, the mass spectra are relatively unaffected by chemical reactions at the electron emitter or by variations in the speed of the pumps. Without it, the chemical alteration of some samples by reaction at the filament may be very serious; without differential pumping, for example, the apparent oxygen content of air may be as little as 2 to 5%. One of the most serious objections to some of the newer time-of-flight resolving systems (Sections 4.1 and 4.2) is the impossibility of providing adequate differential pumping with them.

2.2.2. Sample Inlet Systems. Sample inlet systems for use with gas ion sources are divisible into two main functional classes: systems for batch sampling, and systems which employ continuous sample flow. They are also divisible into two classes on another basis: those intended for chemical mixture analysis, and those intended for measurement of isotope ratios. We shall first discuss some of the requirements that are fundamental to all of them.

We have already mentioned that the sample pressure within an ion source must be so low that intermolecular collisions are infrequent; that is to say, the gas transport through the ion source must be by free-molecule flow. In such flow, the partial pressure of a given component of a gas mixture will be proportional to the admission rate of that particular component and to the square root of its molecular weight, regardless of the partial pressure of the other components that may be present. If, now, the component flows into the ion source from a reservoir such that free-molecule flow occurs at the exit from the reservoir as well, the gas flow rate into the ion source will be proportional to the pressure in the reservoir and *inverse* to the square root of its molecular weight, being independent again of any other components that may be present. Thus if (and only if) the flow into the ion source from a reservoir is by free-molecule flow, the partial pressure of a particular gas in the ion source depends only on the intrinsic properties of the system and the partial pressure of that gas in the reservoir and is independent of the partial pressure of any other components that may be present. Under such conditions, light molecules flow out of a static sample reservoir faster than heavy ones, so that the composition of a heterogeneous mixture changes continually during an analysis; but such changes can be canceled out by careful programming. The important feature of such inlet systems is that a given initial partial pressure of (say) hydrogen will give a fixed indication at any stated future time regardless of whether the hydrogen is mixed with some other gases and regardless of the nature or the amount of the other gases present. Thus the mass spectra due to the various gases present are linearly superposable, a requirement that is almost indispensable for doing routine chemical mixture analysis, as Washburn has pointed out and as we shall shortly see.* (Fig. 9).

Under free-molecule flow conditions, the lighter components of a sample escape from a sample reservoir faster than the heavier com-

* A detailed treatment of gas flow conditions in the mass spectrometer has been given by Honig (161).

ponents. This means that, if the mixture under study is a mixture of (say) $C^{12}O_2$ and $C^{13}O_2$, the abundance ratio of the two will change continuously, and thus the intensity ratio of mass 44 to mass 45 will drift continuously during a measurement. To avoid the inaccuracies and

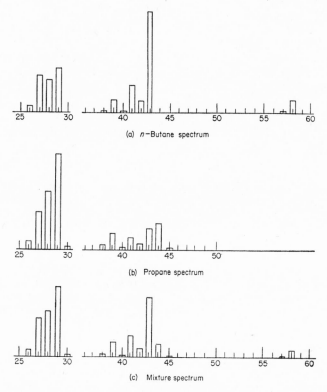

(a) *n*-Butane spectrum

(b) Propane spectrum

(c) Mixture spectrum

Fig. 9. Linear superposition of mass spectra. The spectra shown are (a) normal butane, (b) propane, and (c) a 1:1 mixture of normal butane and propane. Only the principal peaks are shown.

inconveniences that would result from such continual drifts, Halstead and Nier (134) have devised an inlet system particularly suited to measurement of isotope ratios. In this system, the gas flow out of the sample reservoir is not by free-molecule flow but by viscous flow, in which a gas mixture flows as a mixture, each component escaping from the sample reservoir at a rate proportional to the product of the flow rate of the mixture and its relative abundance in the mixture, and independent of its individual properties except as those individual properties may affect those of the mixture. We have seen that such inlet systems cannot be used either for chemical mixture analyses or for measurement of absolute isotope ratios without applying correction factors or using an internal standard, to be discussed (Section 3.1.2). What they are valuable for is the measurement of *relative* isotope ratios with high precision (Fig. 10).

In our discussion of free-molecule flow above, we have mentioned that the lighter components of a mixture escape from the sample reser-

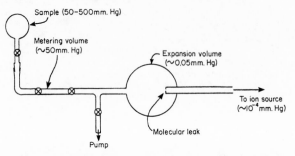

(a) Sample system for mixture analysis with linear superposition of spectra

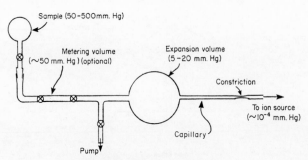

(b) Sample system for isotope-ratio measurements

Fig. 10. Mass spectrometer sample systems. The systems shown are intended (a) for mixture analysis with linearly superposable spectra and minimum gas interference, and (b) for isotope-ratio measurements with time-independent isotope ratios in the expansion volume. The pressures indicated are typical, although wide departures from the indicated pressures will be encountered in special cases.

voir faster than do those of higher molecular weight. We have implied that the intermixing by diffusion of the gases in the sample reservoir is sufficiently rapid that there can be no substantial differences in composition of the mixture between one part of the sample reservoir and another, particularly between the volume immediately upstream of the molecular leak and the main volume of the reservoir. Since interdiffusion rates vary inversely with pressure, it follows that this requirement is more easily satisfied at low pressures than at higher pressures, and this consideration usually limits the pressure in a static sample reservoir to a fraction of a millimeter of mercury. There is one type of sample system, however, in which quite adequate analytical accuracies can be obtained at pressures of 1 mm. Hg or somewhat above, and that is a continuous-flow system in which sample is admitted continuously to the sample volume through a viscous leak and most of the sample is pumped away through a bypass line in which viscous flow conditions are also

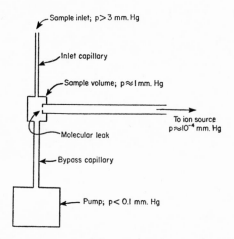

FIG. 11. Mass spectrometer inlet system for continuous sampling. The dimensions of the two capillaries will depend on the upstream sample pressure and the response time desired for the system.

maintained (378). In such a system, one relies on the rapid stirring that results from continuous flow, rather than interdiffusion, to keep the sample well mixed. It can be shown that, in such an arrangement, the pressure in the sample reservoir can be made essentially independent of the viscosity of the gas mixture, and, since the flow conditions are viscous, the partial pressure of each component of a mixture is proportional throughout the system to its abundance in the sample admitted. Such systems are not universally applicable, because the amount of sample demanded by them (sometimes as much as a few atmosphere-cubic centimeters per minute) may be awkward in some cases and because they are not always convenient for samples having vapor pressure substantially less than one atmosphere. For many purposes, however, they are extremely convenient, and for monitoring transient phenomena (as in process control, anesthesia control, lung pathology studies, etc.) they may be indispensable. Such systems have been built with over-all response times as short as a few tens of milliseconds and to operate with upstream sample pressures ranging from several atmospheres to a few millimeters Hg absolute (204) (Fig. 11).

In order for the sample to leave the sample reservoir by free-molecule flow through an aperture of reasonable diameter, the sample pres-

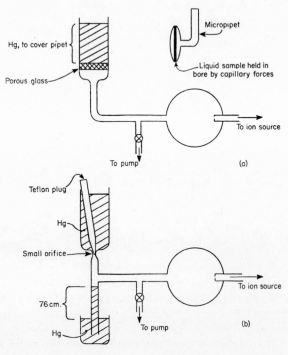

FIG. 12. Liquid sample introduction systems. In (a), the pipet is inserted through the mercury and touched to the porous glass disk, permitting the liquid sample to be drawn through the pores of the disk into the expansion volume. In (b), the Teflon plug is withdrawn and the pipet inserted quickly in its place until the pipet is emptied, when the Teflon plug is replaced. Sysstem (b) avoids hangup of sample in the porous surface of (a) but requires periodic replacement of the mercury in the well.

sure in the reservoir cannot greatly exceed 1 mm. Hg. Since most samples occur at substantially higher pressure, a great variety of techniques have been devised for introducing samples into the sample reservoir of the mass spectrometer. Those means include the gas pipet, the gas or (volatile) liquid ampoule with provisions for breaking the ampoule after it is sealed into the sample reservoir and the reservoir is evacuated, and the fixed-volume liquid pipet in which the sample is introduced either through a mercury-covered porous glass disk or through a mercury-sealed orifice (Fig. 12).

Inlet systems of the general types described above have been built to operate at temperatures ranging up to and beyond 250°C. permitting their use with materials whose volatility is too low to permit their introduction under quantitative conditions at room temperatures (40, 270, 313). There is a second situation in which high temperatures are advantageous; it is the situation where even a volatile sample tends to be adsorbed on the walls of the inlet system. Highly polar molecules tend to be strongly adsorbed on the walls of a vacuum system; molecules having an OH group (water, alcohols, etc.) are outstanding among such materials, and water itself is probably the most common source of trouble from adsorption effects. This difficulty, called "hangup," exhibits itself in two ways. First is the fact that, since a substantial fraction of a sample introduced may be adsorbed on the walls of the container and not participate in the vapor phase, the pressure of vapor in the sample reservoir (and hence the peak heights in the mass spectrometer) will have no reasonable or repeatable relation to the amount of sample introduced. Second is the fact that, since the material is tightly adsorbed on the walls, it cannot be pumped out in a reasonable length of time; it will adhere to the walls until another strongly adsorbed sample is introduced, whereupon some or all of the original sample, which has "hung up" on the walls, will be displaced (eluted) by the second, so that the vapor phase after introduction of the second sample may contain substantial amounts of samples which were run previously and which were thought to have been pumped out (186). This particular aspect of the phenomenon, in which the inlet system appears to remember samples previously run and which was first noticed by Aston in 1920 (6), is called "memory." The effect is particularly troublesome in analyses of mixtures of water (380) and/or alcohols (124), and it can be a source of serious error in measuring isotope ratios in such materials unless appropriate precautions are taken. The precautions, as worked out by Washburn et al. (380) and by Melton et al. (241), are essentially to see to it that each sample is adequately *flushed* out, by repeated introductions either of a strongly adsorbed flushing agent or of the succeeding sample, before analysis of the succeeding sample is attempted; one depends on elution, rather than simple pumping, to rid the inlet system of a sample. Rigorous cleanliness of the sample system is of course assumed.

Inlet systems as well as ion sources must use materials with which the sample does not react. Satisfaction of this requirement may demand special materials, or special operating temperatures, in many cases. In a stainless steel inlet system, for example, oxygen-bearing samples may be so seriously depleted of oxygen, even at 100°C., that no satisfactory analyses for oxygen can be done. In most metal inlet systems, catalytic effects can occur at elevated temperatures so that the character of a sample may be altered almost beyond recognition, and these effects may be enormously exaggerated by very thin surface films of metallic oxides, carbonates, etc. In still other situations, however, where the reaction is thermally reversible, it may be better to operate at elevated tempera-

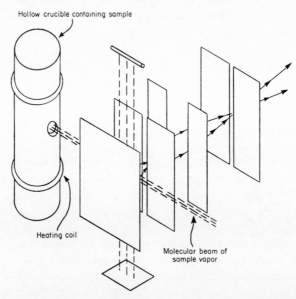

Hollow crucible containing sample

Heating coil

Molecular beam of sample vapor

FIG. 13. Adaptation of a crucible to an ion source otherwise similar to the Bleakney ion source of Fig. 8. The crucible is often surrounded by reflecting shields to reduce the power lost by radiation, and the array is preferably provided with perforated plates (not shown) to collimate the vapor beam from the crucible.

tures to prevent the samples from reacting out on the walls of the inlet system. For inlet systems that are to operate near room temperature, glass is usually used, although it exhibits hangup with some samples. Polyethylene inlet systems appear to exhibit much smaller adsorption effects than glass (84) when used at ordinary temperatures although they are not, of course, usable at elevated temperatures. Inlet systems for use with highly reactive or strongly adsorbed materials tend to require considerable tailoring of the materials and the operating conditions and techniques to the properties of the particular samples being run.

2.2.3. The Crucible Ion Source. In this form the sample, which may be a heavy wax, an oxide or other compound, a simple element, or an alloy, is placed in a crucible which can be heated to a temperature at which the vapor pressure of the material is appreciable, often well over 1000°C. (Fig. 13). The crucible may be internal to the ion source proper, so as to more or less flood the ionizing region with evaporated material (47, 232); more often the crucible proper is external to the ionizing region, and vapors from the crucible enter the ionizing region through apertures which serve to define a molecular beam (85). In either case, material evaporated into the ionizing region is ionized by an electron beam in a manner very similar to that used in the gas ion source. Such ion sources can be used with any material which will exhibit sufficient vapor pressure at temperatures below about 2000°K. and which can be brought to this temperature without decomposition that would impair the analytical results; they have the disadvantage that they may be less sensitive by a factor of 10^3 to 10^6 than the surface ionization ion source (Section 2.2.4) in terms of integrated ion current per unit mass of sample, when materials of low ionization potential are being run. Obviously they cannot be used in structural analyses of materials which decompose at the temperatures necessary for evaporation, such as proteins, amino acids, etc.

Crucible ion sources have been used in certain metallurgical analyses (43, 148, 162). They can be used directly for such work only if the ion current from each constituent of the sample is integrated until that constituent disappears; since the more volatile components of an alloy evaporate first, there is usually no time at which the composition of the vapor stream (and hence of the ion beam) is representative of the composition of the original sample. A second phenomenon which can make their use very awkward in metallurgical analyses is that the composition of the vapor phase over an alloy depends not only on the properties of the constituents but on the properties of the alloy, as such, and of the crucible. The vapor phase in equilibrium with pure Sb, for example, is very rich in the tetramer, Sb_4, but in equilibrium with InSb alloy the antimony in vapor phase is mainly monatomic Sb, and a small part of the Sb may appear as molecular InSb (43). Heated in an alundum crucible, elemental silicon may appear in the vapor phase largely as SiO, with a substantial AlO background from the crucible; in a tantalum crucible, SiO_2 may appear mainly as SiO, with a substantial TaO peak from the crucible (which phenomenon, incidentally, limits the operating temperature not at the melting point of Ta but at the melting point of TaO, some 1400° lower). Tungsten oxide, WO_3, has a strong tendency to polymerize to the trimer, W_3O_9, and thus appear in a part of the mass scale out of the reach of most mass spectrometers, near mass 1000 (21). Thus, although the crucible source is generally useful for isotopic assays, for research into vapor-liquid-solid equilibria in materials, or for routine metallurgical analyses by procedures worked out beforehand for each case, it is much less useful for general analytical work and almost useless in a broad-spectrum search for impurities.

From what has been said, it will be clear that the crucible ion source differs from the gas ion source mainly in that the sample is usually, and preferably, introduced as a molecular beam. There is no intrinsic need

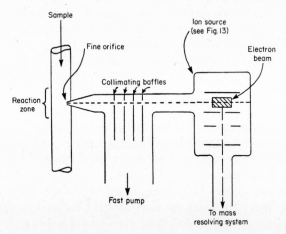

Fig. 14. Sampling arrangement adapted to the study of reaction kinetics. The collimating baffles and the fast pump operate together to minimize the number of uncollimated reaction products reaching the ion source. The reaction zone may be, in pyrolysis, simply a heated section of tubing; in photochemistry, a section subjected to intense ultraviolet radiation; in the study of reaction intermediates, a section where reactants such as H and Cl are mixed at low pressure and controlled temperature, or even an open flame. To study *ions* from the reaction zone, the ion source is rotated (90° counterclockwise, in the figure), the magnetic field at the ion source is removed, the electron beam in the ion source is deleted, and ions are admitted through a small slit (not shown) in the repeller electrode.

for the molecular beam to be formed by evaporation of a high-boiling material; on the contrary the molecular beam may consist of material admitted through a fine orifice from a sample maintained at almost any convenient temperature or pressure. Such arrangements are uniquely valuable for studying gas-phase chemical reactions. The peculiar value of this arrangement lies in the fact that if the orifice is made of appropriate material (quartz, platinum, etc.) it may be immersed directly in the reacting materials (158), and the various lamina of a reaction zone such as a flame (283) may be probed, layer by layer; since the reaction products pass immediately into a region of high vacuum, any further reaction is quenched as soon as the materials pass through the orifice so that very short-lived intermediate compounds or radicals may be studied in detail (Fig. 14).

Aside from quenching any chemical reaction that may be going on in a sample at the instant it is admitted, there are two other advantages in the use of a molecular beam to obtain line-of-sight entry of the sample into the ion source. One is that line-of-sight sample admission makes it possible to pass the sample clear through the ion source and out an exit aperture on the other side, minimizing any tendency for the sample material to condense on or react with the interior surfaces of the ion source whose cleanliness is critically important. Second, as has been noted by Wiley and McLaren (392) and by Brubaker (44), if the sample is admitted in a direction normal both to the optic axis of the ion source and to the electron beam, it can be arranged that the optimum voltage settings on the ion source are different for the sample and for background gases, since the sample molecules have ordered velocities whereas the background molecules do not. Thus it is possible in principle to operate the ion source and its associated circuits in such a way as to reject the signals due to background ions completely while retaining good sensitivity for sample molecules. In practice, substantial improvement in sample/background ratios have been achieved in this way.

2.2.4. The Surface Ionization Ion Source. When a material of high work function is heated in contact with a material of low ionization potential, the first material tends to rob electrons from the second. If the temperature is high enough to evaporate the second material, it will tend to be evaporated as ions, owing to the operation of this effect (123). This provides the basis for the so-called surface ionization ion source, in which a filament of material having a high work function (tungsten, tantalum, platinum, rhenium, etc.) may be either heated in contact with the vapor of the material to be ionized or (more usually) covered with a very thin film of the sample deposited from a dilute solution (67, 68). Such ion sources may be extraordinarily simple; a satisfactory ion source for the alkalis may be no more than a piece of hot Pyrex glass mounted behind a slit.

The efficiency of the surface ionization process, expressed as the ratio of molecules ionized, n^+, to the total number evaporated n^0, is given by

$$\frac{n^+}{n^0} = e^{-(V_i-\phi)/kT} \tag{5}$$

in which ϕ and V_i are the work function of the emitting surface and the ionization potential of the evaporated molecule, respectively, in volts,

k is Boltzmann's constant in electron-volts per degree Kelvin, and T is the absolute temperature of the surface.

In the simplest form in which the sample is both evaporated from and ionized by a single surface, surface-ionization sources have the intrinsic difficulty that many materials are evaporated at temperatures well below those at which the ionization process takes place with high

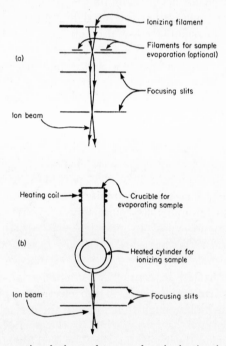

FIG. 15. Cross-sectional views of two surface ionization ion sources. In the usual form (a), either the sample may be painted on the ionizing filament, or it may be deposited on either or both of the filaments for sample evaporation shown. In Hintenberger and Lang's form (b), the sample is carried in a crucible, vapors from the sample passing out the slit after making at least one contact with the heated cylinder shown.

efficiency. A substantial improvement in efficiency is realized by having two surfaces at separately controllable temperatures, so that the sample can be evaporated from one surface (or, if desired, a crucible) at the desired rate onto a second, much hotter, surface on which the ionization takes place. Such compound surface ionization ion sources have been described by Moon and Oliphant (252), by Hintenberger (152), and by Inghram (176); perhaps the most highly developed form of this ion source is the one described by Hintenberger and Lang (153) in which the sensitivity was so high that easily measurable ion currents (5 × 10^{-13} amp.) were derived from as little as 5×10^{-13} g. of material (Fig. 15). From eq. (5) one would expect Pt, with its very high work function, to be a superlative material of which to build the emitter in a surface ionization ion source. Unfortunately the maximum operating temperature (the melting point) of Pt is so much lower than that of W, Ta, or Re that it is less efficient than any of these last three; W has been widely used for work with heavy elements (U, Pu, Th, etc.), but in work with the middle-weight elements Ta is often preferred because it is so difficult to obtain W in a form free of interfering impurities. Robinson *et al.* (302) have shown that rhenium is a very promising material for use in surface ionization ion sources, although it is too early as yet to say to what extent it will replace the older materials.

Surface ionization ion sources have been of extraordinary value in the isotopic analysis of materials of low ionization potential such as the alkali metals, the rare earths, and the actinide elements (133), particularly uranium. They have four outstanding properties which make them the preferred form in problems to which they are applicable. First, the ion beam produced is very nearly monokinetic, particularly in Hintenberger and Lang's form (153), so that the simple magnetic sector resolving system can produce mass resolving power that is adequate for many purposes. Second, the energy spread in the ion beam does not depend on the electric fields applied to the ion source as it does in the gas ion source, so that quite high electric fields can be applied and the effects of space charge in the ion source minimized, permitting relatively high ion currents to be drawn. Third, the background gases in the mass spectrometer are not usually ionized appreciably in this type of ion source, so it exhibits a high degree of selectivity in favor of the sample, thus permitting a search for traces of material, or rare isotopes, that would be very much more difficult if any other ion source were used. Fourth is the fact that for elements of low ionization potential (K, Ru, Cs, etc.) the efficiency of this ion source, in ions produced per atom of sample available, may approach 100% (208), three to five orders of magnitude higher than in the gas ion source, so that extremely minute amounts of some material can be analyzed.

Opposed to the advantages of the surface ionization source are certain deficiencies which limit its usefulness to a rather restricted class of problems. First is the inherent property that only materials of low ionization potential are ionized efficiently. Only a relatively few elements are ionized efficiently in elemental form (principally the alkalis and alkali-like materials), and even as compounds, whose ionization potentials are often lower than those of the constituent atoms, only about half the elements in the periodic table can be used. Second is the fact that, for ionization to proceed efficiently, the material being evaporated must be in very intimate contact with the filament, so that in the single-filament form of this ion source the total ion current formed from a given species is proportional to the amount present only so long as it is present in a very thin layer. Third, the temperature at which the sample evaporates will vary widely from one material to another, so that in a mixed sample there is usually no time at which the composition of the ion beam is representative of the composition of the original sample; ion currents have to be integrated over a substantial length of time, sometimes days, before any inferences can be drawn regarding the amount of material originally present unless an internal standard technique, such as isotope dilution (Section 3.1.2), is used. Fourth, thermal decomposition and other chemical reactions on the surface of the emitter often cause the chemical species evaporated as ions to be markedly different from the species placed on the emitter (178). Finally, although the surface ionization ion source operates without a magnetic field (since there is no electron beam to be collimated), it exhibits some mass discrimination, since the vapor pressures of the various isotopic species in a mixed sample are not quite the same (294). Thus the surface ionization ion source cannot be used for measurements of absolute isotope ratios except through the use of a reference standard.

A rather special form of the surface ionization ion source, useful where substantial amounts of material are to be processed or where for some reason it is desired to draw ions for several days from a single loading, is one in which the sample is contained in a massive but porous matrix, material evaporated from the surface being replenished by diffusion of more material from the interior. Such ion sources were used first by Gehrcke and Reichenheim (123) and developed further by Kunsman (202), by Aston (6), by Smythe et al. (334), and by others. A variant of this form has been described by Williams, who sinters a dilute slurry of TaO, amyl acetate, and cellulose nitrate in the proportions 66:33:1 on a tungsten substrate and absorbs a drop of the sample in the porous coating thus formed, thereby creating an emitter of improved life and stability. Sauereisen cements have been used for this same purpose, as have fused borax fluxes.

2.2.5. The High-Frequency Spark Ion Source. This ion source, originally due to Dempster (72) and developed since by Shaw and Rall (323), by Gorman et al. (127), and by Hannay and Ahearn (135, 136), is one which provides ions from a solid sample in abundances very nearly proportional to their abundance in the sample, which can be operated*

---

* By operating the spark intermittently to avoid bulk heating of the sample.

so that the composition of the ion beam from a homogeneous sample does not change appreciably with time and so that the ion current from a given material is relatively invariant to the nature of the solid matrix in which the sample appears. On account of the unsteady nature of the spark, the ion current from such an ion source is very erratic, and such ion sources have been used either with photographic plate recording in

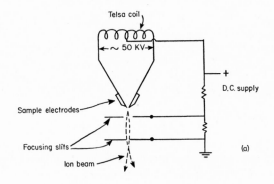

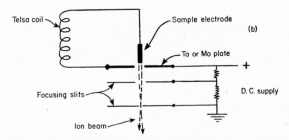

Fig. 16. Two radio-frequency spark ion sources. In Hannay and Ahearn's form (a), the spark is drawn between two similar electrodes; in the form used by Dempster (b), the spark is drawn between a sample electrode and a perforated Ta or Mo plate.

which the currents from all the ions are recorded simultaneously, as by Dempster, by Hannay and Ahearn, by Shaw and Rall, and by Craig *et al.* (65), or with electronic means which records not the individual ion currents but the ratio of the individual currents to the total, as by Gorman *et al.* (127). The high-frequency spark ion source is the only one thus far which can be used for chemical analyses of very refractory materials without prior chemical manipulation of the sample. The techniques for use of such ion sources have thus far been most highly developed by Hannay and Ahearn, who have used it for detecting bulk contaminants in abundances approaching $1:10^8$ and surface contaminants in abundances below 0.1 monolayer. Ions are produced directly from the spark, no auxiliary ionizing means being used (Fig. 16).

The energy spread from the high-frequency spark ion source amounts to several thousand volts (82), so that it must be used with a double-focusing resolving system. Usually additional means must be provided to limit the energy spread of the ions passed by the resolving system to a range of at most a few per cent. It is possible in principle to use the high-frequency spark not as a source of ions directly but simply as a means for nonselective volatilization of the sample, ionization being effected by an electron beam in an ion source similar to the gas ion source already discussed (255). Such an arrangement affords, in principle, the advantages of nonselective volatilization of the sample and the ability to analyze very refractory materials that are characteristic of the spark ion source, combined with the relatively low energy spread that is characteristic of the electron-bombardment ion source. Unfortunately the ion yields realized thus far from such an arrangement have been so low that its usefulness has been very limited, and even if ion currents of useful magnitude were obtained in this way the severe amplitude instabilities of the high-frequency spark ion source would remain.

2.2.6. Sputtering as a Source of Ions (37, 141, 142, 145, 166, 190, 343, 368, 381-384). It is possible to produce ions from a solid sample by bombarding it directly with either electrons or ions. In the case of electron bombardment, the electron beam does no more than heat the sample and ionize the resulting vapor, ion sources based on this principle having all the operating characteristics of the crucible ion source already discussed (278). In the case of ion bombardment, however, the momentum transfer between the bombarding ions and the individual atoms in the solid sample is efficient, and the effects, on a per-atom basis, are highly localized. Thus bombardment of a solid sample with a beam of reasonably heavy positive ions affords relatively nonselective sampling of a highly local nature and may produce a stable ion beam having an energy spread of at most a few tens of volts instead of the several thousand volt spread that is characteristic of the high-frequency spark ion source. Preliminary indications are that this type of ion source has great promise, although it is more complex than any other type and the demands made by it on the vacuum system tend to be more severe (166).

2.3. DETECTION AND RECORDING OF ION CURRENTS

2.3.1. Photographic Plates as Ion Detectors (233, 319). When an energetic ion beam strikes a photographic emulsion, the beam renders the emulsion developable, thus producing a permanent record. The sensitivity of the method depends on the mass and the kinetic energy of the ion beam and, of course, on the emulsion. The threshold for detectability given by various experimenters runs from 2×10^6 ion/cm.[2] given by Lichtblau and Mattauch (215) to 2×10^{11} by Lewis and Hayden (213). Generally speaking, between 10^5 and 10^7 ions are required to make visible a line of 0.001-cm.[2] area (91).

The darkening of a photographic emulsion by an ion beam is proportional to the product It^p, where I is the ion current, t is the exposure time, and p is the well-known Schwartzschild coefficient which is often assumed to be unity but more often is not. Lichtblau and Mattauch, using Ilford Q_1 plates, found $p = 0.86$ (215); Bainbridge found very wide departures from the reciprocity law ($p = 1$) in the case of slow alkali ions (8); Lichtblau found the reciprocity condition well followed for Ilford Q_3 plates (214); and Hannay and Ahearn have found no indication that the reciprocity law does not hold for Ilford Q_2 plates (137). Thus it is possible, with energetic ion beams, suitable emulsions, and appropriate processing, to obtain satisfactory behavior with respect to the reciprocity condition, although it is never safe to assume without experimental verification that this is so.

Photographic plates are advantageous in two situations: first, where the highest possible mass resolving power is required, since there is no resolving slit whose width would contribute to the width of the peak if it were electrically recorded; and second, where it is desired to measure very small or rapidly changing peaks over a wide range of masses, or where an exploratory study of a mass spectrum, where the mass of the peaks of primary interest may not be known, is being done. The last situation is a typical one in the case of an exploratory search for trace impurities in a material. Plates have disadvantages, however, as compared to electrical recording. Aside from the obvious inconvenience of photographic darkroom procedures and the possible failure of the reciprocity condition already mentioned, they have a limited dynamic range, it being difficult or impossible to cover an intensity range wider than about 50:1 in a single exposure; owing to the difficulties of photographic densitometry it is difficult to make relative abundance measurements with accuracy better than several per cent, and a very strong ion beam will in general record as a broad, ill-defined smear due, at least sometimes, to fluorescence in the emulsion (319), excited by the ion beam and darkening the plate far outside the limits of the ion beam itself. These difficulties have resulted in photographic plates being replaced in most situations by electric recording, although there is no doubt that plates have a permanent place in certain areas.

2.3.2. Electrical Measurement of Ion Currents. In electrical measurement of ion currents, a slit is placed at the focal plane of the mass spectrometer, the slit being narrow enough so that only one ion beam at a time can pass through it. Behind the slit is placed an element capable of detecting the ions. Most often, this element is simply a conducting plate or a small Faraday cup connected electrically to an electrometer amplifier, the amplifier being sufficiently sensitive to detect the currents which, in all mass spectrometers except those intended for gross separation of isotopes, range from about 10^{-10} amp. down. Many electrometers having noise levels (detection limits) as low as 10^{-15} amp. or lower have been described in the literature (276) and are available commercially.

For detecting ion currents below 10^{-15} amp., or for measuring ion currents at substantially higher levels with extreme speed (as in cases where it is desired to display the mass spectrum on an oscilloscope), electron multipliers can be used (59). These have been used in two forms: first, one in which the ions impinge on and excite fluorescence in a phosphor or a scintillating crystal and the resulting light is detected by a conventional photomultiplier (360); and second, one where the ions strike the cathode of the multiplier directly and eject secondary electrons which are then multiplied by successive impacts on a dynode array (3). The phosphor-plus-photomultiplier arrangement has an advantage that the light from the phosphor can be piped for a considerable distance to the photomultiplier, which may be necessary when the resolving slit of the mass spectrometer is immersed deeply in a strong magnetic field. A second advantage of the phosphor-plus-photomultiplier is that the secondary-emitting surfaces of the photomultiplier dynode array are permanently sealed and thus protected from changes in secondary emission coefficient which would result from their exposure to the mass spectrometer background gases. The principle disadvantages of the phosphor-plus-photomultiplier arrangement, aside from the transmission losses (which can easily exceed 90%), are that the photocathode must be a material of low work function, which causes the thermal background currents in the photomultiplier to be objectionably high unless it is refrigerated; the photomultiplier itself is extraordinarily sensitive to magnetic fields; and the life may be limited by the formation of deposits on the phosphor surface. In the electron multiplier in which ions strike the cathode directly, all the surfaces can be of material having a relatively high work function so that the thermal background currents may be as little as one count per second even at room temperature. With material of high work function, high voltages can be used—250 volts per stage is a common value—so that the electron multipliers are less sensitive to stray magnetic fields than the photomultipliers which commonly are limited to interstage voltages of 100 to 125 volts; Smith (327) has described an electron multiplier for use in a strong magnetic field.

The number of secondaries ejected from the cathode of an electron multiplier depends on both the kinetic energy and the chemical species of the ion involved (3, 14, 277, 336), and at impact energies of less than about 2500 volts the number of secondary electrons ejected may be small and the statistical fluctuations very large. At impact energies of more than 2500 volts the number of secondary electrons formed, per impacting ion, shows somewhat less variation with ion energy, and there is some indication that the dependence on the chemical species of the ion may also be less at high impact energies. The reasons for such variations appear to be understood only in a very general way (132, 307, 340).

Since the secondary emission coefficient of the dynode surfaces in an electron multiplier is sensitive to adsorbed gases (387), it is exceptional for the gain of an electron multiplier to be constant for any extended period of time. Electron multipliers are more nearly quantitative at current levels at which the ion currents can be measured by counting the individual ions (201, 388)—that is, at current levels below about 10^{-14} amp., although even then the measurements are subject to statistical fluctuations because a statistically variable number of the impinging ions make no secondaries (64). Used carefully, however, electron multipliers can be made to show gain variations that are imperceptible for days at a time, and they can be used for critical work. The conditioning of an electron multiplier so that it will show high and stable gain is a subtle art which is only beginning to be understood in terms of the fundamental processes involved (16, 150, 229, 288, 377).

2.3.3. Intrinsic Limitations on Ion Current Measurements. The ion current in a mass spectrometer is a stream of individual particles formed at statistically independent times, and the total charge delivered to the detecting means during a given time is subject to an intrinsic statistical uncertainty given approximately by the square root of the number of ions collected during that time. Thus the measurement of 1.6×10^{-13} amp. in 0.01 second, or 1.6×10^{-15} amp. in one second (10^4 ions) involves an *intrinsic* uncertainty of 1%, etc. Substitution of an electron multiplier for an electrometer certainly raises the currents to a more conveniently measurable level, sometimes increasing the currents by a factor of a million or more, but such a substitution does nothing to help the intrinsic accuracy of the measurement because it is the *ion current itself, not the measurement,* which is subject to this intrinsic statistical uncertainty. In fact, an electron multiplier worsens the situation quite appreciably because of statistical fluctuations in the gain of the multiplier itself (64, 195).

3. Applications of Mass Spectrometry

3.1. QUANTITATIVE ANALYSIS. THE PRINCIPLES
OF CHEMICAL MIXTURE ANALYSIS BY MASS SPECTROMETER

3.1.1. Matrix Methods. We have mentioned that, to obtain stable operation, mass spectrometers are ordinarily operated in such a way that the ionizing electron beam has several times as much energy as the minimum necessary for forming ions, and we have remarked that such operation always results in extensive fragmentation of the bombarded molecule. Thus a chemically pure substance ordinarily produces not a single mass peak at the position corresponding to the molecular weight of the substance but a complex array of peaks, called a "pattern," which is characteristic not only of the molecular weight of the molecule but of its structure. In the general case, mixtures of considerable complexity may be encountered. The general procedure for analysis is to determine, by calibration of the instrument on pure compounds, a set of sensitivity coefficients A_{ij}, which are the ion current of the ith peak, due to the jth component, per unit partial pressure in the inlet system and under some stipulated conditions of ionizing current and other operating parameters. When the mass spectrum of the mixture is recorded, one obtains a set of peak heights I_i, being the ion currents measured on the various peaks. One then sets up the matrix

$$I_1 = A_{11}P_1 + A_{12}P_2 + A_{13}P_3 + \ldots$$
$$I_2 = A_{21}P_1 + A_{22}P_2 + A_{23}P_3 + \ldots$$
$$I_3 = A_{31}P_1 + A_{32}P_2 + A_{33}P_3 + \ldots \tag{6}$$
$$\ldots \quad \ldots \quad \ldots \quad \ldots \quad \ldots$$

and solves, by conventional methods, for the various P_j, the P_j being the partial pressures of the jth component in the mixture, in the same units as those used to determine the sensitivity coefficients A_{ij}. This procedure yields the partial pressure of each component of the mixture and thus gives the desired analytical result. A useful check on the accuracy of the analysis is the "pressure check" in which the total of the partial pressures deduced from the calculations is compared to the measured pressure at which the mixture is introduced. In the event the two figures fail to agree within 1 or 2%, it can be inferred that an error has been made. Very often this error is in the nature of overlooking some component of the mixture by failing to insert the sensitivity coefficients for this component into the matrix used to perform the calculations.

In practice, particularly in catalogs of published spectra,* the co-efficients shown are often not absolute sensitivity coefficients but so-called "pattern coefficients," which are the heights of the various peaks expressed as a fraction usually of the strongest peak in the spectra but sometimes as a fraction of the height of the "parent peak" (the peak corresponding to the unfragmented molecule). In addition, published spectra are sometimes "polyisotopic spectra," which are the actual peak heights as read from the mass spectrum, and sometimes "monoisotopic spectra," in which the peak heights as catalogued have been corrected for the isotopic contributions of adjacent ions. Although the lack of complete consistency in the method of reporting mass spectra requires some care in their interpretation, the inconsistencies are not so serious as might at first appear, since it is not often feasible to use on one mass spectrometer a set of calibrating coefficients that have been taken on another in any event. Differences between one mass spectrometer and another of the same type, particularly commercial instruments from the same manufacturer, are often small enough, however, that mass spectra taken on two or more instruments can be made to agree with satisfactory accuracy by suitable adjustment of the operating parameters such as temperature, magnetic field strength, and voltage distribution in the ion source.

Clearly, for the matrix approach outlined above to be useful, not only must the sensitivity coefficients, A_{ij}, be constant from day to day but they must be independent of the partial pressure of the corresponding component (that is, the ion current on a given component must be linear with the partial pressure of that component) and independent of the partial pressures of unrelated components. A final requirement, and one that may seem strange at first, is that the resolving power of the mass spectrometer must not be too high; there must be some instant during which all ions having the same *nominal* mass number strike the collector together in order that the spectra be superposable in the linear fashion implied by eqs. (6). The method could not be used, for example, in analyzing mixtures of hydrocarbons containing nitrogen if the mass

* An extensive compilation of mass spectra has been given in API Project 44, Catalog of Mass Spectral Data, published by the U.S. National Bureau of Standards. In addition, various investigators have published spectra for such materials as volatile oxygenated compounds (124, 186, 205, 206, 348, 351), haloalkanes (22, 247, 347), alkylbenzenes (243), ketones (322), thiophenes (192), acids (138-139), lactones (115), amines (60), normal, secondary, and tertiary alcohols (113), aliphatic ethers (226), aliphatic alcohols (117), acetals (111), trimethylsilyl derivatives (321), metallo-organic compounds (73, 246), alcoxy alcohols (275), diols (227), and some miscellaneous compounds (225, 320).

resolving power were higher than about 1:500, since in that event there would be no time when the ion currents due to N_2 (mass 28.0151) and those due to C_2H_4 (mass 28.0403) would combine.

The necessity for solving large numbers of systems of equations similar to eqs. (6) has motivated a search for a means of mechanizing the data-handling process since the earliest days of analytical mass spectrometry, and at least two simple analog computers have been developed for the specific purpose of solving simultaneous linear equation sets, of up to twelfth order, of the type that one obtains from a mass spectrometer analysis (28). Fritts and Peattie (119) have devised a system and equipment for reading mass spectra with an electromechanical apparatus which automatically records the various peak heights, as they are read from the mass spectrum, on an electric typewriter and which simultaneously punches the peak heights into a set of punched cards or perforated paper tape for insertion into a digital computer. In this system, the mass spectrometer operates conventionally and produces a record of the usual type. The analyst is, however, spared the tedious and time-consuming task of measuring the records manually, entering the readings in a table, and manually preparing the input information for a computer.

A very high state of automation in handling of mass spectrometer data has been reached in an apparatus described first by Dudenbostel and Priestley (83) and developed further by King et al. (191). In this arrangement, the mass spectrometer does not scan an entire spectrum but steps discontinuously from one to the next of a preselected group of peaks, the ion current output on each peak being digitized automatically and automatically fed into the input of an appropriate computer which performs the computations and prints the compositional data automatically in tabular form. With such an apparatus, it is possible to report thirty 20-component analyses per 8-hour shift, at an average labor demand of 12 man-hours per shift, including instrument maintenance.

It is possible to perform the calculations indicated by the system of eqs. (6) by a process of simple multiplication if the matrix of sensitivity coefficients is inverted. One can construct a matrix B_{ji}, the inverse of the A_{ij} previously mentioned, such that

$$P_j = B_{ji}I_i \tag{7}$$

and the use of such inverted matrices saves an enormous amount of calculating time and of complexity and cost in the equipment required (66). The calculation of the inverse matrix itself, however, is a task not taken lightly, and the use of the inverted matrix is feasible only when the sensitivity coefficients of the mass spectrometer are sufficiently stable that the inverse matrix, once calculated, can be used for a substantial length of time. Generally speaking, these systems share the characteristics common to all highly automated systems that, the higher the degree of automation and the higher the performance of the system when doing its designed job, the less efficient the system is when operating on a nonstandard task and the less is the ability of the system to operate, at reduced but still reasonable efficiency, in the event of a breakdown of some component. It is not yet clear what the optimum degree of automation is in any given problem situation.

3.1.2. Internal Standard Methods. There are many important situations in which the matrix methods outlined above cannot be used. A situation which occurs frequently is one where an instrument intended primarily for isotope-ratio measurements, and possessing an inlet system designed for this work (and therefore exhibiting gas interference, as discussed in Section 2.2.1), is to be used for chemical mixture analysis. There are also situations in which the sample has such low volatility that a crucible or a thermal emission ion source must be used and no satisfactory measurement of sample pressure can be made, or in which a mixed sample is to be analyzed, in which the various components of the sample may evaporate at different rates (257) or may appear at different times during the evaporating schedule.

In the case of the isotope-ratio inlet system used for chemical mixture analysis, the central difficulty is that the partial pressure of a given component in the ion source depends on the admission rate of that component and on the component's intrinsic properties (molecular weight, temperature), but the admission rate depends not on an intrinsic property of that component alone as it does in an inlet system designed for mixture analysis but on the bulk properties of the mixture in which the component occurs. This difficulty can be circumvented by adding, both to the pure compounds used for calibrating the system and to the mixture to be analyzed, a known amount of some tracer gas such as argon and by using the tracer gas peak height as a measure of the sample admission rate. One may then set up an array of sensitivity coefficients, C_{ij}, which represent the ion current on the ith peak, due to the jth component, *per unit tracer gas peak height,* and proceed by the methods outlined in Section 3.1.1. This method yields abundance measurements, not in terms of partial pressure, but in terms of the tracer gas peak height, and the total of the various component abundances measured must be normalized to 100% to obtain results in per cent concentration. This method has been discussed in more detail by Mattraw *et al.* (237); a variant method has been given by Freeman and Serfass (110).

In the case of a sample evaporated from a crucible or a thermal-emission ion source, the various components of a mixed sample will in general evaporate at different rates so that there is, in general, no time when the composition of the vapor is representative of the composition of the sample. In many cases, even the chemical species present in the vapor may be different from those in the sample. Thus a quantitative analysis of a sample by mass spectrometer using a crucible or thermal-emission ion source involves largely trial-and-error methods which have to be tailored to the requirements of a specific problem. Where a quantitative determination of one or more specific components is desired, the sample may be equilibrated with a known amount of isotopically enriched material of the chemical species to be determined, and the amount of material originally present may be inferred by measurement of the isotope ratio in the evaporated sample in a variant of the *isotope dilution* technique next to be discussed (175, 308).

The analytical chemist is confronted frequently with situations in which a determination of some specific substance is required but in which analytical procedures for separation of that substance may not be sufficiently quantitative or it may be prohibitively laborious to make them so. Such cases include the assay of ores for trace amounts of uranium or lead, the determination of a specific amino acid in a biological specimen, or the determination of a specific atomic species—say oxygen—in a mixed material (194). In such cases, the sample can be equilibrated with a measured amount of isotopically enriched material of the chemical species to be determined. The appropriate extraction procedures (50) are then carried out, and the isotope ratio of the extract is measured. If R is the natural isotope ratio of the element sought, R' the isotope ratio of the isotopically enriched internal standard, W' the weight of internal standard added, and R'' the isotope ratio measured in the extract, then the weight, W, of the material to be determined is given simply by

$$W/W' = (R'' - R')/(R - R'') \tag{8}$$

It is implied in the above derivation that the isotopically normal and the isotopically enriched materials behave identically during chemical processing and during analysis in the mass spectrometer. This they do not do (18, 46, 76, 77, 314-316, 341, 364). In the event the mass of either the original molecule or the evaporated ion is affected substantially by isotopic enrichment, this assumption may be seriously in error, and even in the case of such molecules as $C^{12}O_2^{16}$ and $C^{13}O_2^{16}$ it does not hold exactly. Thus the determination of abundances by isotope dilution methods is subject to intrinsic errors that are usually small but whose control does require some care.

3.1.3. Mass Spectrometry and Gas Chromatography. The combination of a mass spectrometer and a gas chromatograph illustrates the extraordinary synergistic effects which sometimes occur when two techinques are combined and constitutes probably the most powerful tool yet devised for gas and vapor analysis. The gas chromatograph will, at least in principle, take a mixed gas or vapor sample and present the various components consecutively, in pure form, at the output. But in a sample of unknown composition the gas chromatograph by itself offers little clue as to the identity of the separated components. The mass spectrometer can give nearly complete information regarding the identity, including the structure, of an unknown material and has the further advantage over other analytical methods (infrared or ultraviolet absorption, etc.) that an analysis can be performed on a very minute quantity of gas, but may offer almost insuperable difficulties when several unknown materials are run simultaneously. Preliminary gas chromatographic separation of a mixed sample permits the mass spectrometer to deal with the components one at a time, reducing greatly the requirements on both mass resolving power and stability of the mass spectrometer. A comparatively simple and inexpensive mass spectrometer, when combined with a gas chromatograph, may be able to perform analyses which the most complex and costly mass spectrometric installation could not approach alone. The various components separated by the gas chromatograph may be trapped individually and analyzed on a mass spectrometer of conventional type (31, 80, 212), or a mass spectrometer equipped with a continuous-flow inlet system may be attached directly to the output of the gas chromatograph, the mass spectra of the separated components being recorded consecutively on a high-speed recording oscillograph, or an oscilloscope screen, or in various other ways (79, 103, 140, 160, 325). The mass spectrometer-chromatograph combination has been applied to the study of such subtle problems as the chemistry of onion odors (212) and many other difficult problems.

3.1.4. Monitoring and Control of Continuous Processes. The first application of mass spectrometry to the monitoring of a continuous chemical process was in the monitoring of process stream composition of the gaseous diffusion plant for separation of uranium isotopes during World War II (262). The first mass spectrometer devised for monitoring continuously in an industrial plant was described by Robinson *et al.* in 1950 (304); since that time, developments have followed the general development of the mass spectrometer as such (209, 373, 374, 376). More recently, a mass spectrometer specifically designed from the outset with industrial process-monitoring requirements (explosion-proofing, reliability, remote operation, etc.) in mind has appeared (63).

The mass spectrometer is more complex than many other analytical tools, and its use as an industrial process-monitoring device has been confined thus far to applications in which it has something unique to offer. These unique attributes are as follows: (1) The mass spectrometer will perform an analysis of a gas sample whose total pressure may be as low as 10^{-8} mm. Hg, and it can detect and identify components whose partial pressure may be as low as 10^{-11} mm. Hg. Thus the mass spectrometer is the natural instrument for such applications as monitoring the composition of gases during the purification of metals by vacuum fusion. Mass spectrometer monitoring of the vacuum fusion process results in improved product quality and higher product throughput for a given nominal plant capacity. (2) The mass spectrometer can perform a complete analysis of a complex gas or vapor mixture in as little as a few seconds and can monitor continuously the abundance of a given component with a response time of 50 msec. or less. In high-speed processes such as the Wulff process for acetylene, for example, the mass spectrometer is the only analytical tool whose response time is comparable to the time constant of the process itself; continuous monitoring by mass spectrometer results in improved product quality and throughput again. Obviously the mass spectrometer is indispensable in controlling isotope separation processes; other applications in which mass spectrometers have been used successfully for continuous monitoring of industrial processes are monitoring the H_2S/SO_2 ratio in sulfur recovery plants (203), monitoring traces of oxygen in argon (284), monitoring the ethylene/acetylene ratio in the effluent of a plant intended to absorb acetylene selectively from an acetylene: ethylene mixture (203), analysis of automotive exhaust gases (375), and monitoring concentrations of oxygen, carbon dioxide, and anesthetic gases in expired air (168). There is no doubt that the use of mass spectrometers in process control situations will increase as the trend to high-speed processing and to generally more sophisticated control continues.

3.2. QUALITATIVE ANALYSIS

3.2.1. Identification and Estimation of Minor Components. Undoubtedly the largest use for mass spectrometers, in terms of the number of instruments employed, is the detection of leaks in sealed vessels of all descriptions (265, 352). In leak detection, the mass spectrometer is used to analyze the gas on the low-pressure side of the vessel being tested, and the high-pressure side is pressurized with a gas containing a tracer element which the mass spectrometer is adjusted to detect. The tracer gas is preferably one which does not occur naturally in the laboratory surroundings or in the mass spectrometer background, is non-hazardous, does not tend to hang up on the walls of the vessel being tested, and is readily available. In the United States, the tracer gas is usually helium; elsewhere, the unavailability of helium dictates the use of other gases such as argon. In any event it is advantageous for the tracer gas to be one of low molecular weight whenever possible, since the use of low-molecular-weight tracer gases minimizes the demands on the mass resolving power of the mass spectrometer.

In testing of pressure vessels, the vessel may be pressurized with the tracer gas or with air containing the tracer gas, and the seams of the vessel explored with a probe containing a minute orifice which admits a sample directly to the mass spectrometer. In such applications the requirements on the mass spectrometer are very severe, since the mass spectrometer has not only to detect minute amounts of the tracer gas but to do so in the presence of an overwhelmingly greater abundance of the gases which comprise the atmosphere surrounding the pressure vessel —air, steam, or what not. Very often the testing is done under industrial conditions in which substantial amounts of smoke, oil vapor, and other objectionable materials are drawn into the mass spectrometer. Mass spectrometer leak detectors are available which will detect less than one part of helium in two million parts of other gases such as air and which will do so with no more maintenance downtime than an automobile.

The leak testing of evacuated vessels is an area in which the mass spectrometer leak detector is indispensable, since it is unique in its ability to detect and identify gases whose partial pressures may be as low as 10^{-11} mm. Hg. Many hermetically sealed articles of commerce— relays, vacuum tubes, valves, pumps, and other vacuum system components—are subjected to mass spectrometer leak test routinely as part of the inspection procedures during manufacture.

From leak testing of evacuated vessels with a mass spectrometer leak detector attached to the exhaust line it is only a step to the use of a mass spectrometer as an integral part of the vacuum system to analyze the residual gases in the system (19, 35, 295, 371). In the pumpdown of a large particle accelerator, for example, the outgassing of the system may cause the pressure to fall very slowly for many hours even though the system may be vacuum-tight. Mass spectrometer analysis of the residual gases during pumpdown will disclose whether there is a leak or not, since there are some mass peaks (mass 40, from atmospheric argon, for example) which will be present in the event of a leak but which are almost never observable from any other cause. Establishment of the fact that a system is leaking and location of the leak during pumpdown may save days in the time required to put a large vacuum system into operation. Mass spectrometer analysis of the gases in a vacuum system is also used to study the gases given off by heat treatment of materials in vacuum (49, 279, 342). Adsorption and desorption of surface films during heat treatment (49), liberation of gases dissolved in metals during vacuum fusion (122, 272, 391), permeation of gases through glass (306, 357, 358), metals (109), or plastics (370), and the chemical reactions involved in the activation of oxide cathodes (279)— these are only a few examples of the many physical and chemical proc-

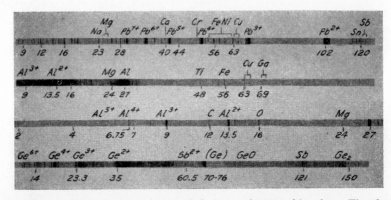

FIG. 17. Mass spectra as recorded on a photographic plate. The first spectrum is of "high-purity" lead. The second and third spectra are of aluminum with the magnetic field adjusted to cover the mass ranges 9 to 125 and 2 to 28, respectively. The fourth spectrum is of very pure Ge doped with 10 p.p.m. Sb. Exposure times are 2 minutes, 20 minutes, and 3 minutes respectively (N. B. Hannay).

esses that can be studied by sealing a comparatively simple mass spectrometer directly into a vacuum system.

In the detection of trace contaminants in solids, two basic approaches are possible (173). The first, applicable in cases where a specific contaminant such as U or Th (356) is being sought, is isotope dilution, already discussed (Section 3.1.2). The second, applicable where a broad-spectrum search for unknown impurities is needed, uses a mass spectrometer with high-frequency spark ion source and photographic plate as the ion detector so that the ion currents can be integrated over a substantial period of time (sometimes several minutes) (135, 136, 372). In direct estimation the mass spectrometer has the following intrinsic merits (326): (1) The mass spectra are comparatively simple. Even though a given nuclide may appear in as many as six or eight different degrees of ionization and there may be as many as six or eight different isotopic species for some chemical elements, there are never as many as a hundred lines per chemical species, and usually there are less than twenty (Fig. 17). An optical emission spectrum, on the other hand, may contain thousands of lines; some elements have so many emission lines that their emission spectra are almost a continuum. (2) The mass spectrometer is relatively nonselective, producing ions from the various chemical species present at nearly equal efficiencies regardless of the ionization cross section, the ionization potential, or the boiling point. Thus elements such as phosphorus and sulfur (for example), to which an emission spectrograph is comparatively insensitive, can be detected readily. Dissolved or chemically combined gases (oxides, nitrides, hydrides, etc.) are also readily detected. Mass spectrometers have exhibited detection limits for bulk impurities in metals somewhat better than 1.10^7 for all elements which are not present in the mass spectrometer background, and these limits will unquestionably be extended by improved instrumentation.

In the high-frequency spark ion source, the consumption of material may be very low, often amounting to less than 100 monolayers per second. Thus there is an appreciable length of time during which the spark is being drawn from the immediate neighborhood of the surface of the sample. If, now, a series of spectra is recorded, the first spectrum is highly preferential to any superficial layers, subsequent spectra disclosing the composition of the deeper layers which constitute the bulk of the sample. This provides an extraordinarily powerful means for studying the nature of surface layers; as little as 0.1 monolayer of surface contaminant can be detected and identified on either metals or insulators (136). This technique promises to be of extraordinary value in the study of corrosion processes and other problems in surface chemistry.

3.2.2. Qualitative Analysis by Operation at Extreme Resolution. In conventional mass spectrometric analysis, it is convenient to lump together all ions which have the same nominal mass number such as CO_2–C_3H_8, N_2–C_2H_4, etc., in order that the matrices on which the analysis is based shall not be overly complex. Where the identity of one or more components of a complex sample is unknown, however, conventional matrix methods may break down because of the inability to select the appropriate calibration spectra. This situation arises in, for example, air pollution studies where the spectrum of a polluted air sample may contain peaks at virtually every mass number, or in exploratory chemical analyses where essentially nothing is known about the chemical composition of a sample even when (as is sometimes the case) it may be known to be chemically pure. In such situations a mass spectrometer operating at extremely high mass resolution may provide information unobtainable in any other way. This comes about because the *exact* weight of a molecule is a virtually unique characteristic; such molecular pairs as (for example) N_2-CO, $N_2-C_2H_4$, $S-O_2$, NH_2-O, CH_2-N, or NH_4-H_2O can be distinguished readily by a mass spectrometer with sufficiently high resolving power. At higher molecular weights, both the complexity of the problem and the power of the mass spectrometer approach become even more impressive. Beynon, the leading exponent of this technique, has listed as an example eleven compounds, all having the nominal molecular weight 84, which can be uniquely identified by a sufficiently precise measurement of the mass of the parent peak alone (29, 31) (See Table I).

TABLE I

Precise Masses for Eleven Compounds All Having the Nominal Molecular Weight 84, Together with the Fractional Mass Differences (the Mass Resolving Power Required to Distinguish between Consecutive Members of the Series on the Basis of Molecular Weight Alone)

Member	Mass	Mass difference
$C_3H_2NO_2$	84.03526	
		1:7473
$C_2H_2N_3O$	84.04650	
		1:62,500
$C_4H_4O_2$	84.04784	
		1:7473
$C_3H_4N_2O$	84.05908	
		1:7473
$C_2H_4N_4$	84.07031	
		1:62,500
C_4H_6NO	84.07166	
		1:7473
$C_3H_6N_3$	84.08289	
		1:62,500
C_5H_8O	84.08424	
		1:7473
$C_4H_8N_2$	84.09547	
		1:6678
$C_5H_{10}N$	84.10805	
		1:6678
C_6H_{12}	84.12063	

3.3. MASS SPECTROMETRY IN CHEMICAL AND PHYSICAL RESEARCH

3.3.1. Molecular Structure and Bond Strengths. When a complex molecule is ionized by an electron beam, the motions of the remaining molecular electrons are so rapid compared to the motions of the heavy nuclei that there is time for essentially complete re-equilibration of the molecular electronic motions before any bond fragmentation takes place. Thus, in the interval between ionization and fragmentation there is what Rosenstock *et al.* (312) have referred to as a "quasi-equilibrium" condition, and the fragmentation process becomes, in this view, an intrinsic property of the molecule with little regard for the details of the ionization process. Prediction of the relative abundances of the various molecular fragments in the mass spectrum then becomes a problem in statistical

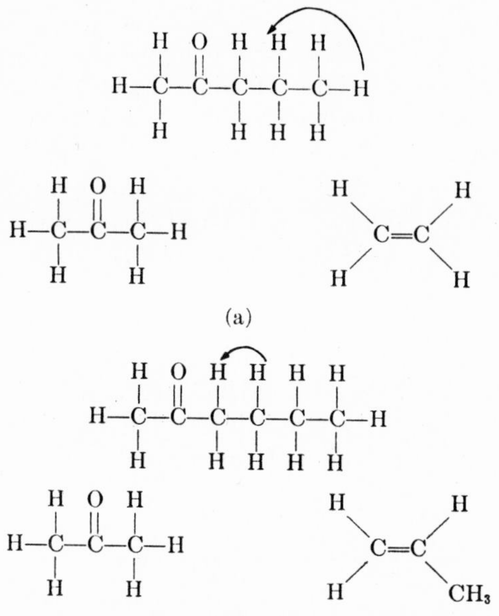

(a)

(b)

Fig. 18. Formation of rearrangement peaks, illustrating (a) formation of acetone and ethylene from methyl-*n*-propyl ketone, and (b) formation of acetone and propylene from methyl-*n*-butyl ketone.

mechanics which is amenable, at least in principle, to analytical treatment (116) and which provides information regarding the bond strengths and bonding mechanisms in the molecule. On the basis that the ionized whole molecule has a certain integrity (albeit a transient one), the existence of rearrangement peaks, due to fragments that cannot be formed by the rupture of any single bond in the original molecule (60, 96, 183, 205), becomes understandable; Beynon has remarked on the tendency for rearrangement peaks to occur such that the *joint* stability of the ionized and the neutral fragments is high, and on the fact that a seemingly improbable rearrangement peak may occur abundantly because its neutral counterpart is one of exceptional stability (30) (see Fig. 18). The quasi-equilibrium theory of mass spectra also accounts for metastable ions by the fact that some ionized whole molecules may persist in the quasi-equilibrium condition for periods comparable with the time required for them to move through the mass resolving system. Thus a study of the detailed structure of a mass spectrum, and of the way in which the structure varies with the energy of the impacting electrons, provides an indispensable tool for the study of the structure of a molecule.

One of the most important phases of molecular structure study by mass spectrometer is the study of the ionization potentials (97)—the so-called appearance potentials—of whole molecules (74, 75, 105, 120, 184, 207, 210, 230, 231, 249, 250, 253) and radicals (88, 92-95, 102, 216-219, 223, 362), and the energy levels for negative ion formation by electron attachment (104, 149) or exchange (256). Measurement of the successive appearance potentials of the CH_4 ion and the CH_3, CH_2, CH, and C fragments from methane, for example, permits the heat of vaporization of carbon, one of the fundamental quantities in organic chemistry, to be calculated. Studies of appearance potentials of the peaks from acetaldehyde permits determination of the dissociation energy of the CH bond on the aldehyde group; by paying attention to the detailed shape of the appearance potential curve it is possible to estimate the difference between the energy of formation of (for example) CH_3CO and CH_2CHO.

The central difficulty in measurement of appearance potentials is that the kinetic energy of the ionizing electron beam is intrinsically ill-defined owing to the Maxwellian distribution of electron energies in thermodynamic equilibrium with an emitter at a temperature of perhaps 2500°K.* These intrinsic thermal energies have the result that the energy of the ionizing electron beam is distributed through a range of about 1 volt. Thus the curve of ion yield versus mean electron beam energy does not show a sharp upward break when the appearance potential is reached; instead, the slope of the curve increases gradually from zero to some finite value through an energy interval of some tenths of a volt. Many methods have been suggested for treating the experimental data

---

* We do not mean to imply that this is the only difficulty simply because it is the only intrinsic one. Other causes of energy spread in the electron beam are electric fields within the ion source, either applied or due to space charge; and space charge, surface charges, and/or contact potentials may cause the mean energy of the electron beam to be uncertain by as much as a volt. For details of experimental technique, the reader is referred to the abundant literature on this subject (97, 100).

so as to circumvent this difficulty; none of the methods is based on really solid theoretical ground, and none of them is really convincing, since they are all based on discussions of what would be the situation if the experimental curves exhibited some idealized shape which they are, in fact, known not to possess.

There are three main techniques for circumventing the thermal spread in electron energies. One, due to Clarke (54) and used also by Hutchison (172), is to pass the electron beam through an energy monochromator. This technique rejects over 90% of the electrons originally available but produces an electron beam whose residual energy spread may be a small fraction of a volt. The second, due to Fox et al. (106, 253), involves modulating the energy of the electron beam through a narrow range and measuring, not the total ion current, but the variation in ion current when the electron beam energy is modulated, this change being due to a small and accurately known change in the energy of the electron beam. The third, due originally to Lossing and Tanaka (220) and extended by Inghram, Morrison, and others (169, 170, 254), involves the use of monochromatic ultraviolet light, rather than electrons, for accomplishing the ionization. This last method avoids completely any difficulties due to contact potentials or space charge, and the energy spread in the ultraviolet light beam may be made very small. Use of this method, however, requires an ultraviolet monochromator, and the experimental difficulties in producing an intense monochromatic ultraviolet light beam at wavelengths of 1000 A. and lower are formidable.

3.3.2. Reaction Kinetics Studies. Mass spectrometers are used to study the progress of chemical reactions both within the ion source and exterior to it. By using a probe consisting of a fine orifice in a sufficiently heat-resistant material, molecules, radicals, or even ions may be admitted directly to the mass spectrometer from a reaction zone. Lossing *et al.* (92, 216-220) have studied the intermediate products from mercury-photosensitized reactions; Eltenton (88), Bradt and Mohler (38) and Straus and Wall (344) have studied the intermediates in pyrolysis processes; Foner and Hudson (101) and others (118, 196, 291-292, 329-332) have studied flames directly; and Boyd (36) has studied chemical processes in arcs.

When a mass spectrometer ion source is operated at pressures high enough that intermolecular collisions within the ionization region become reasonably probable, the mass spectrum will exhibit peaks due to such collisions. These are called secondary ions, since they are formed by secondary processes; typical ones are H_3^+ due to $H^+ + H_2$; H_3O^+ due to $H^+ + H_2O$; and diatomic rare gas ions due to processes of the form $X^+ + X$. Ions due to secondary processes of this form can always be distinguished from normal ions by the fact that their abundance depends on the square of the pressure, whereas the abundance of normal ions is (ideally, at least) linear with pressure. Field *et al.* (98, 99) have used these effects to study reactions of gaseous ions within the ion source itself, operating the ion source at very high pressures to obtain reasonable intensities; ion molecule collision processes have also been described by Wells and Melton (385) and others (240, 242, 256, 309). These are among the first direct measurements of reaction rates and reaction cross sections of radicals and ions that have ever been obtained.

When a solid is evaporated, it will often be found that the composition or the structure of the vapor phase is different from that of the solid. Changes in composition can occur by thermal decomposition or by reaction with the crucible material. In a thermal emission ion source, the molecular species which appear in the mass spectrum may be quite different from those placed on the filament; $CsSO_4$ appears as Cs or CsO; Gd_2O_3 appears as GdO, etc. Inghram, Chupka, and Porter (177, 179, 280-281), Honig (165), Bickel and Holroyd (32), and others have studied metal-metal oxide systems and other vapor-solid equilibria, showing that oxides such as Al_2O_3 may appear either predominantly as AlO or, at much higher temperatures, as Al_2O_3, depending on whether the crucible used is metallic or made of refractory oxides. Often the thermodynamically preferred form of a given material in the vapor phase is different from that in the solid; WO_3, for example, tends to evaporate as W_3O_9; Sb vapor in equilibrium with elemental Sb has the preferred form Sb_4, and in contact with InSb alloy the preferred form is mainly Sb with a small amount of InSb molecule in the vapor phase (44). Many similar cases of vapor-phase association have been reported (39, 52, 81, 114, 163, 164, 180, 185, 188, 245, 310, 355). The necessity for molecular rearrangement in passing from the solid to the vapor phase may cause the evaporation rate of a material to be quite different from what would be predicted in the absence of such a rearrangement.

3.3.3. Metallurgy and Solid-State Physics. Undoubtedly the greatest contribution thus far made by mass spectrometry in the field of metallurgy and solid-state physics is in studying the effects of impurities which are undetectable by older methods. Metallic or solid impurities such as sulfur and phosphorus are detectable by present instruments and methods, using a high-frequency spark ion source and photographic plate ion detector, to levels of the order of $1:10^7$ to $1:10^8$. The detection limit for gaseous impurities depends largely on whether those impurities are present in the mass spectrometer background and whether means are provided to compensate for them if they are; in the case of a reasonably good vacuum system operated without background compensation, the detection limit for elements such as hydrogen, oxygen, and carbon (from the hydrocarbon and water vapor background) may be $1:10^4$ to $1:10^5$. With better vacuums and with compensation for background gases, it should be possible to push these detection limits down two orders of magnitude or more. If the dissolved or chemically combined gases which are to be studied are liberated during vacuum fusion (oxides, nitrides, hydrides, etc.), this can be done with quite simple instrumentation, as we have already mentioned. In some metals, however, vacuum fusion may be impracticable because the melting point is too high (tungsten, tantalum), or it may be unfeasible because the chemically combined material exists in an extraordinarily stable form (tungsten carbide, tantalum carbide, for example). In these cases the high-frequency spark ion source and the double-focusing resolving system must be used.

Certain alloys such as Ag-Be, Ag-Al, Cu-Be, Ni-Cr-Al, Si-B, and many others have the property that, when they are subjected to processing at appropriate temperatures in an atmosphere of appropriate composition, the more reactive component of the alloy can be made to diffuse to and oxidize at the surface so that, after such heat treatment, an alloy containing as little as (for example) a fraction of a per cent of aluminum or silicon may be covered with many monolayers of essentially pure aluminum or silicon oxide (288, 377). It follows that, by appropriate heat treatment, it is sometimes possible to build up a surface layer of contaminant on the surface of a sample and to identify the contaminant by the surface analysis technique of Ahearn, already mentioned (136), even when the bulk abundance is too low to permit direct analysis by any method.

3.3.4. Geology and Geochemistry. Mass spectrometry is applicable to three main problems in geology and geochemistry: (1) direct analysis of ores for minute traces of materials such as uranium or lead, (2) determination of the age of minerals, (3) determination of the conditions of origin of geological specimens. In the analysis of ores, the isotope dilution method already discussed (Section 3.1.2.) is used, although it is often desirable to introduce a refinement of the technique owing to the fact that the isotope ratio of a given material will vary from one natural deposit to another. Thus two samples are often processed, one a straight extract of the mineral and the other an extract containing an isotopically enriched tracer of the element to be determined; this permits the isotope ratio of the unenriched sample to be determined directly. In the most refined practice, three samples are processed: the first, an unenriched portion of the mineral; the second, the mixed sample; and the third, the isotopically enriched material used as a tracer. By this technique, any errors due to contamination by reagents, laboratory atmosphere, or dust, etc., are avoided. It is difficult to state a detection limit for determination of trace impurities by isotope dilution combined with chemical enrichment of the material sought, since so much depends on the efficiency of the chemical processing, the availability of hyperpure reagents, avoidance of cross-contamination, and the amount of material extracted; some elements are detectable in concentrations as low as $1:10^{12}$, and the absolute detection limit may be as low as 10^{-15} g. for some materials.

Geologic age determination rests on the fact that certain nuclides found in ores are the product of radioactive disintegration occurring in coexisting materials. In lead, for example, the Pb^{204} isotope is not a decay product of any radioactive series, whereas Pb^{206}, Pb^{207}, and Pb^{208} are decay products in the radioactive series of U^{238}, U^{235}, and Th^{232}, respectively. In minerals in which the U/Pb or Th/Pb abundance ratios are small, the lead isotope abundances can be taken as characteristic of nonradiogenic lead in that specimen; measurement of the lead isotope abundances in a coexisting mineral containing substantial amounts of U or Th then permits a deduction of the amounts of Pb^{206}, Pb^{207}, and Pb^{208} that are due to radioactive decay processes during the interval since the mineral was formed. This information, combined with a knowledge of the amounts of U or Th present and their known radioactive decay rates, permits a direct measurement of the age of the ore. The measurement can be based on either the Th/Pb^{208}, the U^{238}/Pb^{206}, or the U^{235}/Pb^{207} ratio. Since the U^{238}–Pb^{206} and the U^{235}–Pb^{207} decay processes have very different half-lives (4.56×10^9 years versus 0.71×10^9 years), it is possible to base an age determination on the ratio Pb^{206}/Pb^{207} alone, without knowledge of the abundance of U or Th; this method, due to Nier (258), is less subject to errors caused by leaching of some components of the mineral than any of the other techniques.

Estimates of geological age can also be based on the radioactive decay of K^{40} to A^{40} or Ca^{40} by K-electron capture or β-decay processes, respectively. Thus one would expect the ratio A^{40}/A^{36} to be higher in geologically old minerals than in atmospheric argon, which Aldrich and Nier (1) demonstrated was indeed the case. If one assumes that the A^{40} in the atmosphere was generated by radioactive decay of K^{40} during a period from a time t_0 when the earth was a molten mass to a time t_1 when the earth solidified, and that no substantial evolution of A^{40} occurred after the earth solidified at a time t_1, then a knowledge of the relevant abundances and half-lives permits estimation of time t_1 from an assumed t_0, or vice versa. Such a calculation has been done by Chackett (51), who finds for $t_1 = 2 \times 10^9$ years, $t_0 = 3.5 \times 10^9$; for $t_1 = 1 \times 10^9$, $t_0 = 3.1 \times 10^9$. These figures are in general agreement with other estimates of the age of the earth.

Urey has shown theoretically (365) and confirmed experimentally (363, 367) that conditions of chemical equilibrium are sensitive to the isotopic weights of the chemical species involved so that the isotope distribution between two coexisting chemical compounds, or two phases of the same compound, will be different, the difference depending slightly on the temperature.* Thus, for example, the O^{18}/O^{16} ratio in CO_2 will in general be somewhat greater than the same ratio in water with which the CO_2 is in contact (or in solution), the difference amounting to about 4% at room temperature. This provides a means for estimation of temperatures at which some fossil deposits were laid down (366); in the deposition of $CaCO_3$ by sea animals, for instance, the O^{18} abundance in the $CaCO_3$ deposit depends not only on the oxygen isotope ratios in the ambient water but on the temperature. The temperature coefficients involved are small, and the requirements on the stability and accuracy of the mass spectrometer are extremely stringent; nevertheless McKinney et al. (224) have been able to make the required measurements with accuracy sufficient to permit estimation of paleotemperatures within better than 1°C. Differences in the O^{18}/O^{16} isotope ratio also exist in the case of silicates (57, 171), the ratio being highest in diatomites and lower for basalts and basic rocks generally. Nier and Gulbransen have been able to show (263) that the C^{13}/C^{12} isotope ratio in carbon deposits is greater in limestone than in carbon of organic origin; similar variations in boron (350), sulfur, and nitrogen (349) are known to exist but are not so well understood.

3.3.5. Biochemistry. The course of a specific chemical compound through a biochemical process can be followed by preparing the compound in question from isotopically enriched raw materials so that the compound introduced can be distinguished from the same compound that may already have been present in the system. The isotopic tag may be an artificially radioactive isotope or an abnormal concentration of a stable one. The tagged compound is introduced by a convenient route, and after a suitable time the abundance of the isotopic tag is determined in an appropriate compound isolated from the organs, excreta, etc., of the experimental subject.

For some purposes radioactive isotopes are used as tracers, since the radioactive counting equipment required is comparatively simple. The elements mainly of interest to the biochemist, however, are H, C, N, O, and S, of which only H^3, C^{14}, and S^{35} exhibit radioactivity of convenient half-life. Since none of these elements occurs in nature, there can be some

---

* In the vapor-liquid equilibria of the BF_3–dimethyl ether complex, for example, the $B^{11}F_3$ is dominant in the vapor phase, the $B^{10}F_3$ being sufficiently enriched in the liquid phase that the process forms the basis for a highly efficient method of bulk separation of B^{10}.

doubt whether the reactions of compounds containing them (particularly H^3) will reproduce faithfully the behavior of the isotopically normal counterpart, and many workers find the radioactivity itself objectionable, particularly with human subjects. Stable isotopes can be used as tracers, however; in this event, the isotopes present in the tagged compound may be the same as those occurring naturally, only the relative abundances being different; all five of the elements of interest are available in isotopically enriched form, and there is of course no radiation hazard. In the use of stable isotopes, the isotope ratio of the substance to be studied is determined by mass spectrometer; the mass spectrometric technique has the further advantage over radioactive tracer techniques that, in the case of complex melecules, the position of the isotopic tag within the molecule can often be determined.

The first use of mass spectrometry in studying the fate of compounds tagged with stable isotopes was by Schoenheimer and Rittenberg (318) in 1938. Their results, originally on amino acid metabolism, later extended to the metabolism of fatty acids, led to the then radically new concept of the "dynamic state of body constituents," in which the apparently static, or nearly static, chemical state of many body constituents was shown to be not the result of a low interaction rate with the surroundings but the result of quite rapid opposing reactions at nearly equal rates—a distinction of fundamental importance that could have been made only by the use of isotopically tagged compounds (317). Among the other data obtained by the use of stable isotopes are that the average life span of a water molecule in the human body is about 14 days; that the life of a human red blood cell is about 127 days; and that CO_2 is not merely a metabolic end product, as had previously been thought, but a constituent of some biosynthetic reactions.

Biochemical analyses often require determination of the amount of some substance (121), such as the amount of a specific amino acid in a complex mixture, or the total oxygen in a biological specimen; such determination can be made by the isotope dilution technique already discussed (Section 3.1.2). Continuous breath analysis by mass spectrometer is of value both in monitoring anesthetic gas, CO_2, and oxygen levels during surgery (359) and in studies of lung function (15).

3.3.6. Nuclear Physics and Nuclear Chemistry. Perhaps the first application of mass spectrometry to the study of nuclear chemistry was Aston's demonstration that the isotope ratio of radiogenic lead was markedly different from that of nonradiogenic lead; shortly thereafter Smythe *et al.* determined, by mass spectrometric separation of submicrogram quantities of the isotopes, that it is the K^{40} isotope which is responsible for the radioactivity of potassium (334). The correlation of precise nuclear mass measurements (182, 189, 236, 286, 287) with the energy yields of nuclear reactions is a subject of continuing fundamental interest; more recently, mass spectrometry has been used in a wide variety of other problems. A general discussion of these applications has been given by Inghram (174), and we shall mention only a few, and briefly, here.

The determination of half-lives in a radioactive decay chain, as well as the positive identification of the processes involved, is a problem in which the mass spectrometer may be a very powerful, almost indispensable, tool. In the case of materials having fairly long half-lives the growth of the decay product abundance can often be measured directly; in the case of materials of short half-life (such as 5-day Xe^{123}), it may be more convenient to measure the decay of the parent substance. Determination of neutron absorption cross sections can be done by measuring the isotope abundances of a sample before and after neutron irradiation. In identification and quantitative determination of the products resulting from such processes as spallation or other high-energy nuclear reactions, the ability of the mass spectrometer to perform analyses on very minute samples may make it uniquely powerful; Gordan and Friedman have used mass spectrometric techniques to identify the products of target irradiations on the Brookhaven cosmotron where there were as few as 10^8 atoms of the material to be identified.

In discovery and assignment of mass to radioactive isotopes, the material may be collected in a specially designed target chamber or simply allowed to deposit on a suitable surface such as a photographic plate. Even gases can be collected in measurable quantities, on a metal or other surface, if they are driven into the surface with energies of several thousand volts. Determination of the amount and nature of the radioactivity, and identification of the isotope responsible for it, may then be done by conventional counting techniques or (less quantitatively, but more appropriate for longer-lived isotopes of low specific activity) by placing the surface in contact with a photographic plate for some hours or days and examining the plate, after development, to determine where it is darkened by the radioactivity.

4. Recent Developments in Mass Spectrometry

The typical laboratory mass spectrometer, together with its auxiliary equipment, may easily occupy a volume of 100 cubic feet or more and will incorporate, among other things, a magnet weighing from several score to a few thousand pounds. Yet there are many routine problems in which the high performance and great versatility of such instruments are not fully used, and there has been a growing trend in recent years toward mass spectrometer instrumentation which is lighter, smaller, and less costly than the more conventional laboratory instruments but which retains sufficiently high performance to be useful at least in restricted classes of problems. This trend has resulted in the development of a great variety of instruments, based on both old and new principles, of which we shall mention several here. We shall confine ourselves to instruments of which at least one working model has actually been built; to include the many additional ones which exist only on paper would serve no useful purpose. Since only a small part of the cost of a mass spectrometer installation is accounted for by the cost of the mass resolving system itself, it can be anticipated that the more novel mass spectrometers will have no great cost advantage over older ones of equal versatility; the advantages, where there are any, lie in their detailed adaptability to one or another special problem.

4.1. Linear Transit-Time Mass Resolving Systems

An ion of mass m (atomic mass units), of charge q (units of electron charge), and possessing kinetic energy V (volts), moves with a linear velocity v (centimeters per second) given by

$$v = 9.8 \times 10^5 \, (2qV/m)^{\frac{1}{2}} \tag{9}$$

If a short pulse of ions, initially heterogeneous in mass, is permitted to move down a tube or radially outward from an axis of symmetry, the pulse will disperse because the lighter ions move faster, so that, after moving through an appropriate distance, the initial pulse will have separated into individual groups in which all the ions in any one group have the same mass. Instruments based on this principle seem to have been invented almost simultaneously by Berry (25), by Koppius (200), and by Stephens (338). It is possible to effect a substantial improvement in resolving power in instruments of this type by passing the ion pulses through a "bunching" voltage, exactly analogous to the bunching voltage applied to electrons in a klystron tube, which reduces the time required for a given bunch to pass a given point in the drift tube without affecting the time interval between one bunch and the next, thus improving the mass resolution substantially. Instruments bearing this improvement have been described by Stephens (339), by Glenn (125), by Wiley and McLaren (392), and by Bay (17). Usually, the ion pulses are passed through a grid arrangement biased to prevent any ions getting through except when a narrow voltage pulse—a "gating" pulse—is applied, so that only ions having a narrowly prescribed transit time can pass through the gate grid to an ion collector located behind it. In Bay's form, all the ion pulses are permitted to strike the collector and eject secondary electrons, the grating pulse being applied to the secondary electron collector instead; in Wiley and McLaren's form (Fig. 19) all the ion pulses are permitted to strike the cathode of an electron multiplier, and either one can apply the gating voltage pulse to the electron multiplier, using a conventional electrometer to measure the ion current delivered by ions of a given mass, or one can maintain steady voltages on the electron multiplier and display the entire spectrum on an oscilloscope, as was first done by Stephens (339).

This type of mass spectrometer is interesting mainly because one can, in principle, display with it a complete mass spectrum of ions all of

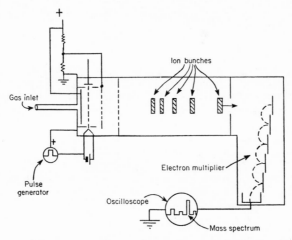

FIG. 19. The pulsed linear transit-time mass resolving system. In this figure, the form described by Wiley and McLaren is shown.

which were formed at a common instant in time, a feature that was formerly possessed only by the Mattauch instrument. Unfortunately, in instruments of reasonable size and operating with reasonable mass resolution, the number of ions per pulse is limited by space charge to about 10^4 ions so that the statistical uncertainty in the charge delivered by any single bunch is about 1%; the intrinsic uncertainty in measurement of a component of 1% abundance is about 10%, and the statistical uncertainty for contaminants (1000 p.p.m. or lower) is hopelessly high, when these instruments are operated on a "one-shot" basis. These are the intrinsic limits. The limits actually obtained in practice are, as discussed in Section 2.3.4, higher than this; Kistiakowsky and Kydd (195) quote an experimental uncertainty somewhat greater than three times the theoretical limit, giving an over-all uncertainty of 13% in determining the abundance of the Ne^{22} isotope (8.8% abundance) and 0.5% as the minimum reliably detectable concentration of minor components.

In a second form of linear nonmagnetic mass spectrometer the ion beam is passed through a series of accelerating gaps to which alternating voltages are applied, the gaps being driven at such frequencies and in such relative phases that ions having a preassigned transit time (velocity) will gain more energy than any others. Instruments based on this principle have been described by Smythe (333), Bennett (20), Redhead and Crowell (290), Townsend (361), Wherry and Karasek (386), and

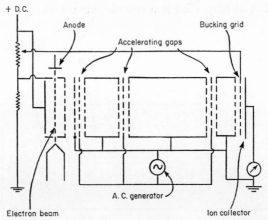

FIG. 20. Continuous linear transit-time mass resolving system. The form shown here, basically similar to Bennett's, is one in which the desired ions gain more energy from the radio-frequency gaps than any others and all but the desired ions are rejected by a bucking grid placed in front of the ion collector.

Donner (78). (Note that the energy gain may be negative, as in Donner's form.) The desired ions, having energy different from the remainder, may be separated either by an electrostatic filter (Smythe, Donner) or simply by biasing the collector so that only the most energetic ions can reach it (Bennett). In resolving systems of this type, ions may be admitted continuously; however, the ions which experience the maximum energy gain from the accelerating gap array are those which not only have optimum transit velocity but enter the gap array at a narrowly defined optimum instant with respect to the phase of the gap voltages. Since these instruments may in principle employ ion beams having a cross-section of several square centimeters (although none has ever actually done so), the total ion currents which can be injected into the gap array may be much higher than can be obtained from conventional ion sources with defining slits, but the phase discrimination in such instruments is so high when they are operated with reasonable mass resolution that the ion currents actually received at the collector are no higher—in fact, they tend to be a little lower—than in mass spectrometers of conventional type (Fig. 20). Mathematical analyses of mass spectrometers of this type have been given recently by Kerr (187) and by Cannon and Testerman (48).

The linear transit-time instruments discussed above have the common property that they are, strictly speaking, velocity spectrometers, not mass spectrometers, so that they are as sensitive to changes in the energy of the ion beam as they are to a difference in the mass of the ions being resolved. Thus they require an accurately monoenergetic ion beam in order to obtain reasonably high mass resolving power, a property that they share with the simple sector-type mass spectrometers.* Since they are velocity spectrometers, they are insensitive to metastable processes; the velocity of the fragments is (approximately) preserved in a metastable transition, and the fragments from a metastable transition proceed through the mass resolving system separately about as well as they would together. Metastables are automatically rejected at the collector because of their kinetic energy deficit, in both the Smythe-Mattauch and the Bennett forms, whereas in the collector-gated (Glenn) and the electron-multiplier (Bay, Wiley and McLaren) forms, metastable fragments are indistinguishable from the unfragmented molecules because the transit times are essentially the same.

There is one linear nonmagnetic mass spectrometer which is a true mass spectrometer and which passes ion current continuously without the low duty cycle that is characteristic of all other instruments of this type. That is the instrument described by Paul and Raether (274), in which ions are injected down the axis of symmetry of an alternating electrostatic field maintained between four long cylindrical conductors. The first-order mathematical analysis of this instrument tends to be somewhat sophisticated, and we know of no studies of second-order aberrations, space charge, or other secondary effects. The instrument appears to offer particular promise in bulk separation of isotopes, although it is too new as yet to permit any prediction as to what its ultimate place will be.

4.2. Instruments Based on Cyclotron Resonance

A singly charged ion of mass m (atomic mass units), moving in a plane normal to a uniform magnetic field of strength B (gauss), describes

---

* In any pulsed mass spectrometer it is possible to operate the ion source in such a way as to compensate, to first order, for energy spreads of a given magnitude, and Wiley and McLaren have done this in their instrument, improving the resolving power substantially.

a circular trajectory at an angular frequency ω (radian per second) given by

$$\omega = 9.6 \times 10^3 \, B/m \qquad (10)$$

If one superposes on the magnetic field a transverse alternating electric field in which there exists a component of frequency ω, then ions of mass m will gain energy continuously, the radii of their circular orbits

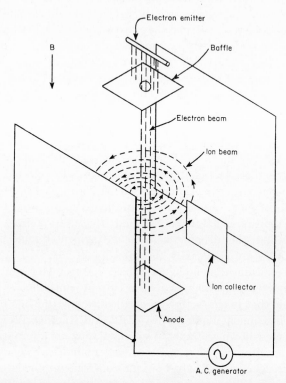

FIG. 21. The ion resonance mass resolving system (omegatron). The entire system is immersed in a magnetic field having the direction shown in the figure.

will therefore increase monotonically and indefinitely, and they will eventually describe an orbit large enough to reach and be collected on a suitable collector electrode, no matter how far from the point of origin it may be placed. An ion of mass $m' \neq m$, on the other hand, will gain energy for a limited time only and will describe a series of roughly circular orbits in which the radii vary cyclically and are bounded. Thus by suitably relating the collector location, the amplitude and frequency of the electric field, and the magnetic field strength, it can be arranged that ions of only one mass at a time can be collected. The first reported use of this principle was in 1939 when Alvarez and Cornog (4) used a cyclotron as a mass spectrometer to establish the existence of He^3. The first published account of an instrument designed specifically as a mass spectrometer based on this principle was by Sommer et al. (335), followed by several others (19, 86, 289, 371); Hipple's designation "omegatron" for instruments based on this principle has become part of the nomenclature of mass spectrometry (Fig. 21). Perhaps the most satisfactory mathematical treatment of the omegatron has been given by Berry (26).

The continuous absorption of energy from the r.f. field by resonant ions constitutes a load on the r.f. supply, and it is possible to detect resonant ions and estimate their abundance by their loading effects on the r.f. power supply as well as by their actual collection on an electrode provided for the purpose; instruments operating on this principle have been described by Lazukin (211) and by Woodford and Gardner (393). Instruments also based on cyclotron resonance, but differing, in some cases materially, from Hipple's omegatron, have been described by Goudsmit (128), by Smith and Damm (328), and by others.

The omegatron has two characteristics which make it very appealing in some cases. First is the fact that the ionizing electron beam may work with very high efficiency, since there are no slits, and high efficiency is not incompatible with high mass resolution as it is in most other instruments. Second is the fact that the operation depends on an intrinsic property of the ions and is comparatively (though not entirely) independent of any initial energies with which ions may be formed. There are several serious problems inherent in this technique, however. The transit time of the ions, between formation and collection, may be tens to hundreds of times as long as in more conventional instruments, and during all this time the ions are exposed to disturbances due to space charge, gas scattering, discrimination, stray accidental surface charges, metastable processes, etc. Thus the omegatron may show very high efficiency, in terms of resolved ion current per unit ionizing current, but space charge effects are so large that the maximum permissible ion current may actually be substantially smaller than in a more conventional instrument; discrimination effects are so high that the ion current efficiency may be essentially zero unless a trapping field is applied to control discrimination and hold the ions near the plane of symmetry until they can be collected, whereupon the instrument may show detuning due to the trapping field itself, harmonic effects due to harmonic content in the alternating electric field or to nonuniformities in the magnetic field, etc. Typical operating parameters in the omegatron have been discussed by Edwards (86); secondary effects and their control have been discussed by Brubaker and Perkins (45).

A final instrument which is also based, in a sense, on cyclotron resonance is the cycloidal-focusing mass spectrometer invented by Bleakney, built first by Bleakney and Hipple (34) and later by Mariner and Bleakney (228), by Monk *et al.* (251), and by Robinson and Hall (301). This instrument shows higher mass resolving power, sensitivity, and analytical accuracy than any other mass spectrometer of comparable size and weight, and there are indications that it may soon become the dominant form in routine analysis of gas and volatile liquid mixtures of molecular weight below about 200 a.m.u., although it is a truly convenient form only in cases where the sample can be piped to the ion source and where ion currents can be measured conveniently without the use of an electron multiplier.

5. The Future of Mass Spectrometry

5.1. MASS RESOLVING SYSTEMS

We believe that the cycloidal-focusing resolving system will become the dominant one in routine gas and volatile liquid analysis, including the identification of background gases and the measurement of total pressure in vacuum systems. In applications where identification of ions from (for instance) a high-temperature reaction zone or an arc is required, the nonmagnetic resolving systems will be found useful; where higher performance is needed than the nonmagnetic systems have thus far shown any signs of being able to give, sector-type or tandem instruments with a nonmagnetic ion source will be found applicable. We believe that in research instrumentation there are the beginnings of a trend toward modular systems in which a single basic mass resolving system can be used with a variety of ion sources or ion detecting means to adapt the system to one or another specific problem, analogous to the modular approach that has become accepted practice in the manufacture of equipment for emission spectroscopy, electron microscopy, etc. In the mass range below about mass 200, or in applications requiring mass resolving power less than about 1:350, we believe that future improvements will lie in the areas of reduced cost, improved reliability, and ease of maintenance, and that simpler and more refined design of presently available hardware will be the rule. In the mass range above about 300 a.m.u., or in applications requiring very high mass resolving power, or in many research situations, we believe that tandem double-focusing instruments, of designs that are now generally known, will see wide use.

5.2. Accessories and Materials

Certain specialized applications of mass spectrometry require specialized accessories. We believe that the use of both electron multipliers and photographic plates for ion detection will increase in absolute (though perhaps not in relative) numbers of instruments involved. For measurement of appearance potentials, we believe that an electron gun incorporating some form of energy monochromator, perhaps similar to Clarke's, will be widely used.

Ion sources containing tungsten emitters have the intrinsic difficulty that the temperature distribution in, and therefore the electron distribution from, the tungsten emitter is affected by carburization and decarburization as it is exposed to hydrocarbons or to oxidizing materials, respectively (112, 129). Indications are that rhenium emitters show these effects to a much smaller degree than tungsten, if needed they exhibit the effects at all (303). Thus we predict that rhenium will replace tungsten in many mass spectrometer applications, perhaps including the thermal emission ion source in which application its merits have already been discussed (Section 2.2.4). As materials technology improves, the performance of heated inlet systems will undoubtedly be made better by improvements in materials or in improved utilization of presently available materials.

Special-purpose mass spectrometers, such as are used in process-monitoring, can almost always provide the desired information from a few selected peaks without displaying the entire mass spectrum. This fact was first exploited by Hipple (155) and a little later by Robinson *et al.* (304); we believe that it will become accepted practice in many situations for an instrument to monitor only a few peaks and to incorporate simple automatic data-processing devices for displaying the analytical results desired in the simplest form. In large plant-control laboratories, automatic digitizing equipment will be used to prepare the mass spectrometer data for insertion into computing equipment.

5.3. Applications

There are three areas in which we believe that mass spectrometry will contribute to major breakthroughs in science and technology in the foreseeable future. The first is in metallurgy, where the ability of the mass spectrometer to detect both bulk and surface contaminants to levels that are in numerous cases several orders of magnitude lower than any competing technique will make it indispensable in studies of the role of impurities in metallurgy and solid-state physics and in corrosion processes. The ability of the mass spectrometer to perform general analyses of solids, largely without the enormous interferences that characterize emission spectroscopy, will, we believe, make it a standard analytical tool in the metallurgical research laboratory.

As mass spectrometers of very high resolving power (over 1:2500) become available, we believe that they will be applied to both qualitative and quantitative analyses where there is now no satisfactory way to obtain the desired information. The combination of such instruments with preliminary separative techniques such as gas chromatography (31, 80) should make possible a true quantum jump in our understanding of such problems as the chemistry of odors, air pollution, and many other presently insoluble problems.

Mass spectrometers of very high resolving power will be applied, as they become available, to the study of very heavy molecules. O'Neal and his co-workers (58, 268, 269) and others (41, 53, 87, 143, 221, 222, 239) have already done substantial work in this area, and indications are that the understanding of the nature of complex materials, especially organics, will be greatly extended by mass spectrometric work in this area when the necessary instrumentation is more highly developed.

6. Acknowledgments

The author's thanks are expressed to C. E. Berry, H. F. Wiley, and G. D. Perkins of Consolidated Electrodynamics Corporation, and to Professor James N. Pitts of the University of California, all of whom have reviewed one or another draft of this presentation and offered helpful comments thereon.

References

1. Aldrich, L. T., and Nier, A. O., *Phys. Rev.* **74**, 876 (1948).
2. Alekseevskii, N. E., Prudkovskii, G. P., Kossourov, G. I., and Filiminov, S. I., *Doklady Akad. Nauk S.S.S.R.* **100**, 229 (1955).
3. Allen, J. S., *Phys. Rev.* **55**, 336, 966 (1939).
4. Alvarez, L. W., and Cornog, R., *Phys. Rev.* **56**, 379 (1939).
5. Aston, F. W., *Proc. Roy. Soc.* **A115**, 487 (1927).
6. Aston, F. W., "Mass Spectra and Isotopes," p. 75. Longmans, New York, 1942.
7. Aston, F. W., and Fowler, R. H., *Phil. Mag.* **43**, 514 (1922).
8. Bainbridge, K. T., *J. Franklin Inst.* **212**, 489 (1931).
9. Bainbridge, K. T., *Phys. Rev.* **44**, 123 (1933).
10. Bainbridge, K. T., and Jordan, E. B., *Phys. Rev.* **50**, 282 (1936).
11. Barber, N. F., *Proc. Leeds Phil. Lit. Soc. Sci. Sect.* **2**, 427 (1933).
12. Barnard, G. P., "Modern Mass Spectrometry." Institute of Physics, London, 1953.
13. Barnard, G. P., "Mass Spectrometer Researches." Dept. Sci. and Ind. Res., Natl. Phys. Lab., London, 1956.

14. Barnett, C. F., Evans, G. E., and Stier, P. M., *Rev. Sci. Instr.* **25**, 1112 (1954).
15. Bartels, J., Severinghaus, J. W., Forster, R. E., Briscoe, W. A., and Bates, O. V., *J. Clin. Invest.* **33**, 41 (1954).
16. Bay, Z. L., *Rev. Sci. Instr.* **12**, 127 (1941).
17. Bay, Z. L., U.S. patent 2,768,303 (1956).
18. Begun, G. M., and Melton, C. E., *J. Chem. Phys.* **25**, 1292 (1956).
19. Bell, R. L., *J. Sci. Instr.* **33**, 269 (1956).
20. Bennett, W. H., *J. Appl. Phys.* **21**, 143, 723 (1950).
21. Berkowitz, J., Chupka, W. A., and Inghram, M. G., *J. Chem. Phys.* **27**, 85 (1957).
22. Bernstein, R. B., Semeluk, G. P., and Arends, C. B., *Anal. Chem.* **25**, 139 (1953).
23. Berry, C. E., *J. Chem. Phys.* **17**, 1164 (1949).
24. Berry, C. E., *Phys. Rev.* **78**, 597 (1950).
25. Berry, C. E., U.S. patent 2,691,108 (1954).
26. Berry, C. E., *J. Appl. Phys.* **25**, 28 (1954).
27. Berry, C. E., *Rev. Sci. Instr.* **27**, 849 (1956).
28. Berry, C. E., Wilcox, D. E., Rock, S. M., and Washburn, H. W., *J. Appl. Phys.* **17**, 262 (1946).
29. Beynon, J. H., *Nature* **174**, 735 (1954).
30. Beynon, J. H., American Society for Testing Materials Committee E-14 on Mass Spectrometry, 1955 (unpublished).
31. Beynon, J. H., *Mikrochim. Acta* **1**, 437 (1956).
32. Bickel, P. W., and Holroyd, L. V., *J. Chem. Phys.* **22**, 1793 (1954).
33. Bleakney, W., *Am. Phys. Teacher* **4**, 12 (1936).
34. Bleakney, W., and Hipple, J. A., *Phys. Rev.* **53**, 521 (1938).
35. Blears, J., *J. Sci. Instr. Suppl.* **1** (1951).
36. Boyd, R. L. F., *Nature* **165**, 142 (1950).
37. Bradley, R. C., *Phys. Rev.* **93**, 719 (1954).
38. Bradt, P., and Mohler, F. L., *Anal. Chem.* **27**, 875 (1955).
39. Bradt, P., Mohler, F. L., and Dibeler, V. H., *J. Research Natl. Bur. Standards* **57**, 223 (1956).
40. Brown, R. A., Melpolder, F. W., and Young, W. S., *Petrol. Processing* **7**, 204 (1952).
41. Brown, R. A., and Young, W. S., *Anal. Chem.* **26**, 1653 (1954).
42. Brubaker, W. M., *J. Appl. Phys.* **26**, 1007 (1955).
43. Brubaker, W. M., American Society for Testing Materials Committee E-14 on Mass Spectrometry, 1957 (unpublished).
44. Brubaker, W. M., private communication (1957).
45. Brubaker, W. M., and Perkins, G. D., *Rev. Sci. Instr.* **27**, 720 (1956).
46. Caldirola, P., and Rossi, G., *Nuovo Cimento* **5**, 1316 (1957).
47. Cameron, A. E., *Rev. Sci. Instr.* **25**, 1154 (1954).
48. Cannon, W. W., and Testerman, M. K., *J. Appl. Phys.* **27**, 1283 (1956).
49. Carpenter, L. G., and Mair, W. N., *J. Sci. Instr.* **34**, 110 (1957).
50. Catch, J. R., *Anal. Chem.* **29**, 1726 (1957).
51. Chackett, K. F., *Phys. Rev.* **81**, 1057 (1951).
52. Chupka, W. A., and Inghram, M. G., *J. Chem. Phys.* **22**, 1472 (1954).
53. Claiborne, E. B., Davis, H. M., and Rivet, C. A., Jr., *Anal. Chem.* **28**, 1104 (1956).
54. Clarke, E. M., *Can. J. Phys.* **32**, 764 (1954).
55. Clarke, W. W. H., and Jacob, L., *J. Appl. Phys.* **27**, 1519 (1956).

56. Classen, W., Jahrbuch I. Hamburg Wiss. Anst., Beiheft (1907).
57. Clayton, R. N., Epstein, S., and Engel, A. E. J., *J. Geol.* **66**, 374 (1958).
58. Clerc, R. J., Hood, A., and O'Neal, M. J., Jr., *Anal. Chem.* **27**, 869 (1955).
59. Cohen, A. A., *Phys. Rev.* **63**, 219 (1943).
60. Collin, J., *Bull. Soc. Roy. Sci. Liège* **21**, 446 (1953).
61. Collins, T. L., Rourke, F. M., and White, F. A., *Phys. Rev.* **105**, 196 (1957).
62. Conrad, W., *Physik. Z.* **31**, 888 (1930).
63. Consolidated Electrodynamics Corporation Model X 5501.
64. Cowan, J. A., *Can. J. Phys.* **32**, 101 (1954).
65. Craig, R. D., Errock, G. A., and Waldron, J. D., American Society for Testing Materials Committee E-14 on Mass Spectrometry, 1957 (unpublished).
66. Dagnall, B. D., "Applied Mass Spectrometry," p. 303. Institute of Petroleum, London, 1954.
67. Datz, S., and Taylor, E. H., *J. Chem. Phys.* **25**, 389 (1956).
68. Datz, S., and Taylor, E. H., *J. Chem. Phys.* **25**, 395 (1956).
69. Dechend, H. von, and Hammer, W., *Proc. Heidelberg Acad. Sci.* **21**, 12 (1910).
70. Dempster, A. J., *Phys. Rev.* **11**, 316 (1918).
71. Dempster, A. J., *Proc. Am. Phil. Soc.* **75**, 755 (1935).
72. Dempster, A. J., *Rev. Sci. Instr.* **7**, 46 (1936).
73. Dibeler, V. H., *J. Research Natl. Bur. Standards* **49**, 235 (1952).
74. Dibeler, V. H., Reese, R. M., and Mohler, F. L., *J. Research Natl. Bur. Standards* **57**, 113 (1956).
75. Dibeler, V. H., Reese, R. M., and Mohler, F. L., *J. Chem. Phys.* **26**, 304 (1957).
76. Dole, M., *Chem. Revs.* **51**, 263 (1952).
77. Dole, M., and Lane, G. A., *J. Chem. Phys.* **22**, 949 (1954).
78. Donner, W., *Appl. Spectroscopy* **8**, 157 (1954).
79. Donner, W., Johns, T., and Gallaway, W. S., American Society for Testing Materials Committee E-14 on Mass Spectrometry, 1957 (unpublished).
80. Drew, C. M., McNesby, J. R., Smith, S. R., and Gordon, A. S., *Anal. Chem.* **28**, 979 (1956).
81. Drowart, J., and Honig, R. E., *J. Chem. Phys.* **25**, 581 (1956).
82. Duckworth, H. E., *Rev. Sci. Instr.* **21**, 54 (1949).
83. Dudenbostel, B. F., and Priestley, W., *Anal. Chem.* **26**, 1275 (1954).
84. Duncan, J. F., and Warren, D. T., *Brit. J. Appl. Phys.* **5**, 66 (1954).
85. Dunning, W. J., "Mass Spectrometry," p. 96. Institute of Petroleum, London, 1952.
86. Edwards, A. G., *Brit. J. Appl. Phys.* **6**, 44 (1955).
87. Ehrhardt, H., and Osberghaus, O., *Z. Naturforsch.* **13a**, 16 (1958).
88. Eltenton, G. C., *J. Chem. Phys.* **15**, 455 (1947).
89. Ennos, A. E., *Brit. J. Appl. Phys.* **4**, 101 (1953).
90. Ennos, A. E., *Brit. J. Appl. Phys.* **5**, 27 (1954).
91. Ewald, H., and Hintenberger, H., "Methoden und Anwendungen der Massenspektroskopie." Verlag Chemie GMBH, Weinheim/Bergstrasse (1953).
92. Farmer, J. B., Henderson, I. H. S., Lossing, F. P., and Marsden, D. G. H., *J. Chem. Phys.* **24**, 348 (1956).
93. Farmer, J. B., and Lossing, F. P., *Can. J. Chem.* **33**, 861 (1955).
94. Farmer, J. B., Lossing, F. P., Marsden, D. G. H., and McDowell, C. A., *J. Chem. Phys.* **24**, 52 (1956).
95. Farmer, J. B., Lossing, F. P., Marsden, D. G. H., and Steacie, E. W. R., *J. Chem. Phys.* **23**, 1169 (1955).

96. Field, F. H., and Franklin, J. L., *J. Chem. Phys.* **22,** 1895 (1954).
97. Field, F. H., and Franklin, J. L., "Electron Impact Phenomena and the Properties of Gaseous Ions." Academic Press, New York, 1957.
98. Field, F. H., Franklin, J. L., and Lampe, F. W., *J. Am. Chem. Soc.* **79,** 2419 (1957).
99. Field, F. H., Franklin, J. L., and Lampe, F. W., *J. Am. Chem. Soc.* **79,** 2665 (1957).
100. Field, F. H., and Hastings, S. H., *Anal. Chem.* **28,** 1248 (1956).
101. Foner, S. N., and Hudson, R. L., *J. Chem. Phys.* **21,** 1374 (1953).
102. Foner, S. N., and Hudson, R. L., *J. Chem. Phys.* **25,** 602 (1956).
103. Forrester, A. T., and Whalley, W. B., *Rev. Sci. Instr.* **17,** 549 (1946).
104. Fox, R. E., *J. Chem. Phys.* **26,** 1281 (1957).
105. Fox, R. E., and Hickam, W. M., *J. Chem. Phys.* **22,** 2059 (1954).
106. Fox, R. E., Hickam, W. M., Grove, D. J., and Kjeldaas, T., Jr., *Rev. Sci. Instr.* **26,** 1101 (1955).
107. Fox, R. E., and Hipple, J. A., *Rev. Sci. Instr.* **19,** 462 (1948).
108. Franck, J., *Z. Elektrochem.* **36,** 581 (1930).
109. Frank, R. C., and Swets, D. E., *J. Appl. Phys.* **28,** 380 (1957).
110. Freeman, J. B., and Serfass, E. J., *Anal. Chem.* **26,** 1403 (1954).
111. Friedel, R. A., and Sharkey, A. G., Jr., *Anal. Chem.* **28,** 940 (1956).
112. Friedel, R. A., Sharkey, A. G., Jr., Schultz, J. L., and Humbert, C. R., *Anal. Chem.* **25,** 1314 (1953).
113. Friedel, R. A., Schultz, J. L., and Sharkey, A. G., Jr., *Anal. Chem.* **28,** 926 (1956).
114. Friedman, L., *J. Chem. Phys.* **23,** 477 (1955).
115. Friedman, L., and Long, F. A., *J. Am. Chem. Soc.* **75,** 2832 (1953).
116. Friedman, L., Long, F. A., and Wolfsberg, M., *J. Chem. Phys.* **26,** 714 (1957).
117. Friedman, L., Long, F. A., and Wolfsberg, M., *J. Chem. Phys.* **27,** 613 (1957).
118. Friedman, R., and Cyphers, J. A., *J. Chem. Phys.* **23,** 1875 (1955).
119. Fritts, B. K., and Peattie, C. G., *Anal. Chem.* **28,** 1518 (1956).
120. Frost, D. C., and McDowell, C. A., *Proc. Roy. Soc.* **A241,** 194 (1957).
121. Gaebler, O. H., American Society for Testing Materials Committee E-14 on Mass Spectrometry, 1957 (unpublished).
122. Garnyk, G. A., and Samarin, A. M., *Izvest. Akad. Nauk S.S.S.R.*, **5,** 77 (1957).
123. Gehrcke, E., and Reichenheim, O., *Verhandl. Deut. Physik. Ges.* **8,** 559 (1906); **9,** 76, 200, 376 (1907); **10,** 217 (1908).
124. Gifford, A. P., Rock, S. M., and Comaford, D. J., *Anal. Chem.* **21,** 1026 (1949).
125. Glenn, W. E., Jr., U. S. patent 2,758,214 (1956); University of California Radiation Laboratory Report 1628 (January 10, 1952).
126. Goldstein, E., *Berlin. Ber.* **39,** 691 (1886).
127. Gorman, J. G., Jones, E. J., and Hipple, J. A., *Anal. Chem.* **23,** 438 (1951).
128. Goudsmit, S. A., *Phys. Rev.* **74,** 622 (1948).
129. Grable, G. F., and Kerr, N. F., *Anal. Chem.* **29,** 1281 (1957).
130. Green, J., "Mass Spectrometry," p. 96. Institute of Petroleum, London, 1952.
131. Gvozdanovic, D. D., *Bull. Inst. Nuclear Sci. "Boris Kidrich" (Belgrade)* **7,** 83 (1957).
132. Hagstrum, H. D., *Appl. Sci. Research* **B5,** 16 (1955).
133. Hall, G. R., and Walter, A. J., *Can. J. Chem.* **34,** 246 (1956).
134. Halstead, R. E., and Nier, A. O., *Rev. Sci. Instr.* **21,** 1019 (1950).
135. Hannay, N. B., *Rev. Sci. Instr.* **25,** 644 (1954).
136. Hannay, N. B., and Ahearn, A. J., *Anal. Chem.* **26,** 1056 (1954).

137. Hannay, N. B., and Ahearn, A. J., private communication (1957).
138. Happ, G. P., and Stewart, D. W., *J. Am. Chem. Soc.* **74,** 4404 (1952).
139. Happ, G. P., Stewart, D. W., and Cooper, H. C., *Anal. Chem.* **29,** 68 (1957).
140. Harrington, D. B., American Society for Testing Materials Committee E-14 on Mass Spectrometry, 1957 (unpublished).
141. Harrison, D. E., Jr., *Phys. Rev.* **102,** 1473 (1956).
142. Harrison, D. E., Jr., *Phys. Rev.* **105,** 1202 (1957).
143. Hastings, S. H., Johnson, B. H., and Lumpkin, H. E., *Anal. Chem.* **28,** 1243 (1956).
144. Henglein, A., and Ewald, H., Proc. NBS Symposium on Mass Spectrometry. *Natl. Bur. of Standards (U.S.) Circ.* **No. 522,** 205 (1953).
145. Henschke, E. B., *Phys. Rev.* **106,** 737 (1957).
146. Herzog, R., *Z. Physik* **89,** 447 (1934).
147. Herzog, R., *Z. Naturforsch.* **10a,** 887 (1955).
148. Hickam, W. M., American Society for Testing Materials on Chemical Analysis of Solids by Mass Spectrometer, Special Technical Problem 149 (1953).
149. Hickam, W. M., and Fox, R. E., *J. Chem. Phys.* **25,** 642 (1956).
150. Higatsberger, M. J., Demorest, H. L., and Nier, A. O., *J. Appl. Phys.* **25,** 883 (1954).
151. Hintenberger, H., *Rev. Sci. Instr.* **20,** 748 (1949).
152. Hintenberger, H., *Helv. Phys. Acta* **24,** 307 (1951).
153. Hintenberger, H., and Lang, C., *Z. Naturforsch.* **11a,** 167 (1956).
154. Hintenberger, H., Wende, H., and König, L. A., *Z. Naturforsch.* **10a,** 605 (1955); **12a,** 140 (1957).
155. Hipple, J. A., U.S. patent 2,331,190 (1943).
156. Hipple, J. A., and Condon, E. U., *Phys. Rev.* **68,** 54 (1945).
157. Hipple, J. A., Fox, R. E., and Condon, E. U., *Phys. Rev.* **69,** 347 (1946).
158. Hipple, J. A., and Stevenson, D. P., *Phys. Rev.* **62,** 121 (1943).
159. Hockly, D. A., and Bull, C. S., *Vacuum* **4,** 40 (1954).
160. Holmes, J. C., and Morrell, F. A., *Appl. Spectroscopy* **11,** 86 (1957).
161. Honig, R. E., *J. Appl. Phys.* **16,** 646 (1945).
162. Honig, R. E., *Anal. Chem.* **25,** 1530 (1953).
163. Honig, R. E., *J. Chem. Phys.* **21,** 573 (1953).
164. Honig, R. E., *J. Chem. Phys.* **22,** 126 (1954).
165. Honig, R. E., *J. Chem. Phys.* **22,** 1610 (1954).
166. Honig, R. E., American Society for Testing Materials Committee E-14 on Mass Spectrometry, 1957 (unpublished).
167. Hoover, H., and Washburn, H. W., *Petrol. Technol.* (May, 1940).
168. Hunter, J. A., Stacey, R. W., and Hitchcock, F. A., *Rev. Sci. Instr.* **20,** 333 (1949).
169. Hurzeler, H., Inghram, M. G., and Morrison, J. D., *J. Chem. Phys.* **27,** 313 (1957).
170. Hurzeler, H., Inghram, M. G., and Morrison, J. D., *J. Chem. Phys.* **28,** 76 (1958).
171. Hutchison, D. A., *J. Chem. Phys.* **22,** 758 (1954).
172. Hutchison, D. A., *J. Chem. Phys.* **24,** 628 (1956).
173. Inghram, M. G., *J. Phys. Chem.* **57,** 809 (1953).
174. Inghram, M. G., Proc. NBS Symposium on Mass Spectrometry. *Natl. Bur. Standards (U.S.) Circ.* **No. 522,** 151 (1953).
175. Inghram, M. G., *Ann. Rev. Nuclear Sci.* **4,** 81 (1954).

176. Inghram, M. G., and Chupka, W. A., *Rev. Sci. Instr.* **24**, 518 (1953).
177. Inghram, M. G., Chupka, W. A., and Porter, R. F., *J. Chem. Phys.* **23**, 2159 (1955).
178. Inghram, M. G., and Hayden, R. J., "A Handbook on Mass Spectroscopy." *Natl. Acad. Sci.—Natl. Research Council Publ.* **311** (1954).
179. Inghram, M. G., Porter, R. F., and Chupka, W. A., *J. Chem. Phys.* **25**, 498 (1956).
180. Johnson, E. G., Hudson, D. E., Caldwell, W. C., Spedding, F. H., and Savage, W. R., *J. Chem. Phys.* **25**, 917 (1956).
181. Johnson, E. G., and Nier, A. O., *Phys. Rev.* **91**, 10 (1953).
182. Johnson, W. H., Jr., and Nier, A. O., *Phys. Rev.* **105**, 1014 (1957).
183. Judson, C. M., Francel, R. J., and Weicksel, J. A., *J. Chem. Phys.* **22**, 1258 (1954).
184. Kandel, R. J., *J. Chem. Phys.* **22**, 1496 (1954).
185. Kane, J. S., and Reynolds, J. H., *J. Chem. Phys.* **25**, 342 (1956).
186. Kelley, H. M., *Anal. Chem.* **23**, 1081 (1951).
187. Kerr, L. W., *J. Electronics* **2**, 179 (1956).
188. Kerwin, L., *Can. J. Phys.* **32**, 757 (1954).
189. Kettner, M. E., *Phys. Rev.* **102**, 1065 (1956).
190. Keywell, F., *Phys. Rev.* **97**, 1611 (1955).
191. King, W. H., Jr., American Society for Testing Materials Committee E-14 on Mass Spectrometry, 1957 (unpublished).
192. Kinney, I. W., and Cook, G. L., *Anal. Chem.* **24**, 1391 (1952).
193. Kirby, W., private communication (1955).
194. Kirshenbaum, A. D., and Grosse, A. V., *Anal. Chem.* **26**, 1955 (1954).
195. Kistiakowsky, G. B., and Kydd, P. H., *J. Am. Chem. Soc.* **79**, 4825 (1957).
196. Knewstubb, P. F., and Sugden, T. M., *Nature* **181**, 475 (1958).
197. König, L. A., and Hintenberger, H., *Z. Naturforsch.* **10a**, 877 (1955).
198. König, L. A., and Hintenberger, H., *Z. Naturforsch.* **12a**, 337 (1957).
199. Königsberger, J., *Physik. Z.* **11**, 848 (1910).
200. Koppius, O. G., U.S. patent 2,582,216 (1952).
201. Koyama, K., and Connally, R. E., *Rev. Sci. Instr.* **28**, 833 (1957).
202. Kunsman, C. H., *Science* **62**, 269 (1925).
203. Landsberg, H., *Oil Gas J.* [4] **55**, 42, 104 (1957).
204. Landsberg, H., Escher, E., and Dawkins, S. A., *Trans. 1955 Symposium Vacuum Technol.* p. 45. Committee on Vacuum Techniques, Boston, Massachusetts (1956).
205. Langer, A., *J. Phys. & Colloid Chem.* **54**, 618 (1950).
206. Langer, A., and Fox, R. E., *Anal. Chem.* **21**, 1032 (1949).
207. Langer, A., Hipple, J. A., and Stevenson, D. P., *J. Chem. Phys.* **22**, 1836 (1954).
208. Langmuir, I., and Kingdon, K. H., *Proc. Roy. Soc.* **A107**, 61 (1925).
209. Lanneau, K. P., *Ind. Eng. Chem.* **45**, 2381 (1955).
210. Law, R. W., and Margrave, J. L., *J. Chem. Phys.* **25**, 1086 (1956).
211. Lazukin, V. N., *Zhur. Eksptl. i. Teoret. Fiz.* **31**, 339 (1956).
212. Levy, E. J., Lawrey, D. M. G., Herk, L. P., Jr., and Stahl, W. H., American Society for Testing Materials Committee E-14 on Mass Spectrometry, 1956 (unpublished).
213. Lewis, L. G., and Hayden, R. J., *Rev. Sci. Instr.* **19**, 599 (1948).
214. Lichtblau, H., *Physik. Z.* **41**, 82 (1940).
215. Lichtblau, H., and Mattauch, J., *Z. Physik* **117**, 502 (1941).

216. Lossing, F. P., *Can. J. Chem.* **35**, 305 (1957).
217. Lossing, F. P., Ingold, K. U., and Henderson, I. H. S., "Applied Mass Spectrometry," p. 102. Institute of Petroleum, London, 1954.
218. Lossing, F. P., Ingold, K. U., and Henderson, I. H. S., *J. Chem. Phys.* **22**, 1489 (1954).
219. Lossing, F. P., Ingold, K. U., and Henderson, I. H. S., *J. Chem. Phys.* **22**, 621 (1954).
220. Lossing, F. P., and Tanaka, I., *J. Chem. Phys.* **25**, 1031 (1956).
221. Lumpkin, H. E., *Anal. Chem.* **28**, 1946 (1956).
222. Lumpkin, H. E., and Johnson, B. H., *Anal. Chem.* **26**, 1719 (1954).
223. McDowell, C. A., Lossing, F. P., Henderson, I. H., and Farmer, J. B., *Can. J. Chem.* **34**, 345 (1956).
224. McKinney, C. R., McCrea, J. M., Epstein, S., Allen, H. A., and Urey, H. C., *Rev. Sci. Instr.* **21**, 724 (1950).
225. McLafferty, F. W., *Anal. Chem.* **28**, 306 (1956).
226. McLafferty, F. W., *Anal. Chem.* **29**, 1782 (1957).
227. McLafferty, F. W., and Peard, W. J., American Society for Testing Materials Committee E-14 on Mass Spectrometry, 1957 (unpublished).
228. Mariner, T., and Bleakney, W., *Rev. Sci. Instr.* **20**, 297 (1949).
229. Marple, D. T. F., *Rev. Sci. Instr.* **26**, 1205 (1955).
230. Marriott, J., and Craggs, J. D., *J. Electronics* **1**, 405 (1956).
231. Marriott, J., and Craggs, J. D., *J. Electronics and Control* **3**, 194 (1957).
232. Matheson, R. M., Nergaard, L. S., and Plumlee, R. H., *RCA Rev.* **18**, 385 (1957).
233. Mattauch, J., and Ewald, H., *Z. Physik* **122**, 314 (1944).
234. Mattauch, J., and Herzog, R., *Z. Physik* **89**, 447, 786 (1934).
235. Mattauch, J., and Herzog, R., *Phys. Rev.* **50**, 617 (1936).
236. Mattauch, J., Wildmann, L., Bieri, R., and Everling, F., *Z. Naturforsch.* **11a**, 525 (1956).
237. Mattraw, H. C., Patterson, R. E., and Pachuki, C. F., *Appl. Spectroscopy* **8**, 117 (1954).
238. Meissner, C. R., *Rev. Sci. Instr.* **26**, 305 (1955).
239. Melpolder, F. W., Brown, R. A., Washall, T. A., Doherty, W., and Young, W. S., *Anal. Chem.* **26**, 1904 (1954).
240. Melton, C. E., Bretscher, M. M., and Baldock, R., *J. Chem. Phys.* **26**, 1302 (1957).
241. Melton, C. E., Gilpatrick, O., Baldock, R., and Healy, R. M., *Anal. Chem.* **28**, 1049 (1956).
242. Melton, C. E., and Rosenstock, H. M., *J. Chem. Phys.* **26**, 568 (1957).
243. Meyerson, S., *Appl. Spectroscopy* **9**, 120 (1955).
244. Meyerson, S., *Anal. Chem.* **28**, 317 (1956).
245. Miller, R. C., and Kusch, P., *J. Chem. Phys.* **25**, 860 (1956).
246. Mohler, F. L., *J. Research Natl. Bur. Standards* **47**, 337 (1951).
247. Mohler, F. L., Bloom, E. G., Lengel, J. W., and Wise, C. E., *J. Am. Chem. Soc.* **71**, 337 (1949).
248. Mohler, F. L., Dibeler, V. H., and Reese, R. M., *J. Chem. Phys.* **22**, 394 (1954).
249. Momigny, J., *Bull. Soc. Roy. Sci. Liège* **25**, 183 (1956).
250. Momigny, J., *J. Chem. Phys.* **25**, 787 (1956).
251. Monk, G. W., Graves, J. D., and Horton, J. L., *Rev. Sci. Instr.* **18**, 796 (1947).
252. Moon, P. B., and Oliphant, M. L. E., *Proc. Roy. Soc.* **A137**, 463 (1932).

253. Morrison, J. D., *J. Chem. Phys.* **22**, 1219 (1954).

254. Morrison, J. D., *J. Appl. Phys.* **28**, 1409 (1957).

255. Muraca, R. F., and Serfass, E. J., "A Mass Spectrometer for Solids." Lehigh University, Bethlehem, Pennsylvania, 1953.

256. Muschlitz, E. E., Jr., *J. Appl. Phys.* **28**, 1414 (1957).

257. Newton, A. S., *Anal. Chem.* **25**, 1746 (1953).

258. Nier, A. O., *Phys. Rev.* **55**, 150 (1939).

259. Nier, A. O., *Phys. Rev.* **52**, 933 (1937).

260. Nier, A. O., *Rev. Sci. Instr.* **18**, 398 (1947).

261. Nier, A. O., *in* "Nuclear Masses and Their Determination" (H. Hintenberger, ed.), p. 185. Pergamon Press, New York, 1957.

262. Nier, A. O., Abbott, T. A., Pickard, J. K., Leland, W. T., Taylor, T. I., Stevens, C. M., Dukey, D. L., and Goertzel, G., *Anal. Chem.* **20**, 188 (1948).

263. Nier, A. O., and Gulbransen, E. A., *J. Am. Chem. Soc.* **61**, 697 (1939).

264. Nier, A. O., and Roberts, T. R., *Phys. Rev.* **81**, 507 (1951).

265. Nier, A. O., Stevens, C. M., Hustrulid, A., and Abbott, T. A., *J. Appl. Phys.* **18**, 30 (1947).

266. Norton, F. J., *J. Chem. Phys.* **22**, 1144 (1954).

267. Norton, F. J., *J. Appl. Phys.* **28**, 34 (1957).

268. O'Neal, M. J., Jr., Proc. NBS Symposium on Mass Spectrometry. *Natl. Bur. Standards (U.S.) Circ.* **No. 522**, 217 (1953).

269. O'Neal, M. J., Jr., "Applied Mass Spectrometry," p. 27. Institute of Petroleum, London, 1954.

270. O'Neal, M. J., Jr., and Wier, T. P., *Anal. Chem.* **23**, 830 (1951).

271. Osborne, J. S., Ademek, S., and Hobbs, M. E., *Anal. Chem.* **28**, 211 (1956).

272. Papazian, H. A., and Wolsky, S. P., *J. Appl. Phys.* **27**, 1561 (1956).

273. Paul, W., Proc. NBS Symposium on Mass Spectrometry. *Natl. Bur. Standards (U.S.) Circ.* **No. 522**, 107 (1953).

274. Paul, W., and Raether, M., *Z. Physik* **140**, 262 (1955).

275. Peard, W. J., and McLafferty, F. W., American Society for Testing Materials Committee E-14 on Mass Spectrometry, 1957 (unpublished).

276. Pelchowitch, I., *Philips Research Repts.* **9**, 2 (1954).

277. Ploch, W., *Z. Naturforsch.* **5a**, 570 (1950); *Z. Physik* **130**, 174 (1951).

278. Plumlee, R. H., Proc. NBS Symposium on Mass Spectrometry. *Natl. Bur. Standards (U.S.) Circ.* **No. 522**, 229 (1953).

279. Plumlee, R. H., and Smith, L. P., *J. Appl. Phys.* **21**, 811 (1950).

280. Porter, R. F., Chupka, W. A., and Inghram, M. G., *J. Chem. Phys.* **23**, 216 (1955).

281. Porter, R. F., Schissel, P., and Inghram, M. G., *J. Chem. Phys.* **23**, 339 (1955).

282. Power, B. D., and Crawley, D. J., *Vacuum* **4**, 415 (1954).

283. Prescott, R., Hudson, R. L., Foner, S. N., and Avery, W. H., *J. Chem. Phys.* **22**, 144 (1954).

284. Priestley, W., and Dudenbostel, B. F., *Ind. Eng. Chem.* **48**, 81A (Feb. 1956).

285. Quiram, E. R., Metro, S. J., and Lewis, J. B., *Anal. Chem.* **26**, 352 (1954).

286. Quisenberry, K. S., Scolman, T. T., and Nier, A. O., *Phys. Rev.* **102**, 1071 (1956).

287. Quisenberry, K. S., Scolman, T. T., and Nier, A. O., *Phys. Rev.* **104**, 461 (1956).

288. Rappaport, P., *J. Appl. Phys.* **25**, 288 (1954).

289. Redhead, P. A., *Trans. Roy. Soc. Can.* **47**, 134 (1953).

290. Redhead, P. A., and Crowell, C. R., *J. Appl. Phys.* **24**, 331 (1953).

291. Reed, J. F., and Rabinovitch, B. S., *J. Phys. Chem.* **59**, 261 (1955).

292. Reed, J. F., and Rabinovitch, B. S., *J. Phys. Chem.* **61**, 598 (1957).
293. Reitlinger, S. A., Maslennikova, A. A., and Yarkho, I. S., *Zhur. Tekh. Fiz.* **26**, 2553 (1956).
294. Reuterswärd, C., *Arkiv Fysik* **11**, 1 (1956).
295. Reynolds, J. H., *Rev. Sci. Instr.* **27**, 928 (1956).
296. Robinson, C. F., *Rev. Sci. Instr.* **20**, 745 (1949).
297. Robinson, C. F., *Rev. Sci. Instr.* **27**, 509 (1956).
298. Robinson, C. F., *Rev. Sci. Instr.* **27**, 512 (1956).
299. Robinson, C. F., *Rev. Sci. Instr.* **28**, 777 (1957).
300. Robinson, C. F., *Rev. Sci. Instr.* **29**, 622 (1958).
301. Robinson, C. F., and Hall, L. G., *Rev. Sci. Instr.* **27**, 504 (1956).
302. Robinson, C. F., Schultz, W. D., and McKinney, C. R., (1958) (unpublished).
303. Robinson, C. F., and Sharkey, A. G., Jr., *Rev. Sci. Instr.* **29**, 250 (1958).
304. Robinson C. F., Washburn, H. W., Berry, C. E., and Perkins, G. D., *Instruments* **24**, 221 (1951).
305. Rock, S. M., *Anal. Chem.* **23**, 261 (1951).
306. Rogers, W. A., Buritz, R. S., and Alpert, D., *J. Appl. Phys.* **25**, 868 (1954).
307. Roos, O. van, *Z. Physik* **147**, 210 (1956).
308. Rosenblum, C., *Anal. Chem.* **29**, 1740 (1957).
309. Rosenstock, H. M., and Melton, C. E., *J. Chem. Phys.* **26**, 314 (1957).
310. Rosenstock, H. M., Sites, J. R., Walton, J. R., and Baldock, R., *J. Chem. Phys.* **23**, 2442 (1955).
311. Rosenstock, H. M., Wahraftig, A. L., and Eyring, H., *J. Chem. Phys.* **23**, 2200 (1955).
312. Rosenstock, H. M., Wallenstein, M. B., Wahraftig, A. L., and Eyring, H., *Proc. Natl. Acad. Sci. U.S.*, **38**, 667 (1952).
313. Rowe, E. H., *Rev. Sci. Instr.* **28**, 1094 (1957).
314. Schaeffer, O. A., and Owen, H. R., *J. Chem. Phys.* **23**, 1309 (1955).
315. Schaeffer, O. A., and Hastings, J. M., *J. Chem. Phys.* **18**, 1048 (1950).
316. Schaeffer, O. A., and Owen, H. R., *J. Chem. Phys.* **23**, 1305 (1955).
317. Schoenheimer, R., "The Dynamic State of Body Constituents." Harvard Univ. Press, Cambridge, Massachusetts, 1942.
318. Schoenheimer, R., and Rittenberg, D., *J. Biol. Chem.* **127**, 285 (1939).
319. Schönheit, E., *Naturwissenschaften* **44**, 278 (1957).
320. Shapiro, I., and Ditter, J. F., *J. Chem. Phys.* **26**, 798 (1957).
321. Sharkey, A. G., Jr., Friedel, R. A., and Langer, S. H., *Anal. Chem.* **29**, 770 (1957).
322. Sharkey, A. G., Jr., Schultz, J. L., and Friedel, R. A., *Anal. Chem.* **28**, 934 (1956).
323. Shaw, A. E., and Rall, W., *Rev. Sci. Instr.* **18**, 278 (1947).
324. Shepard, M., Rock, S. M., Howard, R., and Stormes, J., *Anal. Chem.* **23**, 1431 (1951).
325. Siri, W., *Rev. Sci. Instr.* **18**, 540 (1947).
326. Smales, A. A., *J. Electronics* **1**, 327 (1955).
327. Smith, L. G., *Rev. Sci. Instr.* **22**, 166 (1951).
328. Smith, L. G., and Damm, C. C., *Rev. Sci. Instr.* **27**, 638 (1956).
329. Smith, S. R., and Gordon, A. S., *J. Chem. Phys.* **22**, 1150 (1954).
330. Smith, S. R., and Gordon, A. S., *J. Phys. Chem.* **60**, 759 (1956).
331. Smith, S. R., and Gordon, A. S., *J. Phys. Chem.* **60**, 1059 (1956).
332. Smith, S. R., Gordon, A. S., and Hunt, M. H., *J. Phys. Chem.* **61**, 553 (1957).

333. Smythe, W. R., *Phys. Rev.* **28**, 1275 (1926).
334. Smythe, W. R., Rumbaugh, H., and West, S. S., *Phys. Rev.* **45**, 724 (1934).
335. Sommer, H., Thomas, H. A., and Hipple, J. A., *Phys. Rev.* **82**, 697 (1951).
336. Stanton, H. E., Chupka, W. A., and Inghram, M. G., *Rev. Sci. Instr.* **27**, 109 (1956).
337. Stephens, W. E., *Phys. Rev.* **45**, 513 (1934).
338. Stephens, W. E., U.S. patent 2,612,607 (1952).
339. Stephens, W. E., *Rev. Sci. Instr.* **24**, 616 (1953).
340. Sternglass, E. J., *Phys. Rev.* **108**, 1 (1957).
341. Stevenson, D. P., *J. Chem. Phys.* **15**, 409 (1947).
342. Stoll, S. J., *Brit. J. Appl. Phys.* **7**, 94 (1956).
343. Strachan, J. F., and Harris, N. L., *Proc. Phys. Soc.* (*London*) **B69**, 1148 (1956).
344. Straus, S., and Wall, L. A., *J. Research Natl. Bur. Standards* **60**, 39 (1958).
345. Svartholm, N., *Arkiv Fysik* **2**, 115 (1950).
346. Swann, W. F. G., *J. Franklin Inst.* **210**, 751 (1930).
347. Taylor, R. C., Brown, R. A., Young, W. S., and Headington, C. E., *Anal. Chem.* **20**, 400 (1948).
348. Taylor, R. C., Brown, R. A., Young, W. S., and Headington, C. E., *Anal. Chem.* **20**, 396 (1948).
349. Thode, H. G., and Macnamara, J., Proc. NBS Symposium on Mass Spectrometry. *Natl. Bur. Standards* (*U.S.*) *Circ.* **No. 522**, 235 (1953).
350. Thode, H. G., and Macnamara, J., Lossing, F. P., and Collins, C. B., *J. Am. Chem. Soc.* **70**, 3008 (1948).
351. Thomas, B. W., and Seyfried, W. D., *Anal. Chem.* **21**, 1022 (1949).
352. Thomas, H. A., Williams, T. W., and Hipple, J. A., *Rev. Sci. Instr.* **17**, 368 (1946).
353. Thomson, J. J., *Phil. Mag.* **13**, 561 (1907).
354. Thomson, J. J., *Phil. Mag.* **21**, 225 (1911).
355. Thorn, R. J., and Winslow, G. H., *J. Chem. Phys.* **26**, 186 (1957).
356. Tilton, G. R., Aldrich, L. T., and Inghram, M. G., *Anal. Chem.* **26**, 894 (1954).
357. Todd, B. J., *J. Appl. Phys.* **26**, 1238 (1955).
358. Todd, B. J., *J. Appl. Phys.* **27**, 1209 (1956).
359. Tokoyasu, K., Coblentz, A., and Bierman, H. R., *J. Appl. Physiology* **14**, (1959) (in press).
360. Tove, P. A., *Rev. Sci. Instr.* **27**, 143 (1956).
361. Townsend, J. W., Jr., *Rev. Sci. Instr.* **23**, 538 (1952).
362. Tsuchiya, T., *J. Chem. Phys.* **22**, 1784 (1954).
363. Urey, H. C., *J. Chem. Soc.* **1947**, 562.
364. Urey, H. C., *J. Am. Chem. Soc.* **69**, 562 (1947).
365. Urey, H. C., and Greiff, L. J., *J. Am. Chem. Soc.* **57**, 321 (1935).
366. Urey, H. C., Lowenstam, H. A., Epstein, S., and McKinney, C. R., *Bull. Geol. Soc. Am.* **62**, 399 (1951).
367. Urey, H. C., and Rittenberg, D., *J. Chem. Phys.* **1**, 137 (1933).
368. Veksler, V. I., and Ben'yamovich, M. B., *Zhur. Tekh. Fiz.* **26**, 1671 (1956).
369. Voorhies, H. G., *Rev. Sci. Instr.* **26**, 716 (1955).
370. Waack, R., Alex, N. H., Frisch, H. L., Stannett, V., and Szwarc, M., *Ind. Eng. Chem.* **47**, 2524 (1955).
371. Wagener, J. S., and Marth, P. T., *J. Appl. Phys.* **28**, 1027 (1957).
372. Waldron, J. D., *Research* (*London*) **9**, 306 (1956).
373. Walker, J. K., *Petroleum Engr.* **7:12**, C-7 (November, 1955).

374. Walker, J. K., Gifford, A. P., and Nelson, R., *Ind. Eng. Chem.* **6,** 1400 (1954).
375. Walker, J. K., and O'Hara, C. L., *Anal. Chem.* **27,** 825 (1955).
376. Wall, R. F., *Ind. Eng. Chem.* **49,** 59A (1957).
377. Wargo, P., Haxby, B. V., and Shepherd, W. G., *J. Appl. Phys.* **27,** 1311 (1956).
378. Washburn, H. W., U.S. patent 2,596,032 (1951).
379. Washburn, H. W., and Berry, C. E., *Phys. Rev.* **70,** 559 (1946).
380. Washburn, H. W., Berry, C. E., and Hall, L. G., *Anal. Chem.* **25,** 130 (1953).
381. Wehner, G. K., *Appl. Sci. Research* **B5,** 334 (1955).
382. Wehner, G. K., *Phys. Rev.* **102,** 690 (1956).
383. Wehner, G. K., *Phys. Rev.* **108,** 35 (1957).
384. Wehner, G. K., and Medicus, G., *J. Appl. Phys.* **25,** 698 (1954).
385. Wells, G. F., and Melton, C. E., *Rev. Sci. Instr.* **28,** 1065 (1957).
386. Wherry, T. C., and Karasek, F. W., *J. Appl. Phys.* **26,** 682 (1955).
387. Whetten, N. R., and Laponsky, A. B., *J. Appl. Phys.* **28,** 515 (1957).
388. White, F. A., and Collins, T. L., *Appl. Spectroscopy* **8,** 17 (1954).
389. White, F. A., and Collins, T. L., *Appl. Spectroscopy* **8,** 169 (1954).
390. Wien, W., *Verhandl. Physik. Gese.* **17** (1898).
391. Wieringen, A. van, and Warmoltz, N., *Physica* **22,** 849 (1956).
392. Wiley, W. C., and McLaren, I. H., *Rev. Sci. Instr.* **26,** 1150 (1955).
393. Woodford, H. J., and Gardner, J. H., *Rev. Sci. Instr.* **27,** 378 (1956).

Bibliography

1. "Applied Mass Spectrometry"; Report of a Conference organized by the Mass Spectrometry Panel of The Institute of Petroleum, London, October 29-31, 1953. The Institute of Petroleum, 26 Portland Place, London, 1954.
2. Aston, F. W., "Mass Spectra and Isotopes." Edward Arnold, London, 1933.
3. Barnard, G. P., "Modern Mass Spectrometry." The Institute of Physics, London, 1953.
4. "Electromagnetically Enriched Isotopes and Mass Spectrometry" (M. L. Smith, ed.); Proceedings of Harwell Conference, September 13-16, 1955. Academic Press, New York, 1956.
5. Ewald, H., and Hintenberger, H., "Methoden und Anwendungen der Massenspektroskopie." Verlag Chemie GMBH; Weinheim/Bergstrasse, 1953.
6. Field, F. H., and Franklin, J. L., "Electron Impact Phenomena and the Properties of Gaseous Ions." Academic Press, New York, 1957.
7. Inghram, M. G., and Hayden, R. J., "A Handbook on Mass Spectroscopy"; Nuclear Science Series Report No. 14. National Academy of Sciences, National Research Council Publication 311, Washington, 1954.
8. "Mass Spectrometry"; Report of a Conference organized by the Mass Spectrometry Panel of The Institute of Petroleum, Manchester, April 20-21, 1950. The Institute of Petroleum, 26 Portland Place, London, 1952.
9. "Mass Spectroscopy in Physics Research"; Proceedings of the National Bureau of Standards Semicentennial Symposium on Mass Spectroscopy in Physics Research, Washington, September 6-8, 1951. National Bureau of Standards Circular 522 (1953).
10. "Nuclear Masses and Their Determination" (H. Hintenberger, ed.); Proceedings of the Conference held in the Max Planck Institut für Chemie, Mainz, July 10-12, 1956. Pergamon Press, New York, 1957.

11. Rieck, G. R., "Einführung in die Massenspektroskopie." VEB Deutscher Verlag der Wissenschaften, Berlin, 1956 (translated from the Russian by A. Rakow).
12. Robertson, A. J. B., "Mass Spectrometry." Wiley, New York, 1954.
13. Transactions of the 1955 Symposium on Vacuum Technology, Committee on Vacuum Techniques Inc., Boston, Massachusetts, 1956.
14. Transactions of the 1956 Symposium on Vacuum Technology, Pergamon Press, New York, 1957.
15. Duckworth, Henry E., "Mass Spectroscopy," Cambridge Univ. Press, London and New York, 1958.
16. Proceedings of the Joint Conference on Mass Spectrometry, London, 1958. Pergamon Press, New York, 1959 (in press).

Electron Microscopy

ROBERT D. HEIDENREICH

AND

CHESTER J. CALBICK

Bell Telephone Laboratories, Murray Hill, New Jersey

1. Introduction

The last years have seen the growth of electron microscopy on this continent from the status of an instrument which was a rare curiosity to that of the present day with many hundreds of electron microscopes now being employed in industrial and academic research. The applications of electron microscopy are quite diverse and include bacteriology, biology, chemistry, physics, and metallurgy. As a result, those working with this instrument are likely to apply their efforts chiefly in one of these fields, with only a very general knowledge of the work in others.

In attempting to judge or evaluate the worth of the electron microscope in chemistry and metallurgy at this date, the various phases which any new scientific instrument passes through in its evolution into a useful tool must be recognized. It is evident that the first phase will be one of instrumentation wherein problems of design and construction will constitute the major effort. Following this is a period in which various techniques of application are initiated and in which the individual worker examines a great many substances and tries out his instrument. This phase is one in which many pictures of a great variety of specimens are taken for the sake of becoming familiar with the machine and its operation. There is a considerable satisfaction in the production of pleasing and interesting pictures even though these pictures do not have immediate significance in any particular research program. This exploratory stage of investigation leads to the formulation of problems and gradually works into another phase. In this the instrument takes its place along with other research tools and makes its own contribution to a scientific program. At present, electron microscopy is just achieving the status which x-ray diffraction, spectroscopy, etc., have already attained.

The purpose of this chapter is to acquaint chemists and metallurgists with some of the methods developed up to the present time in such a way that they may recognize problems wherein the electron microscope can contribute to the solution. In the present stage, the directions in which the work may go are quite sensitive to advances in techniques, and hence the methods and interpretations of results are to be carefully considered. Examples illustrating the methods applied to selected problems will be included wherever possible, and suggestions for future work will be made in some instances. The authors have drawn freely on the published literature, and references to the original work are included where it seems advisable. Recognition of private communications will be given. When not otherwise specified, the electron micrographs employed were taken at Bell Telephone Laboratories.

Several books (2, 3, 32, 39, 42, 45, 62, 116, 117, 149, 150) have been published, in English as well as German. Cosslett's book (39) is perhaps the best of the more recently published books in English. That published by the group at RCA (150) is recommended for those interested in the fundamental problems of instruments, electron optics, resolution, etc. That of Burton and Kohl (32) is of a general, nontechnical nature, whereas the book of von Ardenne (3) is more concerned with construction problems. A very good book on general electron microscopy is that of Ramsauer (117). Hall's book (62), in addition to an excellent theoretical section, discusses experiments on the interaction of electrons with matter. Wyckoff's book (149) is a valuable interim discussion on the performance of electron microscopes, replete with beautiful electron micrographs of shadowed virus macrocrystals. Excellent bibliographies are available. Marton's (101) covers the early work; Cosslett's (38) is excellent for work up to 1948; the punched card bibliography (110), published by the New York Society of Electron Microscopists, includes many thousands of references from 1950 to date and is issued approximately quarterly. Reference to the Manual for this bibliography gives a bird's-eye view of the tremendous expansion of the field of electron microscopy during the past decade. The Keysort punched card system provides for classification by subject and author. If the article deals with more than one subject, one or two additional subject zones are punched before issuance. The fourth subject zone is devoted to a single-letter code for sixteen major classifications, e.g., Solid Surfaces. One end zone is left free for the user's own classification, if desired. The system facilitates greatly the rapid retrieval of information.

The reviews published (121, 132, 133) by *Analytical Chemistry* give excellent accounts of the progress of the art of electron microscopy.

The process of imaging by means of an electron beam will be examined first, and the types of instruments will be briefly discussed. The application of the electron microscope to several fields will then be considered along with the various techniques. The types of problems have been roughly divided into two classes: those wherein the substance to be examined is in a colloidal state, and those where the surface of bulk matter is to be studied.

2. Imaging by Means of Electron Beams

In beginning a discussion of electron microscopy as applied to problems of a physical or chemical nature it is instructive to review some of the properties of electron beams and their interaction with matter. These phenomena are reasonably well understood and serve as a starting point in interpreting electron microscope images and in understanding the necessity for certain techniques and methods.

A common source of electrons is a tungsten wire heated to a high temperature such that the conduction electrons within the metal escape in considerable quantity. The electron current density from a region of a clean metal surface in the presence of an accelerating potential is given by

$$i = ADT^2 e^{-\epsilon \chi' / kT} \tag{1}$$

where A is a constant (120 amp./cm.²), D is the transmission coefficient for the potential barrier at the region in question, χ' is the effective work function, ϵ is the electron charge, k is the Boltzmann constant, and T is the absolute temperature. If χ is the work function for zero applied field, then $\chi' = \chi - \epsilon^{1/2}F^{1/2}$, where F is the applied field at the surface. The current by eq. (1) obviously increases rapidly with increasing temperature and is very sensitive to the value of χ, the thermionic work function. The value of χ is found to vary systematically from one metal to another and is different for the various crystal faces of a given metal; χ is also quite sensitive to absorbed films and surface layers of all kinds.* The emission current may vary greatly from one region of the surface to another. The emission electron microscope is designed specifically to study the variations in emission current over the surface of a given emitter.

The emitted electrons exhibit both wave and particle characteristics. The charged particle characteristics are used in the focusing of the beam by means of electric or magnetic fields. The wave properties are exhibited in the images formed by using the electron streams. The wavelength of an electron which has been accelerated through a potential, V, is given by

$$\lambda = \frac{h}{\sqrt{2m\epsilon V}} = \frac{12.3}{\sqrt{V}} \text{ Angstrom units}\dagger \qquad (2)$$

where m is the mass of the electron. For 60-kv. electrons, $\lambda = 0.05$ A. This value is considerably less than the usual x-ray wavelengths and far below that of visible light.

On the basis of the Abbé theory of image formation it would be expected that the resolution obtainable in an image formed by using a stream of electrons would be very much better than in an image formed with light. Boersch (17) gives a more sophisticated theory of formation of electron microscope images. The quantitative expression for resolution is often given as the radius of a disk, the Airy disk, formed by a perfect lens and a point source. The intensity of the disk falls to zero at a distance

$$d = \frac{0.61\lambda}{n \sin \alpha} = \frac{0.61\lambda}{\text{N.A.}} \qquad (3)$$

Here λ is the wavelength, α the objective aperture, n the refractive index, and N.A. the numerical aperture. On the basis of eq. (3) the limit of resolution of the light microscope is about 1100 A. ($\lambda \simeq 2500$ A., $n \sin \alpha \simeq 1.4$), and the useful magnification about 2000 ×. Because of lens aberration in electron optical systems, very small values of α must be utilized, with the result that eq. (3) predicts a resolution of about 6 A.

---

* Cf. J. H. DeBoer, "Electron Adsorption and Emission Phenomena." Cambridge Univ. Press, 1935.

† 1 Angstrom unit (1 A.) $\equiv 10^{-8}$ cm. $\equiv 10^{-4}\,\mu$.

for the present magnetic electron microscope.* As will be seen, there are other factors to be considered in the resolution obtained with an electron microscope which usually result in a limit somewhat higher than eq. (3).

Electrons are very efficiently scattered by matter, and as a result an electron beam must be confined to space that is relatively free of gas. A vacuum of 10^{-4} torr† is necessary to reduce the general scattering below the point where it interferes with the formation of an image.‡ Electron microscope specimens are thus immediately restricted to those that have vapor pressures less than about 10^{-4} torr. A much more drastic limitation is imposed by the requirement that the specimen remain unchanged. A specimen with an equilibrium vapor pressure of 10^{-6} torr evaporates about one molecular layer per second and in a few minutes, necessary for observation, would evaporate several hundred angstroms. In view of the fact that specimen temperature is raised by interaction with the electron beam, the practical limit for equilibrium vapor pressure is at most 10^{-8} torr, and preferably should be less than 10^{-10} torr.

A detailed treatment (150, Chapter 19; 39, Chapter 1) of image formation is not required to gain a general understanding of the type of image formed by an electron microscope. The general aspects will be discussed here only in sufficient length to serve as a basis for the later interpretation of images.

The discussion will be facilitated by the schematic diagram of a simple magnetic type of microscope shown in Fig. 1a. Details concerning the lenses and their properties will be found in the references, particularly refs. 39 and 150, and in the literature of the various manufacturers. Figure 1b shows the objective in more detail. It is here that the image characteristics are determined (17). The illuminating electron stream with a half-angle, α_c, from the condensing lens impinges on the specimen. Of the electrons leaving the specimen plane, only those falling within a cone of half-angle α_{ob} pass through the objective and contribute to the image. Those outside the cone are stopped by the limiting diaphragm. If the limiting diaphragm is removed, as it often is, α_{ob} is considerably larger, and electrons deflected through wider angles find their way to the image plane. In this case, the objective aperture is determined by the electrons leaving the specimen.

It is of interest to note that with the values of α_c and α_{ob} employed in the electron microscope the depth of field is considerably greater

---

* For electrons, $n = 1$, and $\alpha \simeq 5 \times 10^{-3}$ radian.

† 1 torr = pressure of 1 mm. of mercury = 1/760 atmosphere.

‡ Mean free path depends on the gas; for electrons it is in the vicinity of 5 meters at 10^{-4} torr.

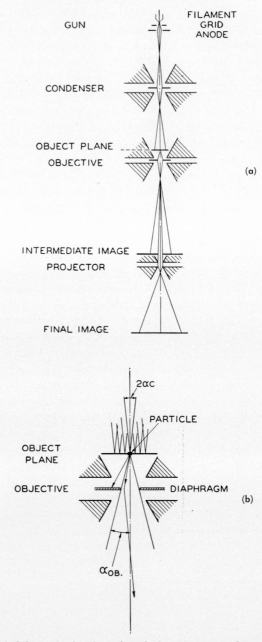

Fig. 1. (a) Schematic drawing of optical components of magnetic, transmission-type electron microscope. (b) Geometry of specimen and objective-limiting diaphram showing rays into and outside cone of aperture.

than that obtained with a light microscope. If δ is the maximum reduction in resolution that can be permitted owing to imperfect focusing resulting from variations in specimen-lens distance, then the depth of field is given by

$$D_f = \frac{2\delta}{\tan \alpha_{ob}} \tag{4}$$

Usually δ is chosen as equal to the experimentally observed resolution. For $\alpha_{ob} \simeq 3 \times 10^{-3}$ radian and $\delta \simeq 30$ A., the value of D_f is about 2 μ. Thus, the depth of field is very large relative to the resolution for the electron microscope. In the case of the light microscope α_{ob} is about $10°$ for low-power and as large as $70°$ for high-power objectives. Correspondingly, D_f varies from about 12.5δ to 0.8δ—at the highest power depth of field is actually smaller than the lateral resolution. These facts are of great importance in the preparation of metallographic specimens and in stereoscopy.

Returning to Fig. 1b, it is seen that the image intensity variations will depend on whether various points in the specimen deflect electrons into the objective cone or not. A point in the object that scatters a large proportion of the incident electrons outside this cone will exhibit a deficiency of electrons in the corresponding image point. Hence the contrast in the image depends on the variation in scattering power in the specimen from point to point. A detailed consideration of intensities requires a detailed treatment of electron scattering in the specimen.

The scattering in the specimen will depend on the type, number, and arrangement of atoms and on the thickness of the specimen and may be classified under the following headings:

1. Incoherent
   (a) Elastic $\begin{cases} \text{single scattering} \\ \text{plural scattering} \\ \text{multiple scattering} \end{cases}$
   (b) Inelastic
2. Coherent
   (a) Diffraction by a crystal
   (b) Diffraction at edges, called Fresnel diffraction

In most electron microscope specimens it is probably safe to say that all types of scattering occur but that the degree to which each type contributes may vary from point to point. If a region in the specimen is amorphous, then single, plural, or multiple scattering may obtain, depending on the thickness. If an edge or sharp step is present, Fresnel diffraction will occur. Single scattering occurs only in exceedingly thin regions, multiple scattering in thick regions. The most likely type in noncrystalline electron microscope specimens is plural scattering; i.e., an electron suffers only a few deflections in passing through the specimen rather than a large number as assumed in multiple scattering.

Restricting the discussion to noncrystalline specimens, it can be shown that the fraction of electrons scattered into the aperture (Fig. 1b) can be written (102) as

$$\frac{I}{I_0} = e^{-x \sum_i N_i \sigma_i} \tag{5}$$

where x is the thickness, $\sum_i N_i \sigma_i$ is the total cross section for scattering outside the aperture, N_i is the number of atoms per cubic centimeter

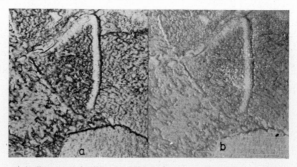

FIG. 2. (a) Image of silica replica photographed with objective-limiting diaphram (approximately 0.004-inch diameter) in place. (b) Same field as (a) photographed with limiting diaphram removed showing loss in contrast due to high background. (4000×)

of type i, σ_i is the cross section for an atom of type i. Methods of computing σ_i will be found in ref. 61, 62, 93, and 102, and it is sufficient for this discussion to point out that σ_i increases with atomic number and decreases with increasing energy of the incident electrons in the case of elastic scattering. As α_{ob} increases (Fig. 1b), the number of electrons scattered into the aperture will increase. If there is scattering from a large fraction of the illuminated area in the specimen plane, the image contrast is strongly dependent on the objective aperture. The objective diaphragm, in this case, removes an appreciable fraction of the inelastically scattered electrons that would otherwise yield a high level of unfocused intensity as illustrated in Fig. 2.

Inelastic scattering in which the incident electrons lose some energy to the specimen results in electrons entering the aperture which are not focused at the image plane owing to chromatic aberration of the objective.* Inelastic scattering (119) increases with increasing thickness and results in elevating the temperature of the specimen (19). This fact is important, since it often results in deterioration (29, 50). It is possible to vaporize a specimen rapidly by increasing the incident beam intensity.

In the case of crystalline specimens the question of diffraction by the crystal becomes important. If a crystal is oriented so that a net plane makes the Bragg angle with the incident beam, a strong diffracted ray is possible and the mass thickness of the crystal becomes secondary

FIG. 3. Electron micrograph of molybdenum oxide crystals taken with limiting objective diaphragm removed. Strong diffracted beam is evident in the slightly defocused image (71).

FIG. 4. Edge contours in electron micrograph of molybdenum oxide crystals (71).

in its effect. In amorphous materials, the mass thickness is the determining factor (7, 94, 124).

Whether or not a diffracted beam enters the image plane depends on the relative magnitudes of objective aperture and angle of diffraction (79). A Bragg reflection will make an angle 2θ with the incident beam, where θ is given by $n\lambda = 2d \sin \theta$. If $2\theta > \alpha_{ob}$, the reflected beam is excluded from the image and the crystal appears dark in bright field. If the usual limiting diaphragm is employed in the objective ($\alpha_{ob} \simeq 3 \times 10^{-3}$), 2θ will nearly always be much larger than α_{ob}. With the diaphragm removed, the diffracted beam will appear in the image and its position will be quite sensitive to focus. Figure 3 shows the appearance of the diffracted beams in a defocused image of molybdenum oxide. A sheet crystal such as mica will produce an interesting pattern (79) in

* The focal power of an electron lens is inversely proportional to electron energy (cf. ref. 150). Equation (1) shows that its wavelength, λ, also varies with energy. By analogy with light optics, the resulting lens defect is called chromatic aberration.

its image as a result of Bragg reflections from local regions throughout the sheet. It has also been shown that the thickness as well as orientation must be considered in interpreting the intensity distribution in the image of a crystal (79).

The question of Fresnel diffraction has been left until the last

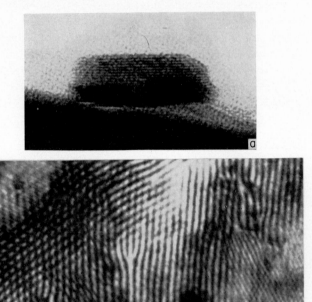

FIG. 5. Observation of best resolution: contrast increased by periodic spacings. (a) MoO_3 (020 planes) showing resolution of 6.93-A. spacing. [G. A. Bassett and J. W. Menter, *Phil. Mag.* [8] **2**, 1482 (1957)]. (b) Moiré pattern obtained by superposition of thin gold and palladium films. Example of an edge dislocation with its Burger's vector oriented perpendicular to set of planes giving rise to moiré pattern (75,000×) (114).

portion of the discussion of image formation. Diffraction at an edge or sharp step does not become a significant factor in interpreting images of specimens of physical or chemical interest until the detail to be discerned is no longer large relative to the width of the edge contour. The appearance of such a contour is shown in Fig. 4, which is a micrograph of molybdenum oxide smoke. If the illuminating aperture, α_c, is reduced from about 10^{-3} radian (at which Fig. 4 was taken) to about

10^{-5} radian, a converging series of fringes becomes visible in a slightly defocused image.* These fringes offer what appears to be the best method for measuring resolving power yet reported (45, 82). Further, the edge contour is very sensitive to ellipicity in the objective lens.

3. Resolution

The optical aberration corresponding to lens asymmetry is astigmatism. Hillier (82) concluded that astigmatism in the objective lens was the chief factor limiting resolution. The asymmetry is caused (1) by residual mechanical asymmetry of the objective lens despite the most precise machining; (2) by magnetic inhomogeneities in the lens material; and (3) by films which deposit on lens surfaces during operation. Compensators for astigmatism are now a part of the design of most commercial instruments. The procedure is similar in principle to that devised by Hillier and Ramberg (84); an electron optical asymmetry adjustable in magnitude and azimuth is introduced in the region of the objective lens to compensate for its astigmatism. Fresnel fringes from a suitable object† are observed, and the compensator is adjusted by means of external controls until they are uniform around the periphery of the object. The objective lens power is then adjusted until the fringes disappear. Resolution of better than 10 A. may be attained. Periodic structures with spacings as small as 6.9 A. (Fig. 5a) and moiré patterns with a periodic spacing of 5.3 A., similar to that illustrated in Fig. 5b, have been observed (114). In practice, however, the highest resolving power is maintained for only a short time before it is degraded by the operation of factor 3 above. With the best of microscopes commercially available at present, it is not too difficult to achieve a resolution of 15 A. and to maintain it at better than 25 A. over considerable periods of operation. Less elaborate microscopes, available at lower cost, have more limited resolving power (e.g., 75 to 100 A.). This is adequate for the study of many specimens.

Observable resolution is a function of the specimen as well as the microscope (35, 81, 119, 136). An early example of a micrograph showing particle separation as small as 15 A. in a crystallized gold film is shown in Fig. 6. Adequate contrast is achieved because of the large scattering cross section of the heavy metal, gold. Similar pictures have been taken of particles from gold and platinum sols; but observation of values of resolution less than 10 A. is limited because of difficulty in preparing

---

* Cf. H. Boersch, *Physik. Z.* **44**, 202 (1943).

† The most suitable object is a carbon film 100–200 A. thick containing numerous small, round holes; a technique for making such films has been devised.

specimens with adequate contrast. Contrast may be enhanced by interference effects in observations of periodic structures such as those of Fig.
5. In general it can be stated that the specimen must contain detail
smaller than the resolution, and with adequate contrast differences over
such exceedingly minute distances, if the actual instrumental resolution
is to be observed. Cosslett (40) has pointed out that chromatic aberration
due to inelastic scattering limits resolution to about a tenth of specimen
thickness. In consequence, a small sharp step on a thick specimen is

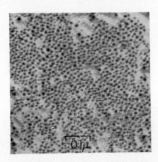

FIG. 6. Electron micrograph illustrating image detail in thin film of evaporated gold (recrystallized) removed from rock salt surface
by means of a silica film (71).

obscured; it would be observed as sharper, i.e., more highly resolved,
on a thinner specimen. Much valuable information is often obtained,
however, from images of specimens that exhibit relatively poor resolution. For example, it is difficult to prepare replicas with resolution
better than 50 A. Frequently the intrinsic resolution (35) of a replica
is no better than 100 A.; it tends to be in the neighborhood of half the
average thickness.

It is evident that the scattering cross section for electrons of solid
matter is so large that films suitable for observation in the transmission-
type microscope must be very thin. To a first approximation, all materials of a given mass thickness have the same scattering power. This
is not rigorously true (cf. Hall, 62), but it can be stated that, for 50-kv.
electrons, specimens must have mass thickness between 1 and 20 γ/cm.^{2}
to produce useful intensity variations in the image. Corresponding linear
thicknesses are given in tabular form. These are only meant to give
some idea of the thickness of specimen that must be adhered to in

Material	Maximum (A.)	Minimum (A.)
Plastic films	2000	100
Silica	800	40
Aluminum	740	37
Platinum	100	5

electron microscopy. Since scattering cross section decreases with electron energy, somewhat thicker specimens can be used for 100-kv. electrons; but in any event, useful thicknesses will not exceed a few thousand angstroms. Obviously, considerable technique is required in working with such thin layers of matter. Thicker objects can be examined only in profile, e.g., silhouettes of particles.

4. Types of Instruments

A detailed discussion of instruments and their characteristics is not warranted here, since the main subject is that of applications. It is worth while to mention several of the various types of instruments, however, particularly since the transmission type of magnetic microscope is being employed almost to the exclusion of all others. Some of the lesser known types yield important information of a specific nature such as the distribution of emission current from electron emitters.

The first electron microscope was of the emission type wherein electrons emitted by heated objects were focused so as to produce an emission pattern of the object. Electrons can be removed from a solid by means other than thermal, however, so that secondary electrons and photoelectrons can also be used to form images of the original emitting surface. These instruments employ an electrostatic immersion objective lens and may or may not use a second stage of magnification or projection lens. An electrostatic, thermionic emission instrument employing a projection lens and yielding high-quality images exhibiting a resolution of about 400 A. has been described by Mechlenberg (104). Several others (28, 99) have been reported in the literature with resolutions quoted of the order of that of the light microscope. An interesting thermionic emission microscope has been described by McMillen and Scott (95) in which an ashed biological specimen served as the emitter. Variations in thermionic work function over the specimen were shown to be due to the presence of sodium, calcium, magnesium, barium, etc., in enhanced concentrations at certain regions in the specimen (127). The location of specific metallic constituents was inferred from the order in which the emission increased as the temperature was raised. This instrument employed an immersion objective and a magnetic projection lens and gave pictures of excellent quality.

The most common and most highly developed instrument is the transmission microscope utilizing magnetic lenses and two or three stages of magnification. Instruments employing electrostatic lenses rather than magnetic have been constructed as well (5, 39, 96, 149). The instrument of Mahl (96) produced high-quality images with a resolution of about

100 A. An electrostatic instrument (5) designed in this country with lenses patterned after those of Mahl was put into production and then withdrawn because of a series of difficulties. As discussed by Wyckoff (149) and by Cosslett (39), electrostatic objective lenses inherently are not capable of producing as good resolution as has been attained with magnetic instruments; the best value so far reported has been about 20 A.

The three types of microscopes mentioned above are the only ones that have been applied to any extent in research problems. Several other types have been built for the purpose of studying their operation. Among these is the scanning microscope of Zworykin and Hillier (150). This instrument utilizes the secondary electrons ejected when a primary beam of about 800 volts of energy impinges on a surface. The resolution of the instrument is determined by, among other things, the cross section of the primary beam at the surface being examined. The problems and equipment involved in moving the specimen during scanning and in final recording of the image result in a rather complicated device. The question of interpretation of images and resolution obtained offers, at present, no advantage over the surface replicas used in the transmission microscope.

The surface of bulk materials may also be examined by reflected electrons. In one form (18, 41) the electron beam is reflected obliquely. In another, the so-called electron mirror (11, 103, 131), the target is at cathode potential; the electrons never strike it but are reflected in the electrostatic field very near the surface. The first form suffers from foreshortening of the image caused by the oblique incidence. The second has rather limited resolving power primarily because of the low energy, and hence long wavelength, of the electrons in the region of reflection. The shadow microscope of Boersch (16) gave images of high quality but suffered from uncertainty in magnification calibration.

There has recently been a considerable revival of interest in reflection, scanning, and shadow microscopes. The NYSEM bibliography gives at least twenty-five references, nineteen to the reflection, four to the scanning, and two to the shadow type. Ohashi and Takeuchi (113) observed growing TiO_2 crystals, and Blackman and Greenbaum (15) magnetic domains, in electron shadow photographs. Smith and Oatley (130) discuss the fields of application of the scanning microscope; it has been applied to direct observation of chemical reactions and to the study of fibers. Bradley et al. (27) describe stereoscopic reflection microscopy. Holland (86) and Bradley (25) describe replica techniques suitable for observations by reflection methods. Fert et al. (47, 48) has applied cylindrical and quadrupolar lenses to reduce the "distortion" of the reflection image. The reported subjects of study have been metal surfaces and fibers.

The applications to be discussed in the following sections are concerned in general with the magnetic transmission microscope. Present electron microscope work is being carried on almost entirely with this instrument. High-quality magnetic microscopes are produced commercially in this country and in Germany, Japan, Holland, and England. A few laboratory-built microscopes are also in use both here (100) and abroad.

5. Comparison of Light and Electron Microscope Images

In dealing with problems in applied electron microscopy, a common approach is one which views the electron microscope as an extension to light microscopy. Many of the conventional methods of attack on problems are carried over to the high-resolution instrument with the hope of supplying missing details. In more than one case, however, this approach has not been fruitful, and it has been necessary to view the problem from a position independent of light microscopy. Nevertheless, it is instructive and logical first to consider applied electron microscopy through a comparison of the images obtained with the two microscopes.

The discussion is facilitated by listing some of the general characteristics of light and electron microscope images and then proceeding to actual examples. Table I will serve to summarize the more pertinent

TABLE I

Comparison of the General Characteristics of Light and Electron Microscope Images

Property	Light microscope	Electron microscope (50-kv. electrons)
Wavelength	Variable (2500-6500 A.)	Variable (0.05-0.06 A.)
Abbe resolution	1100 A. (N.A. = 1.4, λ = 2537 A.)	6 A. (N.A. = 5 $\times$ 10^{-3}, λ = 0.056 A.)
Resolution of usual laboratory equipment	1800 A. (N.A. = 1.4, λ = 4200 A.)	20-50 A. (colloidal systems)
Normal magnifying power	670 $\times$	27,000 $\times$
Depth of field at normal magnifying power	1000 A.	20,000 A.

features. Appearing in this table is the term "normal magnifying power," [*] which has not been previously mentioned. Normal magnifying power is that magnification beyond which no new detail in the image becomes visible to the eye. The resolution of the human eye is at best about 0.1 mm., so that an image containing no detail below 0.1 mm. is at or above the normal magnifying power. Further enlargement does not produce new detail although it facilitates study and measurement of structure. An expression for the normal magnifying power of an image-producing instrument is obtained from the Abbé formula, eq. (3), by multiplying both sides of the equation by the magnification, M, to give $M \cdot d = 0.61 \lambda M / (n \sin)$. Setting $M \cdot d = 0.01$ cm., and writing $M = M_n$, the normal magnifying power, we find the result to be

$$M_n = 0.01 \frac{n \sin \alpha}{0.61 \lambda} \tag{6}$$

with λ in centimeters. The numerical values of this quantity in Table I were computed from eq. (6).

In light microscopy, the presence of inhomogenieties in the object of a size below the resolution of the instrument may still be detected by the light scattered. In this case, the intensity of the scattered radiation is to be taken as a measure of the size of the particle rather than the dimensions of the image.

The comparative figures in Table I[†] refer only to the imaging of size and shape of structural details. In light microscopy, however, other information of value is obtained from the optical properties of the specimen such as refractive index, color, anisotropy, and polarization. The electron optical analogs do not exist as such, and consequently this type of information is not obtained from electron images. The use of electron diffraction techniques with the electron microscope specimen serves partially to overcome this disadvantage where crystalline materials are concerned. In particular, the electron probe diffraction techniques (83) should be of great value in studying colloidal systems and supplying information not obtainable from the electron images alone. Commercial microscopes of higher quality are now equipped for convenient use of an analogous method, called selected area diffraction. A small part of an image, e.g., a single crystal, can be selected by means of a suitable aperture located in the image plane of the objective lens and externally adjustable in position and size. The power of the intermediate lens is then changed to produce an image with zero magnification. The

[*] Cf. C. P. Shillaber, "Photomicrography in Theory and Practice," p. 305. Wiley, New York, 1944.

[†] For more complete data see refs. 31 and 58.

objective aperture is then removed, and the diffraction pattern appears.

The determination of size and shape of opaque particles from both light and electron optical images is worthy of brief consideration, since, in order that the true shape be recognized, the resolution in the image must be considerably below the diameter of the particle. If the particle takes the shape of a regular polygon, its diameter must exceed the resolution of the instrument by a factor about equal to the number of sides of the polygon if the shape is to be recognizable. Borries and Kausche (20) derived a relation between the least diameter of a polygon permitting recognition as such (D_{min}), the resolution of the instrument (d), and the number of sides of the polygon (n):

$$\frac{D_{min}}{d} = 2\left(1 + \cos\frac{\pi}{n}\right)\sqrt{\frac{n}{\pi}\cot\frac{\pi}{n}} \qquad (7)$$

D_{min}/d varies from $0.75n$ for $n = 3$ to $1.27n$ for $n \to \infty$. For $n = 4$, eq. (7) yields $D_{min}/d = 3.7$; for $n = 10$, $D_{min}/d = 12.2$. In the case $n = 4$,

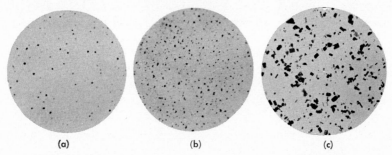

FIG. 7. (a) Photomicrograph of zinc oxide powder taken with $\lambda = 4390$ A. and N.A. = 1.40. (1575×) (b) Photomicrograph of same powder taken with $\lambda = 2750$ A. showing increased definition due to better resolution. (1575×) (c) Electron micrograph of same powder clearly showing shape of particles. (8600×) (58).

a value of $D_{min} = 74$ A. is obtained for a resolution of $d = 20$ A. A light microscope employing $\lambda = 4390$ A., N.A. = 1.40, and $d = 1900$ A. yields $D_{min} = 7030$ A. Thus, square particles of a size less than about 7000 A. would appear as disks in a light optical image but would persist as squares in an electron optical image until their size became less than about 75 A. As an example of this dependence of image shape on resolution, a photomicrograph taken with $\lambda = 4390$ and N.A. = 1.40, one with $\lambda = 2750$ A., and an electron micrograph taken with 60-kv electrons are shown in Fig. 7 (58). The specimen was a finely divided zinc oxide powder with particles of a rectangular shape. The particles appear as circular disks in Fig.

7a, are somewhat better defined in Fig. 7b, but are easily recognized as rectangular in the electron micrograph.

The determination of size is another matter. It is probably true that, as long as the shape of a particle is evident, a measurement of size in the image will yield a value quite close to the true size. When the diameter is such that the shape becomes undiscernible in the image, the size measurements should be closely questioned. As the particle diameter decreases,

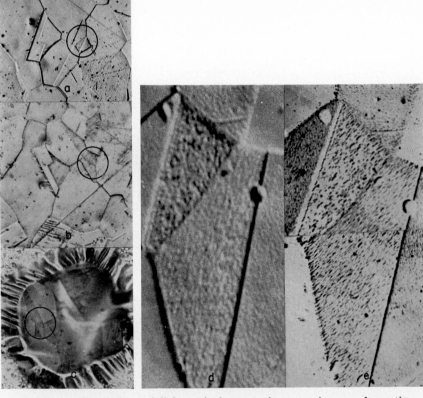

FIG. 8. Comparison of light and electron microscope images of exactly the same spot on a polished and etched stainless steel surface. (a) Photomicrograph of original surface (500×). (b) Photomicrograph of polystyrene molding (500×). (c) Photomicrograph of silica replica on a 200-mesh screen (500×). (d) Photomicrograph of original surface taken at 2000× and enlarged to 3400×. (e) Electron micrograph of silica replica for direct comparison with (d) (3400×). The circles in (a), (b), and (c) include area shown in (d) and (e) (69).

the uncertainty in the location of the edge due to diffraction approaches the diameter of the particle. For very small particles, the diameter of the diffraction halo is roughly independent of particle size and depends chiefly on the optical adjustments. When the particle diameter is small enough that both an internal and an external set of fringes are formed, then the particle is no longer recognizable as such and its edges cannot be located in the image. The particle diameter at which the uncertainty in measurement due to diffraction exceeds a definite value is difficult to predict. The evidence indicates that large errors will occur in measurements of particle size at and below the wavelength of the illumination employed.

A similar situation exists in electron microscope images. Uncertainty

Fig. 9. Comparison of photomicrograph (a) and emission electron micrograph (b) of recrystallized iron strip. Emission micrograph at approximately 30×. From *Physica* **4**, 15 (1937).

in the location of the particle edge may be comparable to the particle diameter when the size is of the order of 50 A. Again, the measured values will be very sensitive to focus of the objective and the angular aperture of the illumination (84).

A comparison of light optical and electron optical results on an etched metal surface has been made (69) which illustrates the advantage of the higher resolution of the electron microscope. Actually, this is a comparison of the light microscope image and the electron image of a replica of the same surface. The details of replica preparation will be described in a separate section, but the results are of interest here and are illustrated in Fig. 8. Figure 8a is a photomicrograph taken at 500× of an electropolished and etched specimen of stainless steel 18-8. Figure 8b is a polystyrene molding of this same surface taken at 500×, and Fig. 8c is a photomicrograph of the silica replica mounted an a 200-mesh screen and ready for the electron microscope. Figure 8d is a high-magnification photomicrograph of the original surface taken at 2000× and enlarged to 3400× for comparison with the electron micrograph of the silica replica, Fig. 8e. The appearance of the two images is very similar, and corresponding spots are easily recognized. The additional detail of Fig. 8e over 8d illustrates the greatly increased resolution of the electron microscope-silica replica combination over the light microscope. Both the light optical and electron optical images result from elevation changes on the etched surface and hence would be expected to be similar at least to a first approximation. The problems of interpretation will be considered in a later section.

For the sake of completeness an emission micrograph and a photomicrograph of a recrystallized iron strip are shown in Fig. 9. Although the magnification is low, the similarity is quite striking.

6. Magnification Calibration

The determination of the magnification is of primary importance in applying the electron microscope. The accepted standard for calibration is a diffraction grating replica for which the constant has been determined (for the replica itself) by light-diffraction methods. In the past, such replicas have been prepared by many of the methods described in Section 8.1, but the superior properties of shadowed carbon replicas (stripped directly from the grating by the use of a parting layer) have led to its general adoption. Such calibrated replicas are now commercially available. The procedure for calibrating, apparently first reported by Burton *et al.* (31), is as follows:

1. The replica is stripped from the grating and mounted on a specimen screen which is inserted in the holder.
2. The holder is mounted in a spectrometer, and the diffraction angle, θ, for a strong spectral line (e.g., the sodium doublet $\lambda 5890$, 5896) is measured on both sides of the undiffracted beam. The grating constant, a, computed from the formula for normal incidence,

$$a = \frac{\lambda}{\sin \theta} \tag{8}$$

is the *average* line spacing in the replica. If the replica does not produce sharp diffraction lines, it is distorted or wrinkled. Of course the holder is adjusted so that the lines are parallel to the slit of the spectrometer.
3. Electron micrographs such as that shown in Fig. 10 are then taken, preferably with the replica oriented with the lines parallel to one edge of the photographic plate. These micrographs then give also the over-all rotation due to the magnetic lenses.

The grating should have at least 30,000 lines per inch, for which the average line spacing is about 8500 A. At low magnification, below 5000×, field distortion may be present, but 10 or more lines are imaged; and a few micrographs suffice both to select a pair of lines with average separation and to determine magnification on the axis. The magnification is then increased and the selected pair used to measure it up to about 50,000×. At still higher M, features in the pattern more closely spaced than 8500 A must be used. Such features, of adequate sharpness and contrast, may be present in the grating replica, but, if not, recourse may be made to other specimens, such as a hole in a carbon substrate, to determine higher magnifications relative to those determined by the grating replica. Of course this procedure may also be used at lower M, provided one picture is related to the magnification accurately determined by the grating replica. At $M > 20,000$ magnification calibration is inseparable from the problem

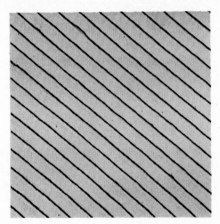

Fig. 10. Shadowed carbon replica of grating with average line spacing 8800 A. Courtesy of E. F. Fullam, Inc., Schenectady, New York.

of accurate focusing, which involves the removal of objective lens astigmatism by adjustment of a compensator.

Some years ago L. A. Matheson and R. D. Heidenreich* conducted some experiments concerning the accuracy and uniformity of grating replicas as calibration standards. Polystyrene-silica replicas, metallized with aluminum to improve the optical reflectivity, exhibited a 2% increase in spacing over that of the original. Successive replicas agreed among themselves to better than 1%. Neither exposure to the electron beam nor prolonged standing in air caused measurable distortion. In contrast, plastic replicas did not exhibit the same degree of dimensional stability, although they can be stabilized to a considerable extent by shadowing with a metal.

Two other methods for determining magnification are often used.

*J. Appl. Phys. **16**, 263A (1945), and unpublished results.

The first is based on data furnished by the manufacturer of the instrument. Since magnification is a product of ratios of distances along the microscope column, a standardized procedure can be specified which results in a known magnification, in much the same way that the optical train in a light microscope yields a known magnification. This is accurate to within a few per cent and is adequate for many problems. The second

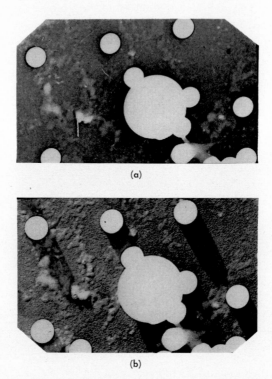

(a)

(b)

Fig. 11. (a) Latex particles before shadowing, average diameter 2590 A. (b) After shadowing, diameter 2840 A. Thickness of metal 10 A. (21,750×) (89).

is the polystyrene sphere method much in vogue a few years ago (6, 56). Certain latexes called monodisperse (22) precipitate spheres of a very uniform size; the one most used was 2590 A. Drops of a very dilute suspension of these spheres are placed on the specimen. Preferably, they are then metallized. Their images appear on the micrograph as an internal calibration. The principal difficulty with the method is that the spheres, although adequately uniform in size, exhibit a certain variability in apparent size in the image. The causes of this variability include possible electrostatic charging, and deposit of carbon from grease vapors present in the microscope; but unexplained differences among various observers also occurred. An example of the application of the method to the study of polished metal surfaces is given in ref. 46. A replica of a grating may also be used as a substrate and internal standard (51).

In our experience, there are few problems in which ultimate accuracy in calibration is essential. Under standard operating conditions the accuracy—about 2%—with which an electron microscope retains its calibration is adequate. Particle size determination might seem to be an exception, but the fact is that the shape factor introduces much greater uncertainty into the calculation of particle parameters—such as equivalent diameter, specific surface (140)—than a minor uncertainty in magnification. It is important that field distortions (i.e., variation in M over the field of the micrograph) be absent or, if present, known and corrected for. Field distortion can seriously increase the apparent width of a particle size histogram; this width is an important constant of the distribution. Another possible exception is the examination of certain periodic structures such as occur in macromolecular crystals (149) and in certain biological fibers (collagen). Once again, however, difficulties of interpretation far outweigh a minor uncertainty in magnification. If an internal magnification marker is desired, it can be built into the microscope mechanically. Some commercial microscopes are so equipped. Of course, the accuracy of this calibration should be checked occasionally by the grating replica method.

7. Stereoscopy

In light microscopy, the small depth of focus offers a means of detecting and measuring elevation changes in the object simply by means of differential focusing. This method cannot be employed in electron microscopy, however, since the focal depth is almost always greater than the changes of elevation occurring in the object. Consequently, other means must be sought.

There are, at present, two methods of detecting and measuring elevation changes in electron microscope specimens. These are stereoscopy and "shadow-casting." The former is an optical method operating on the parallax between two images of an object taken with a known angle between pictures. The latter utilizes the shadows produced on the specimen by condensing a stream of metal atoms directed at oblique incidence (cf., e.g., ref. 46). A knowledge of the angle at which the stream impinges on the structure and the length of the shadow makes it possible to compute the height of the structure. It is frequently difficult, however, to determine the profile edge which actually casts the shadow. Moreover, the shadow edge may fall in a region of irregular topography. In general the determination of height by shadow length is accurate only for isolated particles on flat surfaces.

The use of the stereoscopic technique in electron microscopy appeared in the German literature (3, 57) some time ago for both qualitative and quantitative work. The method is quite simple and consists in taking two micrographs of the specimen with the angle between illuminating beam and object changed between pictures. The stereomicrographs are then viewed with the aid of a stereoscope and the illusion of depth so obtained.

Commercial electron microscopes are now usually equipped with spe-

FIG. 12. Electron stereomicrographs of molybdenum oxide smoke crystals on a silica support film. The stereoscopic base line is shown. (7600×) (71).

cial specimen holders for stereoscopic work. By means of an external control, the angle which the specimen makes with the electron beam can be changed by about ±4°. This is equivalent to looking at an ordinary object at a viewing distance of 17 to 18 inches. Larger angles have occasionally been used.

The rotation of the image by the magnetic lenses introduces a complication. It becomes necessary to determine the tilt axis in the image, since this axis is rotated from its position in the object. The angle can be conveniently determined by using the diffraction grating replica. The grating replica is aligned in the specimen holder with the rulings normal to the axis of tilt. The image of the rulings on the plate then constitute the "stereoscopic base line" for subsequent pictures. Stereomicrographs are indexed according to the rulings in the calibration image and viewed with the eyes parallel to the base line shown in Fig. 12. The electron optical system in some microscopes has been designed so that the angle of rotation is either 0° or 90°, dependent on the magnification range or, more specifically, on whether or not the intermediate lens of a three-lens system is used. This eliminates the necessity for determination of the azimuthal position of the stereoscopic base line.

The micrographs for quantitative stereoscopy are prepared as just described. The additional step is the measurement of parallax between image points by means of a contour finder and then conversion of the parallax readings to elevations (Fig. 12). A detailed discussion will be found in ref. 76 and further examples in ref. 71. Figure 13 shows a profile line taken from a stereoscopic pair.

Practical electron stereoscopy is most effective for elevation changes of the order of 1000 A. and up, although it can be extended to smaller values. Basically, this is because the vertical resolving power is much less

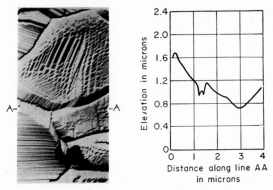

FIG. 13. Profile along the line *A-A* of a micrograph from the surface of a nickel-manganese oxide flake sintered at 1250°C. (34).

than the horizontal. It is not suitable in the case of a dispersion of particles on a flat surface which is ideal for shadow-casting. It is well suited to aggregates of particles, surface replicas, and microsections and can be used to good advantage in interpreting electron micrographs of such objects (34). Fuller (53) has employed stereoscopy in studying the angles between the "spikes" of zinc oxide smoke crystals. Diffraction effects from crystalline materials are often quite evident in stereomicrographs (54, 79).

8. Application to Colloidal Systems

The study of finely divided solid materials is one of the largest fields of electron microscopy and includes bacteriology, colloids, and catalysts. It is evident that each system studied will present its own problems of preparation and image interpretation. In this discussion it would be impractical to attempt to enter into detailed methods or results. The general problem will be taken up, and various factors in preparation common to a variety of materials will be considered. The two main problems in the examination of finely divided materials are: (1) substrates to support the particles in the object plane, and (2) dispersion and application of the material to the support film.

8.1. ORGANIC SUBSTRATE FILMS

It follows from what has been said concerning image formation that the use of a support film, which is often necessary, is a disadvantage due to reduction in image contrast (see Fig. 17). Consequently, the support films should offer a minimum cross section for electron scattering. This is realized by employing materials with atoms of low atomic number and films as thin as is practical. The thickness of film required will be dictated by the strength of the film and the electrical properties and size of particles it must support and by its behavior during electron bombardment. That the support films should contribute no structural details to the image which might interfere with the material being studied goes without saying. This requirement eliminates highly crystalline materials for most applications, since such films nearly always exhibit pronounced diffraction effects in the image (72, 146). Many of the plastic films are crystalline to a certain extent (115), but no difficulty has been observed as a direct consequence.

One of the earliest methods of supporting a finely divided material employed a thin film of nitrocellulose across a fine mesh screen or hole in a plate. The material to be examined was then dusted or deposited from a suspension onto the film and was ready to be examined in the microscope. Modifications of this method are still employed to a large extent. Figure 14a shows a profile of particles mounted on a thin film.

A serious difficulty in the above preparation is that of obtaining a uniform dispersion of particles rather than isolated clusters and aggregates. As a result, modifications have been made wherein the material to be examined is dispersed in the polymer solution and then cast in the film. This situation is illustrated in Fig. 14b, showing the dispersed particles embedded in the film. Satisfactory results are achieved by this method for many materials, although a difficulty is encountered not present in the first-mentioned method. This difficulty may or may not be serious, depending on the information sought. It arises from the thick layer of plastic presented to the electron beam at the edges of the particles. The scattering due to this layer of polymer tends to diffuse the image of edges. If the particles possess a scattering cross section comparable to that of the plastic, the boundaries may be quite indistinct. It has been observed several times that powders dispersed in this manner give no pattern by transmission electron diffraction or sometimes only a diffuse, weak pattern even though the powder is sharply crystalline. It is thought by the authors that the thick layer of polymer at the edges is partially responsible for these observations. This behavior would be due to the scattering of the incident electrons and broadening of the weak diffracted beam. Bombardment of films in the electron microscope greatly increases the chance of attaining a good diffraction pattern because of ill-understood changes occurring in the plastic. This point should be clarified, since electron diffraction patterns from the electron microscope preparations are often required.

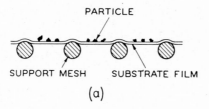

(a)

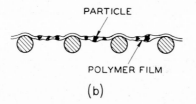

(b)

Fig. 14. Profiles illustrating two ways of mounting powdered material for electron microscope examination. (a) Particles resting on substrate film. (b) Particles dispersed in substrate film.

There are a number of high polymeric materials commonly used for support films, such as cellulose nitrates, ethyl cellulose, cellulose acetate, and polyvinyl formal. Various workers may consider one of these, in conjunction with chosen solvents, as superior to others. Actually, the differences are quite small if the proper solvents are employed with each, since they all possess roughly similar physical properties. The elongations may be expected to vary with solvent content, plasticizing agents, etc. They are all thermoplastic and at 150° to 200°C. are viscous liquids rather than solids unless some degree of crosslinking occurs under electron bombardment. Here again, there are practically no data. Revell and Agar (120) have reported on the preparation of uniform plastic films.

There are several methods of forming films from solutions of the polymers. A very common one is the use of a solvent with a polar end group (such as amyl acetate) which causes the solution to spread on a water surface. As the solution spreads into a thin film, the solvent evaporates leaving behind a polymer film. The thickness of the film is determined by the concentration of the solution and the area attained during spreading.

The film spread on a water surface is transferred to the specimen supports by simply distributing a number of these over a small area of the film while the film is on the water. A microscope slide is then pushed vertically into the water surface at the edge of the region containing the supports whereupon the film folds back onto the slide with the supports between the glass and the film. They then are simply removed from the slide with a pair of tweezers and are ready for use.

Specimen supports take many forms. Perhaps most common is a disk, of diameter appropriate for the specimen holder, punched from 200-mesh screen. Screen with a wide variety of opening size and shape (e.g., slits, hexagons, diamond shapes) is available commercially. Disks with center identification structure are also available, and the manufacturers are prepared to supply any shape for which a drawing is made. This drawing, optically reduced, is used in a photoelectrolytic technique to produce the screen. The authors prefer 500-mesh copper screen, which is available with transparency of 60 to 80%. The more closely spaced metal grids of this screen are only about 10 μ wide, as compared to 25 μ for similar 200-mesh. Some microscopists prefer platinum disks in which small holes (usually 70 μ) have been drilled. Because of their greater rigidity these are desirable for work of highest resolution.

Films can be formed on solid surfaces as well as on water, and there is some advantage in employing a solid with a very smooth surface such as a glass microscope slide. The films cast on water and those applied to a solid surface are generally not of uniform thickness if the top surface of the film is allowed to form at the air interface. On the other hand, a reasonably uniform thin film is obtained from a glass slide by placing a drop of the polymer solution (about 1%) on one end of the slide and then spreading it over the surface by using the edge of another microscope slide. This reduces thickness variations due to uneven flow and evaporation of solvent. When such a film has set, the material at the edges is scraped away so that when the slide is pushed under a clean water surface, at an angle of 20° to 30°, the film moves out onto the water surface. The slide is immersed only to about two-thirds of its length. The specimen screens are then placed on the glass surface beneath the film, and the slide is carefully withdrawn from the water so that the film is redeposited onto the surface and over the screens.

In regard to dispersion methods wherein the pigment or powder is to be included in the plastic films, several workers have reported various methods of accomplishing the desired result. Fuller *et al.* suggest a method (54) using poppyseed oil and amyl acetate as a medium in which the pigment is mulled. To the resulting paste is added nitrocellulose in amyl acetate, and after more working of the mixture it is finally cast from an isopropyl acetate suspension onto a water surface. This method is recommended by these workers for zinc oxide pigments, etc.

Many variations of the technique just described are possible with various media, depending on the material being dispersed. Schuster and Fullam (125) have surveyed some variations of this method, and a table listing solvents, etc. recommended by these workers is included (see Table II).

TABLE II

Table of Resins and Solvents

		Recommended solvents		
Resin	For dispersion[a]	For mounts cast on glass[b]	For mounts spread on water[c]	For mounts drawn down on glass[c]
Nitrocellulose (Parlodion)	Cellosolve acetate	Methyl acetate Ethyl acetate	Methyl acetate Ethyl acetate Amyl acetate Cellosolve acetate Octyl acetate	Ethyl acetate Amyl acetate
Formvar 15/19	1,4-Dioxane plus a few drops of dimethyl dioxane Nitroethane	Ethylene dichloride Nitroethane	Dichloroethylene Propylene dichloride Ethylene dichloride plus 0.1% oleic acid Nitroethane 1,1-dichloro-2-nitroethane	Dioxane Nitroethane
Polystyrene	Xylene	Ethylene dichloride Toluene	Benzene Toluene Xylene	Benzene Toluene
Methyl methacrylate or cellulose acetate	Methyl amyl ketone Methyl ethyl ketone plus 10% isophorone	Acetone	Methyl ethyl ketone Methyl amyl ketone Isophorone	Methyl ethyl ketone

[a] 10 to 20% solutions, approximately.
[b] 0.1 to 0.5% solutions, approximately.
[c] No fixed concentration; suspension allowed to dry to a suitable consistency.

The organic polymer films are subject to certain limitations which, in some instances, make them useless. The main restrictions are their solubility in organic liquids and their deterioration at elevated temperatures. Their dimensional stability during electron bombardment always leaves something to be desired.

8.2. INORGANIC SUBSTRATE FILMS

Inorganic substrates are often very useful. Although they can be made of many substances, by evaporation onto a smooth solid surface, at the present time evaporated carbon films (Bradley, 23, 24, 26) are preferred by most microscopists. The material should be, as nearly as possible, structureless; evaporated films of many inorganic oxides (SiO, SiO_2, TiO_2, GeO, W_2O_3, etc.) are amorphous as shown by electron diffraction patterns. The group IV elements carbon, silicon, and germanium likewise form amorphous evaporated films. Of these carbon has the highest conductivity and the least susceptibility to damage in the electron microscope. It is possible to prepare carbon substrate films so thin that they give rise to a barely detectable contrast difference in electron micrographs. This is true also of the Al-Be alloy suggested by Kaye (87), but, in the authors' experience, this film was more fragile in the microscope. Crystallite size and electron scattering cross section was so small that granularity could not be detected in the micrographs, and broad diffraction rings were observed (87).

The preparation of electrolytic Al_2O_3 films has been described by Hass (66) and will not be repeated here. Although in the past evaporated films have been prepared by using plastic-covered microscope slides as the surface for deposit, it is perhaps more customary now to use the parting-layer method first proposed by Kaye (87).

1. A thin amorphous parting layer is first evaporated onto the slide surface. This may be an organic detergent (87) or boron oxide (21).

2. The film material is then evaporated. (a) Oxides, silicon, and germanium, and the Al-Be alloy may be evaporated from a conical tungsten filament or "basket." (b) Carbon is evaporated by Bradley's method—contact heating of a carbon point held by a suitable spring mechanism against the truncated end of a carbon cone. Heating current is of the order of 50 to 70 amp. when the point and cone are made by grinding down ¼-inch carbon rods. Thickness of films (a) is determined by the amount placed in the tungsten basket. Thickness of carbon films (b) is determined by experience and, in particular, by the duration of heating. In both cases, distance from source to target (microscope slide) should be 8 to 10 cm. Very thin films are perhaps best prepared by increasing this distance.

3. If the parting layer, which is water-soluble, is sufficiently thick, the film can be floated off on water. The inorganic film is then treated similarly to the organic film described above. The authors prefer a somewhat different technique—the film on the slide is backed by a plastic film such as collodion. After drying, the combination strips readily off the glass slide—in fact, thinner parting layers than in the float-off method are adequate. The backed film is cut into squares and transferred to specimen screens. The plastic is then dissolved at the surface of a suitable solvent, leaving the film adhering to the screen. (If the screen is immersed in the solvent, the film drifts free and must be "fished" out of the solvent as in the polystyrene-silica technique (55, 77).

There are many variants to this technique. The essential step is to cover with a thin layer of some material which permits physical removal of the film. This layer must not modify detectably the smoothness characteristic of microscope slides, which are fire-polished and, except for scattered, easily recognizable flaws, yield substrate films without structure detectable in the electron microscope. The objection to using a thin plastic film, deposited from solution, for this purpose is that the molecular structure of the plastic may become visible if metal-shadowing is subsequently used in specimen preparation.

As prepared, substrate films are structureless (115) and preferably very thin—about 1 γ/cm.^{2} Subsequent treatment may develop an observable structure. For example, on heating above 500°C., silica films convert to cristobalite, becoming crystalline. Structure invisible because of lack of contrast in the substrate film itself may become visible when contrast is heightened by shadowing. Heating in the electron beam (or otherwise) may cause chemical reactions to occur between a material being studied and the substrate film. Thus, at elevated temperature a magnesium film reacts with silica to form MgO and Si or SiO. Only a very few materials have been reported as useful for substrate films, but presumably almost any metallic oxide and particularly the more refractory ones could be so used. Because of its low chemical activity, aluminum oxide should be helpful in particular applications.

8.3. Dispersion Methods

Two distinct methods are in use, the mechanical and the electrostatic techniques (111). Both methods aim to break particle aggregates into a primary particle dispersion. The first operates through the shear forces developed by motion in a viscous medium; the second depends on electrostatic repulsion between particles bearing a like charge. Basically, the second method is more attractive because of the small likelihood of breaking up the primary particles as might occur during mulling. Some years ago, however, one of the authors observed that the electrostatic method produced nonrepresentative distributions; a preponderance of larger particles was found on specimen supports located near the source during dispersion, as compared to those farther away.

A mechanical method used by R. D. Heidenreich and H. L. Woods (unpublished) that yielded quite good results is as follows:

1. The dry powder to be dispersed is made into a paste with 1 to 2% solution of ethyl cellulose in 80:20 amyl acetate-ethanol by mulling.
2. This paste is then diluted about 100 times with distilled benzene, and a drop of the resulting suspension is allowed to dry on a silica blank and the resulting deposit examined.

This method does not produce a heavy coating of polymer about each particle, but there is sufficient material to maintain a dispersion during evaporation of the solvent and to anchor the particles to the substrate.

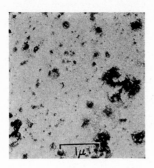

FIG. 15. Electron micrograph of a colloidal iron oxide used in producing magnetic powder patterns. Deposited on a silica substrate from a water suspension containing soap.

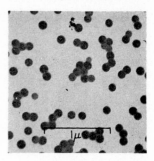

FIG. 16. Spherical particles of emulsion-polymerized polystyrene. Prepared by allowing a drop of the dilute emulsion to dry on a silica substrate. Courtesy of Dow Chemical Co.

If the substrate can be avoided it is advantageous to do so. This again depends on the specific material to be examined. Metallic oxide smokes can be collected on screens with no support film. Watson (139)

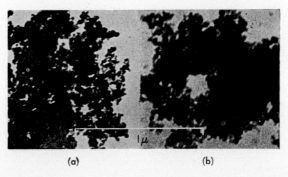

(a)   (b)

FIG. 17. Loss in contrast in image of Halo "C" carbon black resulting from use of substrate with comparable scattering cross section. (a) Applied dry to standard mesh with no support film. (b) Applied dry to silica substrate. (Approximately 125 A. thick.)

has employed fine fibers as a base on which chains and networks of particles are formed from an air suspension. This method is, in part, electrostatic, especially when insulating fibers are used. Excellent micrographs of carbon black have been obtained in this manner with additional information resulting from the absence of the support film.

If the dispersed phase possesses a cross section for scattering com-

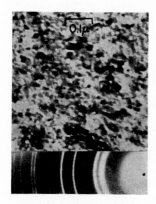

FIG. 18. Electron micrograph and transmission electron diffraction pattern of a film of hydrogen-reduced nickel. A trace of oxide is evident from the diffraction pattern. No substrate film.

parable with the substrate, difficulties with contrast in the image will be encountered. The shadowcast (147) technique for improving contrast is valuable in such cases as well as for aiding in shape determination. It is most effective when the particles are in contact with a flat surface such

FIG. 19. Silica replicas of particles and associated shadows. Silica evaporated at colatitude angle $\theta_a = 60°$. Oval hole in enlargement shows presence of film in shadow. Two small particles in shadow (whitish areas) are replicated by diffusing components only (35).

as a glass slide. Areas of the specimen with no metal possesses a much lower scattering power than do those with a deposit.

The problem of dispersion is greatly ameliorated, and much more information about particles obtained, if surface replicas are used. This method was originally reported by Calbick (33, 34), using silica replicas. The use of carbon and shadowed carbon replicas in a similar manner has since been reported by Bradley (23, 26) and by Watson (141, 142). The chief advantages are that the shape of the individual particles may be displayed stereographically (Fig. 19) and that particles in aggregates can usually be distinguished.

As with all techniques, many variations are possible to accomplish specific purposes. An experimenter usually develops his own preferred methods. Although many electron micrographs illustrating various applications of the electron microscope to colloidal systems could be exhibited, only a few have been included. It is evident that justice cannot be done to any application with a single picture. Therefore, the reader is referred to the bibliographies (38, 101, 110) for specific applications.

As a conclusion to this section and an introduction to the next, Table III gives a classification of electron microscope problems.

TABLE III

Electron Microscope Problems

Particle, or direct examination problems		Surface, or indirect examination problems	
Form of material	Critical technique	Form of surface	Remarks
Bulk powders: pigments, metal, carbon black, ceramic, etc.	Dispersion	Natural surfaces Growth: sintered, from solution, crystals, polymers, etc.	
Colloids, aerosols: nonbiological, also biological, bacteria, viruses, etc.	Precipitation on substrate in dispersed state	Chemically changed: oxidation, decomposition, etc.	Replication method must be adapted to gross shape, detailed structure, and sometimes chemical nature of surface
Crystallites: whiskers, thin films, smokes, etc.	Production of specimens suitable for insertion in microscope	Mechanically modified: polished, wear, cold-worked, etc.	
Thin sections (biology)	Production of specimens suitable for microtomy	Prepared surfaces: metallographic, ceramic, etc.	Polishing, etching, and perhaps other methods determine surface structure

9. Application to Solid Surfaces

The structure of solid surfaces is a subject of great interest from both a fundamental and a practical point of view. Investigations of surface structure can generally be divided into two categories according to their purpose:

1. Chemical constitution, atomic arrangement, and general topography of surfaces and their relation to physical and chemical properties.
2. The deduction of the bulk structure of a solid from the examination of a suitably prepared surface (70).

In Table III these two categories have been called natural and prepared surfaces, respectively. The characteristic of natural surfaces is that they appear as *faits accomplis*—it is desired that the electron micrographs depict what has happened in the course of growth, chemical reactions, mechanical wear, etc. Prepared surfaces occur when the determination of bulk structure is the primary object, as in metallography, or similar studies on nonmetallic materials such as ceramics or plastics. Natural surfaces are, of course, not independent of bulk structure, and sometimes the micrographs furnish information which can be interpreted in terms of bulk structure. But the primary object of the investigation of a natural surface is study of the process which produced the surface, and, in general, it is not permissible to modify the surface. In contrast, etching and perhaps other forms of surface modification are normal procedures for prepared surfaces, and the surface structure revealed is interpreted in terms of bulk structure.

The study of surfaces by means of the transmission microscope yields the same type of information obtained with colloidal systems, namely; size and shape only. As pointed out in the discussion of image formation, 60-kv. electrons are incapable of penetrating thicknesses of matter in excess of a few hundred angstroms and still form satisfactory images. Consequently, the problem of determining surface topography with the electron microscope is one of reproducing the surface contours in a film of material that can be imaged by the transmission instrument. Obviously, the reproduction or replica technique introduces another variable into the already complex problem of studying surfaces. The present state of replica methods is such, however, that the topography of the original surface can be reasonably well deduced from electron images of replicas. The range of size of the topographical details usefully imaged is from about 3 μ down to about 100 A. Above 2 or 3 μ, light microscopy should be employed. Below about 100 A., interpretation should be made with extreme caution. Hence, the role of the conventional electron microscope is at present that of supplying topographical details in the range of 3 μ to 100 A. This information is then to be interpreted in close conjunction with electron diffraction and chemical analyses and correlated with other observed properties.

9.1. Replica Methods

A replica may be defined as a thin film which presents to the electron beam locally varying thicknesses and topography which correspond in some manner to the surface detail. The manner in which the thickness differences correspond, and hence the interpretation of density variations in the micrographs, depends on the method of replication (35, 120). Surface replicas for electron microscopy were first suggested by Mahl (97, 98). Table IV presents a classification of replicas. At present evaporated film replicas, particularly pre- or postshadowed carbon replicas, are in use almost exclusively, at least in this country. Evaporated film replicas include shadowed plastic replicas, because the electron-interaction properties of the replica are predominantly those of the shadowing material rather than the plastic.

TABLE IV

Replication Methods

Type of replica	Intrinsic resolution	Interpretation	Permits repetition	Stability under electron irradiation	Technique of preparation
Electrolytic or thermal oxide	Good, ca. 100 A.	Good	No, surface ᴢstroyed	Good	Simple, but not generally applicable
Plastic	Poor, > 200 A.	Excellent but limited	Yeᵣ	Poor	Simple, but not applicable to particles
Evaporated films (elements and oxides)	Good to best, 200-10 A.	Yields greatest informa-	Yes, except for highest resolution	Good to best	More complex, but of general applicability

9.1.1. Oxide Film Replicas. Mahl's first results were obtained with an anodic oxide film chemically removed from an etched aluminum surface. This oxide film followed the contours of the surface on which it was formed and yielded high-quality micrographs. Unless produced under closely controlled conditions, the aluminum oxide film may exhibit a granular structure (43) which obliterates detail approaching the size of the granules.

Mahl (98) also employed oxide films from copper and nickel in order to study the topography of the etched metals. Gulbransen (60) has used thermal oxide films extensively as replicas. These films are crystalline, however, and much of the detail observed is probably due to diffraction effects. For general work and where satisfactory oxide films cannot be produced, Mahl (98) employed a thin lacquer film stripped from the surface in question. From these plastic lacquer films and some of their disadvantages stemmed the silver-collodion method (151), modifications (122, 123) of Mahl's original lacquer film, and the polystyrene-silica method (27). Calbick (35) showed that evaporated-film replicas can be made from virtually any material with suitable properties. The development of the parting layer method described in Section 8.2 permitted the elimination of one step in two-step processes such as the polystyrene-silica method where an intermediate plastic mold is the surface actually replicated. Many other ingenious replication techniques have been devised, described in some of the articles listed in the bibliographies. Two which should be mentioned are the transfer replica technique of Fisher (44) and the carbon replica technique of Bradley (24, 26).

Anodic aluminum oxide films can be obtained from pure aluminum as follows:

1. The prepared aluminum surface (etched or otherwise) is anodized in a distilled water solution of 2.5% ammonium borate and 0.2% boric acid at 15 to 20 volts for about 2 minutes.

2. The surface is scribed into ⅛-inch squares and then immersed in a saturated solution of mercuric chloride where the mercury is rapidly displaced by aluminum. The mercury deposit moves under the oxide film and frees it from the surface. The released films are transferred to dilute hydrochloric acid for 10 to 15 seconds and then to distilled water. They are picked out of the water on specimen supports and are ready for use. Such a film from a surface etched in 1:1 hydrochloric acid is shown in Fig. 20a. Further discussion of the oxide film preparation is given by Keller and Geisler (88) and in ref. 42.

Substrate films (as discussed in Application to Colloidal Systems) can be produced in this way from an aluminum surface that has been electropolished or uniformly etched in strong sodium hydroxide.

9.1.2. Plastic Film Replicas. The plastic film method is a single-step process wherein the film is first deposited on the surface from a solvent and then mechanically removed with the aid of water or water vapor. Although this appears to be the simplest method and has been represented as very rapid and requiring practically no equipment, it is not so straightforward as might be supposed. The success in stripping a thin plastic film from a surface is apparently dependent both on surface roughness and on the presence of thin, foreign layers that reduce adhesion. Various workers have adopted modifications suited to their own particular problems, and, for that reason, it is difficult to record a procedure that will be generally satisfactory. Two variations of the plastic replica will be briefly described; the "wet" method and the "dry" method.

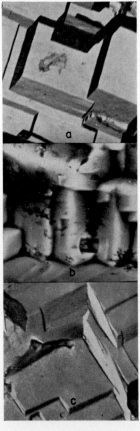

Fig. 20. Replicas of aluminum etched in 1:1 hydrochloric acid-water. (a) Anodic oxide replica. (b) Formvar replica stripped under water. (c) Polystyrene silica replica. (9300×)

Irrespective of the method of removal, the application of the film is the same. It is applied by dipping the surface to be studied into a ½ to 1% solution of the plastic in a suitable solvent. The specimen is removed vertically from the solution and allowed to drain and dry so that the surface to be reproduced has a thick film at the end where the solution drains. Schaefer and Harker (122) recommend Formvar 15/95 (polyvinyl formal) in ethylene dichloride or 1,4-dioxane. Harker and Murphy (63) employ the same polymer in 1,4-dioxane distilled over sodium to remove

water. According to these workers, the films should be applied to the specimen in a dry box to avoid flaws in the film resulting from concentration
of water as the solvent evaporates.

The wet method of removing the lacquer film consists in immersing
the specimen in distilled water the surface of which has been swept clean
with paraffined barriers. The thick end of the film is loosened with a pair
of tweezers, and then the entire film is slowly stripped by pulling back
and up from the starting point. It then may be picked up on a piece of
screen and the disks punched out for the specimen holder. Another
method is to drop specimen supports onto the floating film and then introduce a microscope slide vertically through the surface to fold film and
screen onto the glass as already mentioned in preparation of substrates.

The "dry" method (63, 123) of removal is accomplished by placing
specimen grids on the dried lacquer film (over specific areas if desired).
A piece of Scotch tape is then firmly pressed onto the meshes and film
and worked in closely around the meshes with the fingers. One end of the
tape (at the thick end of the lacquer film) is then pulled in such a manner
that it follows approximately a radius of a circle having as its center the
back or thin film end of the specimen. Practice is required to secure removal of the entire film including that beneath the meshes. The appearance of a Formvar replica stripped by the wet method from an etched
aluminum surface is seen in Fig. 20 b for comparison with the oxide and
polystyrene replicas of similar surfaces.

The question of polymer-solvent combinations arises again and again.
Each observer believes that some particular combination is superior.
There have, however, been few critical studies. The best is that of Revell
and Agar (120), to which the reader is referred for a thorough discussion
of plastic replication films and interpretation of electron micrographs
obtained from them. Although Revell and Agar report only on Formvar,
which is the most generally used plastic, their analysis can be regarded
as applicable to plastic replication in general (Fig. 21).

The defects of plastic replicas—relatively poor resolution, contrast,
and dimensional stability—are removed to a great extent by shadow-
casting (109, 134, 146), in which metal is evaporated at an angle onto the
surface of the thin plastic replica. Since this is a mold of the sample surface, the metal forms a second-step evaporated film replica of the surface.
Since the scattering power of the plastic film should be small compared
to that of the metal, the resulting micrographs are typical of evaporated
film replicas except in regions in which, as a result of surface topography,
either no metal is deposited (i.e., within shadows) or the metal film is very
thin because of near-glancing incidence of the metal during evaporation.
The study of Sub-committee X1 of Committee E-4 of the American

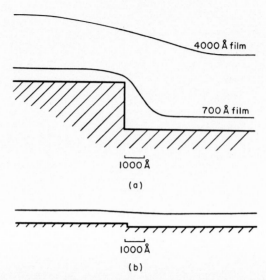

FIG. 21a. Typical cross sections of Formvar replicas on calcite crystal. (a) Films 4000 and 700 A. thick over a step 2500 A. high. (b) Film 700 A. thick over a step 200 A. high.

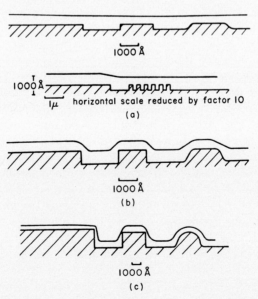

FIG. 21b. Typical cross sections of Formvar replicas. Films 700 Å. thick on pearlite structures. (a) Structure 300 Å. deep. (b) Structure 700 Å. deep. (c) Structure 1600 to 2000 Å. deep (120).

Society for Testing Materials (44) makes a thorough comparison of shadowed plastic and polystyrene-silica replicas for the delineation of surface structures of etched ferrous metals. Such a comparison is shown in Fig. 37 (a) and (c). The papers presented at the ASTM Symposium (44) report many other valuable electron metallographic techniques.

9.1.3. *Evaporated Film Replicas.* The polystyrene-silica replica (55, 77) was the first application, at least in this country, of vacuum evaporation to the production of replicas for electron microscopy. It was followed by metal shadowcasting.

Two-step and one-step processes. In the polystyrene-silica method, the first step consisted in producing an impression of the surface either by pressure-temperature molding or by means of a heavy plastic film. The second step was that of evaporating silica followed by removal of this film by dissolution of the plastic and transferring pieces of suitable size to specimen supports. Many variants of the first step are possible—e.g., polymerizing *in situ* on the surface, softening a plastic block with a solvent which may be the monomer, and pressing this block on the surface. The problem is to obtain a faithful imprint of the surface. One limitation of this step is that a granular structure due to the large plastic molecules appears in the thin film replica, and also in the micrograph if replica resolution is adequate, i.e., better than about 100 A. Since pure silica replicas rarely have resolution better than 200 A. (35), however, they do not show this structure. Many different plastics may and have been used, although in the experience of the authors none is superior to polystyrene.

It may be observed in passing that pressure-temperature molds are usually easily made for prepared surfaces as discussed above, because the gross form of the sample can readily be made a small rectangular block. This may be molded into a block of plastic, from which it can be freed by mechanical means (sawing away the excess plastic, etc.). In contrast, the gross forms of samples whose natural surfaces it is desired to examine often preclude use of the molding technique. As examples, one may wish to observe the growth surface of a small crystal, or the surface of a fiber, or the wear surface on a cylindrical bearing. This problem of gross form of "natural surface" samples on occasion also precludes the use of the one-step parting layer method, because it may not be practical to put the sample itself in the evaporator. In such cases the use of a thick plastic film as an intermediate replica may be nearly unavoidable.

At the present time, whenever possible the evaporated film is produced directly on the sample surface with the use of a parting layer. It is evident that this removes uncertainties due to the use of an intermediate imprint. When it is desired to use an oxide film—and some experimenters still prefer these to carbon (24, 26)—silicon monoxide (65, 67, 68, 90, 148) rather than silica is used, because it is much more easily evaporated.

By either pre- or postshadowing a thin silicon monoxide film, replicas with resolving power equivalent to that of shadowed carbon replicas (50 A. or perhaps a little better) have been produced. If an intermediate plastic replica is used, the final film replica may have as an artifact the granular structure discussed above. Additional artifacts are introduced when heavy film intermediate replicas are used—wrinkles due to drying out of the solvent, and randomly distributed small bumps and pockets of size around 100 A., also due to drying effects. The use of such films, however, is almost the only practical way when the surface is very rough and highly re-entrant. A plastic film is flexible enough to unlock from many re-entrancies; if these are very complex, the film may break off. Because the area of such a break is almost structureless, it is usually possible to identify it. On the other hand, even with a heavy parting layer, the evaporated film is difficult to remove from re-entrant regions, and small holes due to this cause may appear in the replica film. If these are sufficiently numerous, as on a very rough surface, the film is actually removed only in small patches which cannot be transferred satisfactorily to a specimen support for electron microscope examination. It is clear that shadowed plastic replicas are also two-step replicas.

Properties of evaporated film replicas. The films may be of only one material, or of two. In the latter case one film, which may be called the base film, is usually deposited at normal incidence; the other, the shadowing film, at an angle to the surface normal. It is essential that a vacuum better than about 2×10^{-5} torr be maintained during evaporation, and pressure in the 10^{-6} range is recommended. Best results are usually attained with rapid rather than slow evaporation.

At a residual gas pressure of 2×10^{-5} torr, the number of gas molecules striking a surface is sufficient to deposit about twenty molecular layers per second. Fortunately, most of the molecules do not stick, or films evaporated at this pressure would be composed principally of trapped gas molecules. Some do stick, however, and if pressure is allowed to rise to 10^{-4} torr the film is found in subsequent processing to crumble under the action of surface tension forces. This occurs particularly during drying, when the film will be found, not covering the mesh openings of the support, but wrapped around the support members.

It is evident, then, that ability to withstand surface tension forces, a property which will for brevity be called toughness, is important. It is not the same property as dimensional stability, previously discussed, although it is related to it. Toughness is macroscopic, whereas dimensional stability is primarily a microscopic property. A second kind of toughness is ability to withstand the action of the electron beam in the microscope. This is usually called stability in the electron beam. Films with adequate electrical conductivity are superior in this property. Thus plastic films often tear and curl up when under observation, but metal-shadowed films are much tougher. Electrostatic charging evidently occurs with nonconducting films. Local heating is a contributory cause, especially with plastic films. Within the range of thicknesses useful in replicas, heating is proportional to film thickness, and the thinner films ($< 10 \gamma/\text{cm.}^2$) correspondingly are more stable under electron microscope observation than thicker films. Stability also is deleteriously affected by high residual gas pressure during evaporation. *Superiority in this property is the most important advantage of carbon films.* Certain other materials, however—silicon, germanium, and probably also zirconium, and aluminum and the Al-Be alloy—display good stability. All these

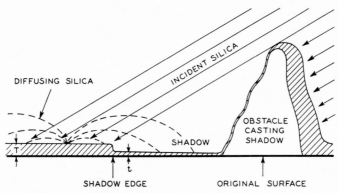

FIG. 22. Diagrammatic representation of condensation of evaporating silica, illustrative of materials condensing with a surface-diffusing component. If all incident material diffused, no shadow edge would be formed. Shadow edges do appear as in Fig. 19 (44).

materials are conducting. Metal-shadowing of nonconducting films such as SiO, SiO_2, TiO_2, Al_2O_3, and plastic improves stability. Unshadowed inorganic films are more stable than plastic.

Toughness of the first kind appears to be related to the noncrystallinity of films. Plastic films are in general noncrystalline and withstand surface tension forces well. Oxides and the semiconductor elements C, Si, Ge, and Zr form amorphous evaporated films (35). During deposition, the molecules or atoms have the ability to wander over the surface; films are found in shadows as well as in regions exposed to the source. The fact that shadows appear, however, indicates that some of the incident atoms or molecules must stick where they strike (Fig. 22). In contrast, the atoms of most metals form crystalline films. The condensing atoms migrate only short distances, of the order of 10 to 100 A., to crystals which initially form on nucleating centers, and subsequently grow (4, 127, 129,

145). Although it is possible to use pure metals as materials for replicas (1, 35) great care must be exercised to prevent their destruction by surface tension forces during processing. Aluminum is an exception. This is believed due to growth of a thin oxide film on the replica surface on exposure to air. This film, however, if present, cannot be detected by electron diffraction. Only the ring pattern of crystalline Al is observed.

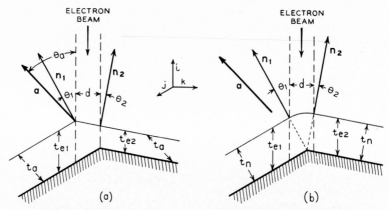

Fig. 23. Diagram illustrating how thickness, t_e, in the direction of the electron beam changes from t_{e1} on one slope to t_{e2} on a different slope. Corresponding to a sharp change in slope, the change occurs over a horizontal distance, d (44). (a) Every atom sticks where it strikes. (b) Diffusing atoms condense into film uniformly thick normal to local surface.

The relation of thickness variations in the replica, which actually produce the electron micrographs, to the corresponding surface features in the sample depends on the material and, in particular, on whether it migrates over the surface during condensation (Fig. 23). When every atom sticks where it strikes, as with metals, the replica is uniformly thick in the direction of the source; and if this direction is the same as that of the subsequently incident electron beam, the only intensity variations observable are those due to the crystalline structure. Hence, to produce contrast due to surface topography, metals must be incident at an angle with the surface normal. The migratory component of oxides and group IV elements, on the other hand, tends to form a film of uniform thickness normal to the local surface; and hence the thickness in the direction of the electron beam varies with local slope. If metal is evaporated at an angle, thickness variations required for replication occur (Figs. 23 and 24). If the colatitude angle of the incident atoms is sufficiently large compared to local slopes on the surface, "shadows" occur in the metal film.

In any replication process the thickness change does not perfectly reproduce sharp steps on the surface; and in general there is a degradation of sharpness which depends on the conditions of formation and observation of the replica. With shadowed replicas (which include single-component replicas evaporated at an angle) this degradation is not constant over a surface but depends on orientation of a feature with respect to the azimuth of incidence (44, p. 45). It tends to be of the order of half the average thickness of the shadowing component but may vary from near zero to perhaps twice the average thickness. Contrast differences representing topographical features also depend on the azimuth and colatitude angles of the shadowing beam. That these differences can

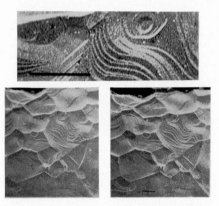

FIG. 24. Aluminum replica formed by single evaporation at $\theta_a = 30°$ (defined in Fig. 23). Thickness 180 A. Replica has torn and curled near top. "Negative shadows" can be observed in this region (35).

be extreme is shown in Fig. 25. Although evaporated film replicas can be interpreted with considerable assurance, especially with the use of stereoscopy, the possible differences in appearance due to angle of incidence must always be remembered. The importance of the property "permits repetition" in Table IV is evident.

Crystallinity (129) of metal films introduces a granularity into micrographs (Fig. 24) which is not related to surface structure. Crystallite size varies greatly for different metals. At thicknesses in the electron microscope range, gold and silver yield large crystals, chromium and platinum much smaller crystals. Because of difficulty in evaporating platinum from a tungsten filament, palladium and palladium-platinum alloys are sometimes used. Chromium is preferred by some investigators, although its crystallinity is usually observable above 20,000×. Because replica resolution depends on linear dimensions, whereas electron-scattering power depends on mass thickness, dense materials such as platinum yield the best resolution. If the very highest resolution is important, pre-shadowing with platinum to an average thickness of 10 to 20 A., fol-lowed by evaporation of carbon to a thickness of about 50 A., will pro-duce about the highest possible resolution. But in the authors' experience, no surfaces requiring such ultimate resolution have been encountered. Replica resolution of about 50 A. can be achieved in either a pure ger-manium replica or in a germanium-shadowed carbon replica. The crys-

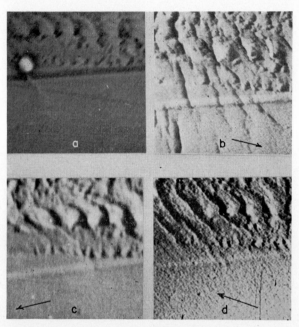

Fig. 25. Series of plastic film (Formvar) strippings from exactly the same region of a scratched glass surface. (a) The stripping before shadowcast. (b), (c), and (d) Chromium-shadowed strippings. The arrows indicate direction of shadowing. Study of corresponding points in this sequence illustrates the necessity for cautious interpretation of shadowcast plastic film replicas. Cour-tesy S. G. Ellis, University of Toronto.

tallinity problem, of course, does not occur with amorphous films (C, Si, Ge, Zr, and oxides). Uranium shadowing has been used, but uranium converts to the oxide on exposure to air.

To sum up, carbon or SiO replicas shadowed, according to the pref-erence of the microscopist, with chromium, germanium, zirconium, palla-dium, or platinum constitute the best present-day practice. Many of the methods discussed above are still in use, however, in some cases for spe-cific reasons, and in others because of the preference and special profi-ciency of the microscopist.

Artifacts and defects. The optical as well as the electron microscopist must be constantly on the alert to detect artifacts. In general, these can be defined as structures which are not germane to the investigation and which may actually interfere with obtaining a satisfactory interpretation of the image. Most commonly they arise in the course of preparation of the sample, which may be one classified under any of the headings in Table III. Of course, the nature of the artifact differs with the nature of the sample. Many examples from the field of biology could be given. A simple one is the effect of the microtome knife on the thin sections used in histological investigations. Agglomeration and fragmentation are examples of artifacts in particle studies.

Because replicas are a substitute for an actual surface, the occurrence of artifacts is more pervasive, and in fact their recognition is almost synonymous with correct interpretation of electron micrographs. Collapse of particle replicas by surface tension forces is a simple example of a process artifact. Wrinkles, bumps, and pockets observed in thick plastic film intermediate replicas are other examples. Barrett (9) has published a series of pictures of artifacts in polystyrene silica replicas. Considerable care must be exercised in the evaporation of parting layers to prevent spattering which can deposit a random distribution of tiny spheres of about 100-A. diameter on the surface being replicated. There are many more obvious artifacts such as dust particles, unwanted surface films, and residue from chemical etches, etc. Distortions and false structures are possible in any replication process. Granularity due to plastic molecules and that due to crystallinity are obvious examples. It is a problem of semantics whether all such effects should be called artifacts, or whether some should be called defects of the replication process. Thus nonobservance of a feature because of the tendency for contrast to vanish in the azimuth of incidence (Fig. 25) is a characteristic of the shadowing process which is a serious defect on occasion. Replica resolution inadequate to see detail actually present is another defect. Nonobservance of a true feature is just as serious as observation of a false one. Perhaps errors of omission should be called defects, and errors of commission artifacts.

The importance of stereoscopy in interpreting micrographs and in the recognition of artifacts is very great. Combined with information deducible from shadows, it usually permits unequivocal characterization of surface features.

The merits of a replica are, in the final analysis, to be judged by the information that can be obtained through its use. For a particular application, one type of replica may be superior to another. Thus, it can be argued that because the simple plastic replica yields pictures more similar to those obtained by optical microscopy than are those obtained from shadowed plastic replicas, the metallurgist obtains more information from them even though the resolution is relatively poor. They are useful in bridging the hundredfold gap between optical and the best electron microscope resolutions.

(a)

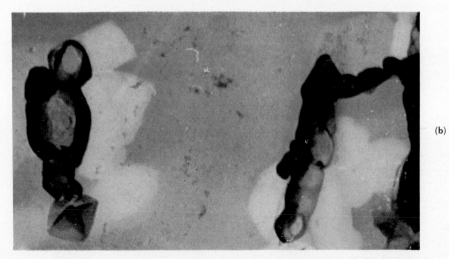

(b)

FIG. 26. (a) Octahedral crystals of nickel physically joined. Beginning of reticulate growth. (b) Continuation of reticulate growth. Germanium replicas. (15,000×)

9.2. PARTICLE STUDIES BY REPLICAS

Originally proposed by one of the authors (33), this is perhaps the most powerful method of examining particles in the size range from about 500 A. to about 5 μ. Smaller particles are best examined directly as described in Section 8. Interpretation of direct particle micrographs is often helped greatly by diffraction, particularly selected area diffraction. But particles above 500 A. rarely give rise to observable electron diffrac-

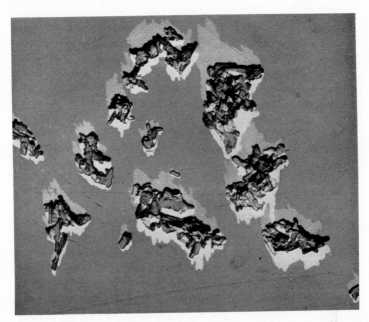

FIG. 27. Germanium-shadowed carbon replica of hematite powder. Both carbon and germanium were evaporated at angles, roughly in opposite azimuths. Most particles in aggregate are distinguishable.

tion patterns, because they are too thick to yield transmission patterns, and too small to yield reflection-type patterns. Substitution of a replica for the particle of course eliminates the possibility of obtaining diffraction patterns, since the particle has been dissolved and is no longer present. The information on particle shape, obtainable from stereoscopic pairs (Fig. 19), is frequently very valuable. Figure 26 shows the process of reticulate growth characteristic of nickel crystals produced by the carbonyl process. Figure 27 is from a germanium-shadowed carbon replica and shows particles of Fe_2O_3; the ability to distinguish particles in agglomerates is evident. Watson (141, 142) has published interesting and valuable papers on the interpretation of unshadowed carbon particle replicas (Fig. 28).

The authors' preferred technique is as follows:

1. The powder is dusted or smeared onto the surface of a microscope slide. Particles in the micron or submicron range adhere to the slide. Excess powder is shaken off.

2. A parting layer film is evaporated. Carbon is then evaporated at normal incidence; thickness should be 100 to 200 A. This is followed by shadowing, at a shadow factor of about 2:1, with germanium, zirconium, platinum, or carbon.

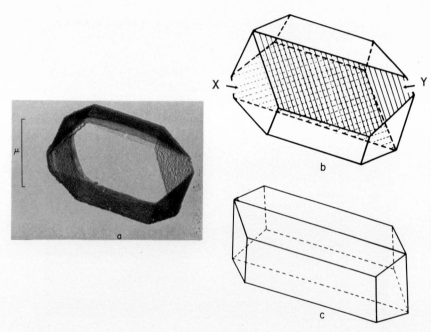

FIG. 28. (a) Aragonite from Staticonia from static labyrinth of a frog. Carbon replica. Unshadowed electron micrograph. (46,000×) (b) Planes of the slightly imperfect orthorhomb shown in (a). Crosshatching at X indicates plane of the crystal facing the carbon source and is oriented perpendicular to the electron beam. Crosshatching at Y indicates plane which supported crystal on slide during carbon evaporation. Doubly crosshatched area represents clear area in (a). (c) Normal orthorhombic crystal of aragonite (143).

3. After the surface has been scored into small squares, the film is floated off onto a water solution of a solvent for the powder. This solvent must not attack the carbon or the shadowing material. The method is thus limited to powders soluble in solvents that will not attack carbon—not a severe limitation.

4. The pieces of film are transferred to the clean surface of a water rinse, with a piece of 200-mesh screen as a transfer tool. This is repeated several times.

5. To reduce surface tension forces during drying, the water should be replaced by a liquid of lower surface tension. A bench made of coarse mesh nichrome screen is placed in a Petri dish. Pure alcohol is added till it just floods the top of this

bench. The film is picked up off the water on 500-mesh screen and transferred to the bench. The screen is then lifted out and allowed to dry. Specimen screens are then punched out from film-covered areas.

The shaking-off process above may eliminate larger particles; these are not suitable to the method because there is a tendency for surface replicas of large particles to collapse. Auxiliary tests employing the cast-film method (Fig. 14b) may be necessary to obtain a complete particle size distribution if particles larger than about 3 μ are present. It should be observed, however, that any method of

FIG. 29. Growth spiral on face of crystal of n-hectane. The vertical edge of the spiral is one molecule or 125 A. high. This face developed from a single screw dislocation. Courtesy *Proc. Roy. Soc.* Reproduced in Heidenreich, *Rev. Sci. Instr.* **23**, 583 (1952).

dispersion, and especially the mulling method employing viscous shear, causes a certain amount of fragmentation, particularly of large particles of irregular shape. The more thorough the dispersion, the greater is the amount of fragmentation. The dusting or smearing method produces poor dispersion and hence little fragmentation. Instead of trying to separate every particle from its neighbors, the microscopist is able to identify particles in aggregates (Fig. 27). The particle shape is observable stereographically.

The study of fibers may be regarded as intermediate between particles and gross surfaces. The ultimate fibers in wood and asbestos, for example, are of diameters in the range of 100 A. or less and may be examined directly. Asbestos fibers appear to be tubular and have led to the concept of a cylindrical lattice (12, 13). Natural and artificial fibers of all kinds have been examined by replica methods (cf. refs. 8, 128, 135, and numerous others in the bibliographies). The advantage of the NYSEM punched card system is here very evident, since the general subject "Thin film and fibers" has the code punch M in subject zone 4. It should be pointed out that the earlier issues were not punched in zone 4.

9.3. NATURAL SURFACES

Inspection of Table III makes it clear that surfaces so classified are "natural" only in the sense that they are the end result of physical or

FIG. 30. Sintering of nickel-manganese oxide powder. Polystyrene-silica replica of natural surfaces. (a) Heated briefly at 900°C., porous structure. (b) Heated briefly at 1250°C., recrystallized compact structure. Note steep detail developed on crystal faces by high-temperature heating. Reproduced in Heidenreich, *Rev. Sci. Instr.* **23**, 583 (1952).

chemical processes. Perhaps the clearest case of a natural surface would be the face of a mineral crystal. Sometimes these faces show growth spirals (59). Such spirals on minerals are usually complex, but simple ones such as that in Fig. 29 may be attributed to a single screw dislocation. This *n*-paraffin crystal was grown from a supersaturated solution. Verma's concise book (137) gives an excellent account of crystal growth and dislocations. The Frank-Read mechanism is discussed thoroughly in ref. 118. Spirals appear frequently on silicon carbide crystals, which are grown by a sintering process. Sintering may be defined as crystal growth below the melting point. An example of crystal growth by sintering is shown in Fig. 30. The crystal facets developed are not usually parts of growth spirals, and the precise mechanism most important in the growth process is probably volume diffusion. Growth such as this appears to be typical of many ceramics such as Al_2O_3, $BaTiO_3$, and various more complex metal oxides. Growth from solution develops diverse surface forms (1), as indicated by the three pictures of Fig. 31. Another process which

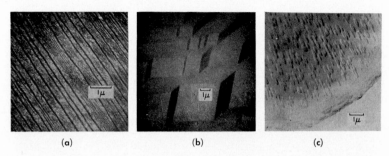

(a)   (b)   (c)

FIG. 31. (a) Ammonium nitrate face (110). Gold-shadowed Formvar replica. (10,500×) (b) Acid magenta-modified ammonium nitrate (high index face). Gold replica. (5500×) (c) Ammonium sulfate face (010). Chromium replica. 7500×) (1).

has been studied by one of the authors is slip. The stepwise nature of slip was first demonstrated in 1947 (78). Figure 32 illustrates the laminar nature of the slip band in aluminum—slip occurs by a maximum glide

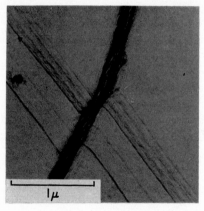

FIG. 32. Anodic oxide replica of intersection slip bands in high-purity aluminum showing stepwise or laminar nature of slip band formation. The distances involved are a glide of 2000 A. on a single atom plane and a distance of 200 A. between active planes. Reproduced in Heidenreich, *Rev. Sci. Instr.* **23,** 583 (1952).

of about 2000 A. with a distance of 200 A. between adjacent active planes. Brown (105) confirmed these findings and extended them over a wide temperature range. Laminar slip has also been observed in nickel, lead, and manganese. Kuhlman-Wilsdorf *et al.* (91) attribute the stepwise slip process to surface defects produced in the crystal at the start of deformation. Fine lines due to steps of the order of 20 to 30 A. spaced 200 to 600 A. apart were found on unslipped surfaces of pure aluminum. The minimum spacing of 200 A. is attributed to the nearest approach allowed by interaction of the stress fields about neighboring dislocations. This elementary structure is actually incipient slip. As deformation proceeds, groups of elementary lines become active slip bands. These authors extended the study to include copper, silver, and α-brass (92).

FIG. 33. Cleavage surface of a crystal of germanium showing crack structure possibly developing from imperfections of the nature of Griffith cracks.

There are, of course, many other processes which produce "natural" surfaces. A few which may be mentioned are: bearing and other forms of wear (37, 126), extrusion, e.g., of plastic fibers (37, 128, 135), polishing, diffusion, electrical erosion by arcing, oxidation and reduction, and electrolysis; no doubt the reader can think of many others. Then there are certain processes which produce surfaces which can be classified either as natural or prepared. Cleavage or fracture surfaces (36, 138) often reveal internal structure but also give information about the fracture process (Fig. 33). Interfaces, of which grain boundaries are an example, usually must be studied in part at least by preparational methods. Figure 34a shows dislocation etch pits along a subgrain boundary in "single-crystal" germanium, as revealed by CP4 etch (143). If etching is by bombardment with mercury ions, these pits disappear and are replaced by others not related to dislocations (Fig. 34b). Such surfaces do not fit neatly into either category.

9.4. ELECTRON METALLOGRAPHY

A common use of surface replicas is the investigation of etched metal surfaces. If electron diffraction methods are employed in close conjunction with the electron microscope, electron metallography is a suitable name for the resulting method. Confusion with light metallography is then avoided.

From the discussion of replica methods it is apparent that the problem of reproducing surface contours was necessarily the first phase of electron microscope examination of surfaces. The use of the replica

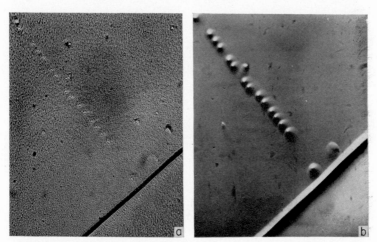

FIG. 34. (a) Germanium crystal (100) surface with 6° tilt boundary etched with CP4 shows assembly of edge dislocations. Optical micrograph. (300×) (b) Same area after sputtering in mercury at 100 ev. for 3 hours. It shows that dislocation edge pits tend to vanish (143).

processes to obtain information about the bulk structures of metals introduces a separate problem that appears to be at least as difficult as the first. The preparation of a metallic surface so that its contours bear an understandable relation to the bulk structure is the basic problem of electron metallography.

This same problem is, of course, present in light metallography, but, over a period of years, metallographers have worked out interpretations of images, at least partially. Although the image formed of a surface by a light microscope is largely due to topography, the presence of color has aided materially. The advantage of color is lost in electron microscope images, and elevation changes alone determine the image through the medium of the replica. For this reason, corrosion products, stains, distorted metal, etc., offer serious complications and must be avoided. Electron diffraction offers a method of detecting undesirable surface contamination and guiding preparation procedures. Electron diffraction is included in electron metallography for this reason as well as for determining the crystallographic nature of the clean surface.

The problem of preparing metal surfaces for electron diffraction and microscopic examination was discussed by Heidenreich and Sturkey (80). The application of a specific preparation to magnesium alloys (75) was demonstrated, and it was shown that valuable information could be obtained by this method that was not obtainable by the light microscope and x-ray diffraction. In this and in subsequent work with other metals the following principles have been adhered to:

1. Sufficient metal must be removed chemically or electrochemically to eliminate distorted metal always produced during polishing. Electropolishing methods are quite satisfactory.

2. The etch reaction must be allowed to proceed sufficiently long to develop a type of attack that is characteristic. That is, in the initial stages the etching reaction is not uniform over the surface, and the contours developed are not characteristic of the particular interfacial reactions occurring. Thus, a relatively deep etch is desirable in many instances.

3. The etch reaction must not deposit reaction products, such as hydroxide, if identification of secondary phases is to be made by electron diffraction.

4. A complete chemical analysis of the metal or alloy including spectrochemical analyses for impurities is necessary. Once the elements present are known and their relative positions in the electrochemical series noted, the question of etchant must be considered.

5. The etchant chosen should be such that metallic impurities (silver, copper, gold, etc.) are not redeposited on the surface during etching (80).

6. The etchant should be displaced from the surface through a series of inert rinses (80) to minimize formation or deposition of surface contaminates.

7. Electron diffraction reflection patterns should be taken from the prepared surface and a light microscope examination made. The replica is then prepared, and the resulting electron micrographs are interpreted in conjunction with the diffraction patterns and chemical data. Contact-deposited metals or very insoluble secondary phases will often be transferred to the replica from the original surface (75, 80).

The general texture of the surfaces obtained by these methods will include:

(a) Crystallographically distinct phases such as intermetallic compounds, carbides, and nitrides. The particle size and distribution as well as a diffraction pattern will result from a properly prepared surface. The surfaces should not be so deeply etched for this type of work.

(b) Etch characteristics of grain boundaries as influenced by impurities, heat treatment, or alloying constituents.

(c) Texture of grain interiors as separate from boundaries and secondary phases. The appearance of an etched crystal facet is quite sensitive to impurity content, etchant, and orientation.

Of these distinct types of structure, (a) is at present the most likely to be understood; (b) and (c) are important and of great interest but it

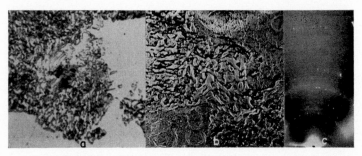

FIG. 35. (a) Photomicrograph of etched molybdenum steel. (2000×) (b) Electron micrograph of etched molybdenum steel. (3000×) (c) Reflection electron diffraction pattern of etched molybdenum steel. Sample furnace cooled after ½ hour at 1650°F. A nodule of Fe_3Mo_3C is seen in (a); (b) shows the shape of the double carbide particles for this particular nodule.

appears that much work will be necessary before the results can be interpreted.

As an example of the structure of type (a), some results on a

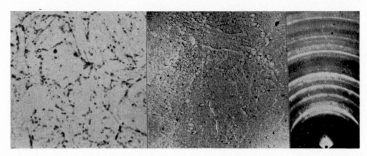

FIG. 36. Series, similar to Fig. 35, of molybdenum steel quenched from 1650°F. and tempered 2 hours at 1300°F. The dispersed Mo_2C particles are evident in both (a) and (b). The rings in (c) are due to Mo_2C, and the spots are apparently due to Fe_3Mo_3C. Magnification: (a) 2000×; (b) 3000×.

molybdenum steel are shown in Figs. 35 and 36.* The surfaces were prepared by abraiding through 4/0 French emery and then electropolishing

* The steel samples and photomicrographs were furnished by J. B. Austin of U.S. Steel Corp. The analysis of the sample was as follows: 0.16 C, 0.43 Mn, 0.015 P, 0.013 S, 0.16 Si, and 1.10 Mo.

in a sulfuric-phosphoric-chromic acid electrolyte. The etchant employed was one part concentrated HCl to ten parts distilled water with 0.2% $FeCl_3$. The ferric chloride is important in etching iron and steel in that contact plating of any copper present is avoided.

After etching, the surfaces were rinsed first in 1:1 methanol-acetone

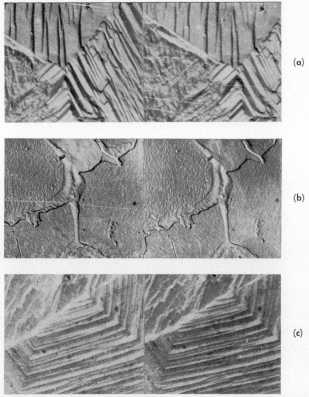

(a)

(b)

(c)

Fig. 37. Stereomicrographs of identically prepared nickel surfaces. Silica replicas. (a) High-purity nickel. (11,000×) (b) Commercial-purity nickel. The effect of impurities on the etch structure of the grains and the deep grooves resulting from accelerated attack of grain boundaries are clearly evident. (5300×). (c) Gold-shadowed plastic replica, for comparison with (a).

and then benzene and dried in a blast of air. Electron diffraction patterns were taken, and the samples molded in polystyrene. Silica replicas were then made. The photomicrographs were taken at U.S. Steel Corp. from surfaces prepared by the usual metallographic methods and etched in alcoholic picric acid. Nevertheless, the structures are not inconsistent.

Figure 35 shows a photomicrograph, an electron micrograph (silica replica), and a diffraction pattern from a sample which was furnace-cooled after ½ hour at 1650°F. Discrete patches of a second phase are in evidence in the photomicrograph. The electron micrograph shows more clearly the particles in the nodule. The electron diffraction pattern

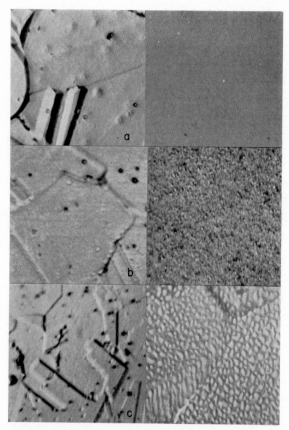

FIG. 38. Photomicrographs, left (2500×), and electron micrographs, right (11,000×), of etched K-Monel samples. (a) Hot roll plus 1 hour at 1550°F.; RC − 1. (b) Aged 16 hours at 1080°F.; RC − 30. (c) Aged 30 days at 1400°F.; RC − 1. In this case, the structural changes evidenced in the electron micrographs are not visible in the photomicrograph.

consists of spotty rings which are attributed to the double carbide Fe_3Mo_3C. A satisfactory standard pattern was not available at the time, or the identification would be more positive.

Figure 36 shows a photomicrograph, an electron micrograph, and a diffraction pattern from a similar sample water-quenched after ½ hour at 1650°F. and then tempered 2 hours at 1300°F. The structure now consists of a dispersed phase made up of particles of Mo_2C with a trace of Fe_3Mo_3C. The particles are visible in both the photomicrograph and electron micrograph. The rings in the electron diffraction pattern are due to Mo_2C; the spots are for Fe_3Mo_3C.

Structures of types (b) and (c) are demonstrated in Fig. 37. These stereoelectron micrographs were taken from nickel samples of high and commercial purity, respectively, and prepared identically. Figure 37

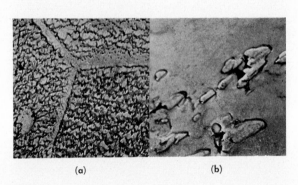

(a)   (b)

FIG. 39. Silica replicas of etched methyl iodide reagent (28) magnesium alloy. (a) Solution heat treat plus water quench. (b) Sample (a) cold-worked and aged to precipitate $Mg_{17}Al_{12}$. (a) illustrates the "fine structure" concluded to be responsible for stress corrosion, and (b) shows the removal of "fine structure" by solution of the iron impurity in the precipitated compound. $(7300\times)$

shows both the great difference in the texture of the individual crystal surfaces and the tendency of the grain boundaries of the less pure nickel to etch deeply. The deep groove between grains can be seen in the stereomicrograph. These differences are attributable to impurity content, but the origin of the structure is not known. Whether the structures result chiefly from surface effects during etching or from heterogeneous distribution of impurity atoms in the bulk crystal is not clear.

An example in an alloy of a dispersed second phase not visible in the light microscope is illustrated in Fig. 38, which shows photomicrographs and electron micrographs of three heat-treated K-Monel * samples. The Rockwell C-scale hardness numbers indicate a great change in hardness of the alloy as a function of heat treatment. The photomicrographs, however, do not show any structural change that could account for

* Samples from International Nickel Co. The photomicrographs were taken by P. F. George of Dow Chemical Co., and the electron micrographs were taken by one of the authors while at Dow Chemical Co.

the hardness values. The electron micrographs show a very highly dispersed structure in the sample of maximum hardness (Fig. 38b) and considerably larger particles in Fig. 38c, which was overaged. Whether or not there is a crystallographically distinct second phase in Fig. 38c cannot be said, since no electron diffraction patterns were taken. The increase in hardness observed as the structure becomes finer agrees with the results reported for tempered martensite (80).

A final example of electron metallography is taken from published results (75) obtained with magnesium alloys. This work was concerned with the etch structure exhibited by magnesium-aluminum solid solutions and the correlation of the observations with stress corrosion

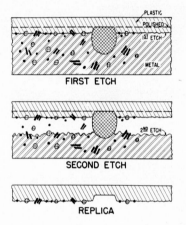

FIG. 40. Diagrammatic representation of extraction replica technique (44).

behavior. It was found that iron, present as an impurity, in conjunction with varying amounts of added aluminum, imparted a "fine structure" to the etched magnesium crystals. The presence of this "fine structure" correlated with stress corrosion tendencies and was concluded to be responsible for the transcrystalline stress cracks in magnesium alloys. The origin of the "fine structure" was attributed to a segregation of FeAl in the magnesium crystal. The distribution of the FeAl was inferred from the electron micrographs, and its identity from electron diffraction results.

The appearance of the fine structure is illustrated in Fig. 39a, taken from the magnesium plus 6% aluminum alloy with 1% zinc and 0.2% manganese. The state is that obtained after solution heat treatment and water quench. If this same material is cold worked and aged to bring about precipitation of the compound $Mg_{17}Al_{12}$, the result is as seen in Fig. 39b. Large particles of compound are visible, but the fine structure has practically vanished, and the stress corrosion susceptibility is considerably lower. This, in conjunction with other data, led to the conclusion that the iron was taken up by the precipitating compound.

The extraction replica technique reported by Fisher (44) is a valuable addition to electron metallographic methods. The technique is illustrated in Fig. 40. The first step is formation of a simple plastic replica on the etched surface—a step that may be replaced by evaporation of a suitably thin carbon film. The next step is to etch again. The etchant is able to penetrate the film and free it from the surface. Small crystals of disperse phases, which project from the surface because of their poor solubility in the etchant, are found embedded in the film

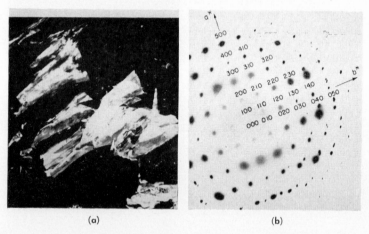

(a)   (b)

FIG. 41. (a) Extraction replica of pearlite, artificially transformed at 1100°F. (2400×) (b) Electron diffraction pattern from area in (a). Pattern is largely due to a single crystal of cementite (44).

(Fig. 41). Such crystals can be examined by electron diffraction, and in particular individual crystals or groups of a few crystals oriented to diffract as one crystal can be examined by the selected area diffraction technique. Figure 42 gives an example, and other very interesting examples are given in the reference.

9.5. Emission Studies

The replica methods and surface preparations described are restricted to specimens at room temperature. Consequently, their application to the structure of a specimen at elevated temperature depends on preserving the stable arrangement attained at high temperature by means of quenching. Quenching is satisfactory for most processes or rearrangements taking place by diffusion. Rearrangements that occur through shear, on the other hand, or small movements of a large number of atoms, take place with great rapidity and cannot be arrested by quenching. The temperatures at which such transformations occur are usually considerably above room temperature, and hence the replica and etch methods are of no value. The transformations $\gamma \rightarrow \alpha$-iron (28) or $\alpha \rightarrow \beta$-zirconium (30) are typical.

X-ray diffraction can be effectively used at elevated temperatures as can electron diffraction. Microscopic data is also desirable, and the indications are that the thermionic emission microscope can be effectively employed in studying high-temperature transformations (600°

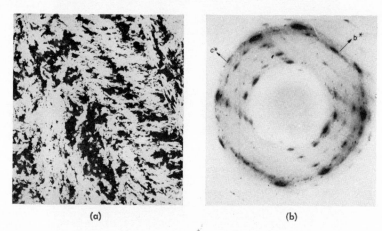

(a)   (b)

Fig. 42. (a) Extration replica of lower bainite, isothermally transformed at 600°F. (1800×) (b) Corresponding electron diffraction pattern (44).

to 1100°C.). The main problem in emission microscope applications to metallurgical processes is the correlation of emission patterns with changes in crystal structure. As pointed out in eq. (1), the current from a crystal face depends on the work function, transmission coefficient, applied electrical field, and temperature of the surface. In order to obtain current densities sufficiently great to form useful images at reasonable temperatures, it is necessary to reduce the work function of the surface by applying a layer of positive ions such as barium. This layer may constitute less than a complete monolayer and still yield greatly enhanced emission currents. The layer is adsorbed on the crystal facets, and it might be expected that the density of adsorbed atoms would be quite different for different faces. Thus, the emission pattern is chiefly a result of variation in density of adsorbed atoms from one face to another, resulting in considerably different work functions among the several crystal faces themselves (74).

It appears that the work function of a crystal face, with adsorbed layer, changes quite rapidly when the crystal passes through that temperature where a crystallographic transformation occurs. Figure 43 illustrates the ability to follow a transformation through the local change in

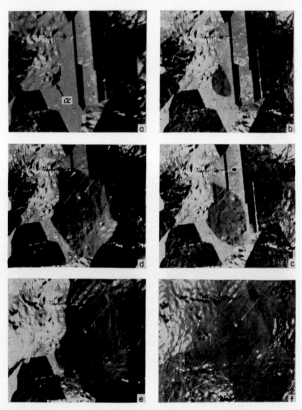

Fig. 43. Sequence of emission micrographs of a 0.22% plain carbon steel at about 810°C. showing the growth of a ferrite grain in an austenite field just below the A₃ line. The sequence (a–f) was taken in a period of about 20 seconds with a 2-second exposure. The variation in local velocity of the "front" with the development of bright streaks parallel to the austenite (111) planes is pointed out. The maximum velocity of the transformation front is parallel to the streaks. From Heidenreich, *J. Appl. Phys.* **24**, 879 (1955).

thermionic emission (2). The formation of a growing nucleus of α-iron in austenite is indicated in Fig. 43a, and its subsequent growth is shown in the sequence of following images. High-speed motion pictures of such transformations taken as they occur* are very significant in studies of

* Private communication from E. Eichen, Ohio State University.

the transformation mechanism. An interesting memory for the original structure is often found in the reverse transformation of metals and alloys (30, 31).

The resolving power of the thermionic emission microscopes constructed thus far is no better than about 500 A. (31). Even so, there are numerous investigations of recrystallization, grain growth, precipitation, and transformations in alloys that can be profitably carried out. Mahl (99) and Mechlenburg (104) have reported a resolving power of

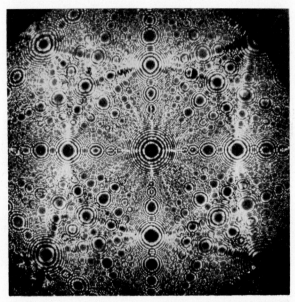

FIG. 44. Ion image of nearly perfect platinum crystal. Tip radius in center region is 1660 A. Surface cleaned by field evaporation. Helium ion image, 21°K., 27,000 volts. Courtesy E. W. Müller, Pennsylvania State University.

about 400 A. in observations of emission from oxide cathode surfaces. Considerable variation in resolution is found, depending on the total emission and contrast in the image.

The field emission microscope described by Müller (107) and Becker (14) exhibits much higher resolving power than the thermionic microscope. In this microscope a pointed wire is employed as an emitter with field emission from the tip supplying the electrons forming the image. Resolution of better than 5 A. has been reported, although there has been controversy over the interpretation of detail in these images. The usefulness of the field emission microscope is chiefly in studies of adsorption of various materials on the tip of the emitter (14). Because of the sensitivity of field emission to small numbers of adsorbed atoms, great care must be exercised in experiments with field emission microscopy. Most of the emission detail is the result of less than a single monolayer of adsorbed atoms. Recently Müller (109) has developed the field ion microscope which is capable of resolving individual atoms (Fig. 44).

9.6. THIN SECTIONS

A technique of growing interest and importance in the study of crystals is the use of thin sections as transmission specimens. It was realized from early images of crystalline materials that Bragg reflections played a major part in determining the image contrast and hence the detail observed. Interpretation of the image detail requires the more general, dynamical theory of electron diffraction (72, 79). This is true not only of crystals occurring in sheetlike form, such as mica and graphite, but in the thin sections of metals and alloys prepared from bulk samples and for crystals produced by evaporation onto suitable substrates.

Thin sections of most metals and alloys can be prepared for electron microscopy by suitable electrolytic polishing baths. Mechanical thinning methods such as slicing or grinding are of little value because of heavy mechanical damage to the crystals. The general technique for metals is to start with rolled sheet about .001 in. thick and electrothin until a small hole is pierced in the sheet. Specimens are cut out in the vicinity of such a hole, and, with some practice, useful specimens can be made for a fair percentage of the tries. The thickness of useful area for transmission microscopy is up to about 1000 A., depending on the atomic number of the metal employed. It is highly advantageous to use 80- or 100-kv. electrons for this work, since the useful range of specimen thickness is considerably greater. The Siemens' Elmiskop 1 is well adapted to studies of thin sections owing to the high-intensity electron gun and condenser system.

Early work in thin sections of metal was done with aluminum (72, 73) because of its low atomic number and ease of electrothinning. Studies of high-purity aluminum indicated a subgrain size of about 2 μ. Outstanding work by Hirsch (85) *et al.* has demonstrated that the motion of single dislocations in metals can be recorded by high-speed photography. The dislocation lines are visible in the images owing to the changed diffracting power of the crystal in the region of a dislocation. This work has resulted in much interest in thin sections and their potentialities in contributing to the understanding of dislocations in metals. Striking demonstrations of deformation stacking faults in stainless steel have been published (144). It seems likely that transmission microscopy of thin sections will be a major factor in future studies of dislocation in metals and the mechanism of deformation.

Precipitation of second phases in alloys can be readily studied by thin sections and should be particularly valuable in the very early stages of precipitation where replica methods are inadequate. Selected area diffraction is a necessary adjunct to the study of thin sections, since variations in diffracting power are the source of image detail.

A phenomenon first recognized by Mitsuishi et al. (106) has proved of considerable worth in studying and understanding aging of crystalline materials. This is the moiré pattern* resulting from an overlap of two periodic scattering structures. If two identical nets of spacing d are superimposed with an angular displacement, θ, a set of fringes of spacing s is observed in the image, where

$$ s = \frac{d}{\theta} $$

This phenomenon can be observed equally well with ruled, translucent paper and a light, or with two thin, overlapping crystals observed by electron transmission (64). An alternate way of producing a moiré pattern is with two overlapping nets of spacings d_1 and d_2 with no angular displacement (Fig. 5). The fringe separation in the image is then

$$ s = \frac{d_1 + d_2}{d_1 - d_2} $$

It has been demonstrated (114) that single dislocations in crystals can be made visible by means of an epitaxial overlap with proper choice of d_1 and d_2. The application of moiré patterns in the study of crystals should be increasingly useful as techniques of superposition of nets are developed.

References

1. Ames, J., Cottrell, T. L., and Sampson, A.M.D., *Trans. Faraday Soc.* **46**, 938 (1950).
2. Anderson, T. F., *Advances in Colloid Sci.* **1**, 353 (1942).
3. Ardenne, M. von, "Elektronen Übermikroskopie." Springer, Berlin, 1940.
4. Aziz, R. A., and Scott. G. D., *Can. J. Phys.* **34**, 731 (1956).
5. Bachman, C. H., and Ramo, S., *J. Appl. Phys.* **14**, 155 (1943).
6. Backus, R. C., and Williams, R. C., *J. Appl. Phys.* **19**, 1186 (1948); **20**, 224 (1949).
7. Baillie, Y., *3rd Interna. Conf. Electron Microscopy, London, 1956.*
8. Barnes, R. B., Burton, C. J., and Scott R. G., *J. Appl. Phys.* **16**, 730 (1945).

---

* From the textile industry where the production of optical effects due to over-lapping of weaves in sheer fabrics is common practice.

9. Barrett, C. S., *Metals Technol.* **10** (September, 1943), *Am. Inst. Mining Met. Engrs., Tech. Publ.* **No. 1637.**

10. Barrett, C. S., *J. Appl. Phys.* **15,** 691 (1944).

11. Bartz, G., Weisenberg, G., and Wiskott, D., Radex Rundschau 1956, H4/5,163; *Proc. Interna. Conf. Electron Microscopy, London, 1954.*

12. Bates, T. F., *Science* **111,** 512 (1950).

13. Bates, T. F., and Comer, J. J., *Proc. 3rd Nat. Conf. Clays Clay Minerals, 1955.*

14. Becker, J. A., *Advances in Catalysis* **7,** 136 (1955).

15. Blackman, M., and Greenbaum, E., *Nature* **178,** 584 (1956).

16. Boersch, H., *Z. tech. Physik* **20,** 346 (1939).

17. Boersch, H., *Natl. Bur. Standards (U.S.) Circ.* **No. 527,** 127 (1954).

18. Borries, B. von, *Z. Physik* **116,** 570 (1940).

19. Borries, B. von, and Glaser, J. W., *Kolloid Z.* **106,** 123 (1943).

20. Borries, B. von, and Kausche, G. A., *Kolloid Z.* **90,** 132 (1940); see also Marton, L., *J. Phys. Chem.* **46,** 1023 (1942).

21. Boswell, F. W. C., *Rev. Sci. Instr.* **28,** 723 (1957).

22. Bradford, E. G., and Vanderhoff, J. W., *J. Appl. Phys.* **26,** 864 (1955).

23. Bradley, D. E., *Brit. J. Appl. Phys.* **5,** 65, 96 (1954).

24. Bradley, D. E., *J. Inst. Metals* **83,** 35 (1954-55).

25. Bradley, D. E., *Brit. J. Appl. Phys.* **6,** 191 (1955).

26. Bradley, D. E., *J. Appl. Phys.* **27,** 1339 (1956).

27. Bradley, D. E., Halliday, J. S., and Hirst, W., *Proc. Phys. Soc. (London)* **B69,** 484 (1956).

28. Brüche, E. and Kueckt, W., *Z. tech. Physik* **15,** 461 (1934).

29. Bryant, P. J., Rhoads, H. U., and Weber, A. H., *J. Appl. Phys.* **25,** 1343 (1954).

30. Burgers, W. G., and Ploos van Amsrel, J.J.A., *Physica* **5,** 305 (1938).

31. Burton, C. J., Barnes, R. B., and Rochow, T. G., *Ind. Eng. Chem.* **34,** 1429 (1942).

32. Burton, E. F., and Kohl, W. H., "The Electron Microscope," 2nd ed. Reinhold, New York, 1946.

33. Calbick, C. J., *J. Appl. Phys.* **19,** 119 (1948).

34. Calbick, C. J., *Phot. Eng.* 696 (December, 1950).

35. Calbick, C. J., *Bell System Tech. J.* **30,** 798 (1951).

36. Calbick, C. J., Christenson, H., and Thomas, E. E., *Phys. Rev.* **92,** 1082 (1953).

37. Chapman, J. A., and Menter, J. W., *Proc. Roy. Soc.* **A226,** 400 (1954).

38. Cosslett, V. E., "Bibliography of Electron Microscopy." Edward Arnold, London, 1950.

39. Cosslett, V. E., "Practical Electron Microscopy." Academic Press, New York, 1951.

40. Cosslett, V. E., *Brit. J. Appl. Phys.* **7,** 10 (1956).

41. Cosslett, V. E., and Jones, D., *J. Sci. Instr.* **32,** 86 (1955).

42. Drummond, D. G. (ed.), The practice of electron microscopy. *J. Roy. Microscop. Soc.* (March, 1950).

43. Edwards, J. D., and Keller, F., *Metals Technol.* **11** (April, 1944), *Am. Inst. Mining. Met. Engrs. Tech. Publ.* **No. 1710.**

44. Electron Metallography, Symposium on Techniques. *Am. Soc. Testing Materials Spec. Tech. Publ.* **No. 155** (1953).

45. Electron Microscope Society of America, Report on Resolution. *J. Appl. Phys.* **17,** 989 (1946).

46. Feng, I. M., *J. Appl. Phys.* **22,** 820 (1951).

47. Fert, C., and Marty, B., *Compt. rend.* **241**, 1454 (1955).
48. Fert, C., and Saporte, R., *Compt. rend.* **243**, 1107 (1956).
49. Fischer, R. B., "Applied Electron Microscopy." Indiana Univ. Press, Bloomington, Indiana, 1953.
50. Fischer, R. B., *J. Appl. Phys.* **25**, 894 (1954).
51. Fullam, E. F., *J. Appl. Phys.* **14**, 677 (1943).
52. Fullam, E. F., and Gessler, A. E., *Rev. Sci. Instru.* **17**, 23 (1946).
53. Fuller, M. L., *J. Appl. Phys.* **15**, 164 (1944).
54. Fuller, M. L., Brubaker, D. G., and Berger, R. W., *J. Appl. Phys.* **15**, 201 (1944).
55. Gerould, C. H., *J. Appl. Phys.* **18**, 333 (1947).
56. Gerould, C. H., *J. Appl. Phys.* **12**, 138 (1950).
57. Gotthardt, E., *Z. Physik* **118**, 714 (1942).
58. Green, H., and Fullam, E. F., *J. Appl. Phys.* **14**, 332 (1943).
59. Griffin, L. J., *Phil. Mag.* [7] **41**, 196 (1949).
60. Gulbransen, E. A., *J. Appl. Phys.* **16**, 619 (1945); see also *Metal Progr.* **49**, 553 (March, 1946); and Phelps, R. T., Gulbransen, E. A., and Hickman, J. W., *Ind. Eng. Chem. Anal. Ed.* **18**, 391 (1946).
61. Haine, M. E., and Agar, A. W., *Proc. Stockholm Conf. Electron Microscopy, September, 1956* 64-66.
62. Hall, C. E., "Introduction to Electron Microscopy." McGraw-Hill, New York, 1953.
63. Harker, D. J., and Murphy, M. J., *Metals Technol.* **12** (June 1945), *Am. Inst. Mining Met. Engrs. Tech. Publ.* **No. 1811.**
64. Hashimoto, J., *Acta Cryst.* **10**, 143 (1957).
65. Hass, G., *J. Am. Ceramic Soc.* **33**, 355 (1950).
66. Hass, G., and Kehler, H., *Kolloid-Z.* **95**, 29 (1941).
67. Hass, G., and Scott, N. W., *Optik* **5**, 48 (1949).
68. Hass, G., and Scott, N. W., *J. phys. radium* **11**, 394 (1950).
69. Heidenreich, R. D., *J. Appl. Phys.* **14**, 312 (1943).
70. Heidenreich, R. D., *S.A.E. Journal* **53**, 588 (1945).
71. Heidenreich, R. D., *J. Opt. Soc. Am.* **35**, 139 (1945).
72. Heidenreich, R. D., *J. Appl. Phys.* **20**, 993 (1949).
73. Heidenreich, R. D., *Bell System Tech. J.* **30**, 867 (1951).
74. Heidenreich, R. D., *J. Appl. Phys.* **26**, 757, 859 (1955).
75. Heidenreich, R. D., Gerould, C. H., and McNulty, R. E., *Metals Technol.* **13**, (April, 1946), *Am. Inst. Mining Met. Engrs. Tech. Publ.* **No. 1979.**
76. Heidenreich, R. D., and Matheson, L. A., *J Appl. Phys.* **15**, 423 (1944).
77. Heidenreich, R. D., and Peck, V. G., *J. Appl. Phys.* **14**, 23 (1943).
78. Heidenreich, R. D., and Shockley, W., *J. Appl. Phys.* **18**, 1029 (1947).
79. Heidenreich, R. D., and Sturkey, L., *J. Appl. Phys.* **16**, 97 (1945).
80. Heidenreich, R. D., Sturkey, L., and Woods, H. L., *J. Appl. Phys.* **17**, 127 (1946).
81. Hibi, T., and Yada, K., *J. Appl. Phys.* **25**, 712 (1954).
82. Hillier, J., *J. Appl. Phys.* **17**, 307 (1946).
83. Hillier, J., and Baker, R. F., *J. Appl. Phys.* **17**, 12 (1946).
84. Hillier, J., and Ramberg, E. G., *J. Appl. Phys.* **18**, 48 (1947).
85. Hirsch, P. B., Horne, R. W., and Whelan, M. J., *Phil. Mag.* [8]**1**, 677 (1956).
86. Holland, L., *Brit. J. Appl. Phys.* **7**, 113 (1956).
87. Kaye, W., *J. Appl. Phys.* **20**, 1209 (1949).
88. Keller, F., and Geisler, H. H., *J. Appl. Phys.* **15**, 696 (1944).

89. Kern, S. F., and Kern, R. A., *J. Appl. Phys.* **21**, 705 (1950).

90. König, H., *Optik* **3**, (5/6), 419 (1948).

91. Kuhlman-Wilsdorf, D., van der Merwe, J. H., and Wilsdorf, H., *Phil. Mag.* **43**, 632 (1952).

92. Kuhlman-Wilsdorf, D., and Wilsdorf, H., *Acta Met.* **1**, 394 (1953).

93. Lenz, F., *Z. Naturforsch.* **9a**, 185 (1954).

94. Lippert, W., *Optik* **13**, 506 (1956).

95. McMillen, J. H., and Scott, G. H., *Rev. Sci. Instr.* **8**, 788 (1937).

96. Mahl, H., "Jahrbuch der AEG Forschungs Institute." Springer, Berlin, 1940.

97. Mahl, H., *Z. tech. Physik* **21**, 17 (1940).

98. Mahl, H., *Naturwissenschaften* **30**, 207 (1942).

99. Mahl, H., *Z. tech. Physik* **23**, 117 (1942).

100. Marton, L., *J. Appl. Phys.* **16**, 131 (1945).

101. Marton, L., and Sass, S., *J. Appl. Phys.* **14**, 522 (1943); **15**, 575 (1944); **16**, 373 (1945).

102. Marton, L., and Schiff, L. I., *J. Appl. Phys.* **12**, 759 (1941).

103. Mayer, L., *J. Appl. Phys.* **26**, 1228 (1955).

104. Mechlenburg, W., *Z. Physik* **120**, 21 (1942).

105. Metallurgical Applications of the Electron Microscope. *Institute of Metals (London) Monograph* **No. 8**, 103 (1950).

106. Mitsuishi, T., Nagasaki, H., and Vyeda, R., *Proc. Japan Acad.* **27**, 86 (1951).

107. Müller, E. W., *Z. Physik* **106**, 132, 541 (1937).

108. Müller, E. W., *J. Appl. Phys.* **27**, 474 (1956); **28**, 1 (1957).

109. Müller, H. O., *Kolloid-Z.* **99**, 6 (1942).

110. New York Society of Electron Microscopists, "International Bibliography of Electron Microscopy." 2 East 63rd Street, New York.

111. O'Brien, H. C., Jr., *J. Appl. Phys.* **16**, 370 (1945).

112. O'Brien, H. C., Jr., and McKinley, G. M., *Science* **98**, 455 (1943).

113. Ohashi, K., and Takeauchi, S., *Kagaku (Tokyo)* **24**, 473 (1954).

114. Pashley, D. W., Menter, J. W., and Bassett, G. A., *Nature* **179**, 752 (1957).

115. Picard, R. G., *J. Appl. Phys.* **15**, 678 (1944).

116. Prebus, A. F., "Colloid Chemistry," Vol. 5. Reinhold, New York, 1944.

117. Ramsauer, C., "Elektronen Mikroskopie." Springer, Berlin, 1942.

118. Read, W. T., "Dislocation in Crystals." McGraw-Hill, New York, 1953.

119. Reimer, L., *Z. angew. Phys.* **9**, 34 (1957).

120. Revell, R. S. M., and Agar, A. W., *Brit. J. Appl. Phys.* **6**, 23 (1955).

121. Rochow, T. G., and Botty, M. C., *Anal. Chem.* **30**, 640 (1958).

122. Schaefer, V. J., and Harker, D. J., *J. Appl. Phys.* **139**, 427 (1942).

123. Schaefer, V. J., *Phys. Rev.* **62**, 495 (1942).

124. Scheffels, W., von Borries, B., and Lenz, F., *3rd Intern. Conf. Electron Microscopy, London, 1956.*

125. Schuster, M., and Fullam, E. F., *Ind. Eng. Chem. Anal. Ed.* **18**, 653 (1946).

126. Scott, D., and Scott, H. M., *Proc. Stockholm Conf. Electron Microscopy, 1956* 331.

127. Scott, G. H., *Proc. Soc. Exptl. Biol. Med.* **95**, 30 (1940).

128. Scott, R. G., and Ferguson, A. W., *Textile Research J.* **26**, 284 (1956).

129. Sennett, R. S., and Scott, G. D., *J. Opt. Soc. Am.* **40**, 203 (1950).

130. Smith, K. C. A., and Oatley, C. W., *Brit. J. Appl. Phys.* **6**, 391 (1955).

131. Spivak, C. V., Prilezhaeva, I. N., and Azovtsev, V. K., *Doklady Acad. Nauk S.S.S.R.* **105**, 965 (1955).

132. Swerdlow, M., *Anal. Chem.* **26,** 34 (1954).

133. Swerdlow, M., Dalton, A. J., and Birks, L. S., *Anal. Chem.* **28,** 597 (1956).

134. Thielsch, H., *Metal Technol.* **13** (February, 1946), *Am. Inst. Mining Met. Engrs. Tech. Publ.* **No. 1977.**

135. Tripp, V. W., Moore, A. T., and Rollins, M. L., *Textile Research J.* **27,** 419 (1957).

136. Tsuchikura, H. J., *Electron Microscopy (Japan)* **2,** (1954).

137. Verma, A. J., "Crystal Growth and Dislocations." Butterworths, London, 1953.

138. Wakashima, H., *J. Japan Inst. Metals* **18,** 528 (1954).

139. Watson, J. H. L., *J. Appl. Phys.* **17,** 121 (1946).

140. Watson, J. H. L., *Anal. Chem.* **20,** 576 (1948).

141. Watson, J. H. L., *Anal. Chem.* **29,** 562 (1957).

142. Watson, J. H. L., and Freeman, M. W., *J. Appl. Phys.* **26,** 1391 (1955).

143. Wehner, G. K., *J. Appl. Phys.* **29,** 217 (1958).

144. Whelan, M. J., Hirsch, P. B., Horne, R. W., and Bollman, W., *Proc. Roy Soc.* **A240,** 524 (1957).

145. Williams, R. C., and Backus, R. C., *J. Appl. Phys.* **20,** 1209 (1949).

146. Williams R. C., and Wykoff, R. W. G., *J. Appl. Phys.* **15,** 712 (1944).

147. Williams, R. C., and Wykoff, R. W. G., *J. Appl. Phys.* **17,** 23 (1946).

148. Wilsdorf, H., *Z. Metallk.* **45,** 14 (1954).

149. Wyckoff, R. W. G., "Electron Miscroscopy." Interscience, New York, 1949.

150. Zworykin, V. K., Morton, G. A., Ramberg, E. G. Hillier, J., and Vance, A. W., "Electron Optics and the Electron Microscope." Wiley, New York, 1945.

151. Zworykin, V. K., and Ramberg, E. G., *J. Appl. Phys.* **12,** 692 (1941).

Electron Diffraction

W. C. Bigelow

Department of Chemical and Metallurgical Engineering,
University of Michigan, Ann Arbor, Michigan

1. Introduction

Compared to many techniques of analytical interest, electron diffraction is of relatively recent origin, for it was not until the development of the present quantum theory with the concept of the wavelike behavior of moving material particles that the possibility of the diffraction of electrons was recognized. This concept originated in 1924 when Louis de Broglie (13) proposed that moving electrons should exhibit some of the characteristics of waves, with a wavelength inversely proportional to their momentum. The first experimental confirmation of this proposal,

619

and also the first demonstration of electron diffraction, was reported in 1927 by Davisson and Germer (21), who studied the scattering of a beam of low-energy electrons from the surface of a nickel single crystal. In the scattered electrons, intensity maxima were observed which varied with the energy of the electrons and with the different arrangements of the atoms in different directions in the crystal surface. Shortly thereafter Thomson and Reid (73, 74, 76) passed high-speed electrons (20 to 60 kv.) through thin films of celluloid and various metals and obtained diffraction patterns analogous to those which were produced when a beam of x-rays was passed through the same materials. From quantitative measurements on these patterns, they also showed that the same general mathematical expressions could be used to describe the geometry of the diffraction of electrons as were used in x-ray diffraction. These results provided the necessary foundation for the practical utilization of the phenomenon of electron diffraction, though it was several years later before electron diffraction techniques became widely used.

It is the present practice to categorize electron diffraction studies according to the energies of the electrons used and whether the specimen under investigation is a solid or a gas. The following discussion refers to the use of fast electrons (with energies greater than about 20 kv.) in studies of solids, since this includes virtually all applications of analytical interest. Slow electrons (having energies ranging from a few hundred to a few thousand volts) are readily scattered by the residual gas in an ordinary vacuum (10^{-4} to 10^{-5} mm. Hg) and are normally used only in a few cases where fast electrons are not applicable (such as in studying the adsorption of monomolecular layers of simple gases on solids) and where the additional experimental difficulties associated with ultrahigh vacuum techniques are justified. The use of fast electrons in studying gas specimens is not discussed in this chapter, since this technique is used almost entirely for determining the arrangement of atoms in molecules of pure gases of known composition (10). The analysis of mixtures of gases can be carried out more conveniently and with greater precision by other methods. In describing the general characteristics of the electron diffraction method it is convenient to compare and contrast it with the more familiar x-ray diffraction method, since these two supplement one another in the information provided.

2. Electron versus X-Ray Diffraction

The differences in the characteristics and applications of electron and x-ray diffraction result largely from the differences in the wavelength of the two types of radiation and the degree to which they are scattered by materials. The x-ray wavelengths commonly used for diffraction purposes lie in the range of 0.7 to 1.5 A., as determined by the K_a-line of the characteristic x-ray spectrum of the target material. The wavelength of electrons, as recognized by de Broglie, is equal to Planck's constant divided by the momentum of the electrons. In practice the momentum is controlled by the voltage used to accelerate the electrons, and the wavelength, λ, is related to this voltage, V, by the expression

$$\lambda = (149.9/V)^{\frac{1}{2}}(1 + 9.782 \times 10^{-7}V)^{-\frac{1}{2}}(1.002 \times 10^{-8}) \text{ cm.} \quad (1)$$

The voltages commonly used range from 30 to 100 kv., giving wavelengths ranging from 0.06 to 0.04 A. One effect of the shorter wavelengths of the electrons is to cause interference maxima in electron diffraction patterns to occur within a much smaller range of scattering angles than corresponding maxima in x-ray diffraction patterns. In the case of diffraction from crystalline materials, this is evident from inspection of the Bragg relationship, $n\lambda = 2d \sin \theta$, which applies for both x-rays and electrons. The maximum value of 2θ for which data are recorded is usually of the order of 6° for electrons, whereas for x-rays it commonly extends nearly to 180°. Flat photographic plates are therefore used in electron diffraction, since cylindrical films of the type commonly used for x-rays offer no advantage. The short wavelength of electrons also permits reflection to occur simultaneously from a large number of planes in a fixed single crystal with monochromatic radiation and leads to types of patterns that are rarely observed when monochromatic x-rays are diffracted by a fixed crystal. This effect is discussed below under the description of single crystal patterns.

The fraction of incident intensity of electrons scattered coherently (i.e., without loss of energy or change of wavelength) by a free atom is given by the expression (57)

$$I/I_0 = C(1/r^2)(Z - f)^2(\lambda/\sin \theta)^4 \quad (2)$$

The corresponding expression for x-rays is

$$I/I_0 = C'(1/r^2)f^2(1 + \cos^2 2\theta) \quad (3)$$

In both equations, 2θ is the angle between the directions of the incident and scattered rays, and f is the atomic scattering factor for x-rays (45) which is equal to Z, the atomic number, at $\theta = 0$, and drops toward zero for large θ. The factors C and C' are collections of physical constants such that at small angles I/I_0 for electrons is about 10^8 as large as for x-rays. The values of I/I_0 for the scattering of electrons and x-rays by an iron atom are plotted in Fig. 1 to show the angular dependence and the relative orders of magnitude of the scattered intensity for the two types of radiation. The magnitudes of these atomic scattering functions indicate the relative scattering power of crystals and other specimens for electrons and x-rays in producing diffraction patterns, since in such cases the total scattering is calculated by summing the waves scattered by the individual atoms, each modified by its own phase factor. In general, the fraction of incident electron intensity scattered by an appropriate specimen is many times as great as for x-rays, so that electron

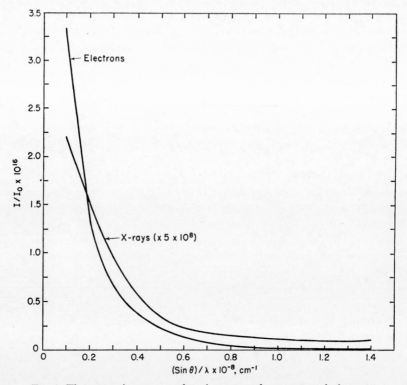

Fig. 1. The scattering power of an iron atom for x-rays and electrons.

diffraction patterns can be obtained from very much smaller amounts of material than x-ray diffraction patterns. Furthermore, exposure times for recording electron diffraction patterns photographically are of the order of 10 seconds, as compared to several hours for x-ray diffraction patterns.

Associated with the relatively strong coherent scattering is a correspondingly strong incoherent scattering and absorption of electrons resulting in a very limited penetrating power for electrons as compared with x-rays. It is generally accepted that electron diffraction patterns cannot be obtained from crystals which are thicker than about 10^{-5} cm., whereas satisfactory x-ray patterns can be obtained from crystals which are 10^4 times as thick. The effective penetration of both x-rays and electrons below smooth surfaces of thick specimens is reduced when the incident beam is directed onto the surface at a small angle. In the case of electrons, the angle of incidence must be reduced to $1°$ or $2°$ in order to obtain diffraction patterns, and the penetration beneath the surface is reduced to about 50 A. This makes electron diffraction techniques particularly useful for following crystallographic changes on surfaces when the affected layer is too thin to be detected by x-rays. The strong scattering of electrons also requires electron diffraction experiments to be carried out in a high vacuum; otherwise, the electron beam is diffused by atmospheric gases.

As a consequence of these differences in the wavelengths and the scattering and absorption of x-rays and electrons, the applications of electron diffraction admirably complement those of x-ray diffraction. Electron diffraction techniques are best suited for studies of fine powders, thin films, and surface layers on thick specimens, especially in cases where the quantity of material is very small. X-ray diffraction techniques are best for studies of coarser powders and particularly for determining the interior or bulk structure of thick specimens which electrons will not penetrate. X-rays are also better suited for general structure determinations using single crystals, as will be discussed later.

3. Electron Diffraction Instruments

Electron diffraction patterns are obtained by directing a fine beam of monochromatic electrons onto the specimen of interest and recording the scattered electrons on a photographic emulsion. Instruments for carrying out electron diffraction studies consist of the following basic elements: (1) an electron gun and a high-voltage supply for generating the electron beam; (2) a system of lenses and diaphragms for focusing and collimating the beam; (3) a specimen chamber containing apparatus for orienting the specimen in the beam and for treating it as desired prior to or during observation; (4) a fluorescent screen and camera for viewing and photographing the diffraction patterns; and (5) a high-vacuum chamber enclosing the entire path of the electron beam. The basic arrangement of these elements in an electron diffraction instrument is shown schematically in Fig. 2, and their characteristics are described briefly below.

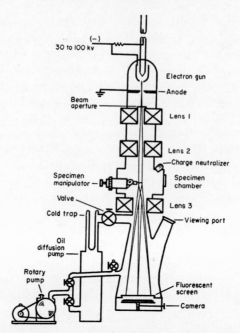

FIG. 2. Schematic diagram showing the principal features of an electron diffraction instrument.

3.1. The High-Voltage Supply and Electron Gun

The beam for electron diffraction experiments is generated by accelerating electrons from a suitable source through a d.c. potential which is in the range from 30 to 100 kv. and allowing them to pass through a hole in an anode plate into the diffraction chamber. For greatest versatility it is desirable to be able to vary the accelerating voltage over a range of values and to be able to reproduce a given voltage setting with accuracy and convenience. At a given setting, the voltage fluctuation should not exceed 0.1%, so that the electron wavelength will not vary by more than 0.05%, thus assuring a sufficiently monochromatic beam to give sharp diffraction patterns. Power supplies vary widely in design, and a description of the details of the circuits and characteristics of the different types which have been used is beyond the scope of this discussion. The simplest ones are similar to x-ray generators with filtering and stabilizing circuits added. These, however, are generally rather bulky, owing to the large size of the transformers and filter condensers required for the low-frequency alternating current. Those of modern commercial instruments employ high-frequency currents for voltage amplification and are much more compact.

The most generally satisfactory electron source presently in use is a self-biased electron gun of the type shown schematically in Fig. 2. In this gun, the electrons are emitted from a V-shaped filament of 0.004- to 0.008-inch-diameter tungsten wire which is accurately centered about ⅛ inch behind a hole about ⅛ inch in diameter in a grid cup. This cup is centrally located approximately an inch from the anode plate which contains a hole about ½ inch in diameter through which the electron beam passes. The grid cup and the filament are connected by a resistor of such value that the cup attains a negative bias of a few hundred volts with respect to the filament at the operating value of the electron space current. This forms a simple electrostatic lens which focuses the electrons to a point in front of the hole in the cup, and this point becomes the virtual electron source. Because of the bias focusing arrangement and the relatively large size of the holes in the grid cup and the anode, this type of gun provides a very intense, yet a very fine and stable beam of electrons. The intensity can be controlled by changing the distance between filament and the cup or by varying the biasing resistor. In another common type of gun of somewhat simpler design, electrons emitted from a shielded tungsten filament are sprayed onto an anode plate containing a hole a few thousandths of an inch in diameter, and those which pass through the hole form the electron beam. The anode hole then becomes the virtual electron source, and its size limits the beam intensity which can also be varied somewhat by changing the temperature of the tungsten filament. In a third type of electron gun which was used extensively in early instruments (75) and which has recently been much improved by the work of Induni (43), electrons generated by a carefully controlled gas discharge pass through a fine hole in the anode plate. The beam intensity is controlled by varying the gas pressure in the discharge tube.

3.2. The Electron Optical System

The basic function of the optical system of an electron diffraction instrument is to collimate the electron beam and focus it to a fine spot at the photographic plate so that the diffracted beams also come to sharp focus at the plate. In most instruments electromagnetic lenses are used, and, since accurate reproduction of an extended image is not required, these are usually simpler in design than those of electron microscopes and do not have accurately machined, small-bore pole pieces or provisions for compensating for astigmatism.

For most electron diffraction work, a relatively simple optical system, consisting of a single lens and one or two apertures, is adequate. The lens is placed between the specimen chamber and the electron gun at the position of lens 2 in Fig. 2. To obtain diffraction patterns large enough to measure conveniently, the distance from the specimen to the photographic plate is usually about 50 cm. The distance from the lens to the plate is then about 60 cm., and the distance from the lens to the gun is made about the same to avoid an undesirable increase in the diameter of the focused spot. With a self-biased gun, an aperture consisting of a thin platinum disk with a 0.002- to 0.005-inch hole is placed just below the anode to prevent stray electrons and light from the filament from reaching the photographic plate. With other types of guns, a somewhat larger aperture is usually located in the lens. With reasonably well-designed single-lens systems of this type the diameter of the focused beam at the specimen is 0.5 to 1.0 mm., and at the photographic plate it is 0.05 to 0.1 mm.

Some instrument designs (42, 43, 67) employ one or two additional lenses which are designated as lenses 1 and 3 in Fig. 2. In such cases, lens 1 is equipped with a pole piece to give it a short focal length and is used to produce a reduced image of the electron source which can be focused by lens 2 to give a finer beam diameter at the photographic plate but a somewhat larger beam diameter at the specimen than is obtained with a single lens. With transmission specimens this arrangement gives better resolution of the diffraction rings, and more continuous (i.e., less spotty) rings, than a single lens system. With reflection specimens, however, there is usually a loss in resolution and a decrease in intensity. If lens 2 is of proper design, a second reduced image of the source can be formed immediately behind the specimen, and an electron shadow micrograph of the specimen can be obtained. Lens 3 is used to magnify the diffraction patterns and shadow micrographs. A still more highly refined system for very high resolution work is described in the literature (19). In most instruments, the path of the beam outside the lenses is surrounded with demagnetized soft iron shields to prevent external magnetic fields from deflecting the beam and distorting the diffraction patterns. To minimize such fields, strong magnets, large electric motors and transformers, and easily magnetized items, such as steel cabinets, should be kept at least 10 feet from the beam column.

3.3. THE SPECIMEN AND PHOTOGRAPHIC CHAMBERS

The basic apparatus of the specimen chamber is the specimen manipulator which provides for the movement of the specimen relative to the beam during observation. Normally five independent motions are provided; three mutually perpendicular translations, one of which is parallel to the beam, and rotations with axes perpendicular to the beam and parallel to the corresponding translations. There is usually a window of lead glass in the specimen chamber which permits the movement of the specimen to be observed, yet protects the operator from x-rays generated as the beam strikes the specimen. Most specimen chambers also contain a charge neutralizer. This is a simple electron gun operating at a few hundred volts potential which is arranged to throw a broad beam of electrons onto the specimen to help eliminate static electric charges which build up on nonconducting materials under the influence of the main beam. In addition to these basic features, provisions may also be made for inserting auxiliary equipment such as instruments for abrading, cutting, or cleaving the specimen in the vacuum, ovens for evaporating materials onto the specimen, manipulators of various types, special holders for heating or cooling the specimen during observation, and devices for cleaning and etching the surface of the specimen by ion bombardment. To a large extent, the versatility of a diffraction instrument depends on the design of the specimen chamber and the specimen manipulator which should be such as to accommodate specimens of a variety of sizes and shapes and to permit the easy installation and use of auxiliary equipment.

The principal apparatus of the photographic chamber is the camera for permanently recording the diffraction patterns. For precision work, patterns are recorded on fine-grain photographic plates rather than on films which tend to change dimensions during development and handling. Therefore, most instruments are equipped with plate cameras, though special roll-film cameras have been introduced (**7, 78**) for continuously recording changes in the pattern as the specimen is heated, cooled, or otherwise treated in the instrument. Geiger-Müller counters have also been used in some cases (51). The plate cameras are designed so that several plates can be exposed successively without breaking the vacuum. Alignment of the electron beam and the selection of the pattern prior to exposure is observed on a fluorescent screen which is located between the specimen and the camera and which may also serve as a manually operated shutter. Many instruments contain a beam stop which can be inserted to intercept the main electron beam and facilitate the observation of faint patterns on the fluorescent screen, and to reduce the fogging of the photographic plate due to scattered electrons and x-rays liberated by the beam.

3.4. THE VACUUM SYSTEM

The normal operating vacuum for an electron diffraction instrument is 5×10^{-5} mm. of Hg or less. To establish and maintain this vacuum, an oil diffusion pump, backed by a rotary mechanical pump, is required. In most instruments air is admitted to the entire column each time the

specimen and photographic plates are changed. Therefore, a system of
vacuum valves is employed so that the diffusion pump oil does not
have to be cooled before the air is admitted, and large vacuum lines and
high-speed pumps are used to reduce the time required to re-establish the
vacuum after the change is completed. A large cold trap for liquid nitrogen located in the vacuum line between the diffusion pump and the
main vacuum chamber is also a decided advantage, for it will condense
water vapor evolved from the photographic plates, markedly reducing the
pump-down time and minimizing reactions between the water vapor and
the specimen. Such a trap will also help remove organic vapors evolved
by the diffusion pump and gasket materials. These vapors are decom-
posed by the electron beam, and their carbonaceous decomposition
products cause very annoying contamination of the specimen and of
the apertures and lens openings. Traps are not normally found on commercial instruments but can often be installed with little difficulty.
Vacuum gauges are required to indicate the vacuum in the instrument
at all times during operation. A combination frequently used consists
of a thermocouple gauge, located in the line between the diffusion and
mechanical pumps, and a cold-cathode discharge gauge, located in the
main vacuum chamber.

3.5. Commercial Instruments

Several different diffraction instruments are described in the literature (2, 26, 29, 31, 34, 42, 49, 50, 52, 59, 67, 72, 75, 80, 81), and commercial models manufactured by the General Electric Company and
Trüb, Täuber and Co., Ltd.,* are presently available in the United
States. The Radio Corporation of America has discontinued manufacturing its Model EMD electron diffraction unit, though a number of these
instruments are still in use. The General Electric instrument has a
single-lens optical system with a nonbiased electron gun. A notable
feature of this instrument is the exceptionally large specimen chamber.
The Trüb, Täuber instrument uses a gas discharge gun and a two-lens
optical system and incorporates a roll-film camera for continuously
recording diffraction patterns. A variety of accessories are available for
use in both of these instruments.

3.6. Electron Microscopes

Because there are many similarities in the power supplies, cameras,
vacuum systems, etc., of electron microscopes and electron diffraction

* Instruments manufactured by Trüb, Täuber and Co., Ltd., are distributed in
the United States by the New England Scientific Instruments Co., Cambridge 42,
Massachusetts.

units, there has been a good deal of interest in the development of a combined instrument. Owing to the basically different functions of the optical systems in the two cases and the special requirements for the specimen chamber in the diffraction instrument, no combination has yet been developed which performs both functions as well and as conveniently as separate instruments. Attempts to provide diffraction adapters for electron microscopes have been rather unsatisfactory for the additional reasons that the size and shape of the specimens which could be accommodated have been severely limited, the motions of the specimen manipulators have been generally quite inadequate, and specimen-to-plate distances have been so short that the patterns had to be magnified by a lens located between the specimen and photographic chambers. The Radio Corporation of America has announced an adapter for the RCA Model EML and EMU-3 electron microscopes which appears to represent a considerable improvement over previous adapters (15, 64). This unit consists basically of a specimen chamber which fits into the microscope column in the place of the intermediate lens. Four independent specimen motions are provided, specimens up to 1 inch in diameter and ¾ inch thick can be accommodated, and the specimen-to-plate distance is 50 cm. In addition, the unit contains a charge neutralizer and a furnace capable of heating specimens to 900° C. The fact that the basic function of the microscope must be interrupted and the intermediate lens and the pole pieces of the objective and projector lenses removed in order to do diffraction work with this adapter is a considerable inconvenience and will undoubtedly serve as a deterrent to its use.

There is one way in which three-stage electron microscopes can be used for diffraction purposes that is both unique and highly advantageous, however, and that is in obtaining the so-called "selected-area" diffraction patterns. When a specimen is viewed in an electron microscope it diffracts electrons, but the diffracted rays come to focus and produce the diffraction pattern in the back-focal plane of the objective lens rather than in the image plane, and so are either stopped by the objective aperture or contribute to the formation of the micrograph image. By removing the objective aperture and suitably altering the currents in the intermediate and projector lenses, however, the diffraction pattern rather than the specimen image can be brought into focus on the viewing screen. Furthermore, since all electrons which are coherently scattered from a given point in the specimen also pass through a common point in the objective image plane, an aperture located in this plane will pass only those diffracted rays which originate from the area of the specimen outlined by the aperture when the specimen is viewed in the normal manner. Most modern microscopes are equipped with adjustable diffraction apertures and have provisions for rapidly changing the lens currents for diffraction. With such instruments it is possible, while observing the specimen, to outline a selected area of it with the diffraction aperture and then immediately obtain a diffraction pattern from any crystalline material in that area. This provides a very powerful method for studying thin films or fine particles which can be mounted for observation in an electron microscope.

4. Electron Diffraction Techniques

Two general methods are used in obtaining electron diffraction patterns: the transmission method in which the electron beam is passed through a thin layer of specimen material, and the reflection method in which the beam is directed across the surface of the specimen at a grazing angle so that diffraction occurs in the surface layers. The transmission method is restricted in use to studies of fine powders and thin films, whereas the reflection method is used in studies of surfaces of thick solid specimens and of thin layers of materials deposited or formed on such surfaces.

4.1. SPECIMEN PREPARATION

Specimens for transmission studies are usually mounted on 100- to 400-mesh wire gauze, the smooth wires of which do not contribute to the diffraction patterns if the gauze has been cleaned before use. In some cases the specimens can be supported by the wire gauze alone, but in others additional support is needed and the specimens are deposited on very thin films of noncrystalline materials such as collodion, Formvar, silicon dioxide, or carbon, which are in turn mounted on the gauze. Films of this type are widely used as replicas and support membranes in electron microscopy, and detailed directions for preparing them can be found in texts on this subject (27, 36) and in the literature (9).

Surfaces for reflection studies should be flat and about 5 to 10 mm. wide in the direction of the beam to afford patterns of good intensity. Surfaces with convex curvature can be used, but the surface area meeting the beam at the correct angle falls off with increasing curvature. When used as substrates on which specimen materials are deposited for examination, surfaces should be as smooth as possible; therefore, polished surfaces of stainless steel, platinum, glass, and other inert materials are usually employed. The preparation of surfaces for direct examination is discussed below.

Of the many methods which have been used in preparing specimens for examination by electron diffraction, only those of fairly general applicability can be described here. Frequently these standard methods must be modified or new methods must be developed to conform with the requirements of new investigations and the characteristics of new specimen materials.

4.1.1. Powders. For best results, powders should be fine enough so that each particle will transmit the electron beam. Large particles block the beam and, if nonconducting or mounted on nonconducting substrates, tend to accumulate static electric charges from the beam which distort the patterns. Suitably fine powders may be prepared from coarser samples by grinding, mulling, or ball-milling; however, precautions must be taken to avoid contamination, phase changes, and segregation of phases. Suitable powders, when available, may be compressed into pills or briquettes with flat surfaces and examined by reflection. They may also be picked up for examination by pressing a wire gauze or support surface into them, or they may be suspended in air or a suitable liquid and allowed to settle onto a support film or surface. Fine particles of many materials may be prepared by placing a drop of a solution of the material on a support film or surface and allowing the solvent to evaporate. When liquids are involved in the mounting technique, the particles frequently tend to clump together as the last of the liquid evaporates, so more uniform dispersions are often obtained if the last of the liquid is removed by freeze-drying in the vacuum of the diffraction instrument. Smokes usually consist of fine particles which are of about the right size for electron diffraction, and can be collected for examination by holding a suitable specimen support above the burning material. Magnesium oxide, zinc oxide, and carbon smokes can be prepared by burning zinc dust, magnesium ribbon, or benzene in air. Smokes of many other metal oxides can be formed by electrically heating wires in air or by striking an arc between metal electrodes, and smokes of metal chlorides can often be prepared by burning the metals in chlorine gas.

4.1.2. Thin Films. Several techniques are commonly used in preparing thin films for electron diffraction studies. Many materials, including metals, alloys, and organic and inorganic compounds, can be evaporated in a vacuum onto a suitable support membrane or surface, and in some cases it is possible subsequently to dissolve away the supporting material and to mount the evaporated film on a fine wire gauze for examination alone. Furthermore, it is often possible to influence the structural characteristics of evaporated films by varying the conditions of evaporation and the nature of the substrate. Thin films of metals may be prepared by slowly withdrawing a small loop of wire from a bath of the molten metal (71), by floating metal foils on suitable etching reagents (65), by electropolishing metal foils under carefully controlled conditions (8, 77), and by bombarding foils with gas ions (16). Once prepared, the metal films may be heated, cooled, or deformed to study phase changes, recrystallization, and grain growth, and they may be treated with oxygen and other gases to study oxidation and other gas-metal reactions or to prepare oxides and other compounds of the metals. Oxide films may also be prepared on surfaces of bulk samples for examination by reflection methods and can often be separated from such surfaces by electrolytic or chemical techniques and examined by transmission (60). Waxes, greases, oils, fats, fatty acids, and similar organic materials can often be smeared on smooth surfaces to form thin films suitable for examination by reflection. Rubbing such films with filter paper will frequently cause partial orientation of the molecules. Oriented films of polar organic compounds such as the fatty acids may be deposited on smooth surfaces by adsorption from solution (3, 5) or by lifting them from a water surface by the Langmuir-Blodgett technique (6, 33). Solutions of polymeric materials may be spread on water or smooth solid surfaces and allowed to evaporate to form films of these materials, and glasses and other vitreous substances may be blown into thin membranes. Ultramicrotome techniques can be used to prepare slices of many substances, including the softer metals (24), which are thin enough for examination by transmission methods.

    4.1.3. Surfaces. In the above discussion, surfaces have been considered mainly as supports for other specimen materials; however, it is often desirable to obtain diffraction patterns from the surface of the solid itself as a means of studying its structure or surface characteristics. In these cases it is usually preferable for the surfaces to be slightly rough, for then the electrons can pass through the peaks of the asperities and stronger patterns are obtained. Smooth surfaces may be roughened slightly by various etching techniques or by abrading them lightly with a fine abrasive. Care must be used, however, to assure that such treatments do not destroy a characteristic of the surface which is of interest in the investigation at hand, and excessive roughening is to be avoided, since then only a few asperities will be struck by the electron beam and inferior patterns will result. Chemically attacked surfaces and films formed on smooth surfaces by oxidation, corrosion, condensation, electrodeposition, etc., usually have surface textures which make them satisfactory for examination without modification. Single crystals of many substances, such as mica, calcite, rock salt, zinc blende, and diamond, can be cleaved to obtain surfaces for diffraction. Cleavage surfaces of metal single crystals may be obtained in many cases by fracturing a single-crystal rod at liquid nitrogen or liquid hydrogen temperatures. Otherwise surfaces with preferred crystallographic orientations may be ground on single crystals by methods similar to those described by Rowland (65).

Surfaces of polycrystalline materials are usually prepared by cutting or machining followed by one or more grinding and polishing operations which leave the outer layers of material disturbed so that they must be removed by etching or electropolishing before the true structures of the specimens can be determined from studies of their surfacs. Considerable care is required in selection of electropolishing or etching treatments for this purpose. In general, treatments are desired which produce uniform, easily controlled attacks, but which do not form insoluble reaction products or allow the redeposition of dissolved constituents onto the surfaces. With multiphase materials, certain phases may be attacked more slowly than others during etching or electropolishing so that they stand in relief in the surfaces and contribute more strongly to the diffraction patterns. Heidenreich et al. (38-40) have taken advantage of these preferential etching effects in developing methods for identifying trace amounts of precipitate phases in alloy systems.

4.1.4. Specimen Contamination. It is of the utmost importance to exercise care at all times to avoid contaminating electron diffraction specimens, for slight traces of foreign crystalline materials may produce "extra" diffraction rings and confuse the interpretation of the patterns produced by the specimens, and even monomolecular layers of grease and similar amorphous materials are often sufficient to obscure patterns from the specimens, particularly when present on surfaces being examined by the reflection method. There are several precautions which should be observed routinely to avoid difficulties of these kinds. In general, specimens should not be handled with the fingers, for these are notorious sources of grease and other contaminants. Instead, implements of glass, platinum, stainless steel, and similar easily cleaned inert materials should be used. Specimens should be transferred to the diffraction instrument and examined as soon as possible after preparation, since prolonged exposure to laboratory air will provide an opportunity for them to accumulate dust and lint, absorb moisture, corrode, or react with gases such as NH_3, HCl, and H_2S, which are frequently present in laboratory atmospheres. Surfaces which have been mechanically polished are almost always contaminated with particles of the polishing abrasives, and these are usually partially embedded into the surfaces and are therefore fairly difficult to remove. Heavy etching, ultrasonic cleaning, and buffing on a clean degreased polishing cloth (12) are cleaning techniques which have proved effective in some cases. Contamination of metallic specimens with polishing powders may of course be avoided through the use of electrolytic or chemical polishing techniques. After the polishing, etching, or cleaning treatments, the surfaces must be carefully rinsed and dried. With inert specimens, an aqueous rinse may be used if advantageous; however, organic solvents are usually used for the final rinse to facilitate drying. Rowland (65) recommends propyl and butyl alcohols as being generally satisfactory for such purposes; Heidenreich *et al.* (38, 40) have found that two rinses in a 1:1 mixture of acetone and methanol followed by a final rinse in purified benzene works well with metallurgical specimens. After rinsing, it is generally preferable to drain the surfaces on clean filter paper and allow them to dry by evaporation. Wiping with cotton, cloths, or tissues will usually contaminate them with lint and other materials. Most laboratory air lines are contaminated with oil from the compressor, and if the common practice of using a blast of air from such lines to hasten drying is to be avoided unless adequate filtering is provided. All reagents used in the preparation of electron diffraction specimens should be of the highest purity available. Even the best commercial grades of organic solvents sometimes contain small amounts of dissolved greases and other organic materials, and distilled and tap water from laboratory lines may carry grease and oil from pipe connections as well as dissolved inorganic salts. Where such contamination is suspected, the liquids should be distilled from an all-glass fractionating column prior to use. Reagents are best stored in glass-stoppered bottles and should not be allowed to come into contact with corks, rubber stoppers, rubber tubing, etc. Wide-mouth weighing bottles are convenient containers for rinses and for storing samples for short periods. Glass apparatus and containers can be cleaned conveniently and effectively with the standard chromic–sulfuric acid cleaning solution. Specimens and small implements which have been contaminated with grease and certain other soluble materials can often be cleaned by treatment with an appropriate solvent in a Soxhlet extractor.

4.2. Obtaining Diffraction Patterns

In order to obtain sharp, clear diffraction patterns, the beam should be focused to give the smallest possible spot on the fluorescent screen, and all apertures and other optical elements should be accurately centered on the beam so that plates exposed for 30 seconds in the absence of a specimen show negligible background. For transmission patterns the specimen is brought into the beam at normal incidence, and the fluorescent screen is observed as the specimen is moved relative to the beam to find a spot giving good scattering. With high beam intensities and a good specimen, it is normally possible to observe the pattern on the fluorescent screen and to position the specimen so that the best pattern is obtained. With low beam intensities or poor specimens, patterns may be too weak to observe. In this case a strong general background scattering is usually evidence for a diffraction pattern except for specimens approaching the limiting thickness (1000 A.) which give strong multiple scattering.

Reflection specimens are brought up with the surface to be examined parallel to the beam, and small adjustments are made in the angle of incidence until a sharp shadow line appears on the screen. Further adjustments are then made in the angle of incidence to bring the shadow line as close as possible to the undeviated beam in order not to lose small-angle reflections, and the surface of the specimen is then moved past the beam until a pattern is obtained. The observation of weak patterns is greatly facilitated by using a beam stop, for the undeviated beam usually forms such an intense spot on the fluorescent screen that it blinds the observer to weak diffraction patterns. It is also desirable to work in a darkened room and to keep the eyes as sensitive as possible by avoiding looking at the main beam spot or other bright objects. When it is desired to examine specific areas of a specimen, special diaphragms with slits or holes may be mounted on the specimen holder to help locate the desired areas.

Nonconducting specimens such as glass, ceramics, and minerals, and even large particles of nonconducting materials like carbides and oxides embedded in metals, when struck by the electron beam, acquire an electrostatic charge which may distort and even destroy diffraction patterns. This effect is particularly annoying but can usually be overcome by bathing the surface of the specimen with low-voltage electrons from the charge neutralizer or auxiliary electron gun (14) described above (Section 3.3). The use of the charge neutralizer is sometimes beneficial in obtaining patterns from conducting specimens. An effect of the neutralizing beam and sometimes of the main electron beam is the formation of a layer of carbonaceous contamination on the specimen due to decomposition of organic vapors from pump oils, gaskets, etc. (22, 23). This layer tends to accumulate a charge, increase the background scattering, and even obscure the pattern completely. To prevent formation of the layer an ultra-clean vacuum system operating below 10^{-7} mm. Hg would be required; however, the rate of formation can be reduced to a negligible value in ordinary vacuum systems by several means including the proper use of cold traps, heating the specimen to above 150°C. (55), spraying jets of oxygen on the specimen (64), and bombarding the specimen with a beam of positive ions (25). Moving the specimen slowly back and forth during the exposure will reduce the effects of both charging and contamination, and in many cases will give improved patterns by bringing more of the specimen into contact with the beam.

Patterns are normally recorded on fine-grain, high-contrast, orthochromatic emulsions; Kodak medium lattern slide plates or Kodak process plates are types which are generally satisfactory. The estimation of exposure time is largely a matter of experience. With patterns that can be seen clearly on the fluorescent screen, from 3 to 5 seconds is normal; for weaker patterns exposures of several minutes may be required, and an exceptional case of a one-hour exposure has been reported (44) in experiments on large-angle scattering. For the usual purposes, accurate control and reproduction of exposure time is not necessary, and hand-operated shutters are used. When a beam stop is used, it is usually desirable to withdraw it a second or two before closing the shutter so that the position of the undeviated beam is clearly marked on the photographic plate to indicate the center of the pattern for subsequent measurements.

5. Interpretation of Patterns

The problem of interpreting electron diffraction patterns from solid specimens is greatly simplified by the extensive background of information that is available from x-ray diffraction investigations of crystalline materials, for much of the crystallographic and diffraction theory is the same for both types of radiation. In the following sections, the types of electron diffraction patterns which are most commonly encountered are described, and the more important points involved in the interpretation of each type are discussed briefly. It should be noted that the same general types of patterns are obtained by both the transmission and reflection methods, the only difference being that reflection patterns appear on only one side of the undeviated beam because the other side is screened by the specimen.

5.1. POWDER PATTERNS

The type of pattern most frequently encountered in electron diffraction work with solids is the "powder" pattern which is produced when the diffracting material consists of a large number of randomly oriented microcrystals. Here each microcrystal gives rise to a single-crystal pattern consisting of a limited number of diffraction spots as described in the following section, but because of the large number of crystals and their random orientations the spots combine to form patterns consisting of concentric rings. If the number of microcrystals struck by the beam is sufficiently large and their orientation is truly random, the rings appear to be uniform and continuous as in Figs. 3 and 4. If, however, the number of crystallites is not sufficiently great, discontinuous or "spotty" rings like those in Fig. 5 are obtained, and nonrandom or "preferred" orientations of the crystallites result in nonuniform distributions of intensities

FIG. 3. Transmission powder pattern of continuous rings. Zinc oxide smoke.

of the types shown in Figs. 6 and 7. In Fig. 6 the rings are continuous but are heavier in some sectors than in others, but in Fig. 7 some of the rings are broken into incomplete arcs. Figure 8 shows an extreme case of preferred orientation produced by rubbing graphite on a smooth surface. The rubbing caused the graphite flakes to orient nearly parallel to the surface, and the strong diffraction spots which appear in a line above the undeviated beam spot are successive orders of diffraction from the

FIG. 4. Reflection powder pattern of continuous rings; α-Fe_2O_3 on iron.

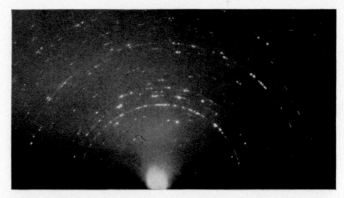

Fig. 5. Reflection powder pattern of spotty rings; α-Mn particles in Al-Mn alloy.

basal planes of the hexagonal graphite unit cell which lie parallel to the surfaces of the graphite flakes.

Powder patterns are used primarily for chemical identification by the Hanawalt method (37) in which the interplanar spacings (the Bragg d values) and the relative intensities of the diffraction rings from the unknown are compared with values tabulated for known materials. This

Fig. 6. Transmission powder pattern with nonuniform intensity distribution characteristic of preferred orientation. Thin gold foil.

FIG. 7. Reflection powder pattern with arced rings indicating preferred orientation; α-Fe$_2$O$_3$ on iron.

method is described in more detail in another chapter of this volume.* As is the case in x-ray diffraction, the Bragg equation $\lambda = 2d \sin \theta$ is used to calculate the interplanar spacings; however, in electron diffraction the values of θ encountered are always sufficiently small that $\sin \theta$

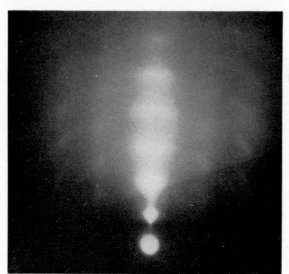

FIG. 8. Reflection pattern indicating extreme preferred orientation. Graphite rubbed on a polished metal surface.

* See pp. 27–128, chapter by Davidson.

$= \tan\ \theta = (\tan\ 2\theta)/2 = R/2L$ within the limits of accuracy required, and the Bragg equation simplifies to

$$d = L\lambda/R = K/R \tag{4}$$

in which L is the distance from the specimen to the photographic plate, λ is the wavelength of the electrons, R is the radius of the diffraction ring, and K is an instrument calibration factor. Analysis of patterns thus requires evaluation of the calibration factor and measurement of the radii of the diffraction rings for calculation of the d values, and estimation of the relative intensities of the rings for the final comparison with known data.

In principle the specimen-to-plate distance and the accelerating voltage could be measured and the product $L\lambda$ evaluated, using equation 1 to obtain λ from the measured voltage. In practice these measurements are sufficiently difficult to make that it is generally more convenient and more accurate to use a crystalline material whose d values are accurately known as a calibration standard. A pattern of the standard is then taken using the same specimen position and accelerating voltage as was used with the unknown, and the radii of the rings of the standard pattern are measured and multiplied by the corresponding d values to obtain K. If the diffracted rays from the specimen are not acted on by electron lenses (or residual electric or magnetic fields), K is constant (for a given combination of L and voltage) over the entire range of radii that is of interest for identification purposes. On the other hand, when lenses are active between the specimen and the photographic plate, K is generally not constant and must be determined as a function of the radius.

With the common type of electron diffraction instrument, the standard specimen is usually mounted beside the unknown, and a standard pattern is recorded immediately after the pattern from the unknown is recorded. It is not difficult to have the specimen-to-plate distance for the standard and the unknown the same within 1 or 2 mm., so, if L is of the order of 50 cm. and reasonable voltage stabilization is available, calibration to better than 1% can readily be achieved in this manner. Zinc oxide smoke is a convenient standard material for this method, since it gives an intense pattern with a large number of sharp rings which have radii in the range of interest and which can be easily and accurately measured. Zinc oxide specimens are prepared by sprinkling a small amount of reagent-grade zinc dust into a red-hot porcelain crucible and collecting the smoke on a fine wire gauze. Swanson and Fuyat (69) have published accurate d values for zinc oxide, although it is still advisable to examine samples of the smoke occasionally by x-ray diffraction to be sure proper preparations are being obtained. If very accurate calibration is desired, the standard material may be deposited directly on the unknown speci-men. For this purpose, standard materials such as magnesium oxide, so-dium chloride, thallium chloride, and various metals may be preferred to zinc oxide, since they give fewer diffraction rings and are therefore less likely to obscure the unknown pattern. In selected-area diffraction work with the electron microscope this method of using an internal stand-ard is almost a necessity if reasonable accuracy is desired, for here the radii depend on the objective, intermediate, and projector lens currents as well as on the location of the specimen relative to the objective lens. The latter factor is especially difficult to control experimentally; for ex-ample, with a typical objective lens of 3-mm. focal length, the specimen position must be reproduced to within 30 microns if the calibration factor is to be maintained within 1% from one specimen to the next. These considerations have been discussed more fully by Reisner (64).

The measurement of the radii of the diffraction rings is greatly facili-tated by a comparator of the type shown in Fig. 9, which features an

FIG. 9. Comparator for measuring electron diffraction patterns. (Designed by L. Niebylski and C. Pohlman of the Ethyl Corporation, and the author.)

accurate measuring scale, a fine parallax-free pointer, a diffuse light source of variable intensity, and a rotating stage for the photographic plate. In use, the plate is positioned with the center of the pattern at the center of rotation of the stage which corresponds to a scale reading of zero, so that readings can be made in any radial direction. This feature is particularly advantageous when working with single-crystal patterns and powder patterns with spotty or arced rings. With average patterns, measurements of the radii can be reproduced to about ±0.01 cm., giving an uncertainty in calculated d values which ranges from about ±0.1 A. to ±0.01 A. as the value of d ranges from 5 A. to 1.0 A. (for an accelerating potential of 50 kv. and a specimen-to-plate distance of about 50 cm.). This is about ten times as great as the uncertainty in x-ray determinations over the same range of d values, and, although somewhat better accuracy can be obtained with very sharp, clear patterns, it generally is not possible to equal that attainable by x-ray methods.

Highly accurate intensity data are generally not required for chemical identification by powder methods; therefore, the relative intensities of powder patterns are usually estimated by visual comparison of the densities of the diffraction rings on the photographic plates. The estimated values are reported either on a semiquantitative basis, with a value of 1 or 100 for the densest ring and proportionately smaller values for weaker rings, or on a somewhat more qualitative basis by rating the rings as strong, medium strong, medium, weak medium, weak, very weak, etc. A facility for estimating diffraction intensities can be developed with relatively little effort by practicing with x-ray patterns of known materials for which accurate intensity data are available. More quantitative intensity determinations can be obtained from photometric measurements of the densities of the rings, although in practice this procedure is applicable to only the very best patterns, for the patterns usually encountered

TABLE I

Comparison of Measured and Estimated Intensities for Electron and X-Ray Powder Diffraction Patterns of Zinc Oxide Smoke

X-ray pattern[a]				Electron pattern[a]	
I_p	I_v	d	hkl	I_p	I_v
71	s	2.816	100	35	ms
34	m	2.601	002	100	s
100	s	2.476	101	82	s
22	m	1.912	102	34	ms
43	ms	1.626	110	20	m
28	m	1.477	103	55	s
8	w	1.408	200	14	w
27	m	1.379	112	26	m
19	wm	1.358	201	12	w

[a] I_p = Intensities based on photometric measurements. I_v = Visually estimated intensities: s = strong, m = medium, w = weak.

have such relatively high background intensities and so frequently contain very weak and spotty or discontinuous rings that they are not well suited for photometric measurements.

In making the final identification it is the normal procedure to compare the observed electron diffraction data with x-ray data for known materials listed in the ASTM Card File of Powder Diffraction Data (1). Here it is important to recognize that, although the interplanar spacings are a property of the crystal and are the same (within the limits of experimental uncertainties) for both electron and x-ray diffraction, the relative intensities in electron diffraction patterns are frequently different from those in x-ray patterns obtained from the same material, as is illustrated by the data for zinc oxide smoke listed in Table I. These intensity differences are due largely to the relatively high scattering and absorption of electrons as compared to x-rays and are most pronounced in cases where the electron diffraction specimens consist of irregularly shaped crystallites (i.e., needles, rods, plates, etc.) so that the path lengths inside the crystallites are considerably different for rays diffracted from different crystal planes, as shown in Fig. 10. The electron rays which have the

FIG. 10. Different path lengths within elongated crystallites for rays diffracted from different crystal planes.

longer paths within the crystal are relatively strongly attenuated, causing the electron diffraction intensities to show a dependence on crystal shape that is not shown by the more penetrating x-rays. Since the effect is one of attenuation by absorption and scattering, the rings of high intensity (i.e., medium or higher) are generally the same for both x-rays and electrons, but the ranking in order of intensity may be different. The practical consequence of this is to make the identification procedure for electron diffraction relatively more complicated in many cases. For x-rays the usual procedure is to search the card file on the basis of the three or four strongest reflections. In electron diffraction it may be necessary to consider all but the weaker reflections in making the search, since a ring which would be reported as of strong intensity in the x-ray data may be reduced to a much lower relative intensity in the electron pattern.

For a satisfactory identification it is usually necessary to have electron diffraction rings corresponding to at least the high-intensity reflections reported in the x-ray data, with "reasonable" correspondence in relative intensities; the number of additional rings corresponding to weaker reflections will depend on the character of the electron patterns. Two somewhat extreme cases are illustrated by the data in Tables II and III. The data in Table II were obtained in the course of an electron diffraction investigation of the oxide phase in a sintered aluminum product (11). As shown in Fig. 11, the pattern obtained was of very poor

TABLE II

Comparison of Electron Diffraction Data from a Sintered Aluminum Product with Data Reported for γ-Al₂O₃

Electron data[a]		γ-Al₂O₃ data[a]	
d	I	d	I
		5.59	w
4.6	vw	4.59	w
		3.54	w
2.80	w	2.80	m
		2.65	vw
		2.50	vw
2.39	s	2.38	s
		2.28	w
		2.20	vw
2.13	w	2.12	wm
1.98	ms	1.98	ms
		1.92	vw
		1.87	vw
		1.73	vw
		1.69	vw
		1.65	vw
		1.61	w
		1.55	vw
1.52	w	1.52	m
		1.47	vw
		1.44	vw
1.39	s	1.40	s

[a] s = strong, m = medium, w = weak, v = very.

quality; however, all the rings present corresponded to the higher intensity reflections reported for γ-Al₂O₃, and this was considered a satisfactory identification. The data in Table III were obtained in the investigation of the carbide phases present in heat-treated specimens of a heat-resistant stainless steel. The x-ray pattern was taken from a sample of carbides obtained by treating the steel with a chemical reagent which dissolved the metallic phase but did not affect the carbide particles. The

TABLE III

*Data Illustrating the Identification of Complex Carbide Phases of a
Heat-Resistant Stainless Steel by Electron and X-Ray Diffraction*

X-ray data[a]		Electron data[a]			M_6C data[a]		$M_{23}C_6$ data[a]	
d	I	d	I	hkl	d	I	d	I
		6.3	vw	111				
		5.4	vw	200				
		3.8	w	220				
3.27	w	3.2	w	311	3.28	vw	3.21	vw
3.13	w	3.1	w	222			3.07	vw
2.71	m	2.70	vw	400	2.72	m	2.66	w
2.49	m	2.49	w	331	2.49	m	2.43	vw
		2.40	vw	420				
		2.38	vw				2.38	s
2.22	s	2.22	s	422	2.22	s		
		2.17	vw				2.17	s
2.09	s	2.10	s	511	2.09	vs		
		2.04	w				2.04	s
1.92	s	1.92	m	440	1.92	m	1.88	m
				531	1.84	w	1.79	s
1.81	m	1.82	m	600	1.81	w	1.77	m
		1.72	m	620	1.72	vw	1.68	vw
1.65	w	1.66	w	533	1.66	w	1.62	vw
		1.63	w	622	1.64	w	1.60	vw
		1.56	vw	444				
1.52	m	1.52	w	711	1.52	wm	1.49	vw
				640	1.51	w	1.48	vw
		1.46	vw	642				
1.42	m	1.43	wm	731	1.42	wm	1.38	vw
		1.36	vw	800	1.36	vw	1.33	w
1.33	m	1.33	wm	733	1.33	m		
				644	1.31	wm		
1.28	s	1.29	m	822				
				555				
1.26	ms	1.26	w	662	1.26	ms	1.26	s
		1.23	vw	840			1.23	w
		1.20	wm	911			1.22	w

[a] s = strong, m = medium, w = weak, v = very.

electron patterns were obtained by the reflection method from surfaces
that were etched so that the carbide particles were exposed in relief
above the matrix metal. Here there is very good general agreement between data from the x-ray and electron diffraction patterns and the data
reported for a metallic carbide of complex composition designated as
M_6C which has a face-centered cubic unit cell with $a_0 = 10.87$ A. The

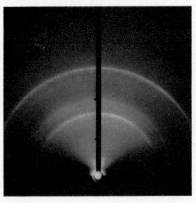

FIG. 11. Pattern of γ-Al₂O₃ from a sintered aluminum product.

electron diffraction pattern, however, which was of especially good quality in this case as shown in Fig. 12, contained a number of weak rings which were not reported for this carbide. Three of these were found to agree with the strongest reflections of a related carbide ($M_{23}C_6$) as shown in the table, indicating the presence of trace amounts of this phase in the alloy. The remainder could not be identified as belonging to any other phase which might be expected in the alloy. Finally, calculations showed that these corresponded to weak reflections permitted by the M_6C structure, but which had not been observed in x-ray patterns. Their

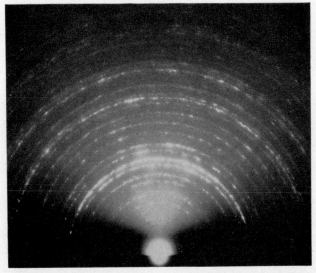

FIG. 12. Pattern of M_6C carbide from heat-resistant stainless steel.

presence in the electron diffraction pattern may be attributed to the high sensitivity of the electron method. This emphasizes the necessity for always checking the reported data, for in addition to the situation indicated here, where all possible reflections are not reported, a number of cases have been found where reflections have been listed which were inconsistent with the known structure of the compound in question. In the past there has been considerable concern about the appearance of "forbidden" reflections in electron diffraction patterns. Such reflections can occur owing to dynamical scattering effects not accounted for by the simple kinematic theory used in crystal structure calculations; however, their occurrence is relatively rare, and extra rings are usually due to traces of contaminants, or else they represent previously unreported reflections as in the present example.

Miller indices may be assigned to the rings of electron diffraction powder patterns, and the patterns may be used to determine the type and dimensions of the crystallographic unit cell by the same methods described for x-ray powder patterns on pp. 27-128. Indexing of patterns having arced lines is generally necessary if the direction of preferred orientation is to be determined. In this connection it should be noted that the arcing of diffraction rings is not infallible proof of preferred orientations. Several cases have been observed (46) in which an etchant used on a metal surface produced a surface structure on grains of certain orientations which was exceptionally favorable for diffraction. Patterns obtained from these surfaces showed rings with strong arcs suggesting preferred orientation, but which were more accurately an indication of the special selective action of the etching reaction. The absence of arcing in transmission patterns from thin films taken at normal incidence also is not proof of the absence of preferred orientation; additional patterns taken at oblique incidence are required to establish this point. In all cases it should be recognized that the information afforded by the diffraction pattern is determined entirely by the crystals which are reached by the electron beam, and, if the preparation or examination of the specimen is carried out in such a manner as to limit the access of the beam, then the information obtained will be biased or incomplete.

5.2. SINGLE-CRYSTAL PATTERNS

Single-crystal electron diffraction patterns consist of discrete spots, as shown in Fig. 13, with the number and arrangement of the spots depending on the structure and orientation of the crystal. The most striking feature of these patterns as compared with corresponding x-ray patterns is the large numbers of spots obtained by using a fixed position of the crystal and monochromatic radiation. As indicated above, this is primarily the result of the very short wavelengths of the electrons, which allows a whole series of crystallographic planes of different d values to come into position to reflect within a range of 1° or 2° in θ. An effective range in θ of this amount can easily occur without movement of the crystal as a result of slight distortions of the crystal or the crystal lattice and the slight range of directions of the electrons in the incident beam. If the crystal is very thin (a few atom layers) in the direction of the beam, the Laue conditions for reflection are slightly relaxed in this direction, also permitting more reflections to occur than would be the case for a thicker crystal. This effect for extremely thin crystals is never observed

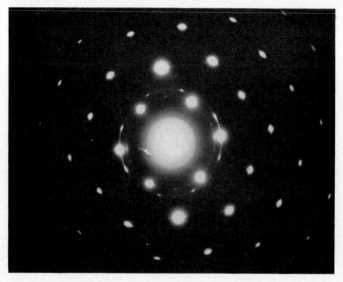

Fig. 13. Single crystal pattern from NiO film.

in x-ray diffraction because the amount of scattering material present would be too small to produce detectable reflections.

Single-crystal patterns may be treated as extreme cases of spotty powder patterns and used for purposes of chemical identification. The underlying principle here is that each spot can be considered as a small segment of an incomplete powder ring. Thus the distance from a given spot to the center of the pattern is equivalent to a ring radius and can be used to calculate an interplanar spacing. The sets of d values obtained in this way generally do not include all those which would be present in a powder pattern, however; and, since the intensities of the spots are rather difficult to estimate, identifications from single-crystal patterns are somewhat more difficult than from powder patterns. This general approach must often be used in analyzing selected-area electron diffraction patterns obtained in the electron microscope where the number of crystals observed is usually insufficient to give powder rings.

By indexing single-crystal patterns, additional information can frequently be obtained concerning the orientation of the crystal and the type and size of its unit crystallographic cell. It is also possible to make crystal structural determinations from single-crystal electron diffraction patterns. The procedures here are similar to those used in x-ray diffraction except that special problems are encountered in accurately determining the diffraction intensities due to secondary and dynamic scattering effects and absorption of the diffracted electrons. The application of electron diffraction techniques to crystal structure determinations has been reviewed by Pinsker (61, 62) and by Cowley and Rees (20).

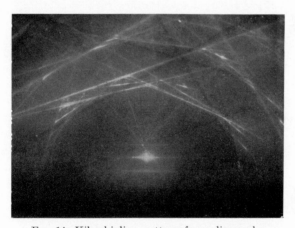

Fig. 14. Kikuchi line pattern from diamond.

Two additional interesting diffraction phenomena which are sometimes observed in single-crystal electron diffraction patterns are the formation of Kikuchi lines and the refraction of electrons. Kikuchi lines are formed when diffusely scattered electrons, which form the normal background scattering, are diffracted from a set of parallel planes in the crystal. The diffracted electrons form cones about the normal to the diffracting planes, and these cones intersect the photographic plate in nearly straight lines which always occur in pairs, one of which is stronger in intensity than the average background, and the other lighter, as shown in Fig. 14. In order for detectable intensities to develop, the path length within the crystal for the diffusely scattered electrons must be relatively long; therefore, Kikuchi lines are normally obtained only from relatively thick transmission specimens or from smooth surfaces of large single crystals. Furthermore, the crystals must be highly perfect in order to produce sharp Kikuchi lines. The uses of Kikuchi lines include determination of crystal orientations, measurement of the "inner potentials" of crystals, and detection of plastic deformation and crystalline imperfections (40, 41). The refraction of electrons results from the periodically varying potential field within the crystal and from the potential discontinuity at the crystal surface. Refraction effects may occur in a variety of circumstances but usually are manifest by small displacements or distortions of the diffraction spots or by the formation of "fine structure" within the spots. These effects are observable only under conditions of high resolution and are usually sufficiently small as to be negligible in making chemical identifications. Detailed discussions of the theoretical and practical aspects of Kikuchi lines and refraction effects are given by Thomson and Cochrane (75) and Pinsker (61).

5.3. LAYER LINE PATTERNS

Long-chain organic compounds such as paraffin hydrocarbons, waxes, the fatty acids, and the corresponding alcohols, amines, and amides may be deposited onto smooth solid surfaces to form films in which the long hydrocarbon chains of the molecules stand more or less upright on the surface. Such films characteristically produce patterns consisting of several diffuse, parallel diffraction bands or "layer lines" as shown in Figs. 15 to 18. These layer lines originate from the fact that the hydrocarbon molecules consist of a zigzag hydrocarbon chain which for diffraction purposes may be considered as two independent, parallel rows of equally spaced atoms. The conditions for diffraction from such a row of atoms is given by the Laue interference expression of equation 5.

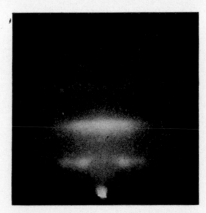

FIG. 15. Horizontal layer line pattern from cerotic acid monolayer.

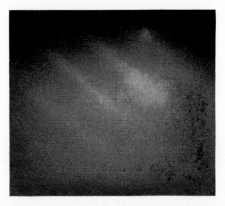

FIG. 16. Pattern of tilted layer lines from stearic acid film.

$$n\lambda = a(\cos \gamma_n - \cos \gamma_0) \tag{5}$$

Here n is the order of diffraction, λ is the electron wavelength, a is the separation of successive atoms in a row, and γ_0 and γ_n are the angles between the line of atoms and the incident and diffracted rays, respectively. The diffracted rays form a set of cones having the direction of the line of atoms as their common axis, with each cone corresponding to a different value of n. These cones intersect the photographic plate as very flat hyperbolae which appear as straight lines. The orientation of these lines on the plate is thus dependent on the orientation of the molecules on the surface.

Patterns of straight, equally spaced layer lines lying parallel to the shadow line of the type shown in Fig. 15 are produced by films in which

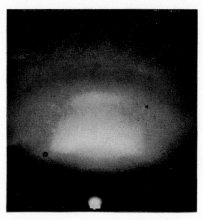

FIG. 17. Pattern of crossed layer lines from cerotic acid monolayer.

the molecules all stand at right angles to the surface (with the beam incident on the surface at a small grazing angle and the photographic plate normal to the beam.) Under these conditions equation 5 reduces to

$$n\lambda = a \sin (90 - \gamma_n) = a \sin 2\theta \tag{6}$$

since γ_0 is now $90°$. The slanting layer lines of Fig. 16 are obtained when all the molecules are tilted from the normal to the surface through the

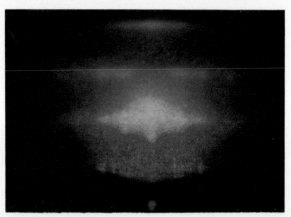

FIG. 18. Layer line pattern with superimposed spots from film of paraffin wax.

same angle and in the same azimuth. The parallel lines of both Figs. 15 and 16 may be represented by the expression

$$y = \frac{nL\lambda}{a \cos \alpha} + x \tan \alpha \sin \phi \tag{7}$$

in which x and y are Cartesian coordinates on the photographic plate with the origin at the position of the undeviated beam, L is the distance from specimen to plate, α is the angle of declination from the normal to the surface, and ϕ is the azimuth measured from the plane normal to both the photographic plate and the surface of the specimen. When α and ϕ are the same for all the molecules on the surface, their values are readily determined from a series of photographs having successive rotations of the specimen in its own plane. The maximum slope observed is $\tan \alpha$, and from the intercepts of the lines the value of a is calculated. The crossed line pattern of Fig. 17 occurs when the molecular axes have random azimuths. In this case the parallel line patterns produced by the separate molecules deviate from the horizontal by all values from $-\alpha$ to $+\alpha$, the resultant composite pattern being shown in the figure. Variation in the declinations of the molecules leads to unequal intervals in the y intercepts. Patterns of the type just described are frequently observed in thin films of oils and greases or of almost any long-chain hydrocarbon derivative. When the amount of material on the surface is sufficient to lead to crystallization, single-crystal spots appear on the layer lines as shown in Fig. 18.

6. Applications

Electron diffraction techniques have been used in a great variety of investigations during recent years. It is beyond the purpose and scope of this discussion to present a comprehensive review of this work; however, some of the general areas where the method is particularly useful have been indicated in the discussion of techniques above. Specific references to published work can be found in various abstract journals (especially the *Bulletin Signaletique,* which is published by the Centre National de la Recherche Scientifique, Paris, and which has sections devoted to electron optics and to structural studies by electron methods). In the following sections a few typical investigations will be discussed to indicate the types of results which can be obtained.

6.1. OXIDATION OF METALS AND ALLOYS

A systematic study of the controlled oxidation of a number of metals and alloys has been reported by Gulbransen *et al.* (35, 60). Polished specimens of the metals were mounted in a high-temperature specimen holder, and electron diffraction patterns were taken by reflection at the temperature of the experiment before oxidation, after oxidation for a specified time with oxygen at a controlled pressure, and again after the surface had cooled back to room temperature. The oxide film was stripped in an electrolytic apparatus and mounted for examination by transmission electron microscopy and diffraction to determine whether the body of the film had the same composition as observed for the surface by reflection. Possible contamination of the oxide film in the stripping treatment was checked by taking reflection photographs from an oxidized Nichrome V surface subjected to the stripping procedure for a time too short to remove the film from the metal; no change in the chemical structure was observed. Electron and optical microscopic examinations gave information on particle size distribution, particle shape, film uniformity, and grain structure. The diffraction patterns were used for identifying the oxides formed at various stages in the oxidation and for checking the cell dimensions of the compounds identified.

Chromium, cobalt, copper, iron, molybdenum, nickel, aluminum, columbium, and tungsten were studied at oxidation temperatures ranging from 200° to 600°C. for times ranging from 5 to 60 minutes in oxygen at 0.1 atmosphere. The first six metals all showed diffuse oxide patterns on being raised to the treatment temperature but before oxygen was admitted. Some of the metals showed different oxides according to the temperature and time of treatment. Tungsten showed no oxide pattern by reflection after 5 minutes in oxygen at 450°C., but the stripped film gave diffuse lines of WO_3. In all cases it appeared that the oxidation started with the adsorption of a layer of oxygen on the surface and the rapid formation of a thin oxide film. This was followed by the growth of the oxide from crystallization nuclei such that the thicker films were non-uniform.

The results of a similar study of sixteen alloys composed principally of iron, cobalt, nickel, and chromium are summarized in Table IV. From

TABLE IV

Electron Diffraction Results from Oxidation of Alloys

| Alloy | Oxidizing conditions | | Composition | |
	Temp. (°C.)	Time (min.)	Transmission	Reflection
Protective				
13 CrFe	600	5	$Fe_3O_4,$[a] Cr_2O_3	Cr_2O_3
18-8 SS	600	5	Cr_2O_3	$Fe_3O_4,$[a] α-Fe_2O_3
Refractory				
K42B	600	30	$Fe_3O_4,$[a] Cr_2O_3	Fe_3O_4, α-Fe_2O_3
Inconel	600	30	Cr_2O_3, NiO	Fe_3O_4
Nichrome V	600	30	Cr_2O_3	Cr_2O_3
Magnetic				
Mild steel	250	5	Fe_3O_4	Fe_3O_4
Hipernik	400	5	Spinel, Fe_2O_3 NiO	Fe_3O_4, α-Fe_2O_3
30 CoFe	300	30	Spinel	Fe_3O_4
Miscellaneous				
Fe + 5%x (x = Cr, Ni, or Mn)	300	5	Spinel type	Fe_3O_4
Fe + 5Si	300	5	Fe_2O_3	Fe_3O_4
Fe + 4W	300	5	Fe_2O_3	Fe_2O_3

[a] Trace.

these results several interesting conclusions were drawn concerning the oxidation characteristics of alloys of this type. The fact that iron and chromium oxides were always observed in the surface of the oxide films indicated that ions of these metals diffused rapidly through the oxide films. Nickel oxide was never observed on the surface of the oxide layer, although it sometimes occurred in the body of the layer. Compositional variations within the oxide layers occurred even when the layers were only 100 to 300 A. thick. Cr_2O_3 was always observed in the films on alloys which were classified as protective or refractory; this oxide was always in contact with the substrate in films showing variable composition. Solid phase reactions occurred between simple oxides to form the spinel type of oxide structure. Except for iron and chromium, metals constituting less than 5% of the alloy did not occur as simple oxides on the outer surface of the film, although they sometimes appeared in complex oxides in the body of the film. Simple oxides of cobalt, manganese, silicon, vanadium, and tungsten were not observed.

6.2. Secondary Phases in Alloys

The method of Heidenreich and associates (38, 39) which was referred to above has proved very effective for identifying precipitated phases in various alloy systems. In this method, surfaces of the alloy specimens are prepared by etching them so that the matrix metal is leached away, and the particles of the precipitate phases remain standing in relief so that they can be struck by the electron beam when the surfaces are examined by the reflection method. In this way strong diffraction patterns can be obtained from phases which constitute only a very small part of the total alloy structure. The principal problems encountered are the selection of a proper etching reagent and the development of a rinsing technique which will displace the etchant and etching products without contaminating the surfaces. Techniques for low-carbon steels and for magnesium, aluminum, and copper alloys have been described by Heidenreich et al. (38, 39), and procedures for a number of more inactive heat-resistant alloys have been developed by Bigelow et al. (4, 11). A particular advantage of the method arises from the fact that the surfaces used in the diffraction studies can subsequently be examined by optical and electron microscopy to correlate the distribution of the precipitate particles with the diffraction results. Here, as in most other areas of research, the combined use of electron microscopy and electron diffraction is particularly effective. The electron microscopic aspects of this method are discussed in the chapter by Heidenreich and Calbick (pp. 547-617).

Heidenreich and associates applied this method to the study of the decomposition of martensite and showed that at temperatures under 200°C. highly dispersed particles of Fe_3N are formed which transform to Fe_3C on annealing above 350°C. The decomposition of martensite at 400°C. yields Fe_3C directly. Bigelow *et al.* (4, 11) used this method in studying several heat-resistant alloys. In a stainless steel containing 16% Cr, 25% Ni, and 6% Mo, two complex carbides, $M_{23}C_6$ and M_6C, were identified. (The M in these formulas refers to the fact that several different metals combine with carbon to form these carbides.) The $M_{23}C_6$ carbide was generally the principal phase present after short periods of heat treatment at temperatures from 1200° to 1600°F.; however, with long periods of heat treatment, the M_6C predominated. The data in Table III illustrate the identification of M_6C in a specimen of this alloy aged 1000 hours at 1600°F. Four precipitate phases, $M_{23}C_6$, TiN, CbN, and an intermetallic phase designated as γ', were identified in a nickel base heat-resistant alloy commercially known as Inconel-X. The $M_{23}C_6$ phase was not found in specimens aged at 1600°F., whereas all four phases were found in specimens aged at 1200° and 1400°F. By combining electron microscopic studies with the electron diffraction work, it was possible to show that the γ' particles occurred only within the matrix grains, whereas the other three occurred predominately at the grain boundaries. Furthermore, hardness and certain other physical properties of the alloy were correlated with the dispersion of the γ' particles within the grains.

Selected-area electron diffraction investigations with the electron microscope have proved particularly effective in identifying precipitates in alloy systems. Here the usual procedure is to make use of the extraction replica technique (28) which permits small precipitate particles to be isolated from the etched surface of an alloy specimen and mounted on a support film so that they retain the same relative positions as they had in the surface. Since the particles from which the diffraction patterns are obtained can actually be observed in the electron microscope, this provides a conclusive method of phase identification. This method has been applied successfully to the identification of precipitates in various types of steels (28, 66, 68) and other alloys (4, 53). Castaing (16, 17) and Takahashi (70) have also studied phase transformations in alloy systems by selected-area electron diffraction and transmission electron microscopic investigations of very thin metal films.

Other studies (54, 56) of substances occurring in the grain boundaries of metals have been made by completely dissolving the metal and examining the residue. Commercial cadmium was found to contain boundary films of $CdCO_3$ and basic lead carbonate, and iron dissolved in ammonium persulfate left Fe_3C and α-FeOOH; a possibility of chemical reaction between the boundary material and the chemical reagent must be considered. Other metallurgical problems studied by electron diffraction include grain growth in thin evaporated films of metal, the formation of various types of protective surfaces on metals, and the general problem of the chemical reactions which occur at the interface between the metal and liquid or gaseous reagents.

6.3. Amorphous "Polish" Layer

The formation of a layer of amorphous material (Beilby layer) on metals or other substances by polishing has been widely discussed in relation to the two very diffuse rings in the electron diffraction pattern from polished surfaces. Diffuse rings obtained on reflection of electrons from a surface are not a reliable indication of the existence of amorphous material because refraction effects for electrons entering and leaving a very smooth crystalline surface at small angles will cause diffuseness in the pattern. Definite indication of amorphous character is given by diffuse patterns from transmission specimens. This question has been discussed in several studies of the surface disturbance caused by rolling and polishing of metals (30, 48, 63, 79).

6.4. Layers of Polar Hydrocarbon Derivatives

Films of long-chain organic molecules formed by melting or rubbing a fatty acid or soap onto a smooth surface or by lifting a floating film by the Langmuir-Blodgett technique have been studied extensively (3, 18, 32, 33, 47, 58). Germer reports that stearic acid molecules in the first layer stand with their axes normal to the supporting surface but with no regular sidewise packing. Subsequent layers are inclined to the surface and are clustered into true crystals showing the monoclinic symmetry and characteristic parameters of the solid crystalline acid. The upper layers are easily removed by rubbing, but the first layer adheres firmly to the surface and is removed only by abrading the metal or washing with an excess of solvent. The strong adhesion of the first layer to the metal is important in the field of lubrication. Observations (3, 12) also have been made on films of long-chain molecules adsorbed from solution in hydrocarbon solvents which show the interesting property of being repellant to the solution from which they were formed (5). Diffraction patterns from films of cerotic acid adsorbed on platinum from solutions in cetane are shown in Figs. 15 and 17. In the first, the molecules are standing normal to the surface, and the attractions between adjacent molecules have led to some regularity in the sidewise spacing as shown by the spots in the first layer line. Layers of stearic acid formed on the same surface do not show the side-spacing spots, and, accordingly, the intermolecular attractions are less effective in the shorter acid. In Fig. 17 the cerotic acid molecules show declinations from the normal reaching 30° and in random azimuths; the platinum surface here has a small-scale waviness which prevents the parallel alignment of the molecules. These studies are of interest in tracing the connection between film structure and contact angle with hydrocarbons; the close-packed nonwetting films may be useful for corrosion inhibition.

The use of electron diffraction both alone and as a supplement to x-ray diffraction and electron microscopy in the examination of materials has become well established as a standard physical method of analysis.

Acknowledgment

The author wishes to express his appreciation to Professor L. O. Brockway for his helpful suggestions and criticisms of this manuscript and for permission to incorporate into this chapter figures, tables, and portions of the text from the previous edition.

References

1. American Society for Testing Materials, Card File of X-Ray Diffraction Data. Philadelphia, 1942, 1944.
2. Bagdyk'Janc, G. O., *Izvest. Akad. Nauk. S.S.S.R.* **17**, 253 (1953).
3. Bigelow, W. C., and Brockway, L. O., *J. Colloid Sci.* **11**, 60 (1956).
4. Bigelow, W. C., Brockway, L. O. and Freeman, J. W., *in* Symposium on Advances in Electron Metallography. *ASTM Spec. Tech. Publ.* **No. 245**, 88 (1958).
5. Bigelow, W. C., Pickett, D. L., and Zisman, W. A., *J. Colloid Sci.* **1**, 513 (1946).
6. Blodgett, K. B., *J. Am. Chem. Soc.* **57**, 1007 (1935).
7. Boettcher, A., Thun, R., and Treupel, H., *J. Appl. Phys.* **25**, 926 (1954).
8. Bollman, W., *Phys. Rev.* **103**, 1588 (1956).
9. Bradley, D. E., *Brit. J. Appl. Phys.* **5**, 65 (1954).
10. Brockway, L. O., *in* "Physical Methods of Organic Chemistry" (A. Weissberger, ed.), Vol. I, Part 2, p. 1109. Interscience, New York, 1949.
11. Brockway, L. O., and Bigelow, W. C., WADC Technical Report 54-589, Wright Air Development Center, Wright-Patterson Air Force Base, Ohio, 1955.
12. Brockway, L. O., and Karle, J., *J. Colloid Sci.* **2**, 277 (1947).
13. Broglie, L. de, *Phil. Mag.* **47**, 446 (1924).
14. Brubaker, D. G., and Fuller, M. L., *J. Appl. Phys.* **16**, 128 (1945).
15. Cardile, A. J., *RCA Sci. Instr. News* **3**, 6 (1958).
16. Castaing, R., *Rev. universelle mines,* **12**, 454 (1956).
17. Castaing, R., *in* "Techniques recentes en Microscopie electronique et corpusculaire, Toulouse, 1955," p. 117. Centre Nationale de la Recherche Scientifique, France, 1956.
18. Coumoulos, G. D., and Rideal, E. K., *Proc. Roy. Soc.* **A178**, 415, 421 (1941).
19. Cowley, J. M., and Rees, A. L. G., *J. Sci. Instr.* **30**, 33 (1953).
20. Cowley, J. M., and Rees, A. L. G., *Repts. Progr. in Phys.* **21**, 165 (1958).
21. Davisson, C., and Germer, L. H., *Phys. Rev.* **30**, 707 (1927).
22. Ellis, S. G., *in* Electron Physics. *Nat. Bur. Standards (U.S.) Circ.* **527**, 359 (1954).
23. Ennos, A. E., *Brit. J. Appl. Phys.* **4**, 101 (1953); **5**, 27 (1954).
24. Fernandez-Moran, H., *J. Biophys. Biochem. Cytol. Suppl.* **2**, 29 (1956).
25. Fert, C., and Dupouy, G., *Compt. rend. acad. sci.* **238**, 333 (1954).
26. Finch, G. I., and Wilman, H., *Ergeb. exakt. Naturw.* **16**, 353 (1937).

27. Fischer, R. B., "Applied Electron Microscopy." Indiana University Press, Bloomington, 1953.
28. Fisher, R. M., *in* Symposium on Techniques for Electron Metallography. *ASTM Spec. Tech. Publ.* **No. 155,** 49 (1953).
29. Fuller, M. L., *Metals & Alloys* **10,** 84, 122 (1939).
30. Fuller, M. L., *Am. Inst. Mining Met. Engrs. Tech. Publs.* **965** (1938).
31. Germer, L. H., *Rev. Sci. Instr.* **6,** 138 (1935).
32. Germer, L. H., and Storks, K. H., *J. Chem. Phys.* **6,** 280 (1938).
33. Germer, L. H., and Storks, K. H., *Phys. Rev.* **55,** 648 (1939).
34. Gulbransen, E. A., *J. Appl. Phys.* **16,** 718 (1945).
35. Gulbransen, E. A., Phelps, R. T., and Hickman, J. W., *Ind. Eng. Chem., Anal. Ed.* **18,** 640 (1946).
36. Hall, C. E., "Introduction to Electron Microscopy." McGraw-Hill, New York, 1953.
37. Hanawalt, J. D., Rinn, H. W., and Frevel, L. K., *Ind. Eng. Chem., Anal. Ed.* **8,** 244 (1936); **10,** 457 (1938).
38. Heidenreich, R. D., Sturkey, L., and Woods, H. L., *J. Appl. Phys.* **17,** 127 (1946); *Nature* **157,** 518 (1946).
39. Heidenreich, R. D., Gerould, C. H., and McNulty, R. E., *Trans. Am. Inst. Mining Met. Engrs., Inst. Metals Div. Tech. Publ.* **1979** (1946).
40. Heidenreich, R. D., *in* "Modern Research Techniques in Physical Metallurgy," p. 51. American Society for Metals, Cleveland, 1953.
41. Heidenreich, R. D. and Shockley, W., Bristol Conference Report, p. 57. Physical Society, 1948.
42. Hillier, J., *J. Appl. Phys.* **17,** 12 (1946).
43. Induni, G., *in* "Techniques récentes en microscopie électronique et corpusculaire, Toulouse, 1955," p. 189. Centre National de la Recherche Scientifique, France, 1956.
44. Jackson, A., and Quarrel, A. G., *Proc. Roy Soc.* **50,** 776 (1938); **51,** 237 (1939).
45. James, R. W., and Brindley, G. W., *Z. Krist.* **78,** 370 (1931).
46. Johnson, R. P., and Grams, W. R., *Phys. Rev.* **62,** 77 (1942).
47. Karle, J., and Brockway, L. O., *J. Chem. Phys.* **15,** 213 (1947).
48. Kirchner, F., *Ann. Physik* **28,** 21 (1937).
49. Lafourcade, L., *Ann. fac. sci. univ. Toulouse sci. math. et. sci. phys.* **17,** 143 (1953-54).
50. Lees, C. S., *J. Sci. Instr.* **31,** 86 (1954).
51. Lennander, S., *Ark. Fysik Sverige* **5,** 391 (1952).
52. LePoole, J. B., Corbet, H. C., Van Koppen, G. M., Kramer, J., Van Ments, M., and Van Reijen, L. L., *Physik Verhandl.*, **4,** 121 (1953).
53. Mihalisin, J. R., *Trans. Am. Inst. Mining Met. Petroleum Engrs.* **212,** 349 (1958).
54. Miller, B. L., *J. Franklin Inst.* **237,** 443 (1944).
55. Mollenstedt, G., and Keller, M., *Radex Rundschau,* **4/5,** 153 (1956).
56. Morgan, R., Steckler, S., and Miller, B. L., *J. Chem. Phys.* **5,** 953 (1957).
57. Mott, N. F., *Proc. Roy. Soc.* **A127,** 658 (1930).
58. Murison, C. A., *Phil. Mag.* **17,** 201 (1934).
59. Page, R. S., and Garfitt, R. G., *J. Sci. Instr.* **29,** 398 (1952).
60. Phelps, R. T., Gulbransen, E. A., and Hickman, J. W., *Ind. Eng. Chem., Anal. Ed.* **18,** 391 (1946).
61. Pinsker, Z. G., "Electron Diffraction" (English translation by J. A. Spink and E. Feigl). Butterworths, London, 1953.

62. Pinsker, Z. G., and Vajnshtejn, B. K., *Kristallografiya* **2**, 552 (1957).
63. Plessing, E., *Z. Physik* **113**, 36 (1939).
64. Reisner, J. H., *RCA Sci. Instr. News* **3**, 1 (1958).
65. Rowland, P. R., *Vacuum* **3**, 133 (1953).
66. Schrader, A., *Rev. universelle mines* **12**, 537 (1956).
67. Simard, G. L., Burton, C. J., and Barnes, R. B., *J. Appl. Phys.* **16**, 833 (1945).
68. Smith, E., and Nutting, J., *J. Iron Steel Inst. (London)* **187**, 314 (1957).
69. Swanson, H. E., and Fuyat, R. K., Standard X-Ray Diffraction Powder Patterns. *Natl. Bur. Standards (U.S.) Circ.* **539**, Vol. II. p. 25 (1953).
70. Takahashi, N., and Ashinuma, K., *Compt. rend. acad. sci.* **246**, 3930 (1956); *J. Inst. Metals* **87**, 19 (1958-59).
71. Takahashi, N., and Kazato, K., *Compt. rend. acad. sci.* **243**, 1408 (1956).
72. Thiessen, P. A., and Schoon, T., *Z. physik. Chem. (Leipzig)* **B36**, 195 (1937).
73. Thomson G. P., *Nature* **120**, 802 (1927).
74. Thomson, G. P., *Proc. Roy. Soc.* **A119**, 651 (1928).
75. Thomson, G. P., and Cochrane, W., "Theory and Practice of Electron Diffraction." Macmillan, London, 1939.
76. Thomson, G. P., and Reid, A., *Nature* **119**, 890 (1927).
77. Tomlinson, H. M., *Phil. Mag.* **3**, 867 (1958).
78. Trillat, J. J., and Takahashi, N., *Acta Cryst.* **7**, 15 (1954).
79. Wulff, J., *Trans. Am. Inst. Mining Met. Engrs.* **145**, 295 (1941).
80. Yamaguchi, S., *J. Appl. Phys.* **24**, 1305 (1953).
81. Yearian, H. J., and Howe, J. D., *Rev. Sci. Instr.* **7**, 26 (1936).

Books and Reviews

Beeching, R., "Electron Diffraction." Methuen, London, 1946.

Cowley, J. M., and Rees, A. L. G., Fourier methods in structure analysis by electron diffraction. *Repts. Progr. in Phys.* **21**, 165 (1958).

Heidenreich, R. D., Electron diffraction and microscopy of metals. *In* "Modern Research Techniques in Physical Metallurgy, pp. 51-71. American Society for Metals, Cleveland, 1953.

Newberry, S. P., and Alessandrini, E. I., Practical applications of electron diffraction. *Instruments* **25**, 907 (1952).

Pinsker, Z. G., "Electron Diffraction" (English translation by J. A. Spink and E. Feigl). Butterworths, London, 1953.

Pinsker, Z. G., (Applications of electron diffraction in the study of materials.) *Izvest. Akad. Nauk. S.S.S.R.* **17**, 170 (1953).

Pinsker, Z. G., (The present state and the future possibilities for electronographic methods in the study of materials.) *Zavodskaya Lab.* **24**, 597 (1958).

Pinsker, Z. G., and Vajnshtejn, B. K., (Electronographic analysis of the structure of crystals.) *Kristallografiya* **2**, 552 (1957).

Ress, A. L. G., Electron diffraction in the chemistry of the solid state (1952 Liversidge Research Lecture). *Proc. Roy. Soc. N.S. Wales* **86**, 38 (1952).

Thomson, G. P., and Cochrane, W., "Theory and Practice of Electron Diffraction." Macmillan, London, 1939.

Trillat, J. J., Etude des réactions chimiques par diffraction électronique. *Cahiers phys.* **49**, 44-60 (1954).

Trillat, J. J., Récent progrès dans les techniques de diffraction électronique. *Cahiers phys.* **83**, 269-276 (1957).

Author Index

Numbers in parentheses are reference numbers and are included to assist in locating references when the authors' names are not mentioned in the text. Numbers in italics refer to the page on which the reference is listed.

A

Abbott, T. A., 511 (262), 512 (265), *541*
Aborn, R. H., 7, *23*
Achhammer, B., 383 (71), *388*
Adams, G. D., *16*
Ademek, S., 471 (271), *541*
Aebersold, P. C., 17, *23*
Agar, A. W., 554 (61), 573, 582 (120), 585, 586 (120), *615, 616*
Aggarwal, S. L., 150 (1), 168, *181*
Agnew, W. G., 370 (16), *386*
Ahearn, A. J., 471 (136), 500 (136), 503 (137), 514 (136), 515 (136), 521, *537*
Alcock, T. C., 165, *182*
Aldrich, L. T., 514 (356), 522, *534, 543*
Alekseevskii, N. E., 474, *534*
Alessandrini, E. I., *660*
Alex, N. H., 514 (370), *543*
Alexander, L. E., 17, *23*, 66 (2), 68, 75, 77, 78, 96, *125, 127*, 153 (68), 160 (68), 169, *182*
Allen, H. H., 523 (224), *540*
Allen, J. S., 504 (3), 505 (3), *534*
Allison, S. K., 15 (19), *24*
Almin, A., 101 (102), *128*
Alpert, D., 514 (306), *542*
Alpert, N. L., 394 (56), *409*
Alvarcz, L. W., 531, *534*
Ames, J., 590 (1), *613*
Andant, A., *408*
Anderson, J. S., 441, 443, *459*
Anderson, T. F., 548 (2), 610 (2), *613*
Andranow, A. A., 283 (1a), *325*
Andress, K., 446 (3), 447 (3), *459*
Ardenne, M. von, 548 (3), 570 (3), *613*
Arends, C. B., 507 (22), *535*

Arndt, R. P., 383, *386*
Arndt, U. W., 66, *125*, 153 (2), 164 (2), *181*
Asbury, W. C., 85 (24), *126*
Ashinuma, K., 656 (70), *660*
Ashkin, J., 16, *23*
Ashmann, K. E., 453 (42), *460*
Astbury, W. T., 132 (5, 6, 7, 8), 137 (7), 152 (7, 8, 9), 174 (4), 175 (5, 8), *181*
Aston, F. W., 470 (5), 474, 479, 493, 500, *534, 544*
Avery, W. H., 496 (283), *541*
Ayton, M. W., 385 (9), *386*
Aziz, R. A., 589 (4), *613*
Azovtsev, V. K., 560 (131), *616*

B

Bachman, C. H., 559 (5), 560 (5), *613*
Backus, R. C., 590 (145), *613, 617*
Bagdyk'Janc, G. O., 628 (2), *658*
Baillie, Y., 555 (7), *613*
Bainbridge, K. T., 470, 475, 503 (8), *534*
Baker, R. F., 562 (83), 568 (6), *615*
Baker, W. O., 130 (10), 136 (39), 140, 143 (39), 144 (11, 12, 39, 40), 145 (39), 146 (12), 152 (10, 11, 12), 157 (10), 164 (13), 178 (10, 12, 13, 40), *181, 182*
Baldock, R., 479 (240), 493 (241), 520 (240, 310), *540, 542*
Ballard, J. W., 78 (4), *125*
Baly, E. C., 251 (2), *325*
Banerje, S. B., 396 (4), *408*
Barber, N. F., 473, *534*
Barkenbus, C., 458 (89), *461*
Barnard, G. P., 464 (12), 472, 474 (12), 479, 484 (13), *534, 544*

661

Subject Index